A Course in Complex Analysis and Riemann Surfaces

Wilhelm Schlag

Graduate Studies
in Mathematics

Volume 154

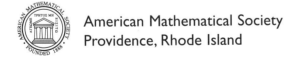

American Mathematical Society
Providence, Rhode Island

2010 *Mathematics Subject Classification.* Primary 30-01, 30F10, 30F15, 30F20, 30F30, 30F35.

For additional information and updates on this book, visit
www.ams.org/bookpages/gsm-154

Library of Congress Cataloging-in-Publication Data

Schlag, Wilhelm, 1969–
  A course in complex analysis and Riemann surfaces / Wilhelm Schlag.
    pages cm. – (Graduate studies in mathematics ; volume 154)
  Includes bibliographical references and index.
  ISBN 978-0-8218-9847-5 (alk. paper)
  1. Riemann surfaces–Textbooks. 2. Functions of complex variables–Textbooks. I. Title.

QA333.S37   2014
515′.93–dc23
                                                                          2014009993

Contents

Preface

During their first year at the University of Chicago, graduate students in mathematics take classes in algebra, analysis, and geometry, one of each every quarter. The analysis courses typically cover real analysis and measure theory, functional analysis and applications, and complex analysis. This book grew out of the author's notes for the complex analysis classes which he taught during the Spring quarters of 2007 and 2008. These courses covered elementary aspects of complex analysis such as the Cauchy integral theorem, the residue theorem, Laurent series, and the Riemann mapping theorem, but also more advanced material selected from Riemann surface theory.

Needless to say, all of these topics have been covered in excellent textbooks as well as classic treatises. This book does not try to compete with the works of the old masters such as Ahlfors [1, 2], Hurwitz–Courant [44], Titchmarsh [80], Ahlfors–Sario [3], Nevanlinna [67], and Weyl [88]. Rather, it is intended as a fairly detailed, yet fast-paced introduction to those parts of the theory of one complex variable that seem most useful in other areas of mathematics (geometric group theory, dynamics, algebraic geometry, number theory, functional analysis).

There is no question that complex analysis is a cornerstone of a mathematics specialization at every university and each area of mathematics requires at least some knowledge of it. However, many mathematicians never take more than an introductory class in complex variables which ends up being awkward and slightly outmoded. Often this is due to the omission of Riemann surfaces and the assumption of a computational, rather than a geometric point of view.

The author has therefore tried to emphasize the intuitive geometric underpinnings of elementary complex analysis that naturally lead to Riemann surface theory. Today this is either not taught at all, given an algebraic slant, or is presented from a sophisticated analytical perspective, leaving the students without any foundation, intuition, historical understanding, let alone a working knowledge of the subject.

This book intends to develop the subject of Riemann surfaces as a natural continuation of the elementary theory without which basic complex analysis would indeed seem artificial and antiquated. At the same time, we do not overly emphasize the algebraic aspects such as applications to elliptic curves. The author feels that those students who wish to pursue this direction will be able to do so quite easily after mastering the material in this book. Because of this, as well as numerous other omissions (e.g., zeta, theta, and automorphic functions, Serre duality, Dolbeault cohomology) and the reasonably short length of the book, it is to be considered as an "intermediate introduction".

Partly due to the fact that the Chicago first year curriculum covers a fair amount of topology and geometry before complex analysis, this book assumes knowledge of basic notions such as homotopy, the fundamental group, differential forms, cohomology and homology, and from algebra we require knowledge of the notions of groups and fields, and some familiarity with the resultant of two polynomials (but the latter is needed only for the definition of the Riemann surfaces of an algebraic germ). However, for the most part merely the most elementary familiarity of these concepts is assumed and we collect the few facts that we do need in Appendix A. As far as analytical prerequisites are concerned, they are fairly low, not extending far beyond multi-variable calculus and basic Hilbert space theory (in Chapter 6 we use orthogonal projections). One exception to this occurs in Sections 3.3, 3.4, and 3.5, which use the weak and weak-$*$ topologies in L^p and the space of measures (Riesz representation theorem). Again, what we need is recalled in the appendix.

Let us now describe the contents of the individual chapters in more detail. Chapter 1 introduces the concept of differentiability over $\mathbb{C}$, the calculus of $\partial_z, \partial_{\bar{z}}$, the Cauchy-Riemann equations, power series, the Möbius (or fractional linear) transformations and the Riemann sphere. Applications of these transformations to hyperbolic geometry (the Poincaré disk and the upper half-plane models) are also discussed. In particular, we verify the Gauss-Bonnet theorem for this special case.

Next, we develop complex integration and Cauchy's theorem in various guises, as well as the Cauchy formula and estimates (with the fundamental theorem of algebra as an application), and then apply this to the study of analyticity, harmonicity, and the logarithm. We also prove Goursat's theorem, which shows that complex differentiability without continuity of the derivative already implies analyticity.

A somewhat unusual feature of this chapter is the order: integration theory and its basic theorems appear after Möbius transforms and applications in non-Euclidean geometry. The reason for this is that the latter can be considered to be more elementary, whereas it is hoped that the somewhat miraculous integration theory becomes more accessible to a student who has seen many examples of analytic functions. Finally, to the author it is essential that complex differentiability should not be viewed as an ad hoc extension of the "limit of difference quotients" definition from the real field to the complex field, but rather as a geometric property at the infinitesimal level: the linearization equals a rotation followed by a dilation, which are precisely the linear maps representing multiplication by a complex number. In other words, *conformality* (at least at non-degenerate points). If there is any one basic notion that appears in every chapter of this book, then it is that of a conformal transformation.

Chapter 2 begins with the winding number, and some brief comments about cohomology and the fundamental group. It then applies these concepts in the "global form" of the Cauchy theorem by extending the "curves that can be filled in without leaving the region of holomorphy" version of the Cauchy theorem, to zero homologous cycles, i.e., those cycles which do not wind around any point outside of the domain of holomorphy. We then classify isolated singularities, prove the Laurent expansion and the residue theorems with applications. More specifically, we derive the argument principle and Rouché's theorem from the residue theorem. After that, Chapter 2 studies analytic continuation—with a demonstration of how to proceed for the Γ-function—and presents the monodromy theorem. Then, we turn to convergence of analytic functions and normal families. This is applied to Mittag-Leffler's "partial fraction representation", and the Weierstrass product formula in the entire plane. The Riemann mapping theorem is proved, and the regularity at the boundary of Riemann maps is discussed. The chapter concludes with Runge's approximation theorem, as well as a demonstration of several equivalent forms of simple connectivity.

Chapter 3 studies harmonic functions in a wide sense, with particular emphasis on the Dirichlet problem on the unit disk. This means that we solve the boundary value problem for the Laplacian on the disk via the Poisson kernel. The Poisson kernel is also identified from its invariance properties under the automorphisms of the disk, and we sketch some basic probabilistic aspects as well. We then present the usual L^p-based Hardy classes of harmonic functions on the disk, and discuss the question of representing them via their boundary data both in the sense of L^p and the sense of "almost everywhere". A prominent role in this analysis is played by compactness ideas in functional analysis (weak-∗ compactness of the unit ball, i.e., Alaoglu's theorem), as well as the observation that *positivity* can be substituted for compactness in many instances. This part therefore requires some analytical maturity, say on the level of Rudin's book [**73**]. However, up to the aforementioned basic tools from functional analysis, the presentation is self-contained.

We then sketch the more subtle theory of holomorphic functions in the Hardy class, or equivalently, of the boundedness properties of the conjugate harmonic functions, culminating in the classical F. & M. Riesz theorems.

The chapter also contains a discussion of the class of entire functions of exponential growth, the Jensen formula which relates zero counts to growth estimates, and the Hadamard product representation which refines the Weierstrass formula. We conclude with a gallery of conformal plots that will hopefully be both inspiring and illuminating.

The theory of Riemann surfaces begins with Chapter 4. This chapter covers the basic definition of such surfaces and of the analytic functions between them. Holomorphic and meromorphic functions are special cases where the target is either $\mathbb{C}$ or $\mathbb{C}P^1$ (the latter being conformally equivalent to the compactification of $\mathbb{C}$ obtained by "adding infinity"). The fairly long Section 4.2 introduces seven examples, or classes of examples, of Riemann surfaces. The first three are elementary and should be easily accessible even to a novice, but Examples 4)–7) are more involved and should perhaps only be attempted by a more experienced reader.

Example 4) shows that compact smooth orientable surfaces in $\mathbb{R}^3$ carry the structure of a Riemann surface, a fact of great historical importance to the subject. It means that we may carry out complex analysis on such surfaces rather than on the complex plane. The key idea here is that of *isothermal coordinates* on such a manifold, which reduces the metric to the one conformal to the standard metric. Example 5) discusses covering spaces, quotients etc., Example 6) is devoted to algebraic curves and how they are best viewed as Riemann surfaces. Example 7) presents Weierstrass' idea of looking for all possible analytic continuations of a power series and building a Riemann surface from this process.

After these examples, we investigate basic properties of functions on Riemann surfaces and how they relate to the topology of the surface as reflected, for example, by the genus in the compact case.

Elementary results such as the Riemann-Hurwitz formula relating the branch points to the genera of the surfaces are discussed. We then show how to define Riemann surfaces via discontinuous group actions and give examples of this procedure.

The chapter continues with a discussion of tori and some aspects of the classical theory of meromorphic functions on these tori. These functions are precisely the doubly periodic or elliptic functions. We develop the standard properties of the Weierstrass $\wp$ function, some of which foreshadow much more general facts which we will see in a much wider Riemann surface context in later chapters. We briefly discuss the connection between the Weierstrass function and the theory of integration of the square root of cubic polynomials (the so-called elliptic integrals).

In Section 4.7 the covering spaces of the doubly punctured plane are constructed and applied to Picard's small and big theorems, as well as the fundamental normality test of Montel. The chapter concludes with a discussion of groups of Möbius transforms, starting off with an analysis of the fixed points of maps in the automorphism group of the disk.

Then the *modular group* $\mathrm{PSL}(2, \mathbb{Z})$ is analyzed in some detail. We identify the fundamental region of that group, which implies, in particular, that the action of the group on the upper half-plane is discontinuous. As a particular example of an automorphic function, we introduce the basic modular function λ, which is constructed by means of the $\wp$ function. Remarkably, this function provides an explicit example of the covering map from Section 4.7.

Chapter 5 presents another way in which Riemann surfaces arise naturally, namely via analytic continuation. Historically, the desire to resolve unnatural issues related to "multi-valued functions" (most importantly for algebraic functions) led Riemann to introduce his surfaces. Even though the underlying ideas leading from a so-called analytic germ to its Riemann surface are geometric and intuitive, and closely related to covering spaces in topology, their rigorous rendition requires some patience as ideas such as "analytic germ", "branch point", "(un)ramified Riemann surface of an analytic germ", etc., need to be defined precisely. The chapter also develops some basic aspects of algebraic functions and their Riemann surfaces. At this point the reader will need to be familiar with basic algebraic constructions.

In particular, we observe that *every* compact Riemann surface is obtained through analytic continuation of some algebraic germ. This uses the machinery of Chapter 5 together with a potential-theoretic result that guarantees the *existence of a non-constant meromorphic function* on every Riemann surface. The reference to potential theory here means the we employ basic results on elliptic PDEs to obtain this (in fact, we will phrase the little we need in terms of harmonic functions and differentials).

This, as well as other fundamental existence results, is developed in Chapter 6. It turns out that differential forms are easier to work with on

Riemann surfaces than functions, and it is through forms that we construct functions. One of the reasons for this preference for forms over functions lies with the fact that it is meaningful to integrate 1-forms over curves, but not functions.

The chapter concludes with a discussion of ordinary differential equations with meromorphic coefficients. We introduce the concept of a *Fuchsian equation*, and illustrate this term by means of the example of the Bessel equation.

Chapter 6 introduces differential forms on Riemann surfaces and their integrals. Needless to say, the only really important class of linear forms are the 1-forms and we define harmonic, holomorphic and meromorphic forms and the residues in the latter case. Furthermore, the Hodge $*$ operator appears naturally (informally, it acts like a rotation by $\pi/2$). We then present some examples that lead up to the Hodge decomposition, which is established later in that chapter. This decomposition states that every 1-form can be decomposed additively into three components: a closed, co-closed, and a harmonic form (the latter being characterized as being simultaneously closed and co-closed). In this book, we follow the classical L^2-based derivation of this theorem. Thus, via Hilbert space methods one first derives this decomposition with L^2-valued forms and then uses Weyl's regularity lemma (weakly harmonic functions are smoothly harmonic) to upgrade to smooth forms.

Chapter 6 then applies the Hodge decomposition to establish some basic results on the existence of meromorphic differentials and functions on a general Riemann surface. In particular, we derive the striking fact that **every Riemann surface** carries a non-constant meromorphic function which is a key ingredient for the result on compact surfaces being algebraic in Chapter 5.

The chapter concludes with several examples of meromorphic functions and differentials on Riemann surfaces, mostly for the class of hyper-elliptic surfaces (compact surfaces that admit a meromorphic function of degree 2).

Chapter 7 presents the Riemann-Roch theorem which relates the dimension of certain spaces of meromorphic differentials with the dimension of a space of meromorphic functions, from properties of the underlying *divisor* and the genus of the compact Riemann surface. Before proving this theorem, which is of central importance both in historical terms as well as in applications, there are a number of prerequisites to be dealt with, such as a linear basis in the space of holomorphic differentials, the Riemann period relations, and the study of divisors.

Section 7.5 studies a diverse collection of applications of the Riemann-Roch theorem, such as the fact that every compact Riemann surface of genus g is a branched cover of S^2 with $g+1$ sheets, as well as the fact that surfaces of genus 2 only require 2 sheets (and are thus hyper-elliptic). Section 7.6 completes the identification of compact surfaces M as projective algebraic curves. Moreover, we show that every meromorphic function on such a surface M can be expressed by means of a *primitive pair* of meromorphic functions; see Theorem 7.24.

Section 7.7 discusses the *Abel and Jacobi theorems*. The former result identifies all possible divisors associated with meromorphic functions (the so-called *principal divisors*) on a compact Riemann surface by means of the vanishing of a certain function of the divisor modulo the period lattice. This implies, amongst other things, that every compact surface of genus 1 is a torus. For all genera $g \geq 1$ we obtain the surjectivity of the Jacobi map onto the Jacobian variety; in other words, we present the Jacobi inversion. In this chapter we omit the theta functions, which would require a chapter of their own.

Chapter 8 is devoted to the proof of the uniformization theorem. This theorem states that the only simply-connected Riemann surfaces (up to isomorphisms) are $\mathbb{C}$, $\mathbb{D}$, and $\mathbb{C}P^1$. For the compact case, we deduce this from the Riemann-Roch theorem. But for the other two cases we use methods of potential theory which are motivated by the proof of the Riemann mapping theorem. In fact, we first reprove this result in the plane by means of a *Green function* associated with a domain.

The idea is then to generalize this proof strategy to Riemann surfaces. The natural question of when a Green function exists on a Riemann surface leads to the classification of non-compact surfaces as either hyperbolic (such as $\mathbb{D}$) or parabolic (such as $\mathbb{C}$); in the compact case a Green function cannot exist.

Via the Perron method, we prove the existence of a Green function for hyperbolic surfaces, thus establishing the conformal equivalence with the disk. For the parabolic case, a suitable substitute for the Green function needs to be found. We discuss this in detail for the simply-connected case, and also sketch some aspects of the non-simply-connected cases.

As in other key results in this text (equivalence between compact Riemann surfaces and algebraic curves, Riemann-Roch) the key here is to establish the existence of special types of functions on a given surface. In this context, the functions are harmonic (or meromorphic for the compact surfaces). Loosely speaking, the classification theorem then follows from the mapping properties of these functions.

Finally, Appendix A collects some of the material that arguably exceeds the usual undergraduate preparation which can be expected at the entry level to complex analysis. Naturally, this chapter is more expository and does not present many details. References are given to the relevant sources.

This text does perhaps assume more than other introductions to the subject. The author chose to present the material more like a landscape. Essential features that the reader encounters on his or her guided tour are pointed out as we go along. Since complex analysis does have to do with many basic features of mathematical analysis it is not surprising that examples can and should be drawn from different sources. The author hopes that students and teachers will find this to be an attractive feature.

How to use this book: On the largest scale, the structure is linear. This means that the material is presented progressively, with later chapters drawing on earlier ones. It is not advisable for a newcomer to this subject to "pick and choose". In the hands of an experienced teacher, though, such a strategy is to some extent possible. This will be also necessary with a class of varying backgrounds and preparation. For example, Sections 3.3–3.6 require previous exposure to basic functional analysis and measure theory, namely L^p spaces, their duals and the weak-$*$ compactness (Alaoglu's theorem). This is, however, the only instance where that particular background is required. If these sections are omitted, but Chapter 8 is taught, then the basic properties of subharmonic functions as presented in Section 3.5 will need to be discussed.

As far as functional analysis is concerned, of far greater importance to this text are rudiments of Hilbert spaces and L^2 spaces (but only some of the most basic facts such as completeness and orthogonal decompositions). These are essential for the Hodge theorem in Chapter 6.

As a general rule, all details are presented (with the exception of the appendix). On rare occasions, certain routine technical aspects are moved to the problem section which can be found at the end of each chapter. Some of the problems might be considered to be more difficult, but essentially all of them are to be viewed as an integral part of this text. As always in mathematics courses, working through at least some of the exercises is essential to mastering this material. References are not given in the main text since they disturb the flow, but rather collected at the end in the "Notes". This is the same format employed in the author's books with Camil Muscalu [65]. By design, this text should be suitable for both independent—but preferably guided—study and the traditional classroom setting. A well-prepared student will hopefully be able to read the eight main chapters in linear succession, occasionally glancing at the appendix if needed.

The main motivation for writing this book was to bridge a gap in the literature, namely between the introductory complex analysis literature such as Lang [55], and to a lesser extent perhaps Ahlfors [1] on the one hand, and on the other hand, well-established pure Riemann surface texts such as Forster [29], Farkas, Kra [23]. Ideally, this book could serve as a stepping stone into more advanced texts such as [23], as well as the recent ones by Donaldson [18] and Varolin [84]. The author hopes that the somewhat higher-level machinery that is used in the latter two books (complex line bundles, Serre duality, etc.) will become more natural as well as more easily accessible after the classical approach, which we employ here, has been understood.

Acknowledgments

The author was partially supported by the National Science Foundation during the preparation of this book. He is indebted to his colleagues Vladimir Gershonovich Drinfeld and Benson Farb at the University of Chicago, as well as Fritz Gesztesy at the University of Missouri, for many helpful comments on an earlier version of this book. Through their influence much more material was added to the original set of complex analysis course notes. Tom Church made numerous corrections to these course notes. Genevieve Raugel at Orsay, France, and Jackson Hance, Jack Sempliner, Ana Balibanu, Zev Chonoles, Gong Chen, and Nick Salter, all at the University of Chicago, helped with the proofreading of the final version of the book. The combined efforts of all of these mathematicians played an essential role in the completion of this project.

Chapter 1

From i to z: the basics of complex analysis

1.1. The field of complex numbers

The field $\mathbb{C}$ of complex numbers is obtained by adjoining i to the field $\mathbb{R}$ of reals. The defining property of i is $i^2 + 1 = 0$ and complex numbers $z_1 = x_1 + iy_1$ and $z_2 = x_2 + iy_2$ are added componentwise and multiplied according to the rule

$$z_1 \cdot z_2 = x_1 x_2 - y_1 y_2 + i(x_1 y_2 + x_2 y_1),$$

which follows from $i^2 + 1 = 0$ and the distributional law. The *complex conjugate* of $z = x + iy$ is $\bar{z} = x - iy$ and we have $|z|^2 := z\bar{z} = x^2 + y^2$. Therefore, every $z \neq 0$ has a multiplicative inverse given by $\frac{1}{z} := \bar{z}|z|^{-2}$ and $\mathbb{C}$ becomes a field. Since complex numbers z can be represented as points or vectors in $\mathbb{R}^2$ in the Cartesian way, we can also assign polar coordinates (r, θ) to them. By definition, $r = |z|$ and $z = r(\cos\theta + i\sin\theta)$. The addition theorems for cosine and sine imply that

$$z_1 \cdot z_2 = |z_1||z_2|(\cos(\theta_1 + \theta_2) + i\sin(\theta_1 + \theta_2)),$$

which reveals the remarkable fact that complex numbers are multiplied by *multiplying their lengths and adding their angles.* In particular, $|z_1 z_2| = |z_1||z_2|$. This shows that power series behave as in the real case with respect to convergence, i.e.,

$$\sum_{n=0}^{\infty} a_n z^n \text{ converges on } |z| < R \text{ and diverges for every } |z| > R,$$

$$\text{where } R^{-1} = \limsup_{n \to \infty} |a_n|^{\frac{1}{n}},$$

where the sense of convergence is relative to the length metric $|\cdot|$ on $\mathbb{C}$ which is the same as the Euclidean distance on $\mathbb{R}^2$ (the reader should verify the triangle inequality). The formula for R of course follows from comparison with the geometric series, and $R = 0$ and $R = \infty$ are allowed. Note that the convergence is absolute on the disk $|z| < R$ and uniform on every compact subset of that disk. Moreover, the series diverges for *every* $|z| > R$ as can be seen by the comparison test. We can also write $R = \lim_{n\to\infty} \left|\frac{a_n}{a_{n+1}}\right|$, provided this limit exists. The first example that comes to mind here is

$$\frac{1}{1-z} = \sum_{n=0}^{\infty} z^n, \qquad |z| < 1.$$

Another example is of course

(1.1)
$$E(z) := \sum_{n=0}^{\infty} \frac{z^n}{n!},$$

which converges absolutely and uniformly on every compact subset of $\mathbb{C}$. Expanding $(z_1 + z_2)^n$ via the binomial theorem shows that $E(z_1 + z_2) = E(z_1)E(z_2)$. In particular, we see that $E(z) \neq 0$ for any $z \in \mathbb{C}$. Indeed, if $E(z_0) = 0$, then $1 = E(0) = E(z_0)E(-z_0) = 0$, a contradiction.

Next, recall the definition of the Euler constant e: consider the ordinary differential equation $\dot{y} = y$ with $y(0) = 1$ which has a unique solution $y(t)$ for all $t \in \mathbb{R}$. Then set $e := y(1)$. Let us solve our differential equation iteratively (this is an example of the general Picard method). Indeed, let us assume that there is a C^1 solution up to some time $t > 0$. Applying the fundamental theorem of calculus then yields

$$y(t) = 1 + \int_0^t y(s)\,ds.$$

Now replace $y(s)$ in the integral by the right-hand side and iterate:

$$y(t) = 1 + \int_0^t y(s)\,ds = 1 + t + \int_0^t (t-s)y(s)\,ds = \cdots$$
$$= \sum_{j=0}^{n} \frac{t^j}{j!} + \frac{1}{n!}\int_0^t (t-s)^n y(s)\,ds.$$

We bound

$$\frac{1}{n!}\left|\int_0^t (t-s)^n y(s)\,ds\right| \leq \frac{t^{n+1}}{(n+1)!} \max_{0 \leq s \leq t} |y(s)|,$$

which vanishes as $n \to \infty$. Therefore, our presumed C^1 solution is uniquely represented by the infinite series

$$y(t) = \sum_{j=0}^{\infty} \frac{t^j}{j!},$$

which of course is nothing other than the usual series expansion for e^t. To finish the argument, one now verifies that the series is in fact infinitely differentiable and satisfies the differential equation and initial condition. For the differentiability see Lemma 1.3 below.

Viewing the exponential function as the solution of $\dot{y} = y$ allows for a transparent derivation of the homomorphism property of the exponential. Indeed, it is none other than the group property of flows which implies

$$y(t_2)y(t_1) = y(t_1 + t_2)$$

which proves that $y(t) = e^t$ for every rational t, and then by continuity for every real t, and motivates why we *define*

$$e^t := \sum_{j=0}^{\infty} \frac{t^j}{j!} \qquad \forall\, t \in \mathbb{R}.$$

Hence our series $E(z)$ above is used as the *definition* of e^z for all $z \in \mathbb{C}$. We have the group property $e^{z_1+z_2} = e^{z_1}e^{z_2}$, and by comparison with the power series of cos and sin on $\mathbb{R}$, we arrive at the famous Euler formula

$$e^{i\theta} = \cos\theta + i\sin\theta$$

for all $\theta \in \mathbb{R}$. This, in particular, shows that $z = re^{i\theta}$ where (r, θ) are the polar coordinates of z. This in turn implies that

$$(\cos\theta + i\sin\theta)^n = \cos(n\theta) + i\sin(n\theta)$$

for every $n \geq 1$ (de Moivre's formula). Now suppose that $z = re^{i\theta}$ with $r > 0$ (this just means that $z \neq 0$). Then by the preceding,

$$z = e^{\log r + i\theta} \quad \text{or} \quad \log z = \log r + i\theta.$$

Note that the logarithm is not well-defined since θ and $\theta + 2\pi n$ for any $n \in \mathbb{Z}$ both have the property that exponentiating leads to z. Similarly,

$$\left(r^{\frac{1}{n}} e^{i\frac{\theta}{n}} e^{\frac{2\pi i k}{n}} \right)^n = z \quad \forall\, 1 \leq k \leq n,$$

which shows that there are n different possibilities for $\sqrt[n]{z}$. Later on we shall see how these functions become single-valued on their natural Riemann surfaces. Let us merely mention at this point that the complex exponential is most naturally viewed as the covering map

$$\mathbb{C} \to \mathbb{C}^* := \mathbb{C} \setminus \{0\},$$

$$z \mapsto e^z.$$

showing that $\mathbb{C}$ is the universal cover of $\mathbb{C}^*$.

1.2. Holomorphic, analytic, and conformal

But for now, we of course wish to differentiate functions defined on some open set $\Omega \subset \mathbb{C}$. There are two relevant notions of derivative here and we will need to understand how they relate to each other.

The first is the crucial linearization idea from multivariable calculus and the second copies the idea of difference quotients from calculus. In many ways, the former is preferable to the latter. In what follows we shall either use U or Ω to denote planar regions, i.e., open and connected subsets of $\mathbb{R}^2$. Also, we will identify $z = x + iy$ with the real pair (x, y) and will typically write a complex-valued function as $f(z) = u(z) + iv(z) = (u, v)(z)$ where $u, v : \mathbb{C} \to \mathbb{R}$.

Definition 1.1. Let $f : \Omega \to \mathbb{C}$.

(a) We say that $f \in C^1(\Omega)$ if there exists df, a continuous 2×2 matrix-valued function, such that

(1.2) $$f(z + h) = f(z) + df(z)(h) + r(z, h) \qquad \forall\, z, z + h \in \Omega,$$

(1.3) $$\lim_{h \to 0} \frac{r(z, h)}{|h|} = 0,$$

where $df(z)(h)$ means the matrix $df(z)$ acting on the vector h. It is understood that $h \neq 0$ in the limit $h \to 0$.

(b) We say that f is *holomorphic* on Ω if

$$f'(z) := \lim_{w \to z} \frac{f(w) - f(z)}{w - z}$$

exists for all $z \in \Omega$ and is continuous on Ω. We denote this by $f \in \mathcal{H}(\Omega)$. A function $f \in \mathcal{H}(\mathbb{C})$ is called *entire*.

The function $r(z, h)$ is the deviation of the function $f(z + h)$ from its linear approximation $f(z) + df(z)h$. Differentiability means that this deviation vanishes faster than linearly as $h \to 0$. Note that (b) is equivalent to the existence of a function $f' \in C(\Omega)$ such that

$$f(z + h) = f(z) + f'(z)h + o(|h|) \qquad |h| \to 0,$$

where $f'(z)h$ is the product between the complex numbers $f'(z)$ and h. Hence we conclude that the holomorphic functions are precisely those functions in $C^1(\Omega)$ in the sense of (a) for which the differential $df(z)$ acts as a linear map via multiplication by a complex number.

We should remark that the condition $f' \in C(\Omega)$ can be dropped from part (b) of Definition 1.1 and replaced by complex differentiability alone. We shall elucidate this issue in Goursat's theorem below; see Theorem 1.34. But for now we prefer to add the continuity assumption on the derivative.

Obvious examples of holomorphic maps are the powers $f(z) = z^n$ for all $n \in \mathbb{Z}$ (if n is negative, then we exclude $z = 0$). They satisfy $f'(z) = nz^{n-1}$ by the binomial theorem. Also, since we can do algebra in $\mathbb{C}$ the same way we did over $\mathbb{R}$ it follows that the basic differentiation rules like the sum, product, quotient, and chain rules continue to hold for holomorphic functions. Let us demonstrate this for the chain rule: if $f \in \mathcal{H}(\Omega)$, $g \in \mathcal{H}(\Omega')$ and $f(\Omega) \subseteq (\Omega')$, then we know from the C^1-chain rule that

$$(g \circ f)(z + h) = (g \circ f)(z) + Dg(f(z))Df(z)h + o(|h|) \qquad |h| \to 0.$$

From (b) above we infer that $Dg(f(z))$ and $Df(z)$ act as multiplication by the complex numbers $g'(f(z))$ and $f'(z)$, respectively. Thus, we see that $g \circ f \in \mathcal{H}(\Omega)$ and $(g \circ f)' = g'(f)f'$. We leave the product and quotient rules to the reader.

It is clear that all polynomials are holomorphic functions. In fact, we can generalize this to all power series within their disk of convergence. Let us make this more precise.

Definition 1.2. We say that $f : \Omega \to \mathbb{C}$ is *analytic* (or $f \in \mathcal{A}(\Omega)$) if f is represented by a convergent power series expansion on a neighborhood around every point of Ω.

We now establish that analytic functions are holomorphic.

Lemma 1.3. $\mathcal{A}(\Omega) \subset \mathcal{H}(\Omega)$.

Proof. Suppose $z_0 \in \Omega$ and

$$f(z) = \sum_{n=0}^{\infty} a_n (z - z_0)^n \qquad \forall\, z \text{ such that } |z - z_0| < r(z_0),$$

where $r(z_0) > 0$. For simplicity, we may assume that $z_0 = 0$ and set $r_0 = r_0(0)$. Fix $|z| < r_0$ and write

$$f(z + h) = f(z) + g(z)h + r(z, h),$$

where $g(z) := \sum_{n=1}^{\infty} na_n z^{n-1}$. It is important to note that this series still converges on $|z| < r_0$ as can be seen from the formula for the radius of convergence, for example. We need to prove that $\frac{r(z,h)}{|h|} \to 0$ as $h \to 0$. If $z = 0$, then this is immediate since in that case $g(z) = a_1$. We have

$$r(z, h) = \sum_{n=2}^{\infty} a_n B_n(z, h),$$

$$B_n(z, h) = (z + h)^n - z^n - nz^{n-1}h = \sum_{k=2}^{n} \binom{n}{k} h^k z^{n-k},$$

since $B_0 = B_1 = 0$. Let $|z| + |h| < r_1 < r_2 < r_0$. Then we have $|a_n| \leq \frac{M}{r_2^n}$ for all $n \geq 0$ and some $M < \infty$. Also,

(1.4)
$$|B_n(z,h)| \leq |h|^2 \sum_{k=0}^{n-2} \binom{n}{k+2} |h|^k |z|^{n-2-k}$$
$$\leq |h|^2 \sum_{k=0}^{n-2} n^2 \binom{n-2}{k} |h|^k |z|^{n-2-k}$$
$$= |h|^2 n^2 (|z| + |h|)^{n-2},$$

for any $n \geq 2$. Hence

(1.5)
$$|r(z,h)| \leq \sum_{n=2}^{\infty} \frac{M}{r_2^n} n^2 |h|^2 (|z| + |h|)^{n-2}$$
$$\leq \frac{|h|^2 M}{r_2^2} \sum_{n=0}^{\infty} (n+2)^2 \left(\frac{r_1}{r_2}\right)^n.$$

We conclude that for some constant C,

$$|r(z,h)| \leq C |h|^2,$$

which is more than we need. Thus,

$$f'(z) = \sum_{n=0}^{\infty} n a_n (z - z_0)^{n-1} \qquad \forall \, |z - z_0| < r(z_0),$$

as desired.   □

In fact, one can differentiate any number of times and

$$f^{(k)}(z) = \sum_{n=0}^{\infty} (n)_k \, a_n (z - z_0)^{n-k} \qquad \forall \, |z - z_0| < r(z_0),$$

where

$$(n)_k = n(n-1)\cdots(n-k+1) = \frac{n!}{(n-k)!}.$$

This establishes the well-known relation $a_n = \frac{f^{(n)}(z_0)}{n!}$ for all $n \geq 0$.

We note that with e^z defined as above, $(e^z)' = e^z$ from the series representation (1.1). It is a remarkable fact of basic complex analysis that one has equality in Lemma 1.3, i.e., $\mathcal{A}(\Omega) = \mathcal{H}(\Omega)$. In order to establish this equality, we need to be able to integrate; see the section about integration below. Before we delve into the fundamental integration theory, we first develop the geometric aspects of holomorphic functions in some detail.

Recall that $f = u + iv = (u, v)$ belongs to $C^1(\Omega)$ if and only if the partials u_x, u_y, v_x, v_y exist and are continuous on Ω. If $f \in \mathcal{H}(\Omega)$, then by letting w (in Definition 1.1) approach z along the x or y-directions, respectively,

$$f'(z) = u_x + iv_x = -iu_y + v_y$$

so that

(1.6) $$u_x = v_y, \qquad u_y = -v_x,$$

which is the same as

$$f_x + if_y = 0.$$

These relations are known as the *Cauchy-Riemann equations*. They are equivalent to the property that

$$df = \begin{bmatrix} u_x & u_y \\ v_x & v_y \end{bmatrix} = \rho A \quad \text{for some} \quad \rho \geq 0, \quad A \in \mathrm{SO}(2, \mathbb{R}).$$

In other words, at each point where a holomorphic function f has a non-vanishing derivative, its differential df is a conformal matrix: it preserves angles and the orientation between vectors. Conversely, if $f \in C^1(\Omega)$ has the property that df is proportional to a rotation everywhere on Ω, then $f \in \mathcal{H}(\Omega)$. Let us summarize these important observations.

Theorem 1.4. *A complex-valued function $f \in C^1(\Omega)$ is holomorphic if and only if the Cauchy-Riemann equations hold in Ω. This is equivalent to df being the composition of a rotation and a dilation (possibly by zero) at each point in Ω.*

Proof. We already saw that the Cauchy-Riemann equation is necessary. Conversely, since $f \in C^1(\Omega)$ as $(\xi, \eta) \to 0$,

$$u(x + \xi, y + \eta) = u(x, y) + u_x(x, y)\xi + u_y(x, y)\eta + o(|(\xi, \eta)|),$$
$$v(x + \xi, y + \eta) = v(x, y) + v_x(x, y)\xi + v_y(x, y)\eta + o(|(\xi, \eta)|).$$

Using that $u_x = v_y$ and $u_y = -v_x$ we obtain, with $\zeta = \xi + i\eta$,

$$f(z + \zeta) - f(z) = (u_x + iv_x)(z)(\xi + i\eta) + o(|\zeta|),$$

which of course proves that $f'(z) = u_x(z) + iv_x(z) = v_y(z) - iu_y(z)$ as desired. The second part was already discussed above. $\qquad \square$

The following notion is of central importance for all of complex analysis:

Definition 1.5. A function $f \in C^1(\Omega)$ is called *conformal* if $df \neq 0$ in Ω and df preserves the angle and orientation at each point.

Thus, the holomorphic functions are precisely those C^1 functions which are conformal at all points at which $df \neq 0$. Note that $f(z) = \bar{z}$ belongs to $C^1(\mathbb{C})$ but is not conformal since it reverses orientations. Also note that $f(z) = z^2$ is holomorphic everywhere but doubles angles at $z = 0$ (in the sense that curves crossing at 0 at angle α get mapped onto curves intersecting at 0 at angle 2α), so conformality is lost there.

A particularly convenient—as well as insightful—way of distinguishing holomorphic functions from C^1 functions is given by the $\partial_z, \partial_{\bar{z}}$ calculus. Assume that $f \in C^1(\Omega)$. Then the real-linear map $df(z)$ can be written as the sum of a complex-linear (meaning that $T(\lambda v) = \lambda T(v)$ for all complex λ) and a complex anti-linear transformation (meaning that $T(\lambda v) = \bar{\lambda} T(v)$). We now make this simple linear algebra fact completely explicit.

Lemma 1.6. *If $T : V \to W$ is an $\mathbb{R}$-linear map between complex vector spaces, then there is a unique representation $T = T_1 + T_2$ where T_1 is complex linear and T_2 complex anti-linear. The latter property means that $T_2(\lambda \vec{v}) = \bar{\lambda} T_2(\vec{v})$.*

Proof. Uniqueness follows since a $\mathbb{C}$-linear map which is simultaneously $\mathbb{C}$-anti-linear vanishes identically. For existence, set

$$T_1 = \frac{1}{2}(T - iTi), \qquad T_2 = \frac{1}{2}(T + iTi).$$

Then $T_1 i = iT_1$ and $T_2 i = -iT_2$, $T = T_1 + T_2$, as desired. $\square$

In other words, there exist complex numbers $w_1(z), w_2(z)$ such that

$$df(z) = w_1(z) \, dz + w_2(z) \, d\bar{z},$$

where dz is the identity map and $d\bar{z}$ the reflection about the real axis; in the previous formula, these maps are then followed by multiplication by the complex numbers w_1 and w_2, respectively. We are using here that all complex-linear transformations on $\mathbb{R}^2$ are given by multiplication by a complex number, whereas the complex anti-linear ones become complex linear by composing them with a reflection. To find w_1 and w_2 observe that since $dz = dx + idy$, $d\bar{z} = dx - idy$,

$$df = \partial_x f \, dx + \partial_y f \, dy = \partial_x f \frac{1}{2}(dz + d\bar{z}) + \partial_y f \frac{1}{2i}(dz - d\bar{z})$$

$$= \frac{1}{2}(\partial_x f - i\partial_y f) \, dz + \frac{1}{2}(\partial_x f + i\partial_y f) \, d\bar{z}$$

$$=: \partial_z f \, dz + \partial_{\bar{z}} f \, d\bar{z}.$$

Thus, $f \in \mathcal{H}(\Omega)$ if and only if $f \in C^1(\Omega)$ and $\partial_{\bar{z}} f = 0$ in Ω. This means that the Cauchy-Riemann system is the same as $\partial_{\bar{z}} f = 0$. To see this explicitly, we write $f = u + iv$ whence $\partial_{\bar{z}} f = 0$ becomes the familiar form

$$u_x - v_y = 0, \quad u_y + v_x = 0;$$

see (1.6).

As an application of this formalism we record the following crucial fact: for any $f \in \mathcal{H}(\Omega)$,

$$d(f(z)\,dz) = \partial_z f\,dz \wedge dz + \partial_{\bar{z}} f\,d\bar{z} \wedge dz = 0,$$

which means that $f(z)\,dz$ is a *closed differential form*. This property is *equivalent* to the homotopy invariance of the Cauchy integral that we will encounter below. As a further example of the $dz, d\bar{z}$ formalism, we leave it to the reader to verify the chain rules (where we write $f = f(z), g = g(w)$)

$$(1.7) \qquad \begin{aligned} \partial_z(g \circ f) &= \left[(\partial_w g) \circ f\right] \partial_z f + \left[(\partial_{\bar{w}} g) \circ f\right] \partial_z \bar{f}, \\ \partial_{\bar{z}}(g \circ f) &= \left[(\partial_w g) \circ f\right] \partial_{\bar{z}} f + \left[(\partial_{\bar{w}} g) \circ f\right] \partial_{\bar{z}} \bar{f}, \end{aligned}$$

as well as the representation of the Laplacian $\Delta = 4\frac{\partial^2}{\partial z \partial \bar{z}}$.

These ideas will be of particular importance once we discuss differential forms on Riemann surfaces.

1.3. The Riemann sphere

To continue our introductory chapter, we next turn to the simple but important idea of extending the notion of analyticity to functions that take the value ∞. In a similar vein, we can make sense of functions being analytic at $z = \infty$. To start with, we define the one-point compactification of $\mathbb{C}$, which we denote by $\mathbb{C}_\infty$, with the usual basis for the topology: the neighborhoods of ∞ are the complements of all compact sets. Thus, $\mathbb{C}_\infty \simeq S^2$ in the homeomorphic sense. Somewhat deeper as well as much more relevant for complex analysis is the fact that $\mathbb{C} \simeq S^2 \setminus \{p\}$ in the sense of *conformal equivalence* where $p \in S^2$ is arbitrary. Conformality here is expressed in terms of the standard Euclidean metric applied to the respective tangent spaces.

This equivalence is realized by the well-known stereographic projection; see the problems to this chapter, Chapter 4 below, as well as Figure 1.1. If the circle in that figure is the unit circle, $N = (0, 1)$, and $X = (x, y)$, then $Z = \frac{x}{1-y}$ as the reader will easily verify using similarity of triangles. This identifies the stereographic projection as the map

$$\Phi : S^2 \setminus \{(0,0,1)\} \to \mathbb{C}, \ X = (x_1, x_2, x_3) \mapsto \frac{x_1 + ix_2}{1 - x_3}.$$

The stereographic projection preserves angles as well as circles; see Problem 1.6. We will see in Chapter 4 that

$$\mathbb{C}_\infty \simeq S^2 \simeq \mathbb{C}P^1$$

in the sense of conformal equivalences, and each of these Riemann surfaces are called the *Riemann sphere*. The space $\mathbb{C}P^1$ is the complex projective line.

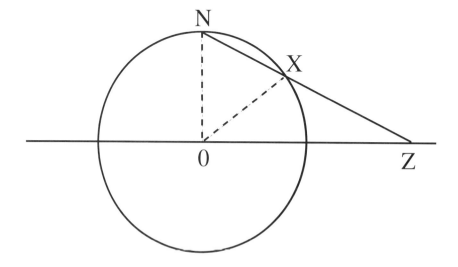

Figure 1.1. Stereographic projection

It is now clear how to extend the domain and range of holomorphic maps to

$$(1.8) \qquad f : \mathbb{C} \to \mathbb{C}_\infty, \quad f : \mathbb{C}_\infty \to \mathbb{C}, \quad f : \mathbb{C}_\infty \to \mathbb{C}_\infty.$$

First, we need to require that f is continuous in each case. Second, we require f to be holomorphic both near points where it assumes values in the complex plane, as well as where ∞ is attained. In the latter case, it is natural to reduce to the finite case by considering $1/f$. To be specific, if $f(z_0) = \infty$ for some $z_0 \in \mathbb{C}$, then we say that f is holomorphic close to z_0 if and only if $\frac{1}{f(z)}$ is holomorphic around z_0. To make sense of f being analytic at $z = \infty$ with values in $\mathbb{C}$, we require that $f(\frac{1}{z})$ is holomorphic around $z = 0$. For the final example in (1.8), if $f(\infty) = \infty$, then f is analytic around $z = \infty$ if and only if $1/f(1/z)$ is analytic around $z = 0$. We remark that $z \mapsto \frac{1}{z}$ is conformal as a map from $\mathbb{C}_\infty \to \mathbb{C}_\infty$; this is a tautology in view of our choice of chart at $z = \infty$. On the other hand, if we interpret $\mathbb{C}_\infty$ as the Riemann sphere, then one needs to use here that stereographic projection is a conformal map.

We shall see later in this chapter that the holomorphic maps $f : \mathbb{C}_\infty \to \mathbb{C}$ are constants (indeed, such a map would have to be entire and bounded and therefore constant by Liouville's theorem, see Corollary 1.22 below). On the other hand, the maps $f : \mathbb{C} \to \mathbb{C}_\infty$ are precisely the *meromorphic ones* which we shall encounter in the next chapter. Finally, the holomorphic maps $f : \mathbb{C}_\infty \to \mathbb{C}_\infty$ are precisely the rational functions $\frac{P(z)}{Q(z)}$ where P, Q are polynomials. To see this, one shows that any such f is necessarily meromorphic with only finitely many poles in $\mathbb{C}$ and possibly a pole at $z = \infty$; see the following chapter for an explanation of these terms.

1.4. Möbius transformations

If we now accept that the holomorphic, and thus conformal, maps $\mathbb{C}_\infty \to \mathbb{C}_\infty$ are precisely the rational ones, then it is clear how to identify the *conformal automorphisms* (or *automorphisms*) amongst these maps. By this we mean the bijections whose inverse is also conformal. Indeed, in that case the fundamental theorem of algebra implies that P and Q both have degree one or less. This naturally leads to the following definition, which of course can be read ad hoc without the preceding motivation. Based on the argument of the previous paragraph (which the reader can safely accept on first reading), the lemma identifies all automorphisms of $\mathbb{C}_\infty$.

Lemma 1.7. *Every $A \in \mathrm{GL}(2, \mathbb{C})$ defines a transformation*

$$T_A(z) := \frac{az + b}{cz + d}, \qquad A = \begin{bmatrix} a & b \\ c & d \end{bmatrix},$$

which is holomorphic as a map from $\mathbb{C}_\infty \to \mathbb{C}_\infty$. It is called a fractional linear *or Möbius transformation. The map $A \mapsto T_A$ only depends on the equivalence class of A under the relation $A \sim B$ if and only if $A = \lambda B$, $\lambda \in \mathbb{C}^*$. In other words, the family of all Möbius transformations is the same as*

$$(1.9) \qquad \mathrm{PSL}(2, \mathbb{C}) := \mathrm{SL}(2, \mathbb{C})/\{\pm \mathrm{id}\}.$$

We have $T_A \circ T_B = T_{A \circ B}$ and $T_A^{-1} = T_{A^{-1}}$. In particular, every Möbius transformation is an automorphism of $\mathbb{C}_\infty$.

Proof. It is clear that each T_A is a holomorphic map $\mathbb{C}_\infty \to \mathbb{C}_\infty$. The composition law $T_A \circ T_B = T_{A \circ B}$ and $T_A^{-1} = T_{A^{-1}}$ are simple computations that we leave to the reader. In particular, T_A has a conformal inverse and is thus an automorphism of $\mathbb{C}_\infty$. If $T_A = T_{\widetilde{A}}$ where $A, \widetilde{A} \in \mathrm{SL}(2, \mathbb{C})$, then

$$T_A'(z) = \frac{ad - bc}{(cz + d)^2} = T_{\widetilde{A}}'(z) = \frac{\widetilde{a}\widetilde{d} - \widetilde{b}\widetilde{c}}{(\widetilde{c}z + \widetilde{d})^2}$$

and thus $cz + d = \pm(\widetilde{c}z + \widetilde{d})$ under the assumption that

$$ad - bc = \widetilde{a}\widetilde{d} - \widetilde{b}\widetilde{c} = 1.$$

Hence A and $\widetilde{A}$ are the same matrices in $\mathrm{SL}(2,\mathbb{C})$ possibly up to a choice of sign, which establishes (1.9). $\qquad\square$

Fractional linear transformations enjoy many important properties which can be checked separately for each of the following four elementary transformations. In particular, Lemma 1.8 below proves that the group $\mathrm{PSL}(2,\mathbb{C})$ has four generators (in the sense of group theory).

Lemma 1.8. *Every Möbius transformation is the composition of four elementary maps:*

- *translations $z \mapsto z + z_0$, $z_0 \in \mathbb{C}$,*
- *dilations $z \mapsto \lambda z$, $\lambda > 0$,*
- *rotations $z \mapsto e^{i\theta} z$, $\theta \in \mathbb{R}$,*
- *inversion $z \mapsto \frac{1}{z}$.*

Proof. If $c = 0$, then $T_A(z) = \frac{a}{d}z + \frac{b}{d}$. This is generated by the first three types of transformations. If $c \neq 0$, then we also require an inversion. In fact, one has

$$T_A(z) = \frac{bc - ad}{c^2} \frac{1}{z + \frac{d}{c}} + \frac{a}{c},$$

and we are done. $\qquad\square$

We now consider some examples. Since the imaginary axis is the perpendicular bisector of the segment $(-1,1)$, it follows that the map $z \mapsto w = \frac{z-1}{z+1}$ takes the imaginary axis onto the circle $\{|w| = 1\}$ (since $|z - 1| = |z + 1|$ for $z \in i\mathbb{R}$). Moreover, $1 \mapsto 0$ so the right half-plane is taken onto the disk $\mathbb{D} := \{|w| < 1\}$. Similarly, $z \mapsto \frac{2z-1}{2-z}$ takes $\mathbb{D}$ onto itself with the boundary going onto the boundary. If we include all lines into the family of circles (they are circles passing through ∞), then these examples can serve to motivate the following lemma.

Lemma 1.9. *Fractional linear transformations take circles; onto circles.*

Proof. In view of the previous lemma, the only case requiring an argument is the inversion. Thus, let $|z - z_0| = r$ be a circle and set $w = \frac{1}{z}$. Then

$$\begin{aligned} 0 &= |z|^2 - 2\,\mathrm{Re}(\bar{z}z_0) + |z_0|^2 - r^2 \\ &= \frac{1}{|w|^2} - 2\frac{\mathrm{Re}(wz_0)}{|w|^2} + |z_0|^2 - r^2. \end{aligned}$$

If $|z_0| = r$, then one obtains the equation of a line in w. Note that this is precisely the case when the circle passes through the origin. Otherwise, we obtain the equation

$$0 = \left| w - \frac{\bar{z}_0}{|z_0|^2 - r^2} \right|^2 - \frac{r^2}{(|z_0|^2 - r^2)^2},$$

which is a circle. A line is given by an equation

$$2 \operatorname{Re}(z\bar{z}_0) = a,$$

which transforms into $2 \operatorname{Re}(z_0 w) = a|w|^2$. If $a = 0$, then we obtain another line through the origin. Otherwise, we obtain the equation $|w - z_0/a|^2 = |z_0/a|^2$ which is a circle.

An alternative argument invokes the Riemann sphere and uses the fact that stereographic projection preserves circles; see the problem section. Indeed, note that the inversion $z \mapsto \frac{1}{z}$ corresponds to a rotation of the Riemann sphere about the x_1 axis (the real axis of the plane). Since such a rotation preserves circles, a fractional linear transformation does, too. $\square$

Since $Tz = \frac{az+b}{cz+d} = z$ is a quadratic equation[1] for any Möbius transformation T, we see that T can have at most two fixed points unless it is the identity.

It is also clear that every Möbius transformation has at least one fixed point. The map $Tz = z + 1$ has exactly one fixed point, namely $z = \infty$, whereas $Tz = \frac{1}{z}$ has two, $z = \pm 1$.

Lemma 1.10. *A fractional linear transformation is determined completely by its action on three distinct points. Given distinct points $z_1, z_2, z_3 \in \mathbb{C}_\infty$, there exists a unique fractional linear transformation T with $Tz_1 = 0$, $Tz_2 = 1$, $Tz_3 = \infty$.*

Proof. For the first statement, suppose that S, T are Möbius transformations that agree at three distinct points. Then the Möbius transformation $S^{-1} \circ T$ has three fixed points and is thus the identity. For the second statement, let

$$Tz := \frac{z - z_1}{z - z_3} \frac{z_2 - z_3}{z_2 - z_1}$$

in case $z_1, z_2, z_3 \in \mathbb{C}$. If any one of these points is ∞, then we obtain the correct formula by passing to the limit here. $\square$

Lemma 1.10 suggests the following definition.

---

[1]Strictly speaking, this is a quadratic equation provided $c \neq 0$; if $c = 0$ one, obtains a linear equation with a fixed point in $\mathbb{C}$ and another one at $z = \infty$.

Definition 1.11. The cross ratio of four points $z_0, z_1, z_2, z_3 \in \mathbb{C}_\infty$ is defined as

$$[z_0 : z_1 : z_2 : z_3] := \frac{z_0 - z_1}{z_0 - z_3} \frac{z_2 - z_3}{z_2 - z_1}.$$

The relevance of this quantity lies with its invariance under Möbius transformations.

Lemma 1.12. *The cross ratio of any four distinct points is preserved under Möbius transformations. Moreover, four distinct points lie on a circle if and only if their cross ratio is real.*

Proof. Let z_1, z_2, z_3 be distinct and let $Tz_j = w_j$ for T be a Möbius transformation and $1 \le j \le 3$. Then for all $z \in \mathbb{C}$,

$$[w : w_1 : w_2 : w_3] = [z : z_1 : z_2 : z_3] \quad \text{provided } w = Tz.$$

This follows from the fact that the cross ratio on the left-hand side defines a Möbius transformation $S_1 w$ with the property that $S_1 w_1 = 0, S_1 w_2 = 1, S_1 w_3 = \infty$, whereas the right-hand side defines a transformation S_0 with $S_0 z_1 = 0, S_0 z_2 = 1, S_0 z_3 = \infty$. Hence $S_1^{-1} \circ S_0 = T$ as claimed. The second statement is an immediate consequence of the first and the fact that for any three distinct points $z_1, z_2, z_3 \in \mathbb{R}$, a fourth point z_0 has a real-valued cross ratio with these three if and only if $z_0 \in \mathbb{R}$. $\qquad \square$

It is evident what symmetry of two points relative to a line means: they are reflections of each other relative to the line. While it is less evident what symmetry relative to a circle of finite radius means, the cross ratio allows for a reduction to the case of lines.

Definition 1.13. Let $z_1, z_2, z_3 \in \Gamma$ where $\Gamma \subset \mathbb{C}_\infty$ is a circle. We say that z and z^* are symmetric relative to Γ if

$$\overline{[z : z_1 : z_2 : z_3]} = [z^* : z_1 : z_2 : z_3].$$

Obviously, if $\Gamma = \mathbb{R}$, then $z^* = \bar{z}$. In other words, if Γ is a line, then z^* is the reflection of z across that line. If Γ is a circle of finite radius, then we can reduce matters to this case by an inversion.

Lemma 1.14. *Let $\Gamma = \{|z - z_0| = r\}$. Then for any $z \in \mathbb{C}_\infty$,*

$$z^* = \frac{r^2}{\bar{z} - \bar{z}_0}.$$

Proof. It suffices to consider the unit circle. Then

$$\overline{[z : z_1 : z_2 : z_3]} = [\bar{z} : z_1^{-1} : z_2^{-1} : z_3^{-1}] = [1/\bar{z} : z_1 : z_2 : z_3].$$

In other words, $z^* = \frac{1}{\bar{z}}$. The general case now follows from this via a translation and dilation. $\qquad \square$

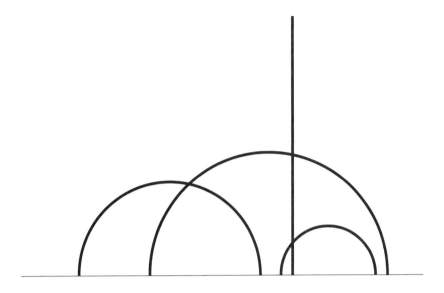

Figure 1.2. Geodesics in the hyperbolic plane

1.5. The hyperbolic plane and the Poincaré disk

Möbius transformations are important for several reasons. We now present a connection to geometry, which can be skipped on first reading. It requires familiarity with basic notions of Riemannian manifolds, such as metrics, isometry group, and geodesics. In the 19th century there was much excitement surrounding non-Euclidean geometry and there is an important connection between Möbius transformations and hyperbolic geometry: the isometries of the hyperbolic plane $\mathbb{H}$ are precisely those Möbius transformations which preserve it. Let us be more precise. Consider the upper half-plane model of the hyperbolic plane given by

$$\mathbb{H} = \{z \in \mathbb{C} \ : \ \operatorname{Im} z > 0\}, \quad ds^2 = \frac{dx^2 + dy^2}{y^2} = \frac{d\bar{z}\,dz}{(\operatorname{Im} z)^2}.$$

The subgroup of $\mathrm{PSL}(2, \mathbb{C})$ which preserves the upper half-plane is precisely $\mathrm{PSL}(2, \mathbb{R})$. Indeed, considering the action on three points on the real line, one sees that $z \mapsto \frac{az+b}{cz+d}$ preserves $\mathbb{R}_\infty := \mathbb{R} \cup \{\infty\}$ if and only if $a, b, c, d \in \lambda\mathbb{R}$ for some $\lambda \in \mathbb{C}^*$. In other words, the stabilizer of $\mathbb{R}$ (as a set) is $\mathrm{PGL}(2, \mathbb{R})$ which contains $\mathrm{PSL}(2, \mathbb{R})$ as an index two subgroup. The latter preserves the upper half-plane, whereas those matrices with negative determinant interchange the upper with the lower half-plane. It is easy to check (see the problems at the end of this chapter) that $\mathrm{PSL}(2, \mathbb{R})$ operates transitively on $\mathbb{H}$ and preserves the metric: for the latter, one computes

$$w = \frac{az+b}{cz+d} \implies \frac{d\bar{w}\,dw}{(\operatorname{Im} w)^2} = \frac{d\bar{z}\,dz}{(\operatorname{Im} z)^2}.$$

In particular, the geodesics are preserved under $\mathrm{PSL}(2,\mathbb{R})$. Since the metric does not depend on x it follows that all vertical lines are geodesics. Now consider $\mathrm{Stab}(i)$, which are all Möbius transformations that fix i. Thus, $\frac{ai+b}{ci+d} = i$ whence $a = d, b = -c$. Since we can assume that $a^2 + b^2 = 1$, it follows that we can set $a + bi = e^{i\theta}$. But then

$$T'(i) = \frac{1}{(ci+d)^2} = e^{2i\theta}$$

acts as a rotation in the tangent space of $\mathbb{H}$ at $z_0 = i$. This property carries over to other $z_0 \in \mathbb{H}$.

Since isometries preserve geodesics, the latter are precisely all circles which intersect the real line at a right angle (with the vertical lines being counted as circles of infinite radius). From this it is clear that the hyperbolic plane satisfies all axioms of Euclidean geometry with the exception of the parallel axiom: there are many "lines" (i.e., geodesics) passing through a point which is not on a fixed geodesic that do not intersect that geodesic. Let us now prove the famous Gauss-Bonnet theorem which describes the hyperbolic area of a triangle whose three sides are geodesics (those are called geodesic triangles). We remark in passing that the following theorem is a special case of a much more general statement about integrating the Gaussian curvature over a geodesic triangle on a general two-dimensional Riemannian manifold. From this perspective, Theorem 1.15 expresses that $\mathbb{H}$ has constant sectional curvature equal to -1. But we shall make no use of this fact here.

Theorem 1.15. *Let T be a geodesic triangle with angles $\alpha_1, \alpha_2, \alpha_3$. Then* $\mathrm{Area}(T) = \pi - (\alpha_1 + \alpha_2 + \alpha_3)$.

Proof. There are four essentially distinct types of geodesic triangles, depending on how many of its vertices lie on $\mathbb{R}_\infty$. Up to equivalences via transformations in $\mathrm{PSL}(2,\mathbb{R})$ (which are isometries and therefore also preserve the area) we see that it suffices to consider precisely those cases described in Figure 1.3. Let us start with the case in which exactly two vertices belong to $\mathbb{R}_\infty$ as shown in that figure (the second triangle from the right). Without loss of generality one vertex coincides with 1, the other with ∞, and the circular arc lies on the unit circle with the projection of the second

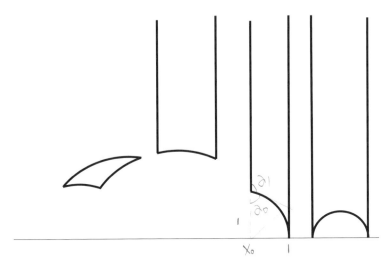

Figure 1.3. Geodesic triangles

finite vertex onto the real axis being x_0. Then

$$\text{Area}(T) = \int_{x_0}^{1} \int_{y(x)}^{\infty} \frac{dx\,dy}{y^2} = \int_{x_0}^{1} \frac{dx}{\sqrt{1-x^2}} \qquad x_0 = \cos\phi$$

$$= \int_{\alpha_0}^{0} \frac{d\cos\phi}{\sqrt{1-\cos^2(\phi)}} = \alpha_0 = \pi - \alpha_1,$$

as desired since the other two angles are zero. By additivity of the area we can deal with the other two cases in which at least one vertex is real. We leave the case where no vertex lies on the (extended) real axis to the reader; the idea is to use Figure 1.4. $\qquad\square$

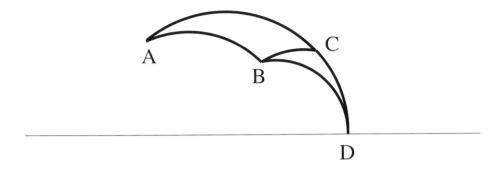

Figure 1.4. The case of no real vertex

We leave it to the reader to generalize the Gauss-Bonnet theorem to geodesic polygons. Many interesting questions about Möbius transformations remain, for example, how to characterize those that correspond to rotations of the sphere, or how to determine all finite subgroups of $\mathrm{PSL}(2, \mathbb{C})$.

The upper half-plane is mapped onto the disk $\mathbb{D}$ by the Möbius transformation $z \mapsto \frac{z-i}{z+i}$. This allows us to map the non-Euclidean geometry that we established on the upper half-plane onto the disk. For example, since Möbius transformations take circles onto circles, we conclude that the geodesics in this geometry on the disk are segments of circular arcs that intersect $\partial \mathbb{D}$ at right angles.

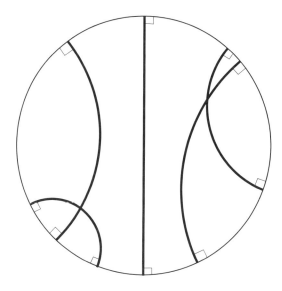

Figure 1.5. The Poincaré disk

Problem 1.13 introduces the natural metrics in these non-Euclidean geometries. Relative to these metrics, the geodesics we observed above are the shortest paths between any two points on them.

1.6. Complex integration, Cauchy theorems

We now develop our complex calculus further. The following definition introduces the complex integral. Indeed, it is the only definition which preserves the fundamental theorem of calculus for holomorphic functions.

Definition 1.16. For any C^1 curve $\gamma : [0, 1] \to \Omega$ and any complex-valued $f \in C(\Omega)$ we define

$$(1.10) \qquad \int_\gamma f(z)\, dz = \int_0^1 f(\gamma(t))\gamma'(t)\, dt.$$

If γ is a closed curve ($\gamma(0) = \gamma(1)$), then we also write $\oint_\gamma f(z)\,dz$ for this integral (note that an orientation needs to be specified). By taking sums, this definition extends to continuous curves γ which are piecewise C^1 on finitely many closed intervals.

The integral is $\mathbb{C}$-valued, and $f(\gamma(t))\gamma'(t)$ is understood as multiplication of complex numbers. From the chain rule, we deduce the fundamental fact that the line integrals of this definition do not depend on any particular C^1 parametrization of the curve as long as the orientation is preserved (hence, there is no loss in assuming that γ is parametrized by $0 \le t \le 1$).

We shall repeatedly encounter the question of estimating the absolute value of the integral in (1.10). Passing the absolute values inside of the integral yields

$$(1.11) \quad \begin{aligned} \left| \int_\gamma f(z)\,dz \right| &\le \int_0^1 |f(\gamma(t))|\,|\gamma'(t)|\,dt \\ &\le \sup_{0 \le t \le 1} |f(\gamma(t))| \int_0^1 |\gamma'(t)|\,dt = ML(\gamma), \end{aligned}$$

where $L(\gamma)$ is the length of γ, and M is an upper bound for $|f|$ on γ. This is our standard estimate on the size of complex integrals.

Let us now investigate the fundamental theorem of calculus in this context.

Proposition 1.17. *From the chain rule, we immediately obtain the following: if $f \in \mathcal{H}(\Omega)$, then*

$$\int_\gamma f'(z)\,dz = f(\gamma(1)) - f(\gamma(0))$$

for any γ as in the definition. In particular,

$$\oint_\gamma f'(z)\,dz = 0 \qquad \forall \text{ closed curves } \gamma \text{ in } \Omega.$$

Proof. It follows from the chain rule that

$$\int_\gamma f'(z)\,dz = \int_0^1 f'(\gamma(t))\gamma'(t)\,dt = \int_0^1 \frac{d}{dt} f(\gamma(t))\,dt = f(\gamma(1)) - f(\gamma(0))$$

for any γ as in the definition. $\qquad \square$

Perhaps the most fundamental complex line integral is the one in the following lemma. It shows that not every integral over a closed loop vanishes.

Lemma 1.18. *Let γ_r be the circle $\{|z| = r\}$, $r > 0$ fixed, with the counter-clockwise orientation. Then*

$$(1.12) \qquad \oint_{\gamma_r} z^n \, dz = \begin{cases} 0 & \text{if } n \neq -1, \\ 2\pi i & \text{if } n = -1, \end{cases}$$

where n is an arbitrary integer.

Proof. By direct computation, with $\gamma_r(t) := re^{it}$, $r > 0$,

$$\oint_{\gamma_r} z^n \, dz = \int_0^{2\pi} r^n e^{int} \, rie^{it} \, dt = \begin{cases} 0 & \text{if } n \neq -1, \\ 2\pi i & \text{if } n = -1. \end{cases}$$

In $\Omega = \mathbb{C}^*$, the function $f(z) = z^n$ has the primitive $F_n(z) = \frac{z^{n+1}}{n+1}$ provided $n \neq -1$. This explains why we obtain 0 for all $n \neq -1$. $\square$

From the $n = -1$ case of the previous lemma, we realize that $\frac{1}{z}$ *does not* have a (holomorphic) primitive on $\mathbb{C}^*$. This issue merits further investigation (for example, we need to answer the question whether $\frac{1}{z}$ has a *local primitive* on $\mathbb{C}^*$—this is indeed the case and this primitive is a branch of $\log z$).

In order to answer such questions, we need to develop some general tools. The most fundamental of those, the Cauchy theorem, gives a sufficient criterion for the path independence of complex line integrals.

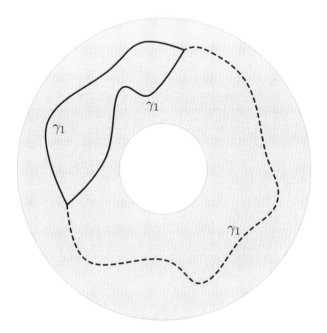

Figure 1.6. Two homotopic curves γ_1 and γ_2. The curve γ_3 is not homotopic to γ_1 or γ_2

Figure 1.6 shows two curves, namely γ_1 and γ_2, which are homotopic within the annular region they lie in. The dashed curve γ_3 is not homotopic to either of them within the annulus.

Theorem 1.19. *Let $\gamma_0, \gamma_1 : [0,1] \to \Omega$ be C^1 curves[2] with $\gamma_0(0) = \gamma_1(0)$ and $\gamma_0(1) = \gamma_1(1)$ (the fixed endpoint case) or $\gamma_0(0) = \gamma_0(1)$, $\gamma_1(0) = \gamma_1(1)$ (the closed case). Assume that they are C^1-homotopic[3] in the following sense: there exists a continuous map $H : [0,1]^2 \to \Omega$ with $H(t,0) = \gamma_0(t)$, $H(t,1) = \gamma_1(t)$ and such that $H(\cdot, s)$ is a C^1 curve for each $0 \le s \le 1$. Moreover, in the fixed endpoint case we assume that H freezes the endpoints, whereas in the closed case we assume that each curve from the homotopy is closed. Then*

$$\int_{\gamma_0} f(z)\,dz = \int_{\gamma_1} f(z)\,dz$$

for all $f \in \mathcal{H}(\Omega)$. In particular, if γ is a closed curve in Ω which is homotopic to a point, then

$$(1.13) \qquad \oint_{\gamma} f(z)\,dz = 0.$$

In particular, this is the case if γ is the boundary of a subregion $\Omega_1 \subset \Omega$ such that $\overline{\Omega_1}$ is diffeomorphic to a closed disk.

Proof. We first note the important fact that $f(z)\,dz$ is a closed form. Indeed,

$$d(f(z)\,dz) = \partial_z f(z)\,dz \wedge dz + \partial_{\bar{z}} f(z)\,d\bar{z} \wedge dz = 0,$$

by the Cauchy-Riemann equation $\partial_{\bar{z}} f = 0$. Thus, Cauchy's theorem is a special case of the homotopy invariance of the integral over closed forms which in turn follows from Stokes's theorem. Let us briefly recall the details: since a closed form is locally exact, we first note that

$$\oint_{\eta} f(z)\,dz = 0$$

for all closed curves η which fall into sufficiently small disks, say. But then we can triangulate the homotopy so that

$$\int_{\gamma_0} f(z)\,dz - \int_{\gamma_1} f(z)\,dz = \sum_j \oint_{\eta_j} f(z)\,dz = 0,$$

where the sum is over a finite collection of small loops which constitute the triangulation of the homotopy H. The more classically minded reader might

---

[2] This can of course be relaxed to piecewise C^1, which means that we can write the curve as a finite concatenation of C^1 curves. The same comment applies to the homotopy.

[3] In light of commonly used terminology it is probably best to refer to this as *homotopic through C^1 curves*, but for simplicity, we shall continue to abuse terminology and use C^1-homotopic.

prefer to use Green's formula, which we now recall: if R is a rectangle, say, and if a, b are C^1 on R, up to the boundary, then

$$\oint_{\partial R} a(x, y)\, dx + b(x, y)\, dy = \iint_R (-a_y(x, y) + b_x(x, y))\, dx\, dy.$$

This formula extends to far more general regions such as those diffeomorphic to a disk and bounded by finitely many C^1 curves. Suppose therefore that $U \subset \Omega$ is such a region. Then returning to our function f as above we obtain

$$\begin{aligned} \oint_{\partial U} f(z)\, dz &= \oint_{\partial U} u\, dx - v\, dy + i(u\, dy + v\, dx) \\ &= \iint_U (-u_y - v_x)\, dx\, dy + i \iint_U (-v_y + u_x)\, dx\, dy = 0, \end{aligned}$$

where the final equality sign follows from the Cauchy-Riemann equations. $\qquad\square$

For the Cauchy theorem it is of course absolutely essential that curves (or "contours" as they are commonly referred to) are deformed *within* the region of holomorphy. Indeed, Lemma 1.18 with $n = -1$ shows that an integral around a closed loop need not vanish. The issue here is, of course, that the circle γ_r cannot be contracted to a point *without hitting the origin*. In a similar vein, (1.13) might fail if γ cannot be "filled in" to a region Ω_1 which lies entirely within Ω; see Lemma 1.18.

The Cauchy theorem is typically applied to simple configurations, such as two circles which are homotopic to each other in the region of holomorphy of some function f. As an example, we now derive the Cauchy formula, a tool of fundamental importance to mathematics.

Proposition 1.20. *Let* $\overline{D(z_0, r)} \subset \Omega$ *and* $f \in \mathcal{H}(\Omega)$. *Then*

$$(1.14) \qquad f(z) = \frac{1}{2\pi i} \oint_\gamma \frac{f(\zeta)}{\zeta - z}\, d\zeta \quad \text{where } \gamma(t) = z_0 + re^{it}$$

for all $z \in D(z_0, r)$.

Proof. Fix any $z \in D(z_0, r)$ and apply Theorem 1.19 to the region $U_\varepsilon := D(z_0, r) \setminus D(z, \varepsilon)$ where $\varepsilon > 0$ is small. The importance of U_ε of course lies with the fact that $\zeta \mapsto \frac{f(\zeta)}{\zeta - z}$ is holomorphic in this region for any $\varepsilon > 0$. Moreover, the two boundary circles of U_ε are homotopic to each other relative to the region $\Omega \setminus \{z\}$. Therefore, by Theorem 1.19,

(1.15)
$$
\begin{aligned}
0 &= \frac{1}{2\pi i} \int_{\partial U_\varepsilon} \frac{f(\zeta)}{z - \zeta} \, d\zeta = \frac{1}{2\pi i} \int_{\partial D(z_0, r)} \frac{f(\zeta)}{z - \zeta} \, d\zeta \\
&\quad - \frac{1}{2\pi i} \int_{\partial D(z,\varepsilon)} \frac{f(\zeta) - f(z)}{z - \zeta} \, d\zeta - \frac{f(z)}{2\pi i} \int_{\partial D(z,\varepsilon)} \frac{1}{z - \zeta} \, d\zeta \\
&= \frac{1}{2\pi i} \int_{\partial D(z_0, r)} \frac{f(\zeta)}{z - \zeta} \, d\zeta + O(\varepsilon) + f(z) \quad \text{as} \ \ \varepsilon \to 0.
\end{aligned}
$$

To pass to the last line we bounded the first integral in (1.15), which involves the ratio $\frac{f(\zeta) - f(z)}{z - \zeta}$, via (1.11), noting that differentiability implies that

$$
\left| \frac{f(\zeta) - f(z)}{z - \zeta} \right| \leq M \quad \forall \, 0 < |z - \zeta| \leq \varepsilon_0,
$$

where $\varepsilon_0 > 0$ is small and fixed. This gives the $O(\varepsilon)$ in the final equality. Furthermore, we used the $n = -1$ case of (1.12) to pass to the third term of the last line:

$$
-\frac{f(z)}{2\pi i} \int_{\partial D(z,\varepsilon)} \frac{1}{z - \zeta} \, d\zeta = f(z)
$$

and we are done. $\qquad\square$

It is clear both from the statement and the proof that Cauchy's formula is intimately tied up with the $n = -1$ case of (1.12). The Cauchy formula is remarkable for many reasons. Indeed, it implies that a holomorphic function in a disk is determined by its values on the boundary of the disk.

1.7. Applications of Cauchy's theorems

It also implies the astonishing fact that holomorphic functions are in fact analytic. This is done by noting that the integrand in (1.14) is analytic relative to z. In other words, we reduce ourselves to the geometric series.

Corollary 1.21. $\mathcal{A}(\Omega) = \mathcal{H}(\Omega)$. *In fact, every $f \in \mathcal{H}(\Omega)$ is represented by a convergent power series on $D(z_0, r)$ where $r = \mathrm{dist}(z_0, \partial\Omega)$.*

Proof. We proved in Lemma 1.3 that analytic functions are holomorphic. For the converse, we use the previous proposition to conclude that with γ

given by a circle $\{|\zeta - z_0| = r_0\} \subset \Omega$ and z lying inside of this circle,

$$f(z) = \frac{1}{2\pi i} \oint_\gamma \frac{f(\zeta)}{\zeta - z_0 - (z - z_0)} \, d\zeta$$

$$= \frac{1}{2\pi i} \oint_\gamma \frac{f(\zeta)}{\zeta - z_0} \sum_{n=0}^\infty \left(\frac{z - z_0}{\zeta - z_0}\right)^n d\zeta$$

$$= \sum_{n=0}^\infty \frac{1}{2\pi i} \oint_\gamma \frac{f(\zeta)}{(\zeta - z_0)^{n+1}} \, d\zeta \, (z - z_0)^n.$$

The interchange of summation and integration is justified due to uniform and absolute convergence of the series which follows from $\left|\frac{z-z_0}{\zeta-z_0}\right| = \frac{|z-z_0|}{r_0} < 1$. Thus, we obtain that f is analytic and, moreover,

$$f(z) = \sum_{n=0}^\infty \frac{f^{(n)}(z_0)}{n!} (z - z_0)^n$$

converges on $|z - z_0| < \operatorname{dist}(z_0, \partial\Omega)$ with

(1.16)
$$f^{(n)}(z_0) = \frac{n!}{2\pi i} \oint_\gamma \frac{f(\zeta)}{(\zeta - z_0)^{n+1}} \, d\zeta$$

for any $n \geq 0$. $\square$

Consider the function $f(x) = \frac{1}{1+x^2}$ on the real line. Around $x = 0$ this function has a convergent Taylor series

$$f(x) = \sum_{n=0}^\infty (-1)^n x^{2n}, \quad |x| < 1.$$

But there is no apparent reason why the radius of convergence should be $R = 1$ in this case. Indeed, $f(x)$ remains smooth on the whole real line. However, when viewed over the complex numbers, $f(z) = \frac{1}{1+z^2}$ immediately reveals the reason for this barrier: f ceases to be holomorphic at $z = \pm i$ whence $R = 1$.

In summary, in contrast to power series over $\mathbb{R}$, over $\mathbb{C}$ there is an explanation for the radius of convergence: $f(z) = \sum_{n=0}^\infty a_n (z - z_0)^n$ has finite and positive radius of convergence R if and only if $f \notin \mathcal{H}(\Omega)$ for every Ω which compactly contains $D(z_0, R)$. We immediately obtain a number of corollaries from this. Recall that an entire function is holomorphic on the whole complex plane.

Corollary 1.22. *(a) Cauchy's estimates: Let $f \in \mathcal{H}(\Omega)$ with $|f(z)| \leq M$ on Ω. Then*

$$|f^{(n)}(z)| \leq \frac{Mn!}{\operatorname{dist}(z, \partial\Omega)^n}$$

for every $n \geq 0$ and all $z \in \Omega$.

(b) Liouville's theorem: If $f \in \mathcal{H}(\mathbb{C}) \cap L^\infty(\mathbb{C})$, then f is constant. In other words: bounded entire functions are constant. More generally, if $|f(z)| \le C(1 + |z|^N)$ for all $z \in \mathbb{C}$, for some fixed integer $N \ge 0$ and a finite constant C, then f is a polynomial of degree at most N.

Proof. (a) follows by putting absolute values inside (1.16), in other words we use (1.11). For

(b) apply (a) to $\Omega = D(0, R)$ and let $R \to \infty$. This shows that $f^{(k)} \equiv 0$ for all $k > N$. $\qquad\square$

Part (b) has a famous consequence, namely the *fundamental theorem of algebra*.

Proposition 1.23. *Every polynomial $P \in \mathbb{C}[z]$ of positive degree has a complex zero; in fact, it has exactly as many zeros over $\mathbb{C}$ (counted with multiplicity) as its degree.*

Proof. Suppose $P(z) \in \mathbb{C}[z]$ is a polynomial of positive degree and without zero in $\mathbb{C}$. Then $f(z) := \frac{1}{P(z)}$ is an entire function. We claim that this function vanishes at infinity. Indeed,

$$P(z) = a_n z^n + a_{n-1} z^{n-1} + \cdots + a_1 z + a_0$$

with $n \ge 1$ and $a_n \ne 0$. Thus,

$$|P(z)| \ge |a_n||z|^n - \sum_{k=0}^{n-1} |a_k||z|^k \ge \frac{1}{2}|a_n|R^n$$

for all $|z| = R$, with R large. Hence $|P(z)| \to \infty$ as $|z| \to \infty$, and f is bounded. By Liouville, f is constant and so P is constant contrary to the assumption of positive degree. So $P(z_0) = 0$ for some $z_0 \in \mathbb{C}$. Factoring out $z - z_0$ we conclude inductively that P has exactly $\deg(P)$ many complex zeros, as desired. $\qquad\square$

We now return to the problem of finding holomorphic primitives to complex-valued functions f on a region Ω. Since holomorphic functions are analytic, and therefore have holomorphic derivatives of any order, it follows that f needs to be itself holomorphic. However, as the example $f(z) = z^{-1}$ on $\Omega = \mathbb{C} \setminus \{0\}$ shows, not every region Ω is admissible (compare Lemma 1.18 and Proposition 1.17). Of key importance here is the notion of simple connectivity.

Definition 1.24. A region Ω is called simply-connected if every closed curve can be contracted to a point. In other words, if there is a homotopy between any closed curve and a constant curve.

In the definition it makes no difference if we use continuous curves or (piecewise) C^1 curves.

Also, by the assumed connectivity of Ω we conclude that the point to which we contract can be chosen arbitrarily.

Proposition 1.25. *Let Ω be simply-connected. Then for every $f \in \mathcal{H}(\Omega)$ such that $f \neq 0$ everywhere on Ω there exists $g \in \mathcal{H}(\Omega)$ with $e^{g(z)} = f(z)$. The function g is unique up to additive constants $2\pi i n$, $n \in \mathbb{Z}$ and any such choice of g is called a branch of the logarithm of f. Furthermore, for any $n \geq 1$ there exists $f_n \in \mathcal{H}(\Omega)$ with $(f_n(z))^n = f(z)$ for all $z \in \Omega$.*

In particular, if $\Omega \subset \mathbb{C}^*$ is simply-connected, then there exists $g \in \mathcal{H}(\Omega)$ with $e^{g(z)} = z$ everywhere on Ω. Such a g is called a branch of $\log z$. Similarly, there exist holomorphic branches of any $\sqrt[n]{z}$ on Ω, $n \geq 1$.

Proof. If $e^g = f$, then $g' = \frac{f'}{f}$ in Ω. So fix any $z_0 \in \Omega$ and define

$$g(z) := \int_{z_0}^z \frac{f'(\zeta)}{f(\zeta)}\, d\zeta,$$

where the integration path joins z_0 to z and consists of a finite number of line segments (say). We claim that $g(z)$ does not depend on the choice of path. First note that $\frac{f'}{f} \in \mathcal{H}(\Omega)$ due to analyticity and nonvanishing of f. Second, since Ω is simply-connected, any two curves with coinciding initial and terminal points are homotopic to each other via a piecewise C^1 homotopy. Thus, Theorem 1.19 yields the desired equality of the integrals. It is now an easy matter to check that $g'(z) = \frac{f'(z)}{f(z)}$. Indeed,

$$\frac{g(z+h) - g(z)}{h} = \int_0^1 \frac{f'(z+th)}{f(z+th)}\, dt \to \frac{f'(z)}{f(z)} \quad \text{as } h \to 0.$$

So $g \in \mathcal{H}(\Omega)$ and $(fe^{-g})' \equiv 0$ shows that $e^g = cf$ where c is some constant different from zero and therefore $c = e^k$ for some $k \in \mathbb{C}$. Hence $e^{g(z)-k} = f(z)$ for all $z \in \Omega$ and we are done with the logarithm.

For the roots, set $f_n(z) := e^{g(z)/n}$. Then $(f_n(z))^n = e^{g(z)} = f(z)$ as desired. $\qquad\square$

The equivalence between holomorphic and analytic functions clearly has far-reaching consequences. We now present some results in this direction which heavily rely on properties of power series.

We begin with the *uniqueness theorem*. The name derives from the fact that two functions $f, g \in \mathcal{H}(\Omega)$ are identical if the set $\{z \in \Omega : f(z) = g(z)\}$ has an accumulation point inside of Ω.

Throughout, for any disk D, the punctured disk D^* denotes D with its center removed.

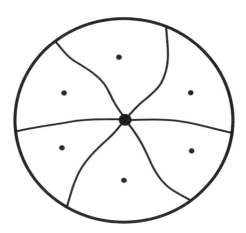

Figure 1.7. A branch point

Proposition 1.26. *Let $f \in \mathcal{H}(\Omega)$. Then the following are equivalent:*

- $f \equiv 0$,
- *for some $z_0 \in \Omega$, $f^{(n)}(z_0) = 0$ for all $n \geq 0$,*
- *the set $\{z \in \Omega : f(z) = 0\}$ has an accumulation point in Ω.*

Proof. We only need to show that third property implies the identical vanishing. Let $z_n \to z_0 \in \Omega$ as $n \to \infty$, where $f(z_n) = 0$ for all $n \geq 1$. Suppose $f^{(m)}(z_0) \neq 0$ for some $m \geq 0$. Then

$$f(z) = \sum_{k=0}^{\infty} a_k (z - z_0)^k = a_N (z - z_0)^N (1 + O(z - z_0)) \quad \text{as } z \to z_0$$

locally around z_0 where $N \geq 0$ is minimal with the property that $a_N \neq 0$. But then it is clear that f does not vanish on some punctured disk $D(z_0, r)^*$, contrary to assumption. Thus, $f^{(n)}(z_0) = 0$ for all $n \geq 0$ and thus $f \equiv 0$ locally around z_0. Since Ω is connected, it then follows that $f \equiv 0$ on Ω. Indeed, define $S := \{z \in \Omega \mid f \text{ vanishes locally around } z\}$. Then S is evidently open, but it is also closed by what we have just shown. Since $S \neq \emptyset$ it follows that $S = \Omega$ (recall Ω connected). This settles the equivalences. $\square$

Next, we describe the rigid mapping properties of holomorphic functions via a *normal form* representation (1.17). Amongst other things, this yields the *open mapping theorem* for nonconstant analytic functions.

Proposition 1.27. *Assume that f is holomorphic and is not constant. Then at every point $z_0 \in \Omega$ there exist a positive integer n and a holomorphic function h locally at z_0 such that*

$$(1.17) \qquad f(z) = f(z_0) + [(z - z_0)h(z)]^n, \qquad h(z_0) \neq 0.$$

In particular, there are disks $D(z_0, \rho), D(f(z_0), r)$ with the property that every $w \in D(f(z_0), r)^*$ has precisely n pre-images under f in $D(z_0, \rho)^*$. If $f'(z_0) \neq 0$, then f is a local C^∞ diffeomorphism. Finally, every nonconstant holomorphic map is an open map (i.e., it takes open sets to open sets).

Proof. If f' does not vanish identically, let us first assume that $f'(z_0) \neq 0$. We claim that *locally* around z_0, the map $f(z)$ is a C^∞ diffeomorphism from a neighborhood of z_0 onto a neighborhood of $f(z_0)$ and, moreover, that the inverse map to f is also holomorphic. Indeed, in view of Theorem 1.4, the differential df is invertible at z_0. Hence by the usual inverse function theorem from multivariable calculus[4] we obtain the statement about diffeomorphisms. Furthermore, since df is conformal locally around z_0, its inverse is, too, and so f^{-1} is conformal and thus holomorphic. If $f'(z_0) = 0$, then there exists some positive integer n with $f^{(n)}(z_0) \neq 0$. But then from the power series representation

$$f(z) = f(z_0) + (z - z_0)^n g(z)$$

with $g \in \mathcal{H}(\Omega)$ satisfying $g(z_0) \neq 0$. By Proposition 1.25 we can write $g(z) = (h(z))^n$ for some $h \in \mathcal{H}(U)$ where U is a neighborhood of z_0 and $h(z_0) \neq 0$, whence (1.17). Now consider the function

$$\varphi(z) := (z - z_0)h(z).$$

By construction, $f(z) = f(z_0) + \varphi(z)^n$. We note that

$$\varphi'(z_0) = h(z_0) \neq 0.$$

By the preceding analysis of the $n = 1$ case we conclude that $\varphi(z)$ is a local diffeomorphism. But this implies that any $w \neq f(z_0)$ which lies in a small neighborhood of $f(z_0)$ admits exactly n solutions to the equation $f(z) = w$. Indeed, this equation is equivalent with the equation $w - f(z_0) = \varphi(z)^n$. Indeed, each of the nth roots of $w - f(z_0)$ (which are all distinct) has a unique pre-image under $\varphi(z)$. In summary, f has the stated n-to-one mapping property. The openness is now also evident. $\square$

Figure 1.7 shows the case of $n = 6$. The dots symbolize the six pre-images of some point. We remark that any point $z_0 \in \Omega$ for which $n \geq 2$ is called a *branch point*. The branch points are precisely the zeros of f' in Ω and therefore form a discrete subset of Ω (this means that every point of this subset is isolated from the other ones).

Corollary 1.28. *Suppose f is analytic on Ω and a bijection between Ω and Ω'. Then $f' \neq 0$ on Ω and $f^{-1} : \Omega' \to \Omega$ (the inverse map of f) is analytic.*

---

[4]In the following chapter we will use Rouché's theorem of complex analysis to circumvent this recourse through real calculus.

Proof. Proposition 1.27 implies that $f'(z) \neq 0$ for every $z \in \Omega$ so f is conformal. By real-variable calculus, the differential of f^{-1} at $w = f(z)$ is the inverse of the differential of f at z, in symbols $Df^{-1}(w) = (Df(z))^{-1}$. This matrix is again a composition of a rotation with a dilation and so f^{-1} is conformal and thus analytic. By the open mapping theorem, Ω' is open and is also connected. $\qquad\square$

The maps described by the previous corollary play a central role in complex analysis and geometry.

Definition 1.29. A mapping as in Corollary 1.28 is called a *conformal isomorphism* between Ω and Ω', or simply an *isomorphism*. This establishes an equivalence relation between regions. If $\Omega = \Omega'$, then we call the map an *automorphism*. These maps form a group, denoted by $\mathrm{Aut}(\Omega)$.

It is of course a natural problem to determine when two regions are isomorphic. In other words, we wish to classify regions up to conformal equivalence. We shall discuss this problem in the wider and more suitable framework of Riemann surfaces, where the solution goes by the name of *uniformization theorem*.

Proposition 1.27 has an important implication known as the *maximum principle*.

Corollary 1.30. *Let $f \in \mathcal{H}(\Omega)$. If there exists $z_0 \in \Omega$ with $|f(z)| \leq |f(z_0)|$ for all $z \in \Omega$, then f is constant. If Ω is bounded and f is continuous on $\overline{\Omega}$, then $|f(z)| \leq \max_{\zeta \in \partial\Omega} |f(\zeta)|$ for all $z \in \Omega$. Equality can occur here only if f is constant.*

Proof. If f is not constant, then $f(\Omega)$ is open contradicting that $f(z_0) \in \partial f(\Omega)$, which is required by $|f(z)| \leq |f(z_0)|$ on Ω. The second part is a consequence of the first one and the fact that continuous functions on compact domains attain their supremum. $\qquad\square$

In the second part of the maximum principle it is essential to assume that Ω is bounded. Indeed, consider $f(z) = e^{e^z}$ on the strip $-\frac{\pi}{2} < \mathrm{Im}(z) < \frac{\pi}{2}$. Then on the boundary lines f is bounded, but it is clearly unbounded on the strip. A positive statement can still be made, provided we exclude rapid growth of the type exhibited by this function. This goes by the name of Phragmen-Lindelöf theorems; see for example Problem 3.7 below.

The following Schwarz lemma serves both as a useful tool as well as a nice illustration of the maximum principle. $\mathbb{D}$ denotes the open unit disk centered at the origin.

Lemma 1.31. *Suppose $f : \mathbb{D} \to \mathbb{D}$ is analytic and $f(0) = 0$. Then $|f(z)| \leq |z|$ for all $z \in \mathbb{D}^*$ with equality if and only if f is a rotation. If f is bijective, from $\mathbb{D}$ onto itself, then f is a rotation.*

Proof. The power series of f around $z = 0$ converges on $\mathbb{D}$ and does not contain a constant term. Consider $g(z) := \frac{f(z)}{z}$, which is therefore analytic on $\mathbb{D}$. Let $0 < r < 1$ and set

$$\max_{|z|=r} |g(z)| =: M_r.$$

Then $\limsup_{r \to 1^-} M_r \leq 1$ whence $|f(z)| \leq |z|$ by the maximum principle. If $|g(z)| = 1$ for some $z \neq 0$, then g is a constant. In other words, $f(z) = e^{i\theta} z$ for some real θ. Now suppose that f is invertible. Then we can apply the same reasoning to f^{-1} which implies that $|f^{-1}(w)| \leq |w|$ which is the same as $|f(z)| \geq |z|$ for all z. So the first part implies that f is a rotation. $\qquad\square$

Natural examples for Lemma 1.31 are $f(z) = e^{i\theta} z^k$ where $k \geq 1$ is an integer and $\theta \in \mathbb{R}$. Note that the only case of a bijection is $k = 1$.

In Problem 1.12 the reader will find some extensions of the Schwarz lemma. The main application of the Schwarz lemma is in characterizing all conformal automorphisms of the disk.

Proposition 1.32. *All conformal automorphisms of the disk are given by*

$$\left\{ \varphi_{a,\theta}(z) := e^{i\theta} \frac{z - a}{1 - z\bar{a}} \;\middle|\; |a| < 1, \theta \in \mathbb{R} \right\}.$$

Proof. It is elementary to check that $|\varphi_{a,\theta}(z)| = 1$ for all $|z| = 1$ (see the first problem of this chapter). Moreover, $\varphi_{a,\theta}(a) = 0$ so the Möbius transform $\varphi_{a,\theta}$ takes $\mathbb{D}$ to itself. Furthermore, we leave it to the reader to check that all Möbius transformations that preserve the disk are of this form.

Now suppose $\psi \in \mathrm{Aut}(\mathbb{D})$. Then $\psi(a) = 0$ and $\varphi_{a,\theta} \circ \psi^{-1} \in \mathrm{Aut}(\mathbb{D})$ and it preserves the origin. So by the Schwarz lemma, this map is a rotation whence the result follows. $\qquad\square$

To conclude our presentation of integration theory, we present Morera's theorem (a kind of converse to Cauchy's theorem).

Theorem 1.33. *Let $f \in C(\Omega)$ and suppose $\mathcal{T}$ is a collection of triangles in Ω which contains all sufficiently small triangles*[5] *in Ω. If*

$$(1.18) \qquad\qquad \oint_{\partial T} f(z)\, dz = 0 \qquad \forall\, T \in \mathcal{T},$$

then $f \in \mathcal{H}(\Omega)$.

---

[5] This means that every point in Ω has a neighborhood in Ω such that all triangles which lie inside that neighborhood belong to $\mathcal{T}$.

Proof. The idea is to find a local holomorphic primitive of f. Thus, assume $D(0, r) \subset \Omega$ is a small disk and set

$$F(z) := \int_0^z f(\zeta)\, d\zeta = z \int_0^1 f(tz)\, dt$$

for all $|z| < r$. Writing out our assumption (1.18) over each of the three line segments bounding the triangle with vertices $\{0, z, z + h\}$, we conclude for $|z| < r$ and h small that

$$F(z + h) - F(z) = \int_z^{z+h} f(\zeta)\, d\zeta$$

where the integration is along a straight line segment connecting z to $z + h$. Parametrizing this line segment as $z + th$ with $0 \le t \le 1$ we obtain

$$\frac{F(z + h) - F(z)}{h} = \int_0^1 f(z + th)\, dt \to f(z)$$

as $h \to 0$. This shows that $F \in \mathcal{H}(D(0, r))$ and therefore also $F' = f \in \mathcal{H}(D(0, r))$. Hence $f \in \mathcal{H}(\Omega)$ as desired. $\qquad\square$

Now suppose $\{f_n\}_{n \ge 1}$ is a sequence of analytic functions on Ω which converges uniformly on compact subsets to some function f. Then f is clearly continuous. Furthermore, using the notation of Theorem 1.33 we see that (1.18) holds since it does for each f_n by Cauchy's theorem; taking limits then yields the same property for f. So f is again analytic. We shall develop this powerful principle in more detail in the next chapter.

A well-known consequence of Morera's theorem is the fact that complex differentiability of a function everywhere in a region implies holomorphy. In other words, the continuity of the derivative need not be imposed in the definition of holomorphic functions. This fact is known as Goursat's theorem.

Theorem 1.34. *Let f be complex differentiable everywhere in a region Ω. Then $f \in \mathcal{H}(\Omega)$.*

Proof. Given a triangle Δ which lies entirely within Ω (with its interior), we define the basic subdivision process as follows: mark the three midpoints of the sides of the triangle and draw a new triangle with these points as vertices. This divides Δ into four congruent subtriangles. Denote them by $\Delta^{(j)}$, $1 \le j \le 4$.

Suppose $\left| \oint_\Delta f(z)\, dz \right| = \delta > 0$. Then for some $1 \le j \le 4$,

$$\left| \oint_{\Delta^{(j)}} f(z)\, dz \right| \ge \frac{\delta}{4}.$$

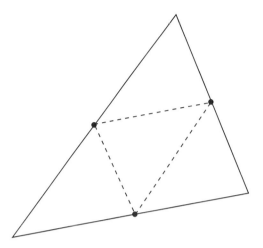

Figure 1.8. The triangle division in Goursat's theorem

Applying the basic subdivision process repeatedly, we see that there exists a sequence Δ_ℓ of nested triangles with $\Delta_0 := \Delta$ such that $\Delta_{\ell+1} \subset \Delta_\ell$ is obtained from Δ_ℓ by a Euclidean motion and a dilation by a factor $\frac{1}{2}$. Moreover,

$$(1.19) \qquad \left| \oint_{\Delta_\ell} f(z)\, dz \right| \geq \frac{\delta}{4^\ell} \qquad \forall\, \ell \geq 0.$$

To lead this to a contradiction, we denote z_0 the unique point in the intersection:

$$\{z_0\} = \bigcap_\ell \Delta_\ell.$$

By the definition of differentiability,

$$f(z) = f(z_0) + f'(z_0)(z - z_0) + r(z)$$

where for any $\varepsilon > 0$ we have $|r(z)| < \varepsilon |z - z_0|$ provided $|z - z_0|$ is small enough. But since

$$\oint_{\Delta_\ell} (f(z_0) + f'(z_0)(z - z_0))\, dz = 0,$$

we see that

$$\left| \oint_{\Delta_\ell} f(z)\, dz \right| \leq L(\Delta_\ell) \max_{z \in \partial \Delta_\ell} |r(z)| \leq \varepsilon 4^{-\ell}$$

for large ℓ. This contradicts (1.19). By Morera's theorem we conclude that f is analytic. $\qquad\qquad \square$

1.8. Harmonic functions

This section is merely an introduction to this rich area which is explored in more detail in a later chapter.

Definition 1.35. A function $u : \Omega \to \mathbb{C}$ is called harmonic if $u \in C^2(\Omega)$ and $\Delta u = u_{xx} + u_{yy} = 0$.

Typically, harmonic functions are taken to be real-valued but there is no need to make this restriction in general. The following result explains the ubiquity of harmonic functions in complex analysis.

Proposition 1.36. *If $f \in \mathcal{H}(\Omega)$, then $\mathrm{Re}(u), \mathrm{Im}(v)$ are harmonic in Ω.*

Proof. First, $u := \mathrm{Re}(f), v := \mathrm{Im}(f) \in C^\infty(\Omega)$ by analyticity of f. Second, by the Cauchy-Riemann equations,

$$u_{xx} + u_{yy} = v_{yx} - v_{xy} = 0, \qquad v_{xx} + v_{yy} = -u_{yx} + u_{xy} = 0,$$

as claimed. $\qquad\qquad\square$

This motivates the following definition.

Definition 1.37. Let u be harmonic on Ω and real-valued. We say that v is the harmonic conjugate of u if v is harmonic and real-valued on Ω and $u + iv \in \mathcal{H}(\Omega)$.

Let us first note that a harmonic conjugate, if it exists, is unique up to constants; indeed, if not, then we would have a real-valued harmonic function v on Ω such that $iv \in \mathcal{H}(\Omega)$. But from the Cauchy-Riemann equations we would then conclude that $\nabla v = 0$ or v is constant by connectedness of Ω.

This definition presents us with the question of whether every harmonic function on a region of $\mathbb{R}^2$ has a harmonic conjugate. The classical example for the failure of this is $u(z) = \log|z|$ on $\mathbb{C}^*$; in view of the complex logarithm, the unique harmonic conjugate v with $v(1) = 0$ would have to be the polar angle which is not defined on $\mathbb{C}^*$. However, in view of Proposition 1.25 it is defined and harmonic on every simply-connected region in $\mathbb{C}^*$. As the following proposition explains, this is a general fact.

Proposition 1.38. *Let Ω be simply-connected and u real-valued and harmonic on Ω. Then $u = \mathrm{Re}(f)$ for some $f \in \mathcal{H}(\Omega)$ and f is unique up to an additive imaginary constant.*

Proof. We already established the uniqueness property. To obtain existence, we need to solve the Cauchy-Riemann equations. In other words, we need to find a potential v to the vector field $(-u_y, u_x)$ on Ω, i.e., $\nabla v = (-u_y, u_x)$. If v exists, then it is $C^2(\Omega)$ and

$$\Delta v = -u_{yx} + u_{xy} = 0,$$

hence v is harmonic. Define

$$v(z) := \int_{z_0}^{z} -u_y \, dx + u_x \, dy$$

where the line integral is along a curve connecting z_0 to z which consists of finitely many line segments, say. If γ is a closed curve of this type in Ω, then by Green's theorem,

$$\oint_{\gamma} -u_y \, dx + u_x \, dy = \iint_{U} (u_{yy} + u_{xx}) \, dx \, dy = 0$$

where $\partial U = \gamma$ (this requires Ω to be simply-connected). So the line integral defining v does not depend on the choice of curve and v is therefore well-defined on Ω. Furthermore, as usual one can check that $\nabla v = (-u_y, u_x)$ as desired. A quick but less self-contained proof is as follows: the differential form

$$\omega := -u_y \, dx + u_x \, dy$$

is closed since $d\omega = \Delta u \, dx \wedge dy = 0$. Hence it is locally exact and by simple connectivity of Ω, exact on all of Ω. In other words, $\omega = dv$ for some smooth real-valued function v on Ω as desired. □

From this, we can easily draw several conclusions about harmonic functions. We begin with the important observation that a conformal change of coordinates preserves harmonic functions.

Corollary 1.39. *Let u be harmonic in Ω and $f : \Omega_0 \to \Omega$ holomorphic. Then $u \circ f$ is harmonic in Ω_0.*

Proof. Locally around every point of Ω, there is a v such that $u + iv$ is holomorphic. Since the composition of holomorphic functions is again holomorphic, the statement follows. There is of course a direct way of checking this: since $\Delta = 4\partial_z \partial_{\bar{z}}$ one has from the chain rule (1.7)

$$\partial_z(u \circ f) = (\partial_w u) \circ f \, \partial_z f + (\partial_{\bar{w}} u) \circ f \, \overline{\partial_{\bar{z}} f} = (\partial_w u) \circ f \, f'$$

and thus, furthermore,

$$\Delta(u \circ f) = 4\partial_{\bar{z}} \partial_z (u \circ f) = 4(\partial_{\bar{w}} \partial_w u) \circ f |f'|^2 = |f'|^2 \, (\Delta u) \circ f$$

whence the result. □

Next, we describe the well-known mean-value and maximum properties of harmonic functions.

Corollary 1.40. *Let u be harmonic on Ω. Then $u \in C^\infty(\Omega)$, u satisfies the mean-value property*

$$(1.20) \qquad u(z_0) = \int_0^1 u(z_0 + re^{2\pi it}) \, dt \qquad \forall \, r < \text{dist}(z_0, \partial\Omega),$$

and u obeys the maximum principle: if u attains a local maximum or mini-mum in Ω, then u is constant. In particular, if Ω is bounded and $u \in C(\overline{\Omega})$, then

$$\min_{\partial\Omega} u \leq u(z) \leq \max_{\partial\Omega} u \qquad \forall\, z \in \Omega,$$

where equality can be attained only if u is constant.

Proof. Let $U \subset \Omega$ be simply-connected, say a disk. By Proposition 1.38, $u = \mathrm{Re}(f)$ where $f \in \mathcal{H}(U)$. Since $f \in C^\infty(U)$, so is u. Moreover,

$$f(z_0) = \frac{1}{2\pi i} \oint_\gamma \frac{f(z)}{z - z_0}\, dz = \int_0^1 f(z_0 + re^{2\pi it})\, dt.$$

Passing to the real part proves (1.20). For the maximum principle, suppose that u attains a local extremum on some disk in Ω. Then it follows from (1.20) that u has to be constant on that disk. Since any two points in Ω are contained in a simply-connected subregion of Ω, we conclude from the existence of conjugate harmonic functions on simply-connected regions as well as the uniqueness theorem for analytic functions that u is globally constant. □

The mean-value property already characterizes harmonic functions. For this, see the chapter on harmonic functions. It is important to note that harmonic functions are not tied to dimension two. The defining equation $\Delta u = 0$ applies to any dimension. The concept of a conjugate harmonic function of course does not apply in the same form as we saw it here. However, the mean-value property and maximum principles do apply. See the final problem of this chapter.

Notes

All of this material is standard, but the presentation and organization of all the basic results in this chapter, as well as the following one is perhaps unusual. The section on non-Euclidean geometry is meant to illustrate the concept of complex differentiability, which should be seen as a geometric one. For the same reason, we discuss Möbius transformations before complex integration. The Poincaré disk will appear again numerous times in this text, for example in Chapter 4 in the construction of the covering space of the twice punctured plane, but of course also in Chapter 8 as part of the Uniformization Theorem.

For much more on Möbius transformations and how they relate to geome-try, group theory, etc., we urge the reader to consult the nice book by Jones and Singerman [47]. Later in the text we will study groups of Möbius transforms by the name of Fuchsian groups, which play a crucial role in the classification of non-simply-connected Riemann surfaces. See Chapters 4 and 8, as well as the book by Katok [50].

Some texts, such as Lang [55], establish the Cauchy theorem without any reference to Green (or Stokes) and the Cauchy-Riemann equations. Rather, one argues directly as in Goursat's theorem; see Theorem 1.34. The author believes, however, that the approach through Cauchy-Riemann is much more fundamental, as it shows that the 1-form $f'(z)\,dz$ being closed is the reason why Cauchy's theorem is true. The extra C^1 condition required in the definition of holomorphic functions is a small price to pay in comparison to the loss of transparency. The $dz, d\bar{z}$ formalism is known as Wirtinger calculus.

1.9. Problems

Problem 1.1. Let $\{z_j\}_{j=1}^n \subset \mathbb{C}$ be distinct points and $m_j > 0$ for $1 \le j \le n$. Assume $\sum_{j=1}^n m_j = 1$ and define $z = \sum_{j=1}^n m_j z_j$. Prove that every line ℓ through z *separates* the points $\{z_j\}_{j=1}^n$ unless all of them are collinear. Here "separates" means that there are points from $\{z_j\}_{j=1}^n$ on both sides of the line ℓ (without being on ℓ).

Problem 1.2. Suppose $p_0 > p_1 > p_2 > \cdots > p_n > 0$. Prove that all zeros of the polynomial $P(z) = \sum_{j=0}^n p_j\, z^j$ lie in $\{|z| > 1\}$.

Problem 1.3. Let $P(z) = \sum_{j=0}^n a_j\, z^j$ be a polynomial of degree $n \ge 1$ with all roots inside the unit circle $|z| < 1$. Define $P^*(z) = z^n \bar{P}(z^{-1})$ where $\bar{P}(z) = \sum_{j=0}^n \bar{a}_j\, z^j$. Show that all roots of

$$P(z) + P^*(z) = 0$$

lie on the unit circle $|z| = 1$. Do the same for $P(z) + e^{i\theta} P^*(z) = 0$, with $\theta \in \mathbb{R}$ arbitrary.

Problem 1.4. In the problem we express simple geometric shapes via relations between complex numbers.

(a) Let $a, b \in \mathbb{C}$ and $k > 0$. Describe the set of points $z \in \mathbb{C}$ which satisfy

$$|z - a| + |z - b| \le k.$$

(b) Let $|a| < 1$, $a \in \mathbb{C}$. The plane $\mathbb{C}$ is divided into three subsets according to whether

$$w = \frac{z - a}{1 - \bar{a}z}$$

satisfies $|w| < 1$, $|w| = 1$, or $|w| > 1$. Describe these sets (in terms of z).

Problem 1.5. Find a Möbius transformation that takes $\{|z - i| < 1\}$ onto $\{|z - 2| < 3\}$. Do the same for $\{|z + i| < 2\}$ onto $\{x + y \ge 2\}$. Is there a Möbius transformation that takes

$$\{|z - i| < 1\} \cap \{|z - 1| < 1\}$$

onto the first quadrant? How about $\{|z - 2i| < 2\} \cap \{|z - 1| < 1\}$ and $\{|z - \sqrt{3}| < 2\} \cap \{|z + \sqrt{3}| < 2\}$ onto the first quadrant?

Problem 1.6. Let $\Phi : S^2 \to \mathbb{C}_\infty$ be the stereographic projection

$$(x_1, x_2, x_3) \mapsto \frac{x_1 + ix_2}{1 - x_3}.$$

(a) Give a detailed proof that Φ is conformal.

(b) Define a metric $d(z, w)$ on $\mathbb{C}_\infty$ as the Euclidean distance of $\Phi^{-1}(z)$ and $\Phi^{-1}(w)$ in $\mathbb{R}^3$. Find a formula for $d(z, w)$. In particular, find $d(z, \infty)$.

(c) Show that circles on S^2 go to circles or lines in $\mathbb{C}$ under Φ.

Problem 1.7. Prove (1.20) without using complex analysis. In other words, use only real-variable methods. Show that your proof carries over to all dimensions, and thus obtain the maximum principle for harmonic functions in all dimensions.

Problem 1.8. Find the holomorphic function $f(z) = f(x + iy)$ with real part

$$\frac{x(1 + x^2 + y^2)}{1 + 2x^2 - 2y^2 + (x^2 + y^2)^2}$$

and such that $f(0) = 0$.

Problem 1.9. This exercise highlights properties of infinite series of complex numbers, and how they differ from real series:

(a) Suppose $\{z_j\}_{j=1}^\infty \subset \{z \in \mathbb{C} : \mathrm{Re}\, z \geq 0\}$ is a given sequence. True or false: if both $\sum_{j=1}^\infty z_j$ and $\sum_{j=1}^\infty z_j^2$ converge, then $\sum_{j=1}^\infty |z_j|^2$ also converges.

(b) True or false: there are sequences of complex numbers $\{z_j\}_{j=1}^\infty$ such that for *each* integer $k \geq 1$ the infinite series $\sum_{j=1}^\infty z_j^k$ converges, but fails to converge absolutely.

Problem 1.10. Discuss the mapping properties of $z \mapsto w = \frac{1}{2}(z + z^{-1})$ on $|z| < 1$. Is it one-to-one there? What is the image of $|z| < 1$ in the w-plane? What happens on $|z| = 1$ and $|z| > 1$? What is the image of the circles $|z| = r < 1$, and of the ray $\mathrm{Arg}\, z = \theta$ emanating from zero?

Problem 1.11. Let $T(z) = \frac{az+b}{cz+d}$ be a Möbius transformation.

(a) Show that $T(\mathbb{R}_\infty) = \mathbb{R}_\infty$ if and only if we can choose $a, b, c, d \in \mathbb{R}$.

(b) Find all T such that $T(\mathbb{T}) = \mathbb{T}$, where $\mathbb{T} = \{|z| = 1\}$ is the unit circle.

(c) Find all T for which $T(\mathbb{D}) = \mathbb{D}$, where $\mathbb{D} = \{|z| < 1\}$ is the unit disk.

Problem 1.12. Let $f \in \mathcal{H}(\mathbb{D})$ with $|f(z)| < 1$ for all $z \in \mathbb{D}$.

(a) If $f(0) = 0$, show that $|f(z)| \leq |z|$ on $\mathbb{D}$ and $|f'(0)| \leq 1$. If $|f(z)| = |z|$ for some $z \neq 0$, or if $|f'(0)| = 1$, then f is a rotation.

(b) Without any assumption on $f(0)$, prove that

$$(1.21) \qquad \left| \frac{f(z_1) - f(z_2)}{1 - \overline{f(z_1)}f(z_2)} \right| \leq \frac{|z_1 - z_2|}{|1 - \bar{z}_1 z_2|} \quad \forall\, z_1, z_2 \in \mathbb{D}$$

and

$$(1.22) \qquad \frac{|f'(z)|}{1 - |f(z)|^2} \leq \frac{1}{1 - |z|^2} \quad \forall\, z \in \mathbb{D}.$$

Show that equality in (1.21) for some pair $z_1 \neq z_2$ or in (1.22) for some $z \in \mathbb{D}$ implies that $f(z)$ is a fractional linear transformation.

Problem 1.13. This problem discusses the metric properties of the non-Euclidean geometries on the upper half-plane and the disk as introduced in this chapter. Endow $\mathbb{H}$ with the Riemannian metric

$$ds^2 = \frac{1}{y^2}(dx^2 + dy^2) = \frac{1}{(\operatorname{Im} z)^2} dz\, d\bar{z}.$$

The power in the dominator is no accident: it is unique with the property that the resulting metric is scaling invariant. Similarly, equip $\mathbb{D}$ with the metric

$$ds^2 = \frac{4}{(1 - |z|^2)^2} dz\, d\bar{z}.$$

With this metric, $\mathbb{D}$ is known as Poincaré disk. These Riemannian manifolds, which turn out to be isometric, are models of *hyperbolic space*. By definition, for any two Riemannian manifolds M, N a map $f : M \to N$ is called an *isometry* if it is one-to-one, onto, and preserves the metric.

(a) The distance between any two points z_1, z_2 in hyperbolic space (on either $\mathbb{D}$ or $\mathbb{H}$) is defined as

$$d(z_1, z_2) = \inf_{\gamma} \int_0^1 \|\gamma'(t)\|\, dt$$

where the infimum is taken over all curves joining z_1 and z_2 and the length of $\dot{\gamma}$ is determined by the hyperbolic metric ds. Show that any holomorphic $f : \mathbb{D} \to \mathbb{D}$ or holomorphic $f : \mathbb{H} \to \mathbb{H}$ satisfies

$$d(f(z_1), f(z_2)) \leq d(z_1, z_2)$$

for all z_1, z_2 in hyperbolic space.

(b) Determine all orientation preserving isometries of $\mathbb{H}$ to itself, $\mathbb{D}$ to itself, as well as from $\mathbb{H}$ to $\mathbb{D}$.

(c) Determine all geodesics of hyperbolic space as well as its scalar curvature (we are using the terminology of Riemannian geometry).

Problem 1.14. Let $f \in \mathcal{H}(\mathbb{D})$ be such that $\operatorname{Re} f(z) > 0$ for all $z \in \mathbb{D}$, and $f(0) = a > 0$. Prove that $|f'(0)| \leq 2a$. Is this inequality sharp? If so, which functions attain it?

Problem 1.15. Give another — more elementary — proof of the fundamental theorem of algebra; see (Proposition 1.23) following these lines: Let $p(z)$ be a nonconstant polynomial. Show that $|p(z)|$ attains a minimum in the complex plane, say at z_0. If the polynomial $q(z) = p(z + z_0)$ starts with a nonzero constant term, obtain a contradiction by showing that we may find a small z such that $q(z)$ is nearer to the origin than $q(0)$.

Chapter 2

From z to the Riemann mapping theorem: some finer points of basic complex analysis

2.1. The winding number

In the previous chapter we encountered the complex logarithm $\log z$, defined for $z \neq 0$ and unique up to addition of some number of the form $2\pi i n$, $n \in \mathbb{Z}$. As we already realized above, the logarithm plays a central role in the theory of analytic functions.

We shall now see further evidence of this by means of the real part of $\log z$, i.e., the harmonic function $u(z) := \log |z|$ defined on $\mathbb{C}^*$. Let us now attempt to find a conjugate harmonic function by means of the procedure of the proof of Proposition 1.38. There is an obvious obstruction to doing this in all of $\mathbb{C}^*$ as evidenced by the integral over the closed loop $\gamma_r(t) = re^{it}$:

$$\oint_{\gamma_r} -u_y \, dx + u_x \, dy = \int_0^{2\pi} (\sin^2(t) + \cos^2(t)) \, dt = 2\pi.$$

This is essentially the same calculation as (1.12) with $n = -1$. Indeed, on the one hand, the differential form

$$(2.1) \qquad \omega = -\frac{y}{r^2} \, dx + \frac{x}{r^2} \, dy$$

pulls back to any circle as the form $d\theta$, the derivative of the angle. Note that while this angle is only defined up to a constant, and also not well-defined on all of $\mathbb{C}^*$, its differential $d\theta$ is. In the right-hand plane we write

$$\theta = \arctan\left(\frac{y}{x}\right), \quad x > 0,$$

and $d\theta$ then clearly agrees with (2.1).

On the other hand, the local primitive of $\frac{1}{z}$ is (any branch of) $\log z$. So integrating over a loop that encircles the origin once, we create a jump by 2π. On the one hand, this property shows that $\log|z|$ does not have a conjugate harmonic function on $\mathbb{C}^*$ and on the other hand, it motivates the following definition.

Lemma 2.1. *Let $\gamma : [0,1] \to \mathbb{C}$ be a closed curve. Then for any $z_0 \in \mathbb{C} \setminus \gamma([0,1])$ the integral*

$$n(\gamma; z_0) := \frac{1}{2\pi i} \oint_\gamma \frac{dz}{z - z_0}$$

is an integer, called the index *or* winding number *of γ relative to z_0.*

The winding number is a homotopy invariant (relative to $\mathbb{C} \setminus \{z_0\}$). It is constant on each connected component of $\mathbb{C} \setminus \gamma([0,1])$ and vanishes on the unbounded component.

Proof. Let

$$g(t) := \int_0^t \frac{\gamma'(s)}{\gamma(s) - z_0}\, ds.$$

The integrand equals $\frac{d}{ds}\log(\gamma(s) - z_0)$ for an arbitrary branch of $\log$. In fact,

$$\frac{d}{dt}\left(e^{-g(t)}(\gamma(t) - z_0)\right) = -e^{-g(t)}\gamma'(t) + e^{-g(t)}\gamma'(t) = 0,$$

which implies that

$$e^{-g(1)}(\gamma(1) - z_0) = e^{-g(0)}(\gamma(0) - z_0) = e^{-g(0)}(\gamma(1) - z_0),$$

and thus $e^{g(0)-g(1)} = 1$; in other words, $g(0) - g(1) \in 2\pi i\mathbb{Z}$ as claimed. The homotopy invariance is a direct consequence of Cauchy's theorem; see Theorem 1.19. To establish the constancy on the components, observe that

$$\frac{d}{dz_0} \oint_\gamma \frac{dz}{z - z_0} = \oint_\gamma \frac{dz}{(z - z_0)^2} = -\oint_\gamma \frac{d}{dz}\left[\frac{1}{z - z_0}\right] dz = 0.$$

Alternatively, we observe that $n(\gamma; z_0)$ is continuous as z_0 varies in $\mathbb{C} \setminus \gamma([0,1])$. Since it is integer valued, it is locally constant and thus constant on each connected component of this set. Finally, on the unbounded component we can let $z_0 \to \infty$ to see that the winding number vanishes. $\qquad\square$

It is convenient to introduce cycles, which are formal sums of closed curves. To be specific, let $c := \sum_{j=1}^J n_j\gamma_j$ where each γ_j is a closed curve and $n_j \in \mathbb{Z}$. If $n_j < 0$, then $n_j\gamma_j$ means that we take $|n_j|$ copies of γ_j with the opposite orientation. An integral over a cycle is the same type of sum with integrals over the individual curves:

$$\oint_c f(z)\,dz := \sum_{j=1}^J n_j \oint_{\gamma_j} f(z)\,dz.$$

In particular, the winding number (or *index*) of a cycle c relative to a point z_0 not on the cycle is

$$n(c; z_0) := \sum_{j=1}^J n_j\, n(\gamma_j; z_0).$$

Observe that

$$n(c; z_0) = \frac{1}{2\pi i} \oint_c d\log(\zeta - z_0) = \frac{1}{2\pi} \oint_c d\theta_{z_0},$$

where θ_{z_0} is the argument relative to the point z_0. The real part of $\log(\zeta - z_0)$ does not contribute since c is made up of closed curves. The differential form[1] (we set $z_0 = 0$)

$$d\theta_0 = -\frac{y}{r^2}\,dx + \frac{x}{r^2}\,dy$$

is closed but not exact. In fact, it is essentially the only form with this property in the region $\mathbb{C}^* = \mathbb{R}^2 \setminus \{0\}$, the punctured plane. To understand this, note that a closed form ω on a region Ω is exact if and only if

$$(2.2) \qquad \oint_c \omega = 0 \qquad \text{for all closed curves } c \subset \Omega.$$

Indeed, it is clearly necessary. For the sufficiency set

$$f(z) := \int_{z_0}^z \omega,$$

where the integral is along an arbitrary path in Ω connecting z_0 to z. It is well-defined due to the vanishing condition (2.2) and satisfies $df = \omega$.

Now let ω be an arbitrary closed form on $\mathbb{C}^*$ with real coefficients and set

$$\widetilde{\omega} := \omega - \frac{\lambda}{2\pi} d\theta_0, \quad \lambda := \oint_{[|z|=1]} \omega.$$

Then $d\widetilde{\omega} = 0$ and (2.2) holds due to the homotopy invariance of integrals of closed forms (Stokes's theorem). Finally, this implies that the map $\omega \mapsto \lambda$ is one-to-one on the space

$$\mathcal{H}^1(\mathbb{C}^*) := \frac{\text{closed forms}}{\text{exact forms}}.$$

---

[1]On first reading, it is advisable to skip ahead to the next section. The material starting here until the next section requires a little knowledge of differential forms, such as Stokes's theorem. In addition, we shall make reference to some elementary concepts from algebraic topology and geometry such as cohomology and the fundamental group.

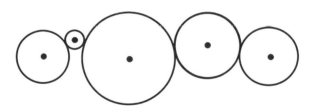

Figure 2.1. Bouquet of circles

The form $d\theta_0$ above ensures that there is a form for which $\lambda \neq 0$. So we have established the well-known fact that $\mathcal{H}^1(\mathbb{C}^*) \simeq \mathbb{R}$ (for forms with real coefficients). Incidentally, it also follows that

$$(2.3) \qquad\qquad [\gamma] \mapsto n(\gamma; 0), \qquad [\gamma] \in \pi_1(\mathbb{C}^*)$$

is an isomorphism of the fundamental group onto $\mathbb{Z}$ (for this, the curves γ have to be rooted at some fixed base-point).

This means, in essence, that two closed curves in $\mathbb{C} \setminus \{0\}$ are homotopic if and only if their winding numbers around the origin coincide. The necessity is Cauchy's theorem, and for the sufficiency we first reduce to the case where the curves actually lie in the circle $|z| = 1$. Then we pass to the universal cover of the circle, which is the line; note that the two curves, which we can assume to start at the same point, will lift to two curves in the cover with the same ending point. But any two such curves can of course be homotopically mapped onto each other on the line.

Let us repeat this analysis on the space $X := \mathbb{C} \setminus \{z_j\}_{j=1}^k$ where $z_j \in \mathbb{C}$ are distinct and $k \geq 2$. As before, let ω on X be a real closed form and set

$$\widetilde{\omega} := \omega - \sum_{j=1}^k \frac{\lambda_j}{2\pi} d\theta_{z_j}, \quad \lambda_j = \oint_{[|z-z_j|=\varepsilon_j]} \omega,$$

where $\varepsilon_j > 0$ is so small that the disks $D(z_j, \varepsilon_j)$ are all disjoint. Then we again conclude that (2.2) holds and thus that $\widetilde{\omega}$ is exact. Since the map

$$\omega \mapsto \{\lambda_j\}_{j=1}^k$$

is a linear map from all closed forms on X onto $\mathbb{R}^k$ with kernel equal to the exact forms, we have recovered the well-known fact,

$$\mathcal{H}^1(X) \simeq \mathbb{R}^k.$$

We note that any closed curve in X is homotopic to a "bouquet of circles", see Figure 2.1; more formally, up to homotopy, it can be written as a word

$$a_{i_1}^{\nu_1} a_{i_2}^{\nu_2} a_{i_3}^{\nu_3} \ldots a_{i_m}^{\nu_m},$$

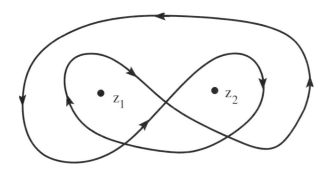

Figure 2.2. 0-homologous but not homotopic to a point

where $i_\ell \in \{1, 2, \ldots, k\}$, $\nu_\ell \in \mathbb{Z}$, and a_ℓ are circles around z_ℓ with a fixed orientation. It is an exercise in algebraic topology to prove from this that $\pi_1(X) = \langle a_1, \ldots, a_m \rangle$, the free group with m generators. Finally, the map

$$[c] \mapsto \{n(c; z_j)\}_{j=1}^m, \quad \pi_1(X) \to \mathbb{Z}^m$$

is a surjective homomorphism, but is not one-to-one; the kernel consists of all curves with winding number zero around each point. See Figure 2.2 for an example with $k = 2$. The phrase "0-homologous" in Figure 2.2 means by definition that the curve has winding number zero around each of the root points z_1, z_2. But note that there is no homotopy which contracts this curve to a point without crossing either of these "roots".

2.2. The global form of Cauchy's theorem

We now use the notion of winding number from the previous section to formulate a more general version of Cauchy's formula. Let c be a cycle. We say that $z \in c$ if z lies on one of the curves that make up the cycle. In general, we write c both for the cycle as well as the points on it. In what follows, we shall call a cycle c in a region Ω a 0-*homologous cycle in* Ω *or relative to* Ω, if $n(c; z) = 0$ for all $z \in \mathbb{C} \setminus \Omega$. From the discussion at the end of the previous section we know that such a cycle is not necessarily homotopic to a point (via a homotopy inside Ω, of course). On the other hand, it is clear that a cycle homotopic to a point is also homologous to zero.

Theorem 2.2. *Let c be a 0-homologous cycle in Ω. Then for any $f \in \mathcal{H}(\Omega)$,*

$$(2.4) \qquad n(c; z_0) \, f(z_0) = \frac{1}{2\pi i} \oint_c \frac{f(z)}{z - z_0} \, dz$$

for all $z_0 \in \Omega \setminus c$. Conversely, if (2.4) holds for all $f \in \mathcal{H}(\Omega)$ and a fixed $z_0 \in \Omega \setminus c$, then c is a 0-homologous cycle in Ω.

Proof. Define

$$\phi(z, w) := \begin{cases} \frac{f(z) - f(w)}{z - w} & \text{if } z \neq w \in \Omega, \\ \\ f'(z) & \text{if } z = w \in \Omega. \end{cases}$$

Then by analyticity of f, $\phi(z, w)$ is analytic in z and jointly continuous (this is clear for $z \neq w$ and for z close to w expand in a Taylor series in z around w). The set

$$\Omega' := \{z \in \mathbb{C} \setminus c \mid n(c; z) = 0\}$$

is open, $\Omega' \cup \Omega = \mathbb{C}$, and $\partial\Omega \subset \Omega'$. This property is due to c being zero homologous as well as the winding number being constant on all components of $\mathbb{C} \setminus c$. The function

$$g(z) := \begin{cases} \oint_c \phi(z, w) \, dw & \text{if } z \in \Omega, \\ \\ \oint_c \frac{f(w)}{w - z} \, dw & \text{if } z \in \Omega', \end{cases}$$

is therefore well-defined and $g \in \mathcal{H}(\mathbb{C})$; for the former, note that for any $z \in \Omega$,

$$(2.5) \quad \oint_c \phi(z, w) \, dw = \oint_c \frac{f(w) - f(z)}{w - z} \, dw = \oint_c \frac{f(w)}{w - z} \, dw - 2\pi i f(z) n(c; z),$$

with $n(c; z) = 0$ for all $z \in \Omega' \cap \Omega$. The analyticity of g on Ω' is clear, whereas on Ω it follows by interchanging integration and from Morera's theorems. Finally, since $g(z) \to 0$ as $|z| \to \infty$, we see that $g \equiv 0$ on $\mathbb{C}$. The theorem now follows from (2.5).

For the converse, fix any $z_1 \in \mathbb{C} \setminus \Omega$ and apply (2.4) to $f(z) = \frac{1}{z - z_1}$. Then $f \in \mathcal{H}(\Omega)$ and, therefore,

$$\begin{aligned} n(c; z_0) f(z_0) &= \frac{1}{2\pi i} \oint_c \frac{1}{(z - z_0)(z - z_1)} \, dz \\ &= f(z_0) \frac{1}{2\pi i} \oint_c \left[\frac{1}{z - z_0} - \frac{1}{z - z_1} \right] dz \\ &= f(z_0) n(c; z_0) - f(z_0) n(c; z_1), \end{aligned}$$

whence $n(c; z_1) = 0$ as claimed. □

We can now derive the following strictly stronger version of Cauchy's Theorem; see (1.13) of Theorem 1.19. The point is of course that we admit curves which cannot be contracted within the region of holomorphy. In heuristic terms, we do not require that we can "fill in" a curve entirely with points from Ω.

As the reader will easily verify, Corollary 2.3 is equivalent to Theorem 2.2.

Corollary 2.3. *With c and Ω as in Theorem 2.2,*

(2.6)
$$\oint_c f(z)\,dz = 0$$

for all $f \in \mathcal{H}(\Omega)$. In particular, if Ω is simply-connected, then (2.6) holds for all *cycles in Ω and $f \in \mathcal{H}(\Omega)$.*

Proof. Apply the previous theorem to $h(z) = (z - z_0)f(z)$ where $z_0 \in \Omega \setminus c$. As for the second statement, it uses the fact that $\mathbb{C} \setminus \Omega$ is connected if Ω is simply-connected (and conversely). But then $n(c; z) = 0$ for all $z \in \mathbb{C} \setminus \Omega$ by Lemma 2.1, and we are done. $\qquad\square$

The final formulation of Cauchy's theorem is the homotopy invariance. We say that two C^1-cycles c_1 and c_2 are *homotopic* if each closed curve from c_1 is C^1-homotopic to exactly one closed curve from c_2.

Theorem 2.4. *Let c_1 and c_2 be two cycles in Ω that are C^1-homotopic. Then*

$$\oint_{c_1} f(z)\,dz = \oint_{c_2} f(z)\,dz$$

for all $f \in \mathcal{H}(\Omega)$. In particular, if c is homotopic to a sum of points, then $\oint_c f(z)\,dz = 0$ for all $f \in \mathcal{H}(\Omega)$.

Proof. By summation, it suffices to consider closed curves instead of cycles. For the case of closed curves one can apply Theorem 1.19 and we are done. $\qquad\square$

This is a most important statement, as it implies, for example, that the winding number is homotopy invariant (a fact that we deduced from the homotopy invariance of integrals of closed forms before); in particular, if a cycle $c \subset \Omega$ is 0-homologous relative to Ω, then any cycle homotopic to c relative to Ω is also 0-homologous. As already noted before the converse of this is false; see Figure 2.2.

We remark that Theorem 2.4 can be proven with continuous curves instead of C^1. For this, one needs to define the integral along a continuous curve via analytic continuation of primitives. In that case, Theorem 2.4 becomes a corollary of the monodromy theorem; see Theorem 2.19 below.

2.3. Isolated singularities and residues

We now consider isolated singularities of holomorphic functions.

Definition 2.5. Suppose $f \in \mathcal{H}(\Omega \setminus \{z_0\})$ where $z_0 \in \Omega$. Then z_0 is called an *isolated singularity* of f. We say that z_0 is *removable* if f can be assigned a value $f(z_0) \in \mathbb{C}$ at z_0 that renders f holomorphic on all of Ω. We say that

z_0 is *a pole* of f provided $f(z) \to \infty$ as $z \to z_0$. Otherwise, z_0 is called an *essential singularity*.

An example of a pole at $z = 0$ is exhibited by $\frac{1}{z}$, whereas an example of an essential singularity at zero is given by $e^{\frac{1}{z}}$. Indeed, consider the behavior of the latter function as $z \to 0$ along the imaginary and real axes, respectively.

We will now give some criteria which allow one to characterize these different types of isolated singularities. As usual, D^* denotes a disk D with the center removed.

Proposition 2.6. *Suppose $f \in \mathcal{H}(\Omega \setminus \{z_0\})$. Then there is the following mutually exclusive trichotomy:*

- *z_0 is removable if and only if $\lim_{z \to z_0}(z - z_0)f(z) = 0$.*
- *z_0 is a pole if and only if there exists a positive integer $n \geq 1$ and $h \in \mathcal{H}(\Omega)$ with $h(z_0) \neq 0$ such that $f(z) = \frac{h(z)}{(z-z_0)^n}$.*
- *z_0 is essential if and only if for every $\varepsilon > 0$, the set $f(D(z_0, \varepsilon)^*)$ is dense in $\mathbb{C}$.*

Proof. Suppose $\lim_{z \to z_0}(z - z_0)f(z) = 0$. Then $g(z) := (z - z_0)f(z_0) \in C(\Omega)$ and from Morera's theorem it follows that $g \in \mathcal{H}(\Omega)$. To apply Morera's theorem, first consider the cases where z_0 lies outside of the triangle. Then g is holomorphic on the entire triangle and we conclude from Cauchy that the integral of g around the triangle vanishes. Next, suppose z_0 lies on the boundary of the triangle. Then we can write this as a limit of the previous case by lightly shifting the respective edge of the triangle away from z_0. Finally, if z_0 lies in the interior of the triangle, then we divide the triangle further into three subtriangles using z_0 as a vertex. Summing the integrals over these subtriangles, which each vanish by the previous case, yields the vanishing of the integral over the original triangle.

In conclusion, Morera's theorem implies that $g(z)$ is analytic and vanishes near z_0. From the power-series representation, we may divide g by $z - z_0$ to obtain another analytic function, which is precisely $f(z)$.

Suppose that z_0 is a pole. Then by the previous criterion, $g(z) := \frac{1}{f(z)}$ has a removable singularity at z_0 (in fact, $g(z) \to 0$ as $z \to z_0$). Hence by Proposition 1.27 for some positive integer n one has the representation $g(z) = (z - z_0)^n \widetilde{g}(z)$ where $\widetilde{g} \in \mathcal{H}(\Omega)$ and $\widetilde{g}(z_0) \neq 0$. This implies that $f(z) = \frac{h(z)}{(z-z_0)^n}$ where $h(z_0) \neq 0$ and $h \in \mathcal{H}(U)$ where U is a small neighborhood of z_0. Conversely, suppose that $f(z)$ has this form. Then $f(z) \to \infty$ as $z \to z_0$ (which is equivalent to $|f(z)| \to \infty$ as $z \to z_0$) and z_0 is a pole of f. Finally, suppose $f(D(z_0, \varepsilon)) \cap D(w_0, \delta) = \emptyset$ for some $\varepsilon > 0$ and $w_0 \in \mathbb{C}$, $\delta > 0$. Then $\frac{1}{f(z) - w_0} \in \mathcal{H}(D(z_0, \varepsilon))$ has a removable singularity at z_0 which then further implies that $f(z)$ has a removable singularity or a pole at z_0. In the converse direction, the density of the sets $f(D(z_0, \varepsilon))$ for every $\varepsilon > 0$ clearly precludes a removable singularity or pole at z_0. $\qquad\square$

Let n be the integer arising in the previous characterization of a pole; then we say that the *order of the pole* at z_0 is n. We also remark that the characterization of essential singularities in Proposition 2.6 is referred to as *Casorati-Weierstrass theorem*. The *great Picard theorem* in fact states that for every $\varepsilon > 0$ such a function necessarily assumes every value—with one possible exception—infinitely often on $D(z_0, \varepsilon)^*$; see Chapter 4.

Definition 2.7. We say that f is a *meromorphic* function on Ω if there exists a discrete set $\mathcal{P} \subset \Omega$ such that $f \in \mathcal{H}(\Omega \setminus \mathcal{P})$ and such that each point in $\mathcal{P}$ is a pole of f. We denote the field of meromorphic functions by $\mathcal{M}(\Omega)$.

A standard and useful tool in the study of isolated singularities are the *Laurent series*.

Proposition 2.8. *Suppose that $f \in \mathcal{H}(\mathcal{A})$ where*
$$\mathcal{A} = \{z \in \mathbb{C} \mid r_1 < |z - z_0| < r_2\}, \quad 0 \le r_1 < r_2 \le \infty$$
is an annulus. Then there exist unique $a_n \in \mathbb{C}$ such that

$$(2.7) \qquad f(z) = \sum_{n=-\infty}^{\infty} a_n (z - z_0)^n,$$

where the series converges absolutely on $\mathcal{A}$ and uniformly on compact subsets of $\mathcal{A}$. Furthermore,

$$(2.8) \qquad a_n = \frac{1}{2\pi i} \oint_{|z-z_0|=r} \frac{f(z)}{(z - z_0)^{n+1}} \, dz$$

for all $n \in \mathbb{Z}$ and any $r_1 < r < r_2$. The series (2.7) is called the Laurent *series of f around z_0, and*

$$\sum_{n=-\infty}^{-1} a_n (z - z_0)^n$$

is its principal part.

Proof. Fix $z \in \mathcal{A}$. Let c be the cycle defined in $\mathcal{A}$ by

$$(2.9) \qquad c = -\gamma_{r_1'} + \gamma_{r_2'} - \eta_\varepsilon,$$

where $\gamma_r(t) := z_0 + r e^{2\pi i t}$, $\eta_\varepsilon(t) := z + \varepsilon e^{2\pi i t}$, and $r_1 < r_1' < |z - z_0| < r_2' < r_2$ and ε is small. Then $n(c; w) = 0$ for all $w \in \mathbb{C} \setminus \mathcal{A}$ and $n(c; z) = 0$. Hence by the Cauchy formula of Theorem 2.2,

$$\frac{1}{2\pi i} \oint_c \frac{f(w)}{w - z} \, dw = 0,$$

which further implies that

$$(2.10) \qquad f(z) = \frac{1}{2\pi i} \oint_{\gamma_{r_2'}} \frac{f(w)}{w - z}\, dw - \frac{1}{2\pi i} \oint_{\gamma_{r_1'}} \frac{f(w)}{w - z}\, dw.$$

Now proceed as in the proof of Corollary 1.21 with $\gamma_{r_2'}$ contributing the a_n, $n \geq 0$ as in (2.8), and the inner curve $\gamma_{r_1'}$ contributing a_n with $n < 0$ as in (2.8). Indeed, we expand:

$$\frac{1}{w - z} = \frac{1}{w - z_0 - (z - z_0)} = \sum_{n=0}^{\infty} \frac{(z - z_0)^n}{(w - z_0)^{n+1}} \qquad \text{if } |w - z_0| > |z - z_0|,$$

$$\frac{1}{w - z} = \frac{1}{w - z_0 - (z - z_0)} = -\sum_{n=0}^{\infty} \frac{(w - z_0)^n}{(z - z_0)^{n+1}} \qquad \text{if } |w - z_0| < |z - z_0|.$$

Inserting these expansions into (2.10) and interchanging summation and integration yields the desired representation (the interchange being justified by the uniform convergence of these series on the integration curves). The absolute and uniform convergence of the resulting series on compact sets follow as well.

For the uniqueness as well as (2.8), divide (2.7) by $(z - z_0)^\ell$ and integrate over a circle $|z - z_0| = r$. Interchanging summation and integration (justified by absolute and uniform convergence on the circle) and invoking (1.12) then shows that all but one of the terms in the resulting series vanishes, concluding the proof.   □

We remark that the cycle in (2.9) could also be replaced by a closed curve. As usual, this is accomplished by introducing (straight) cuts from $\gamma_{r_1'}$ to η_ε, and from $\gamma_{r_2'}$ to η_ε, respectively. Then we move along the cuts in opposite directions so they cancel each other; see Figure 2.3.

Suppose now that $r_1 = 0$ so that z_0 becomes an isolated singularity. Amongst all Laurent coefficients, a_{-1} plays a special role due to its invariance properties (this will only become clear in the context of differential forms on Riemann surfaces). It is called *the residue* of f at z_0 and denoted by $\mathrm{res}(f; z_0)$. It is easy to read off from the Laurent series which kind of isolated singularity we are dealing with:

Corollary 2.9. *Suppose z_0 is an isolated singularity of f and suppose*

$$f(z) = \sum_{n=-\infty}^{\infty} a_n (z - z_0)^n$$

is the Laurent expansion of f around z_0 convergent on $0 < |z - z_0| < \delta$ for some $\delta > 0$. Then z_0 is removable if and only if $a_n = 0$ for all $n < 0$. It has a pole if and only if there exists an integer $n_0 < 0$ such that $a_n = 0$ for all

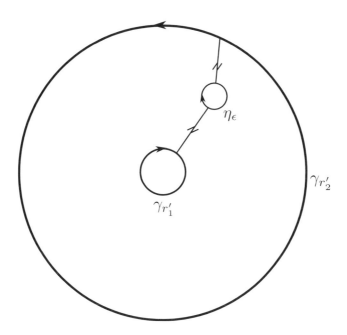

Figure 2.3. The cycle in the proof of Laurent series

$n < n_0$ but $a_{n_0} \neq 0$ *(and n_0 is the order of the pole). Otherwise, z_0 is an essential singularity.*

Proof. Apply Proposition 2.6 to the Laurent series of f at z_0. $\qquad\square$

In the previous chapter we encountered the concept of conformally equivalent regions in the plane. We also identified the automorphism group of the disk. We now do the same for the complex plane and the Riemann sphere.

Proposition 2.10. *The conformal automorphisms of the plane are precisely the invertible linear conformal maps, i.e.,*

$$\{az + b \mid a, b \in \mathbb{C}, \ a \neq 0\}.$$

Proof. It is clear that each such map is an automorphism. Now suppose $f \in \text{Aut}(\mathbb{C})$ with $f(0) = 0$ (by translation). The entire function $f(z)$ is represented by a power series

$$f(z) = \sum_{n=1}^{\infty} a_n z^n \quad \forall \, z \in \mathbb{C}.$$

Then $g(w) := f(1/w)$ exhibits an isolated singularity at $w = 0$. It cannot be essential by the Casorati-Weierstrass characterization. Indeed, since f is, in particular, a homeomorphism, we see that $|f(z)| \geq 1$ for all $|z| > R > 0$. To see this, take the pre-image of the closed unit disk under f. It is some compact neighborhood of the origin by construction, whence the claim. So the image of $0 < |w| < 1/R$ under g is not dense in the plane. But then the Laurent series of g around $w = 0$, viz.,

$$\sum_{n=1}^{\infty} a_n \, w^{-n}$$

is finite. In other words, f is a polynomial. As an automorphism we must have $f' \neq 0$ everywhere. But by the fundamental theorem of algebra this means that f is linear as claimed. $\square$

We now turn to the compactification of $\mathbb{C}$, i.e., the Riemann sphere. In fact, we shall now show that holomorphic maps $\mathbb{C}_\infty \to \mathbb{C}_\infty$ are necessarily rational. Recall that this fact was already mentioned in Chapter 1 in connection with fractional linear transformations.

Lemma 2.11. *The analytic maps $\mathbb{C}_\infty \to \mathbb{C}_\infty$ which are not identically equal to ∞ are precisely the rational functions, i.e., all maps of the form $\frac{P}{Q}$ with P, Q polynomials over $\mathbb{C}$ and $Q \not\equiv 0$. In particular, the automorphism group of the Riemann sphere are all Möbius transforms.*

Proof. All rational maps are analytic from the extended plane to itself. For the converse, suppose $f(z) \in \mathbb{C}$ for all $z \in \mathbb{C}_\infty$. Then f is entire and bounded (by compactness of $\mathbb{C}_\infty$) and thus constant. We can therefore assume that $f(z_0) = \infty$ for some $z_0 \in \mathbb{C}_\infty$. If $z_0 = \infty$, then switch to $f(1/z)$ which is again analytic from $\mathbb{C}_\infty$ to itself, and equals ∞ at $z = 0$. Thus, we may assume that $z_0 \in \mathbb{C}$. By continuity of f the point z_0 cannot be an essential singularity of f; cf. Proposition 2.6.

In other words, z_0 is a pole. By the uniqueness theorem (cf. Proposition 1.26), the poles cannot accumulate in $\mathbb{C}_\infty$. Since the latter is compact, there can thus only be finitely many poles. Hence after subtracting the principal part of the Laurent series of f around each pole in $\mathbb{C}$ from f, we obtain an entire function which grows at most like a polynomial. By Liouville's theorem (see Corollary 1.22), such a function must be a polynomial and we are done. $\square$

A most useful result of elementary complex analysis is the *residue theorem*.

Theorem 2.12. *Suppose $f \in \mathcal{H}(\Omega \setminus \{z_j\}_{j=1}^J)$. If c is a 0-homologous cycle in Ω which does not pass through any of the z_j, then*

$$(2.11) \qquad \frac{1}{2\pi i} \oint_c f(z) \, dz = \sum_{j=1}^{J} n(c; z_j) \mathrm{res}(f; z_j).$$

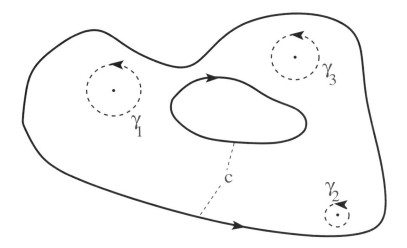

Figure 2.4. An example of the cycle in the residue theorem

Proof. Let $\nu_j := n(c; z_j)$ and define a new cycle

$$c' := c - \sum_{j=1}^{J} \nu_j \gamma_j, \qquad \gamma_j(t) := z_j + \varepsilon e^{2\pi i t},$$

where $\varepsilon > 0$ is small. Then $n(c'; w) = 0$ for all $w \in \mathbb{C} \setminus \Omega$ and $n(c'; z_j) = 0$ for all $1 \le j \le J$. The residue formula (2.11) now follows from Corollary 2.3 applied to $\Omega \setminus \{z_j\}_{j=1}^{J}$. $\qquad\qquad\square$

The residue theorem can be used to evaluate definite integrals; see Problem 2.3. We will apply it now to derive the *argument principle*. To motivate this principle, consider $f(z) = z^n$ with $n \ne 0$. If $\gamma_r(t) = r e^{2\pi i t}$ is the circle of radius r around 0, then $f \circ \gamma_r$ has winding number n around 0. Hence that winding number counts how many zeros of f there are inside of γ_r. If $n < 0$, then we obtain the order of the pole at 0 with a negative sign.

Proposition 2.13. *Let c be a 0-homologous cycle relative to Ω. If $f \in \mathcal{M}(\Omega)$ is such that no zero or pole of f lie on c, then*

$$(2.12) \qquad n(f \circ c\,; 0) = \sum_{z \in \Omega : f(z) = 0} n(c; z) - \sum_{\zeta \in \Omega : f(\zeta) = \infty} n(c; \zeta),$$

where zeros and poles are counted with multiplicity. In other words, suppose that each $n(c;) = 1$ in (2.12). Then the winding number of f along c equals the number of zeros minus the number of poles, counted with multiplicity.

Proof. We first point out the sum on the right-hand side of (2.12) only has finitely many nonzero terms; indeed, zeros and poles can only cluster at the boundary where the winding number necessarily vanishes. By definition,

$$(2.13) \qquad n(f \circ c\,;0) = \frac{1}{2\pi i}\oint_{f \circ c}\frac{dw}{w} = \frac{1}{2\pi i}\oint_c \frac{f'(z)}{f(z)}\,dz.$$

If $f(z) = (z - z_0)^n g(z)$ with $n \neq 0$, $g(z_0) \neq 0$, and $g \in \mathcal{H}(\Omega)$, then

$$\mathrm{res}\left(\frac{f'}{f}\,;z_0\right) = n,$$

and the proposition follows by applying the residue theorem to (2.13). $\square$

Combining the homotopy invariance of the winding number (see Theorem 2.4) with the argument principle yields *Rouche's theorem* to which we now turn. The idea is expressed in Figure 2.5. Denote the solid curve by γ and the dashed curve by η (parametrized over the same interval), respectively, and define a vector $\vec{r}(t) := \eta(t) - \gamma(t)$. Then we have $n(\gamma;0) = n(\eta;0)$ provided the vector $\vec{r}(t)$ can never reach the origin.

In other words, we need to ensure that $|\vec{r}(t)| < |\gamma(t)|$ for all t. Indeed, $\gamma_s(t) := \gamma(t) + s\vec{r}(t)$ for $0 \leq s \leq 1$ defines a homotopy which lies entirely within $\mathbb{C} \setminus \{0\}$. An intuitive way to think about the figure is in terms of a planet circling around a central object. Suppose a moon orbits around the planet in the same plane. Then it encircles the central object as often as the planet— the only way that could change is if the line segment from the planet to the moon were to hit the central object.

We now formulate Rouche's theorem for cycles. A simpler, but more restrictive formulation, is given afterwards.

Proposition 2.14. *Let c be a 0-homologous cycle in Ω such that*

$$\{z \in \mathbb{C} \setminus c \,:\, n(c;z) = 1\} = \Omega_0$$

has the property

$$\{z \in \mathbb{C} \setminus c \,:\, n(c;z) = 0\} = \mathbb{C} \setminus (\Omega_0 \cup c).$$

Let $f, g \in \mathcal{H}(\Omega)$ and suppose that $|g| < |f|$ on c. Then

$$\#\{z \in \Omega_0 \mid f(z) = 0\} = \#\{z \in \Omega_0 \mid (f + g)(z) = 0\},$$

where the zeros are counted with multiplicity.

Proof. The function $(f + sg) \circ c$, $0 \leq s \leq 1$ is a homotopy between the cycles $f \circ c$ and $(f + g) \circ c$ relative to $\mathbb{C}^*$ with the property that Proposition 2.13

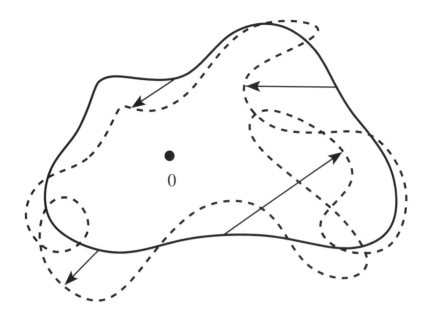

Figure 2.5. The mechanism behind Rouche's theorem

applies to each s-slice (note that by assumption, $f \neq 0$ on c). Consequently,

$$n((f + sg) \circ c; 0) = \sum_{z \in \Omega : (f+sg)(z)=0} n(c; z) = \sum_{z \in \Omega_0 : (f+sg)(z)=0} 1$$

$$= \#\{z \in \Omega_0 \mid (f + sg)(z) = 0\},$$

which does not depend on s and Rouche's theorem follows. $\qquad\square$

The standard formulation of Rouche's theorem concerns zeros of analytic functions that lie within simple closed curves. These are curves without self-intersection.

Corollary 2.15. *Let γ be a simple closed curve in Ω and $f, g \in \mathcal{H}(\Omega)$. Suppose $|g| < |f|$ on γ. Then f and $f + g$ have the same number of zeros within the curve γ.*

Proof. We shall use that γ splits the plane into two regions, the exterior and interior ones which are characterized by $n(\gamma, z) = 0$ or $n(\gamma, z) = 1$, respectively, for $z \in \mathbb{C} \setminus \gamma$. This is known as Jordan's curve theorem. The result is now an immediate corollary of Proposition 2.14. $\qquad\square$

Rouche's theorem allows for yet another proof of the fundamental theorem of algebra: If $P(z) = z^n + a_{n-1}z^{n-1} + \ldots + a_1 z + a_0$, then set $f(z) := z^n$ and $g(z) := a_{n-1}z^{n-1} + \ldots + a_1 z + a_0$. On $|z| = R$ with R large, $|f| > |g|$ and Rouche's theorem applies.

2.4. Analytic continuation

Many special functions, such as the Gamma and zeta functions, are defined by integral or series representations in subdomains of the complex plane (such as a half-plane). The question then arises whether these functions can be *analytically continued* outside of this domain. Historically, this question turned out to be of fundamental importance to complex analysis with many ramifications to other areas of mathematics. Indeed, one of the origins of Riemann surfaces lies in the study of the roots of algebraic equations $P(z, w) = 0$ where $P \in \mathbb{C}[z, w]$. If $P(z_0, w_0) = 0$ and $P_z(z_0, w_0) \neq 0$, then by the implicit function theorem we may solve locally near w_0 for $z = z(w)$ so that $P(z(w), w) = 0$ and z is analytic. As we shall see later in the text, analytic continuation of z to as wide a region as possible naturally leads to the construction of Riemann surfaces.

In this chapter, we discuss the most elementary aspects of this theory and we begin with analytic continuation along curves. First, we define a chain of disks along a continuous curve. Next, we will put analytic functions on the disks which are continuations of one another.

Definition 2.16. Suppose $\gamma : [0, 1] \to \Omega$ is a continuous curve inside a region Ω. We say that $D_j = D(\gamma(t_j), r_j) \subset \Omega$, $0 \leq j \leq J$, is a *chain of disks along γ in Ω* if $0 = t_0 < t_1 < t_2 < \ldots < t_N = 1$ and $\gamma([t_j, t_{j+1}]) \subset D_j \cap D_{j+1}$ for all $0 \leq j \leq N - 1$.

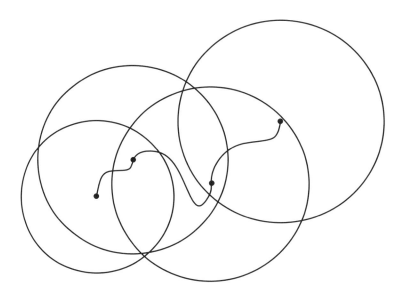

Figure 2.6. A chain of disks

For any γ and Ω as in this definition there exists a chain of disks along γ in Ω, by uniform continuity of γ. Next, we analytically continue along such a chain.

Definition 2.17. Let $\gamma : [0,1] \to \Omega$ be a continuous curve inside Ω. Suppose $f \in \mathcal{H}(U)$ and $g \in \mathcal{H}(V)$ where $U \subset \Omega$ and $V \subset \Omega$ are neighborhoods of $p := \gamma(0)$ and $q := \gamma(1)$, respectively. Then we say that g is an *analytic continuation of f along γ* if there exists a chain of disks $D_j := D(\gamma(t_j), r_j)$ along γ in Ω where $0 \leq j \leq J$, and f_j in $\mathcal{H}(D_j)$ such that $f_j = f_{j+1}$ on $D_j \cap D_{j+1}$ and $f_0 = f$ and $f_J = g$ locally around p and q, respectively.

In what follows, the only relevant information about f and g is their definition locally at p and q, respectively, and not their domains of definition. This is equivalent to saying that we identify f and g with their Taylor series around p and q, respectively. As expected, the analytic continuation of f along γ is unique whenever it exists. In particular, it does not depend on the chain of disks along γ, but only on γ itself. This follows from the uniqueness theorem; see Proposition 1.26 above.

Lemma 2.18. *The analytic continuation g of f along γ as in Definition 2.17 only depends on f and γ, but not on the specific choice of the chain of circles. In particular, it is unique.*

Proof. Suppose that D_j and $\widetilde{D}_k$ are two different chains of disks along γ with underlying partitions $\{t_j\}_{j=1}^J$ and $\{s_k\}_{k=1}^K$, respectively. Denote the chain of analytic functions defined on these disks by f_j and g_k. Then we claim that for any j, k with $t_{j-1} \leq s_k \leq t_j$,

$$f_j = g_k \quad \text{on} \quad D_j \cap \widetilde{D}_k.$$

Applying this claim to the endpoint of γ yields the desired uniqueness. To prove the claim, one uses induction on $j + k$ and the uniqueness theorem. As an exercise, supply the details. $\qquad\square$

We have already encountered a special case of this: suppose that $f \in \mathcal{H}(\Omega)$. Then locally around every point in Ω there exists an anti-derivative (or primitive). Any such primitive can be analytically continued along an arbitrary C^1-curve $\gamma : [0,1] \to \Omega$ by integration:

$$F(z) := \int_\gamma f(\zeta)\, d\zeta,$$

where $\gamma(1) = z$ and $\gamma(0) = z_0$ is kept fixed. This procedure, however, does not necessarily lead to a "global" primitive $F \in \mathcal{H}(\Omega)$. The standard example $\Omega = \mathbb{C}^*$ and $f(z) = \frac{1}{z}$ shows otherwise. On the other hand, it is clear from Theorem 2.4 that we *do obtain a global F* if Ω is simply-connected. This holds in general for analytic continuations and is known as the *monodromy theorem*.

Theorem 2.19. *Suppose γ_0 and γ_1 are two homotopic curves (relative to some region $\Omega \subset \mathbb{C}$) with the same initial point p and endpoint q. Let U be a neighborhood of p and assume further that $f \in \mathcal{H}(U)$ can be analytically continued along every curve of the homotopy. Then the analytic continuations of f along γ_j, $j = 0, 1$ agree locally around q.*

Proof. Let $H : [0,1]^2 \to \Omega$ be the homotopy between γ_0 and γ_1 which fixes the initial and endpoints. Thus, $H = H(t,s)$ where $\gamma_0(t) = H(t,0)$ and $\gamma_1(t) = H(t,1)$, respectively. Denote the continuation of f along $H(\cdot, s)$ by g_s. We need to prove that the Taylor series of g_s around q does not depend on s. It suffices to prove this locally in s. The idea is of course to change s so little that essentially the same chain of disks can be used.

The details are as follows: let $\gamma_s(t) := H(t,s)$, fix any $s_0 \in [0,1]$ and suppose $\{D_j\}_{j=1}^J$ is a chain of circles along γ_{s_0} with underlying partition $0 = t_0 < t_1 < \ldots < t_N = 1$ and functions f_j on D_j defining the analytic continuation of f along γ_{s_0}.

We claim the following: let $D_j(s)$ denote the largest disk centered at $\gamma_s(t_j)$ which is contained in D_j. There exists $\varepsilon > 0$ such that for all $s \in [0,1]$, $|s - s_0| < \varepsilon$, the $D_j(s)$ form a chain of disks along γ_s. In that case, we can use the same f_j, which proves that for all $|s - s_0| < \varepsilon$, the g_s agree with g_{s_0} locally around q. It remains to prove this claim.

For this, we use the uniform continuity of the homotopy H to conclude that there exists $\varepsilon > 0$ so that for all $|s - s_0| < \varepsilon$, each disk $D_j(s)$ contains the ε-neighborhood of $\gamma_s([t_{j-1}, t_j])$ for each $1 \le j \le J$. This of course guarantees that $\{D_j(s)\}_{j=1}^J$ is a chain of disks along γ_s inside Ω as desired. $\square$

Within a simply-connected region, any two curves with the same initial and end points are homotopic. For the particular case of simply-connected regions Ω, the monodromy theorem therefore implies the following: let f be analytic on some disk included in Ω, and suppose that we may analytically continue f to any point in Ω along any path. Then there exists a, necessarily unique, analytic function F on Ω which agrees with f on the original disk. In other words, if there is no local obstruction to analytic continuation anywhere in Ω, then we may obtain a global analytic function on Ω from the "germ" f.

Important examples include the logarithm, initially defined near $z = 1$, say. We encounter the only local obstruction to analytic continuation at $z = 0$, whence we conclude from the monodromy theorem the familiar result that a logarithm exists on any simply-connected domain in the punctured plane. Also note that on non-simply-connected regions we are not able to make such an assertion.

Any reader familiar with universal covers should be reminded here of the homeomorphism between a simply-connected manifold and its universal cover. Making this connection between the monodromy theorem and the universal cover requires the notion of a *Riemann surface* to which we turn in Chapter 4.

An instructive example of how analytic continuation is performed "in practice", as in the context of special functions, is furnished by the Gamma function $\Gamma(z)$ which is ubiquitous in many branches of mathematics. If $\mathrm{Re}(z) > 0$, then it is defined as

$$(2.14) \qquad \Gamma(z) := \int_0^\infty e^{-t} t^{z-1} \, dt.$$

We claim that it is in fact holomorphic in the right half-plane. To see this, we first observe that $z \mapsto t^{z-1} = \exp((z-1)\log t)$ is an entire function for each $t > 0$. Second, since integrals behave in some way like sums and sums of analytic functions are again analytic, we should be able to conclude that (2.14) is analytic. This logic is indeed correct, *provided the defining integral converges locally uniformly*. We shall develop this implication in the following section. For now we analyze the convergence of (2.14) in an ad hoc fashion. Passing absolute values inside, we see that

$$\int_0^\infty \left| e^{-t} t^{z-1} \right| dt = \int_0^\infty e^{-t} t^{x-1} \, dt, \qquad x = \mathrm{Re}(z).$$

Due to $x > 0$ the integral on the right converges at $t = 0$, and due to the fact that $e^{-t} t^{x-1} < e^{-t/2}$ for large t we see that we also have convergence at $t = \infty$.

Moreover, the convergence is uniform in both cases on strips of the form $0 < A^{-1} \le x \le A$ with $A > 1$ arbitrary but fixed. This in fact guarantees that Γ is a continuous complex-valued function in the right half-plane. We apply Fubini's theorem: let γ be a closed curve in $\{z \in \mathbb{C} : x > 0\}$. Then

$$(2.15) \qquad \int_\gamma \int_0^\infty e^{-t} t^{z-1} \, dt \, dz = \int_0^\infty e^{-t} \int_\gamma t^{z-1} \, dz \, dt = 0,$$

since the inner integral vanishes by Cauchy's theorem. By Morera's theorem, we see that Γ is indeed holomorphic in the right half-plane.

One checks via integration by parts that $\Gamma(n+1) = n!$ for each integer $n \ge 0$. The same calculation also establishes the functional equation

$$(2.16) \qquad \Gamma(z+1) = z\Gamma(z) \qquad \forall \, \mathrm{Re}(z) > 0.$$

Indeed,

$$
z\Gamma(z) = \int_0^\infty e^{-t} z t^{z-1}\, dt = \int_0^\infty e^{-t} d(t^z)
$$

(2.17)

$$
= \int_0^\infty e^{-t} t^z\, dt = \Gamma(z+1).
$$

The boundary term here vanished due to $\mathrm{Re}(z) > 0$. Since the left-hand side of (2.16) is defined for all $\mathrm{Re}(z) > -1$, we set

$$
\Gamma(z) := \frac{\Gamma(z+1)}{z}, \quad \forall\, \mathrm{Re}(z) > -1.
$$

Note that $z = 0$ is a pole of first order. Iterating this identity yields, with $k \geq 0$ an arbitrary integer,

$$
\Gamma(z) = \frac{\Gamma(z+k+1)}{z(z+1)(z+2)\dots(z+k)} \qquad \forall\, \mathrm{Re}(z) > -k - 1.
$$

This allows one to analytically continue Γ as a meromorphic function to all of $\mathbb{C}$; it has simple poles at $\{n \in \mathbb{Z} : n \leq 0\}$ with residues $\frac{(-1)^n}{n!}$. For details as well as other examples we refer the reader to Problems 2.11 and 2.14.

Returning to general properties, let us mention that any domain[2] Ω carries analytic functions which cannot be continued beyond any portion of the boundary $\partial\Omega$. Let $\{z_n\}_{n=1}^\infty$ be dense in $\partial\Omega$ and define

(2.18)
$$
f(z) = \sum_{n=1}^\infty 2^{-n} \frac{1}{z - z_n},
$$

which is analytic on Ω (we shall justify this in the next section; see Lemma 2.20). It follows from Corollary 1.21 that a power series with finite and positive radius of convergence cannot be analytically continued across its entire circle of convergence. A natural class of power series with $R = 1$ and which cannot be continued across *any portion* of $\{|z| = 1\}$ are the gap series; see Problem 2.12.

2.5. Convergence and normal families

The next topic we address is that of convergence and compactness of sequences of holomorphic functions. The concept of complex differentiability is so rigid that it survives under uniform limits—this is no surprise as Morera's theorem characterizes it by means of the vanishing of integrals.

Lemma 2.20. *Suppose $\{f_n\}_{n=1}^\infty \subset \mathcal{H}(\Omega)$ converges uniformly on compact subsets of Ω to a function f. Then $f \in \mathcal{H}(\Omega)$ and $f_n^{(k)} \to f^{(k)}$ uniformly on*

---

[2]We use "domain" and "region" interchangeably.

compact subsets of Ω for each $k \geq 1$. Furthermore, suppose that

$$\sup_{n \geq 1} \#\{z \in \Omega \mid f_n(z) = w\} \leq N < \infty.$$

Then either $f \equiv w$ in Ω or

$$\#\{z \in \Omega \mid f(z) = w\} \leq N.$$

The cardinalities here include multiplicity.

Proof. The first assertion is immediate from Cauchy's and Morera's theorems. Indeed, given any triangle which lies entirely within Ω (with its interior) we have

$$\oint_\gamma f_n(z)\,dz = 0 \quad \forall\, n.$$

Passing to the limit yields

$$\oint_\gamma f(z)\,dz = 0,$$

and now Morera gives the desired analyticity since f is continuous as the (locally) uniform limit of continuous functions.

The second assertion follows from Cauchy's formula

$$(2.19) \qquad f_n^{(k)}(z_0) = \frac{k!}{2\pi i} \oint_{|z-z_0|=r} \frac{f_n(z)}{(z-z_0)^{k+1}}\,dz,$$

whereas the third is a consequence of Rouche's theorem: assume that $f \not\equiv w$ and let

$$\{z \in \Omega \mid f(z) = w\} \supseteq \{z_j\}_{j=1}^J$$

with $J < \infty$. Since the set on the left-hand side is discrete in Ω, there exist $\delta, \varepsilon > 0$ small so that $|f(z) - w| > \delta$ on each circle $|z - z_j| = \varepsilon$, $1 \leq j \leq J$; cf. (1.17). Now let n_0 be so large that $|f - f_n| < \delta$ on $|z - z_j| = \varepsilon$ for all $n \geq n_0$ and each $1 \leq j \leq J$. By Rouche's theorem, it follows that $f - w$ has as many zeros counted with multiplicity as each $f_n - w$ with $n \geq n_0$ inside these disks and we are done. $\qquad\square$

Lemma 2.20 implies that (2.18) converges to an analytic function. The following proposition shows that Lemma 2.20 applies to any *bounded* family $\{f_n\}_{n=1}^\infty \subset \mathcal{H}(\Omega)$, or at least subsequences thereof. This is *Montel's normal family theorem.*

Definition 2.21. One says that $\mathcal{F} = \{f_\alpha\}_{\alpha \in \mathcal{A}} \subset \mathcal{H}(\Omega)$ is a *normal family* provided for each compact $K \subset \Omega$ one has

$$(2.20) \qquad \sup_{z \in K} \sup_{\alpha \in \mathcal{A}} |f_\alpha(z)| < \infty.$$

This is equivalent to *local uniform boundedness*, i.e., each point in Ω has a neighborhood K for which (2.20) holds.

Proposition 2.22. *Suppose* $\mathcal{F} = \{f_\alpha\}_{\alpha \in \mathcal{A}} \subset \mathcal{H}(\Omega)$ *is a normal family. Then there exists a sequence* f_n *in* $\mathcal{F}$ *that converges uniformly on compact subsets of* Ω, *the limit again being a holomorphic function.*

Proof. By (2.19), we see that $f_\alpha^{(k)}$ with $\alpha \in \mathcal{A}$ is uniformly bounded on compact subsets of Ω for all $k \geq 0$. By the cases $k = 0$ and $k = 1$, we see that $\{f_\alpha\}_{\alpha \in \mathcal{A}}$ is in particular equi-continuous and bounded. By the Arzela-Ascoli theorem and a diagonal subsequence argument we thus construct a subsequence converging uniformly on all compact subsets of Ω as desired. $\square$

One sometimes uses the convergence expressed in the proposition as the defining property of a normal family. The theorem then being that local boundedness implies normality. However, all of this is equivalent and expresses pre-compactness of a family of holomorphic functions in the local uniform topology. It is also desirable to allow ∞ as a limit. In other words, we say that a family $\mathcal{F} \subset \mathcal{H}(\Omega)$ is normal if for every compact set $K \subset \Omega$, any sequence from $\mathcal{F}$ admits a subsequence which converges uniformly on K to an analytic function or to ∞. A typical example would be

$$\{nz \mid n \geq 1\},$$

which is normal on any domain not containing 0. It clearly fails to be normal if the origin is in the domain. Another example would be

$$\{e^{nz} \mid n \geq 1\},$$

which fails to be normal on any open set.

The notion of normal family carries over to meromorphic functions. In that case we use the metric on the Riemann sphere given by Problem 1.6 to define the notion of convergence in the target. The definition of normality is then convergence of subsequences in this metric. The local uniform boundedness as in Proposition 2.22 has no meaning in this context, but there is the following analogue.

Theorem 2.23. *Let* $\mathcal{F}$ *be a family of meromorphic functions in* Ω *such that for each* $z_0 \in \Omega$ *there is a neighborhood* $U(z_0) \subset \Omega$ *and a constant* $M(z_0)$ *such that either*

$$|f(z)| < M(z_0) \quad or \quad \frac{1}{|f(z)|} < M(z_0) \quad \forall\, z \in U(z_0), \forall\, f \in \mathcal{F}.$$

Then $\mathcal{F}$ *is normal.*

We do not prove this here, see the notes at the end of the chapter.

2.6. The Mittag-Leffler and Weierstrass theorems

Suppose we are given finitely many points $\{z_n\}_{n=1}^N \subset \mathbb{C}$ and we wish to find a meromorphic function in $\mathbb{C}$ which has exactly these points as simple poles with prescribed residues r_n. Then the function

$$(2.21) \qquad f(z) = \sum_{n=1}^N \frac{r_n}{z - z_n}$$

is of this type. If g is another such function, then $f - g$ has removable singularities at z_n, and so is an entire function. We can easily generalize this to arbitrary types of poles. Indeed, given polynomials $p_n(w)$ with $p_n(0) = 0$,

$$f(z) = \sum_{n=1}^N p_n\left(\frac{1}{z - z_n}\right)$$

is meromorphic with poles exactly at the z_n and with pre-assigned *principal parts* in the Laurent expansions at these points. The principal part here refers to all negative powers of $z - z_n$.

It is now natural to ask whether such a construction can be applied to the case of *infinitely many points* $\{z_n\}_{n=1}^\infty \subset \mathbb{C}$. Clearly, we need to impose the condition that these points do not accumulate anywhere in the complex plane. For example, take $z_n = n^2$ for $n \geq 0$. Then (2.21) still applies, i.e.,

$$f(z) = \sum_{n=0}^\infty \frac{r_n}{z - n^2}$$

is meromorphic in $\mathbb{C}$ with simple poles at n^2 and residues r_n. This follows from Lemma 2.20. Indeed, given any disk $|z| \leq R$ we note that

$$\sum_{n > \sqrt{2R}} \frac{r_n}{z - n^2}$$

converges absolutely and uniformly on that disk to a holomorphic function. The finite sum which is excluded here does not pose a problem and of course has the desired properties. This example was still simple since $\sum z_n^{-1}$ is absolutely convergent. Now we will address the general question where such an assumption is not made. We also pose the analogous question with zeros instead of poles.

- Can we find $f \in \mathcal{M}(\mathbb{C})$ so that f has poles exactly at a prescribed sequence $\{z_n\}$ that does not cluster in $\mathbb{C}$, and such that f has prescribed principal parts at these poles (this refers to fixing the entire portion of the Laurent series with negative powers at each pole)?

- Can we find $f \in \mathcal{H}(\mathbb{C})$ such that f has zeros exactly at a given sequence $\{z_n\}$ that does not cluster with prescribed orders $\nu_n \geq 1$?

In both cases the answer is "yes", as we shall now demonstrate.

Theorem 2.24 (Mittag-Leffler). *Given* $\{z_n\}_{n=1}^N \subset \mathbb{C}$, *with* $|z_n| \to \infty$ *if* $N = \infty$, *and polynomials* P_n *with positive degrees and no constant terms, there exists* $f \in \mathcal{M}(\mathbb{C})$ *so that* f *has poles exactly at* z_n *and*

$$f(z) - P_n\left(\frac{1}{z - z_n}\right)$$

is analytic around z_n *for each* $1 \leq n \leq N$.

Proof. If N is finite, there is nothing to do: define

$$f(z) := \sum_{n=1}^N P_n\left(\frac{1}{z - z_n}\right).$$

If $N = \infty$, then we need to guarantee convergence of this series on compact sets by making at most a holomorphic error. Let $D_n := \{|z| < |z_n|/2\}$ for n sufficiently large (so that $z_n \neq 0$) and define $T_n(z)$ to be the Taylor polynomial of $P_n\left(\frac{1}{z-z_n}\right)$ of sufficiently high degree so that

$$\sup_{z \in D_n} \left| P_n\left(\frac{1}{z - z_n}\right) - T_n(z) \right| < 2^{-n}.$$

Then

$$\sum_{n=1}^\infty \left[P_n\left(\frac{1}{z - z_n}\right) - T_n(z) \right]$$

converges on compact subsets of $\mathbb{C} \setminus \{z_n\}_{n=1}^\infty$. By Lemma 2.20 it defines a holomorphic function in that region. Moreover, the z_n are isolated singularities; in fact, they are poles with $P_n\left(\frac{1}{z-z_n}\right)$ as principal parts. $\square$

As an example of this procedure, let $f(z) = \frac{\pi^2}{\sin^2(\pi z)}$. Then $f \in \mathcal{M}(\mathbb{C})$ with poles $z_n = n \in \mathbb{Z}$ and principal part $h_n(z) = (z - n)^{-2}$. Thus, $f(z) - h_n(z)$ is analytic near $z = n$. Clearly,

$$\sum_{n \in \mathbb{Z}} h_n(z)$$

converges uniformly on $\Omega := \mathbb{C} \setminus \mathbb{Z}$ to a function $s(z)$ holomorphic in Ω. Moreover, s and $g := f - s$ are both 1-periodic. In addition, $g \in \mathcal{H}(\mathbb{C})$. Finally, we claim that in the strip $0 \leq \operatorname{Re} z \leq 1$ the function g is uniformly bounded; in fact, it tends to zero as $|\operatorname{Im} z| \to \infty$. Clearly, it suffices to verify this under the additional assumption that $\operatorname{Im}(z) \geq 2$ (the case $\operatorname{Im} z \leq -2$ being symmetric). But then f is analytic and evidently vanishes at infinity.

So it suffices to check the same for $s(z)$. Let $z = x + iy$ with $N \leq y \leq N+1$ with some integer $N \geq 2$ and $0 \leq x \leq 1$. By the triangle inequality,

$$|z - n| \geq n - x \quad \text{for} \quad n > N,$$
$$|z - n| \geq y \quad \text{for} \quad 1 \leq n \leq N.$$

On the one hand,

$$(2.22) \qquad \sum_{n > N} |(z-n)^{-2}| \leq \sum_{n > N} (n - x)^{-2} \leq \sum_{n \geq N} \frac{1}{n(n-1)} = \frac{1}{N-1},$$

and on the other hand,

$$(2.23) \qquad \sum_{1 \leq n \leq N} |(z-n)^{-2}| \leq Ny^{-2} \leq N^{-1}.$$

In conclusion, $|s(z)| \leq 2/(y-1)$ and the claim follows. Hence $g \in \mathcal{H}(\mathbb{C}) \cap L^\infty(\mathbb{C})$ is bounded and in fact vanishes identically. In conclusion,

$$(2.24) \qquad \frac{\pi^2}{\sin^2(\pi z)} = \sum_{n=-\infty}^{\infty} \frac{1}{(z-n)^2}.$$

Setting $z = \frac{1}{2}$ shows that

$$(2.25) \qquad \frac{\pi^2}{8} = \sum_{n=1}^{\infty} \frac{1}{(2n+1)^2} \quad \text{and thus} \quad \frac{\pi^2}{6} = \sum_{n=1}^{\infty} \frac{1}{n^2},$$

where the second series is obtained from the first by splitting into even and odd n. The second series may also be obtained directly from (2.24): Write

$$\frac{\pi^2}{\sin^2(\pi z)} - \frac{1}{z^2} = \sum_{n \neq 0} \frac{1}{(z-n)^2}$$

whence

$$\lim_{z \to 0} \left[\frac{\pi^2}{\sin^2(\pi z)} - \frac{1}{z^2} \right] = 2 \sum_{n=1}^{\infty} \frac{1}{n^2}.$$

By Taylor expansion, the left-hand side is $\frac{\pi^2}{3}$ and (2.25) follows.

As another example, consider $f(z) = \pi \cot(\pi z)$. It has simple poles at each $n \in \mathbb{Z}$ with principal parts $h_n(z) = \frac{1}{z-n}$. In this case we do need to make use of the polynomials T_n from the proof of Theorem 2.24 in order to ensure convergence:

$$s(z) := \frac{1}{z} + \sum_{\substack{n=-\infty \\ n \neq 0}}^{\infty} \left[\frac{1}{z-n} + \frac{1}{n} \right] = \frac{1}{z} + \sum_{n=1}^{\infty} \left[\frac{1}{z-n} + \frac{1}{z+n} \right]$$

$$= \frac{1}{z} + \sum_{n=1}^{\infty} \frac{2z}{z^2 - n^2}.$$

By inspection, $g := f - s$ is 1-periodic and analytic on $\mathbb{C}$. Estimating f and s as above reveals that g is bounded; indeed, the only major difference is that we need to multiply by N in (2.22) and (2.23). Hence $g = \text{const}$, and expanding around $z = 0$ shows that in fact $g \equiv 0$. We have thus obtained the well-known *partial fraction decomposition*

$$(2.26) \qquad\qquad \pi \cot(\pi z) = \frac{1}{z} + \sum_{n=1}^{\infty} \frac{2z}{z^2 - n^2}.$$

Let us now turn to the second question, the construction of an entire function with prescribed zeros.

Definition 2.25. Given $\{z_n\}_{n=1}^{\infty} \subset \mathbb{C}^*$, we say that $\prod_{n=1}^{\infty} z_n$ converges, if

$$P_N := \prod_{n=1}^{N} z_n \to P_\infty \in \mathbb{C}^*.$$

We say that this product converges absolutely if $\sum_{n=1}^{\infty} |1 - z_n| < \infty$. We shall also allow products of the form $\prod_{n=1}^{\infty} z_n$, where all but finitely many z_n do not vanish. In the case that some $z_n = 0$, this product is defined to be 0 provided the infinite product with all vanishing z_n removed, converges in the previous sense.

It is essential here that $P_\infty \neq 0$. This condition is imposed so that we can relate infinite products and infinite sums by means of the complex logarithm. We choose the branch

$$\text{Log } z := \log|z| + i \operatorname{Arg} z, \qquad \operatorname{Arg} z \in (-\pi, \pi].$$

Lemma 2.26. *Let $\{z_n\}_{n=1}^{\infty} \subset \mathbb{C}^*$. Then $\prod_{n=1}^{\infty} z_n$ converges (absolutely) if and only if $\sum_{n=1}^{\infty} \text{Log } z_n$ converges (absolutely). The notion of* uniform *convergence of $\prod z_n$ relative to some complex parameter is also reduced to the same question for the series $\sum \text{Log } z_n$.*

Proof. If the product converges, then $z_n \to 1$ as $n \to \infty$. Moreover, for every $\varepsilon > 0$ there exists N_0 large so that $\left|1 - \prod_{n=N}^{M} z_n\right| < \varepsilon$ for all $M > N \geq N_0$. Applying Log to this shows that the tails of $\sum \text{Log } z_n$ are arbitrarily small.

For the converse direction, we exponentiate. $\square$

We can now easily answer the question concerning entire functions with prescribed zeros.

Theorem 2.27 (Weierstrass). *Let $\{z_n\}_n \subset \mathbb{C}$ be a sequence $\mathcal{Z}$ (finite or infinite) that does not accumulate in $\mathbb{C}$. Then there exists an entire function f that vanishes exactly at z_n to the order which equals the multiplicity of z_n in $\mathcal{Z}$. Conversely, given any entire function $f(z)$ which does not vanish* *identically, there exists another entire function $g(z)$ so that for some integer $\nu \geq 0$,*

$$(2.27) \qquad f(z) = e^{g(z)} z^{\nu} \prod_n E_{m_n}(z/z_n),$$

where the product runs over all zeros $z_n \neq 0$ of f, counted with multiplicity. The factors $E_{m_n}(z/z_n)$ are called the canonical factors *and they are defined as*

$$(2.28) \qquad E_k(z) = (1-z)e^{z+\frac{1}{2}z^2+\ldots+\frac{1}{k}z^k} \qquad k \geq 0.$$

The sequence m_n is a sequence of nonnegative integers.

Proof. We set

$$(2.29) \qquad f(z) := z^{\nu} \overset{\bullet}{\prod_n} \left[\left(1 - \frac{z}{z_n}\right) \exp\left(\sum_{\ell=1}^{m_n} \frac{1}{\ell}\left(\frac{z}{z_n}\right)^{\ell}\right)\right],$$

where ν is the number of times 0 appears in $\mathcal{Z}$ and $\overset{\bullet}{\prod}$ denotes the product from which we have excluded all $z_n = 0$. The $m_n \geq 0$ are integers chosen so that

$$\left| \operatorname{Log}\left(1 - \frac{z}{z_n}\right) + \sum_{\ell=1}^{m_n} \frac{1}{\ell}\left(\frac{z}{z_n}\right)^{\ell}\right| < 2^{-n},$$

on $|z| < \frac{1}{2}|z_n|$. Given any $R > 0$, all but finitely many z_n satisfy $|z_n| \geq 2R$. By our construction, the (tail of the) infinite product converges absolutely and uniformly on every disk to an analytic function. In particular, the zeros of f are precisely those of the factors, and we are done.

For the converse, we apply the first part to the sequence of zeros of f. This gives us a function $\widetilde{f}$ as in (2.29) which has the property that $f/\widetilde{f}$ is entire and does not vanish. Note that all the singularities of $f/\widetilde{f}$ are removable. But then $f = e^g \widetilde{f}$ which gives (2.27). $\qquad \square$

As in the case of the Mittag-Leffler theorem, one typically applies the Weierstrass theorem to give entire functions. Here is an example: let $f(z) = \sin(\pi z)$ with zero set $\mathcal{Z} = \mathbb{Z}$. The zeros are simple. In view of (2.29), we define

$$h(z) := z \overset{\bullet}{\prod_{n \in \mathbb{Z}}} \left(1 - \frac{z}{n}\right) e^{\frac{z}{n}} = z \prod_{n=1}^{\infty} \left(1 - \frac{z^2}{n^2}\right).$$

There exists an entire function g such that $f(z) = h(z)e^{g(z)}$. In other words,

$$f(z) = \sin(\pi z) = z e^{g(z)} \prod_{n=1}^{\infty} \left(1 - \frac{z^2}{n^2}\right),$$

$$\frac{f'(z)}{f(z)} = \pi \cot(\pi z) = g'(z) + \frac{1}{z} + \sum_{n=1}^{\infty} \frac{2z}{z^2 - n^2}.$$

By (2.26), $g' \equiv 0$ or $g = \text{const.}$ Expanding everything around $z = 0$ we conclude that $e^g = \pi$ and we have shown that

$$\sin(\pi z) = \pi z \prod_{n=1}^{\infty} \left(1 - \frac{z^2}{n^2}\right).$$

Setting $z = \frac{1}{2}$, in particular, yields the *Wallis formula*

$$\frac{\pi}{2} = \prod_{n=1}^{\infty} \frac{(2n)^2}{(2n+1)(2n-1)}.$$

It is natural to ask under what circumstances the numbers m_n in the proof of Theorem 2.27 remain bounded. By the proof of Weierstrass's theorem, this questions is tied up with the problem of analyzing the distribution of zeros of an entire function f. More precisely, we will need to control the number $N_f(R)$ of zeros in the disk $D(0, R)$ as $R \to \infty$. It turns out that the growth of $N_f(R)$ is related to the growth of f at infinity. We shall analyze this question in more detail in the following chapter; see Section 3.7.

To conclude the discussion of the Mittag-Leffler and Weierstrass theorems let us note the following: given arbitrary disjoint sequences $\{z_n\}$ and $\{\zeta_m\}$ with no accumulation point in $\mathbb{C}$, there exists a function $f \in \mathcal{M}(\mathbb{C})$ with poles precisely at the $\{z_n\}$ and zeros at the $\{\zeta_m\}$. Moreover, the principal parts at the poles can be arbitrarily prescribed. To see this, apply the Mittag-Leffler theorem which yields a function $f_0 \in \mathcal{M}(\mathbb{C})$ with the prescribed poles and principal parts. Then divide out the zeros of f_0 by means of the Weierstrass function and then multiply the resulting function with another entire function which has the prescribed zeros. In other words, there is no obstruction involving zeros and poles. However, if we consider the compactified plane $\mathbb{C}_\infty$, then there is an important obstruction: first, we know that each (nonconstant) $f \in \mathcal{M}(\mathbb{C}_\infty)$ is a rational function. It is easy to see from this representation that

$$\#\{z \in \mathbb{C}_\infty \,:\, f(z) = 0\} = \#\{z \in \mathbb{C}_\infty \,:\, f(z) = \infty\},$$

where the zeros and poles are counted according to multiplicity (including a possible one at ∞) and the cardinality here is finite. A better way of arriving at the same conclusion is given by the argument principle. We can assume that f has neither a zero or pole at infinity. Indeed, take any point

$z_0 \in \mathbb{C}$ where $f(z_0)$ is neither zero nor infinite. Then replace f by $f(z_0 + \frac{1}{z})$. Then

$$ n(f \circ \gamma_R; 0) = \#\{z \in D(0, R) : f(z) = 0\} - \#\{z \in D(0, R) : f(z) = \infty\}, $$

where γ_R is a circle of radius R centered at the origin so that no zero or pole of f lies on γ_R. Taking the limit $R \to \infty$ now yields the desired conclusion; indeed, the winding number on the left-hand side approaches zero in this limit by our assumption on f at $z = \infty$. We leave it to the reader to verify that this is the only obstruction to the existence of a meromorphic function with the given number of zeros and poles. Of interest is also that in fact

$$ \#\{z \in \mathbb{C}_\infty \mid f(z) = w\} = C, $$

where the left-hand side is counted with multiplicity, where C is independent of $w \in \mathbb{C}_\infty$. We shall see later that this is a general fact about analytic functions on *compact* Riemann surfaces (the constancy of the *valency* or degree).

2.7. The Riemann mapping theorem

We have already encountered several instances of conformal isomorphisms from one region to another. So far, we mainly considered automorphisms, such as for the disk, half-plane, plane, and Riemann sphere. For all of these regions the sought-after maps were Möbius transforms. But this is of course not universally so. For example, the map $z \mapsto z^2$ establishes an isomorphism between the first quadrant $\{x > 0, \ y > 0\}$ and the upper half-plane. Other powers $z^\alpha := \exp(\alpha \log z)$ (with $\alpha > 0$ and a suitable branch of the logarithm) represent automorphisms between different sectors of the plane. The exponential $z \mapsto e^z$ takes horizontal lines onto half-rays emanating at the origin, and vertical lines onto circles. So it conformally maps infinite horizontal strips onto sectors, and vertical strips onto annuli. If a horizontal strip has width less than 2π, then one has an isomorphism. A vertical strip is never mapped isomorphically. Truncating to a rectangle of height less than 2π yields an isomorphism onto an annular sector. In Figure 2.7 the two straight lines of the sector on the right are at angles y_0 and y_1, respectively.

The radii of the circular arcs are e^{x_0} and e^{x_1}, respectively.

It is now natural to ask which regions can be isomorphically mapped onto each other. We shall answer this for the special case where one of the regions is the disk. Since the latter is simply-connected and simple connectivity is a homeomorphism invariant, it is clear that we will need to impose that condition. Furthermore, by Liouville's theorem there can be no isomorphism from the disk onto the plane. As it turns out, this is the only exclusion amongst all simply-connected domains. This is the content of the

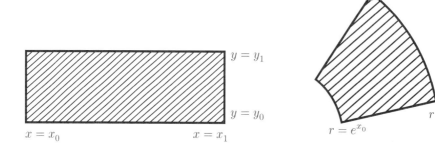

Figure 2.7. The exponential function takes a rectangle onto a sector

famous and fundamental *Riemann mapping theorem.* Later, it will become part of the much wider *uniformization theory* of Riemann surfaces.

Theorem 2.28. *Let $\Omega \subset \mathbb{C}$ be simply-connected and $\Omega \neq \mathbb{C}$. Then there exists a conformal homeomorphism $f : \Omega \to \mathbb{D}$ onto the unit disk $\mathbb{D}$.*

Proof. We first find such a map *into* $\mathbb{D}$. Then we will "maximize" all such f to select the desired homeomorphism. We assume that $0 \notin \Omega$. By Proposition 1.25 there exists a branch of $\sqrt{\cdot}$ on Ω which we denote by ρ. Let $\widetilde{\Omega} := \rho(\Omega)$. Then ρ is one-to-one and if $w \in \widetilde{\Omega}$, then $-w \notin \widetilde{\Omega}$. Indeed, otherwise $\rho(z_1) = w = -\rho(z_2)$ with $z_1, z_2 \in \Omega$ would imply that $z_1 = z_2$ or $w = -w = 0$ contrary to $0 \notin \Omega$. Since $\widetilde{\Omega}$ is open, we deduce that

$$\widetilde{\Omega} \cap D(w_0, \delta) = \emptyset$$

for some $w_0 \in \mathbb{C}$ and $\delta > 0$. Now define $f(z) := \frac{\delta}{\rho(z) - w_0}$ and observe that f is one-to-one and into $\mathbb{D}$. Henceforth, we assume that $\Omega \subset \mathbb{D}$ and also that $0 \in \Omega$ (scale and translate). Define

$$\mathcal{F} := \{ f : \Omega \to \mathbb{D} \mid f \in \mathcal{H}(\Omega) \text{ is one-to-one and } f(0) = 0, f'(0) > 0 \}.$$

Note, in particular, that $f'(0)$ is assumed to be real-valued. Then $\mathcal{F} \neq \emptyset$ (since $\mathrm{id}_\Omega \in \mathcal{F}$) and $\mathcal{F}$ is a normal family and Proposition 2.22 applies. We claim that

$$s_0 := \sup_{f \in \mathcal{F}} f'(0) > 0$$

is attained by some $f \in \mathcal{F}$. Indeed, let $f'_n(0) \to s_0$ with $f_n \in \mathcal{F}$ and $f_n \to f_\infty \in \mathcal{H}(\Omega)$ uniformly on compact subsets of Ω. Then $f_\infty(0) = 0$, $f'_\infty(0) > 0$ and, by the maximum principle and the open mapping theorem, $f_\infty : \Omega \to \mathbb{D}$ since this map is clearly not constant. Finally, from Lemma 2.20 we infer that f_∞ is also one-to-one and thus $f_\infty \in \mathcal{F}$ as claimed.

It remains to prove that f_∞ is onto $\mathbb{D}$. Suppose not, and let $w_0 \in \mathbb{D} \setminus \Omega_1$, $f_\infty(\Omega) =: \Omega_1$. Pick $g_1 \in \mathrm{Aut}(\mathbb{D})$ (a Möbius transform) such that $g_1(w_0) = 0$

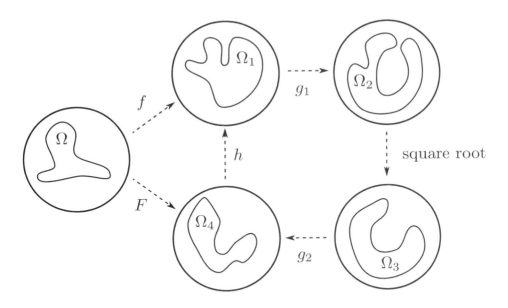

Figure 2.8. The chain of transformations in the Riemann mapping theorem

and let $\Omega_2 := g_1(\Omega_1)$, which is simply-connected and does not contain the origin. It therefore admits a branch of the square root, denoted by $\sqrt{\cdot}$. Let $g_2 \in \mathrm{Aut}(\mathbb{D})$ take $\sqrt{g_1(0)}$ onto 0. By construction,

$$F := g_2 \circ \sqrt{\cdot} \circ g_1 \circ f_\infty$$

satisfies $e^{i\theta}F \in \mathcal{F}$ for suitable θ. The inverse of $g_2 \circ \sqrt{\cdot} \circ g_1$ exists and equals the analytic function

$$h(z) := g_1^{-1}((g_2^{-1}(z))^2) : \mathbb{D} \to \mathbb{D},$$

which takes 0 to 0 and is not an automorphism of $\mathbb{D}$. Hence by the Schwarz lemma (see Lemma 1.31), one has $|h'(0)| < 1$. Since $h \circ F = f_\infty$, we conclude that $h'(0)F'(0) = f'_\infty(0)$ and thus $|F'(0)| > |f'_\infty(0)|$. This yields the desired contradiction. $\qquad\square$

We refer to f as in the theorem as a "Riemann map". It is clear that f becomes unique once we ask for $f(z_0) = 0$, $f'(z_0) > 0$ for some fixed $z_0 \in \Omega$ (this can always be achieved). As already noted, it is clear that $\Omega = \mathbb{C}$ does not admit a Riemann map (constancy of bounded entire functions). Next, we address the boundary behavior of the Riemann map. We begin by imposing a certain regularity condition on the boundary.

Definition 2.29. We say that $z_0 \in \partial\Omega$ is *regular* provided there exists $r_0(z_0) > 0$ such that for all $0 < r < r_0(z_0)$

$$\Omega \cap \{z \in \mathbb{C} \mid |z - z_0| = r\} = \{z_0 + re^{i\theta} \mid \theta_1(r) < \theta < \theta_2(r)\}$$

for some $\theta_1(r) < \theta_2(r)$ which are continuous in r. In other words, $\Omega \cap \partial D(z_0, r)$ is an arc for all small $r > 0$. We say that Ω is regular provided all points of $\partial \Omega$ are regular.

This notion of regularity only applies to the Riemann mapping theorem. In the final chapter we shall encounter another notion of regularity at the boundary which is common in potential theory. An example of a regular domain Ω is a manifold with C^1-boundary and corners; see below.

Theorem 2.30. *Suppose Ω is bounded, simply-connected, and regular. Then any conformal homeomorphism as in Theorem 2.28 extends to a homeomorphism $\bar{\Omega} \to \bar{\mathbb{D}}$.*

Proof. Let $f : \Omega \to \mathbb{D}$ be a Riemann map. We first show that $\lim_{z \to z_0} f(z)$ exists for all $z_0 \in \partial \Omega$, the limit being taken from within Ω. Suppose this fails for some $z_0 \in \partial \Omega$. Then there exist sequences $\{z_n\}_{n=1}^\infty$ and $\{\zeta_n\}_{n=1}^\infty$ in Ω converging to z_0 and such that

$$f(z_n) \to w_1, \qquad f(\zeta_n) \to w_2$$

as $n \to \infty$. Here $w_1 \neq w_2 \in \partial \mathbb{D}$. Let γ_1 be a continuous curve that connects the points $\{f(z_n)\}_{n=1}^\infty$ in this order and let γ_2 do the same with $\{f(\zeta_n)\}_{n=1}^\infty$. Denote $\eta_j := f^{-1} \circ \gamma_j$ for $j = 1, 2$. Then η_j are continuous curves both converging to z_0. Let

$$z_r \in \partial D(z_0, r) \cap \eta_1, \qquad \zeta_r \in \partial D(z_0, r) \cap \eta_2,$$

where we identify the curves with their set of points.

By regularity of z_0 there exists an arc $c_r \subset \Omega \cap \partial D(z_0, r)$ with

$$f(z_r) - f(\zeta_r) = \int_{c_r} f'(z) \, dz,$$

which further implies that

$$|f(z_r) - f(\zeta_r)|^2 \leq \left| \int_{c_r} f'(z) \, dz \right|^2 \leq \left(\int_{\theta_1(r)}^{\theta_2(r)} |f'(re^{i\theta})| \, r \, d\theta \right)^2$$

$$\leq 2\pi r \int_{\theta_1(r)}^{\theta_2(r)} |f'(re^{i\theta})|^2 \, r \, d\theta,$$

using Definition 2.29 and the Cauchy-Schwarz inequality. Dividing by r and integrating over $0 < r < r_0(z_0)$ implies that

$$\int_0^{r_0(z_0)} |f(z_r) - f(\zeta_r)|^2 \, \frac{dr}{r} \leq 2\pi \iint_\Omega |f'(z)|^2 \, dx \, dy = 2\pi \, \text{area}(\mathbb{D}) < \infty,$$

contradicting that $f(z_r) \to w_1$ and $f(\zeta_r) \to w_2$ as $r \to 0$ where $w_1 \neq w_2$.

Hence

$$\lim_{z \to z_0} f(z)$$

does exist and defines a continuous extension $F : \bar{\Omega} \to \bar{\mathbb{D}}$ of f.

The continuity claim can be easily derived from the preceding argument. Indeed, if it fails, then there would have to exist some $z_0 \in \partial\Omega$ and a sequence $z_n \in \partial\Omega$ so that $F(z_n) \not\to F(z_0)$ as $n \to \infty$. Since we can find $z_n' \in \Omega$ which are arbitrarily close to z_n this would then imply that $f(z_n') \not\to F(z_0)$ even though $z_n' \to z_0$. This contradicts the previous step and the continuity holds. Next, apply the same argument to $f^{-1} : \mathbb{D} \to \Omega$.

This can be done since obviously $\mathbb{D}$ is regular in the sense of Definition 2.29 and moreover, since any sequence $z_n \in \Omega$ converging to $z_0 \in \partial\Omega$ can be connected by a continuous curve inside Ω—indeed, use the continuity of $\theta_1(r), \theta_2(r)$ in Definition 2.29. Therefore, f^{-1} extends to a continuous map $G : \bar{\mathbb{D}} \to \bar{\Omega}$. Finally, it is evident that $F \circ G = \mathrm{id}_{\bar{\mathbb{D}}}$ and $G \circ F = \mathrm{id}_{\bar{\Omega}}$ as desired. $\qquad\square$

The same statement applies to unbounded Ω. In that case, we regard Ω as a region in $\mathbb{C}_\infty$ and call ∞ regular provided 0 is regular for $\Omega^{-1} := \{z^{-1} \mid z \in \Omega\}$. The following simple result gives some examples of regular domains.

Lemma 2.31. *Any region $\Omega \subset \mathbb{C}$ so that $\bar{\Omega}$ is a C^1-manifold with boundary and corners is regular. This means that for every $z_0 \in \partial\Omega$ there exists a C^1-diffeomorphism ϕ of a neighborhood U of z_0 onto a disk $D(0, r_1)$ for some $r_1 = r_1(z_0) > 0$ and such that*

$$\phi(\Omega \cap U) = \{re^{i\theta} \mid 0 < r < r_1, \ 0 < \theta < \theta_1 < 2\pi\}.$$

A simple example of such regions are polygons. In that case the conformal maps are given by the Schwarz-Christoffel formulas. For example, the map

$$z \mapsto \int_0^z \frac{d\zeta}{\zeta^{\frac{1}{2}}(\zeta - 1)^{\frac{1}{2}}}, \quad \mathrm{Im}\, z > 0$$

takes the upper half-plane onto the half-strip

$$\{z \in \mathbb{C} \mid \mathrm{Re}\, z \geq 0, \ 0 < \mathrm{Im}\, z < \pi\},$$

where 0 and 1 get mapped to the two finite vertices of the half-strip. In a similar spirit,

$$(2.30) \qquad z \mapsto \int_0^z \frac{d\zeta}{\zeta^{\frac{1}{2}}(\zeta - 1)^{\frac{1}{2}}(\zeta - 2)^{\frac{1}{2}}}, \quad \mathrm{Im}\, z > 0$$

takes the upper half-plane onto a rectangle with 0, 1, and 2 being mapped onto three of the vertices and the fourth vertex being the image of ∞. The square roots $(z-a)^{\frac{1}{2}}$ here are defined to be positive when $z > a$ and to take the upper half-plane into itself.

2.8. Runge's theorem and simple connectivity

Runge's theorem addresses the question as to whether any $f \in \mathcal{H}(\Omega)$ can be approximated on compact sets by a polynomial. Again, there is a topological obstruction: $f(z) = \frac{1}{z}$ cannot be approximated on $1 \leq |z| \leq 2$ by polynomials; otherwise, $\oint_{|z|=1} \frac{dz}{z} = 0$, which is false. However, on **simply-connected domains** this can be done. On general domains, approximation can be achieved by means of *rational functions*.

Theorem 2.32. *Let $K \subset \mathbb{C}$ be compact. Any function holomorphic on a neighborhood of K can be approximated uniformly on K by rational functions all of whose poles belong to $\mathbb{C} \setminus K$. In particular, if $\mathbb{C} \setminus K$ is connected, then the approximation is uniform by polynomials.*

Proof. Let $f \in \mathcal{H}(U)$ where $U \supset K$ is open. Let $\varepsilon > 0$ be sufficiently small that all squares with side-length ε which intersect K belong (together with their interior) entirely to U. Now define a cycle c_K by tracing out the boundaries of all square in an ε-grid with the property that they intersect both K and $U \setminus K$. We can assume that there are no degenerate configurations (squares that intersect ∂K but not K). The cycle is made up of finitely many curves which consist of finitely many line segments.

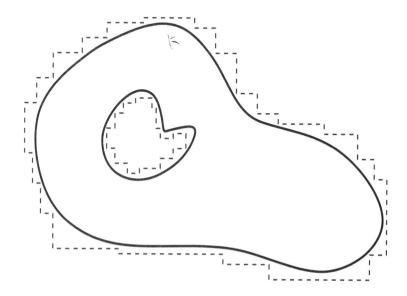

Figure 2.9. The cycle in Runge's theorem

Moreover, equipped with the natural orientation, c_K is 0-homologous relative to U, and the winding number $n(c; z) = 1$ for all $z \in K$. It follows from Cauchy's theorem that

$$f(z) = \frac{1}{2\pi i} \oint_c \frac{f(\zeta)}{\zeta - z} \, d\zeta \qquad \forall \, z \in K.$$

The integral on the right-hand side can be approximated by a Riemann sum uniformly on K and any such Riemann sum defines a rational function with poles on c and thus in $\mathbb{C} \setminus K$. To finish the theorem, we need to show that if $\mathbb{C} \setminus K$ is connected, then the poles can be "pushed to ∞".

In other words, we need to prove that $f(z, \zeta) := \frac{1}{z - \zeta}$ can be approximated uniformly by polynomials if $\zeta \notin K$. To this end, let ϕ be a bounded linear functional on $C(K)$ that vanishes on all polynomials. We remark that the polynomials are in general not dense in $C(K)$, since by Proposition 2.22 uniform limits of analytic functions are analytic. Hence ϕ does not need to vanish.

We claim, however, that $\phi(f(\cdot, \zeta)) = 0$ for all $\zeta \in \mathbb{C} \setminus K$. If $|\zeta| > \sup_{z \in K} |z|$, then this follows from

$$f(z, \zeta) = -\sum_{n=0}^{\infty} \frac{z^n}{\zeta^{n+1}} \qquad \forall \, z \in K.$$

Indeed, ϕ vanishes on each term of the series, and we interchange summation and application of ϕ by continuity of ϕ. Next, observe that $\phi(f(\cdot, \zeta))$ is analytic in ζ. Indeed, again by continuity of the functional ϕ one has

$$\partial_\zeta \phi(f(\cdot, \zeta)) = \phi(\partial_\zeta f(\cdot, \zeta)).$$

We are using here that the difference quotients

$$\lim_{h \to 0} h^{-1}[f(\cdot, \zeta + h) - f(\cdot, \zeta)] \to \partial_\zeta f(\cdot, \zeta)$$

uniformly on K. Alternatively, one can also check analyticity in ζ by Morera's theorem. Finally, we appeal to the uniqueness theorem from the previous chapter to obtain the desired vanishing. Indeed, $\mathbb{C} \setminus K$ is connected by assumption, whence the claim.

We shall now establish by contradiction that

$$f(\cdot, \zeta) \in \overline{\text{span}\{p(z) \mid p \in \mathbb{C}[z]\}} =: L$$

where the closure is with respect to $C(K)$. Indeed, assume this fails. Then

$$\phi(p + tf(\cdot, \zeta)) := t \qquad p \in L, \, t \in \mathbb{C}$$

defines a bounded linear functional on the span of L and $f(\cdot, \zeta)$ which vanishes on L and does not vanish on $f(\cdot, \zeta)$. Extend it as a bounded functional to $C(K)$ using the Hahn-Banach theorem. This can be done without increasing its norm, which equals $\mathrm{dist}(f(\cdot,\zeta), L))^{-1}$. But this is clearly a contradiction to the preceding observation about vanishing of any such functional on $f(\cdot,\zeta)$. $\square$

Runge's theorem has many deep consequences, such as the *local Mittag-Leffler theorem*, which we do not discuss here; for one application of Runge's theorem see Problem 2.13.

We close this chapter with a discussion of simple connectivity, which takes us back to the beginning of this chapter. It is natural to expect that a region Ω is simply-connected if and only if $\mathbb{C} \setminus \Omega$ is connected—the latter being the condition in Runge's theorem (up to the fact that there we removed a compact set). Intuitively, this equivalence expresses the idea that simple connectivity is the same as absence of holes. Let us now make this precise.

Proposition 2.33. *For any open set $\Omega \subset \mathbb{C}$ the following holds: $\mathbb{C}_\infty \setminus \Omega$ is connected if and only if every closed curve (or each cycle) γ in Ω is 0-homologous relative to Ω, i.e., $n(\gamma; z_0) = 0$ for every $z_0 \in \mathbb{C} \setminus \Omega$.*

Proof. The necessity follows from Lemma 2.1, since the winding number vanishes in the unbounded component.

For the sufficiency, assume that $\mathbb{C} \setminus \Omega$ is not connected. Then $\mathbb{C} \setminus \Omega = K_1 \cup K_2$ with closed disjoint sets K_1, K_2 and K_1 unbounded, K_2 compact. We apply Lemma 2.34 below to $\Omega_1 := \mathbb{C} \setminus K_1$ and $K_2 \subset \Omega_1$. Thus, there exists a cycle $c \subset \Omega_1 \setminus K_2 = \Omega$ with the property that $n(c; z_0) = 1$ for each $z_0 \in K_2$ and $n(c; z_0) = 0$ for each $z_0 \notin \Omega_1$. Hence c is not 0-homologous relative to Ω; it winds around a point in $\mathbb{C} \setminus \Omega$. $\square$

The previous proof was based on the following technical fact.

Lemma 2.34. *Let $\Omega \subset \mathbb{C}$ be open and $K \subset \Omega$ be compact. Then there exists a polygonal cycle $c \subset \Omega \setminus K$ so that $n(c; \cdot) = 1$ on K and $n(c; \cdot) = 0$ on $\mathbb{C} \setminus \Omega$.*

Proof. Consider a regular tiling of $\mathbb{C}$ with hexagons $\{\mathcal{H}_j\}_j$ of side length $\varepsilon > 0$. We take the tiles to be closed, so that the boundaries intersect. The parameter $\varepsilon > 0$ is chosen so small that a tile which intersects K lies entirely within Ω. Denote by

$$\mathcal{S} := \{\mathcal{H}_j \mid \mathcal{H}_j \cap K \neq \emptyset\}$$

those tiles that intersect K. We can also assume that if a tile intersects K, then it does so with its interior. Place the positive sense of orientation on each hexagon.

Let $\mathcal{E}$ be those oriented edges of hexagons in $\mathcal{S}$ that are edges (as sets without orientation) of exactly one member of $\mathcal{S}$. Given $\vec{bc} \in \mathcal{E}$, there exist both a unique predecessor as well a unique successor to this edge. I.e., there

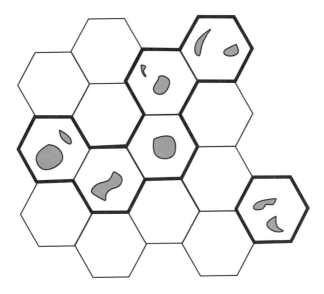

Figure 2.10. The hexagonal tiling

exist unique $\vec{cd} \in \mathcal{E}$ and $\vec{ab} \in \mathcal{E}$ (this is why we use hexagons instead of squares).

Thus, $\mathcal{E}$ is the finite union of closed oriented polygonal paths $\{\gamma_\ell\}_{\ell=1}^k$ consisting of edges of the tiles. Denote the tiles in $\mathcal{S}$ by $\{\mathcal{H}_j\}_{j=1}^J$ and their oriented boundaries by $\partial \mathcal{H}_j$. Then $n(\partial \mathcal{H}_j; z) = 1$ if $z \in \mathrm{int}(\mathcal{H}_j)$ and 0 otherwise. By construction,

$$(2.31) \qquad n\Big(\sum_{j=1}^J \partial \mathcal{H}_j, z \Big) = n\Big(\sum_{\ell=1}^k \gamma_\ell, z \Big) \qquad \forall z \notin \sum_{j=1}^J \partial \mathcal{H}_j + \sum_{\ell=1}^k \gamma_\ell.$$

This follows from the fact that if an edge occurs in two adjacent hexagons, then it cancels out in the sum $\sum_{j=1}^J \partial \mathcal{H}_j$ due to opposite orientations. Otherwise, it occurs exactly once in the sum $\sum_{\ell=1}^k \gamma_\ell$. Figure 2.10 illustrates this procedure.

Hence with $c := \sum_{\ell=1}^k \gamma_\ell$ we have

$$n(c; z) = 1 \qquad \forall\, z \in K$$

and

$$n(c; z) = 0 \qquad \forall\, z \in \mathbb{C} \setminus \Omega$$

as desired. $\qquad\qquad\qquad\qquad\qquad\qquad\qquad\qquad\qquad\qquad\qquad\qquad$ $\square$

We now summarize some of the work of this chapter in the following theorem, which exhibits various equivalencies of the global Cauchy type.

Theorem 2.35. *Let $\Omega \subset \mathbb{C}$ be open. Then the following are equivalent:*

- $\mathbb{C}_\infty \setminus \Omega$ *is connected.*
- $n(c; z) = 0$ *for every cycle c in Ω and every $z \in \mathbb{C} \setminus \Omega$.*
- $\int_c f(z)\, dz = 0$ *for every cycle c in Ω and every $f \in \mathcal{H}(\Omega)$.*
- *Every f holomorphic in Ω has a primitive there.*
- *Every f which is holomorphic and does not vanish in Ω has a logarithm in Ω.*
- *Every f which is holomorphic and does not vanish in Ω has n^{th} roots in Ω for all $n \geq 2$.*
- *Every f which is holomorphic and does not vanish in Ω has a square root in Ω.*

Each of these properties is equivalent to Ω being simply-connected, and each is therefore conformally invariant, meaning that if it holds for Ω, then it also holds on each conformally equivalent region.

Proof. These equivalencies are based on Proposition 2.33, the global Cauchy theorem as in Theorem 2.2 and Corollary 2.3, and the definition of the winding number. In this fashion one obtains the equivalence of the first four properties.

The final three are implied by the proof of Proposition 1.25, which only requires primitives to exist for any analytic function in Ω. Moreover, in the order as they are stated the logarithms imply the roots, which implies the square root.

To conclude the proof, we go back (for example) to Riemann's mapping theorem. Inspection of the proof shows that we only needed the existence of square roots to run the argument, as well as the observation that the existence of roots of nonvanishing analytic functions is a conformal invariant.

So apart from the trivial case $\Omega = \mathbb{C}$ we conclude from the existence of roots that Ω is conformally equivalent to the disk. But then it is simply-connected, and all other properties hold. $\qquad\square$

Notes

This chapter is meant to introduce some of the slightly deeper facts of basic complex analysis. The author needed to make a selection, and hopes to have chosen what can be considered core results which are, moreover, indispensable in other areas of mathematics (such as the Rouché and Riemann mapping theorems, as well as the product representation of entire functions).

The proof of the global Cauchy theorem (cf. Theorem 2.2), is that of Dixon [**14**]. The Γ function, which serves to illustrate some of the concepts that we have developed so far, is studied in more detail in Problems 2.11, 2.14 below. For a proof of Theorem 2.23 see Schiff [**74**, Corollary 3.3.4]. Some of the more glaring omissions, such as the Picard theorems and Montel's normality test, will be covered in Chapter 4. The following chapter on harmonic functions should also be considered as an integral part of complex analysis even though there is a strong "real-variables" component. It does present some essential complex analysis tools, such as Jensen's formula on the zero count, as well as entire functions of finite order and the Hadamard product expansion for this class which is intimately related to the distribution of the zeros of such functions.

We remark that both the Mittag-Leffler and Weierstrass theorems remain valid on regions $\Omega \subset \mathbb{C}$; see Conway [**12**], for example, or Remmert [**70**]. This local theory is something we do not cover in this text. For more on the Schwarz-Christoffel formulas, see for example [**1**].

The tiling with hexagons is from the book by Ash and Novinger [**5**]; see also Taylor's book [**79**].

2.9. Problems

Problem 2.1. In this problem we investigate the problem of "dividing out the zeros" of an analytic function.

(a) Suppose $f \in \mathcal{H}(\mathbb{D})$ satisfies $|f(z)| \leq M$ for all $z \in \mathbb{D}$. Assume further that $f(z)$ vanishes at the points $\{z_j\}_{j=1}^N$ where $1 \leq N \leq \infty$. Prove that

$$|f(z)| \leq M \left| \prod_{j=1}^m \frac{z - z_j}{1 - \bar{z}_j z} \right| \qquad \forall\, z \in \mathbb{D}$$

for any $1 \leq m \leq N$ (or, if $N = \infty$, then $1 \leq m < N$).

(b) If $N = \infty$ and $f \not\equiv 0$, then show that

$$\sum_{j=1}^\infty (1 - |z_j|) < \infty.$$

Problem 2.2. Let $z_1, z_2, \ldots, z_n \in \mathbb{C}$ be distinct points. Suppose γ is a closed (large) circle that contains these points in its interior and let f be analytic on a disk containing γ. Then the unique polynomial $P(z)$ of degree $n - 1$ which satisfies $P(z_j) = f(z_j)$ for all $1 \leq j \leq n$ is given by

$$P(z) = \frac{1}{2\pi i} \oint_\gamma \frac{f(\zeta)}{\omega(\zeta)} \frac{\omega(\zeta) - \omega(z)}{\zeta - z}\, d\zeta,$$

provided $\omega(z)$ is a suitably chosen polynomial. Find ω and prove this formula.

Problem 2.3. The following three problems apply the residue theorem (cf. Theorem 2.12) to the computation of several integrals.

First, compute the value of the following definite integrals.

$$\int_{-\infty}^{\infty} \frac{dx}{1+x^2} =?, \quad \int_{-\infty}^{\infty} \frac{dx}{1+x^4} =?, \quad \int_{-\infty}^{\infty} \frac{x^2\,dx}{1+x^4} =?,$$

$$\int_0^{\infty} \frac{\sin x}{x}\,dx =?, \quad \int_0^{\infty} \frac{1-\cos x}{x^2}\,dx =?,$$

$$\int_0^{\pi} \frac{d\theta}{(a+\cos\theta)^2} =? \quad a>1, \quad \int_0^{\infty} \frac{\log x}{1+x^2} =?, \quad \int_0^{\infty} \frac{(\log x)^3}{1+x^2}\,dx =?,$$

$$\int_0^{\infty} \frac{x^{a-1}}{1+x}\,dx = \int_{-\infty}^{\infty} \frac{e^{at}}{1+e^t}\,dt = \frac{\pi}{\sin\pi a}, \quad 0<a<1,$$

$$\int_{-\infty}^{\infty} e^{-\pi x^2} e^{-2\pi i x \xi}\,dx = e^{-\pi\xi^2} \quad \forall\,\xi\in\mathbb{R}.$$

Problem 2.4. Second, prove that

$$\int_{-\infty}^{\infty} e^{-2\pi i x \xi} \frac{\sin\pi a}{\cosh\pi x + \cos\pi a}\,dx = \frac{2\sinh 2\pi a\xi}{\sinh 2\pi\xi} \quad \forall\,\xi\in\mathbb{R},\ 0<a<1,$$

$$\int_{-\infty}^{\infty} \frac{\cos x}{x^2+a^2}\,dx = \pi\frac{e^{-a}}{a}, \quad \int_{-\infty}^{\infty} \frac{x\sin x}{x^2+a^2}\,dx = \pi e^{-a}, \quad a>0,$$

$$\int_{-\infty}^{\infty} \frac{e^{-2\pi i x \xi}}{(1+x^2)^2}\,dx = \frac{\pi}{2}(1+2\pi|\xi|)e^{-2\pi|\xi|}, \quad \forall\,\xi\in\mathbb{R},$$

as well as

$$\int_{-\infty}^{\infty} \frac{dx}{(1+x^2)^{n+1}} = \frac{1\cdot 3\cdot 5\cdots(2n-1)}{2\cdot 4\cdot 6\cdots(2n)}\cdot\pi,$$

$$\int_0^{2\pi} \frac{d\theta}{(a+\cos\theta)^2} = \frac{2\pi a}{(a^2-1)^{\frac{3}{2}}}, \quad a>1,$$

$$\int_0^{2\pi} \frac{d\theta}{a+b\cos\theta} = \frac{2\pi}{\sqrt{a^2-b^2}}, \quad a,b\in\mathbb{R},\ |a|>b,$$

and finally, show that

$$\int_0^{2\pi} \log|1-ae^{i\theta}|\,d\theta = 0, \quad \int_0^{\infty} \frac{\log x}{x^2+a^2}\,dx = \frac{\pi}{2a}\log a, \quad a>0,$$

$$\int_0^1 \log(\sin\pi x)\,dx = -\log 2,$$

$$\sum_{n=-\infty}^{\infty} \frac{1}{(u+n)^2} = \frac{\pi^2}{(\sin\pi u)^2}, \quad \text{Hint: use } f(z) = \frac{\pi\cot\pi z}{(u+z)^2},$$

$$\int_0^{\pi} \frac{d\theta}{a+\cos\theta} = \frac{\pi}{\sqrt{a^2-1}}.$$

Problem 2.5. Use the residue theorem to carry out the following two computations:

(a) Prove that

$$\int_0^{\frac{\pi}{2}} \frac{x\,d\theta}{x^2 + \sin^2\theta} = \frac{\pi}{2\sqrt{1+x^2}} \qquad \forall\, x > 0.$$

(b) Prove that

$$\int_0^{2\pi} \frac{(1+2\cos\theta)^n \cos(n\theta)}{1 - r - 2r\cos\theta}\, d\theta = \frac{2\pi}{\sqrt{1-2r-3r^2}} \left(\frac{1 - r - \sqrt{1 - 2r - 3r^2}}{2r^2} \right)^n$$

for any $-1 < r < \frac{1}{3}$, $n = 0, 1, 2, \ldots$.

Problem 2.6. This problem introduces the Schwarz reflection principle.

(a) Let Ω be an open set in $\bar{\mathbb{H}}$ and denote $\Omega_0 = \Omega \cap \mathbb{H}$. Suppose $f \in \mathcal{H}(\Omega_0) \cap C(\Omega)$ with $\operatorname{Im} f(z) = 0$ for all $z \in \Omega \cap \partial\mathbb{H}$. Define

$$F(z) := \begin{cases} f(z) & z \in \Omega, \\ \overline{f(\bar{z})} & z \in \Omega^-, \end{cases}$$

where $\Omega^- = \{z : \bar{z} \in \Omega\}$. Prove that $F \in \mathcal{H}(\Omega \cup \Omega^-)$.

(b) Suppose $f \in \mathcal{H}(\mathbb{D}) \cap C(\bar{\mathbb{D}})$ so that $|f(z)| = 1$ on $|z| = 1$. If f does not vanish anywhere in $\mathbb{D}$, then prove that f is constant.

Problem 2.7. This exercise explores conformal mappings of various domains:

(a) Is there a bi-holomorphic map between the punctured disk $\{0 < |z| < 1\}$ and the annulus $\{\frac{1}{2} < |z| < 1\}$? If "yes", then find it; if "no", then prove that it cannot exist.

(b) Prove that $\mathbb{C}$ is not conformally equivalent to any proper subdomain of itself.

Problem 2.8. Let $f(z) = \sinh(\pi z)$,

$$\Omega_0 = \left\{ z \in \mathbb{C} : \operatorname{Re} z > 0, \ -\frac{1}{2} < \operatorname{Im} z < \frac{1}{2} \right\},$$

and $\Omega_1 = -i\mathbb{H}$ (the right half-plane). Prove that $f : \Omega_0 \to \Omega_1$ is one-to-one, onto, and bi-holomorphic (use the argument principle).

Problem 2.9. Let $\lambda > 1$. Show that the equation $\lambda - e^{-z} - z = 0$ has a unique zero in the closed right half-plane $\operatorname{Re} z \geq 0$.

Problem 2.10. This exercise provides examples of Laurent expansions and partial fractions:

(a) Give the partial fraction expansion of $r(z) = \frac{z^2+1}{(z^2+z+1)(z-1)^2}$.

(b) Let $f(z) = \frac{1}{z(z-1)(z-2)}$. Find the Laurent expansion of f on each of the following three annuli:

$$\mathcal{A}_1 = \{0 < |z| < 1\}, \quad \mathcal{A}_2 = \{1 < |z| < 2\}, \quad \mathcal{A}_3 = \{2 < |z| < \infty\}.$$

Problem 2.11. This exercise introduces and discusses some basic properties of the Gamma function $\Gamma(z)$, which appears quite frequently in mathematics:

(a) Show that

$$(2.32) \qquad \Gamma(z) = \int_0^\infty e^{-t} t^{z-1}\, dt$$

defines an analytic function in the half-plane $\operatorname{Re} z > 0$. Also, verify the functional equation $\Gamma(z+1) = z\Gamma(z)$ for all $\operatorname{Re} z > 0$ as well as the identity $\Gamma(n+1) = n!$ for all integers $n \geq 0$.

(b) Using the functional equation, show that there exists a unique meromorphic function on $\mathbb{C}$ which agrees with $\Gamma(z)$ on the right half-plane. Denoting this globally defined function again by Γ, prove that it has poles exactly at the nonpositive integers $-n$ with $n \geq 0$. Moreover, show that these poles are simple with residues $\operatorname{Res}(\Gamma, -n) = \frac{(-1)^n}{n!}$ for all $n \geq 0$.

(c) With $\Gamma(z)$ as in (a), verify the identity

$$(2.33) \qquad \Gamma(z) = \int_1^\infty e^{-t} t^{z-1}\, dt + \sum_{n=0}^\infty \frac{(-1)^n}{n!(z+n)},$$

for all $\operatorname{Re} z > 0$. Now repeat part (b) using (2.33) instead of the functional equation.

(d) Verify that

$$(2.34) \qquad \int_0^\infty \frac{v^{a-1}}{1+v}\, dv = \frac{\pi}{\sin \pi a}, \qquad \forall\, 0 < \operatorname{Re} a < 1.$$

Now apply this to establish that

$$(2.35) \qquad \Gamma(z)\Gamma(1-z) = \frac{\pi}{\sin \pi z}$$

as an identity between meromorphic functions defined on $\mathbb{C}$. In particular, we see that $\Gamma(\frac{1}{2}) = \sqrt{\pi}$. Find an expression for $|\Gamma(\frac{1}{2}+it)|$ with $t \in \mathbb{R}$.

To pass from (2.34) to (2.35), use the identity

$$\Gamma(1-x) = y^{1-x} \int_0^\infty e^{-uy} u^{-x}\, du, \qquad \forall\, y > 0,$$

which holds for any $0 < x < 1$.

(e) Check that

$$\int_0^1 (1-t)^{\alpha-1} t^{\beta-1}\, dt = \frac{\Gamma(\alpha)\Gamma(\beta)}{\Gamma(\alpha+\beta)}, \qquad \forall\ \mathrm{Re}(\alpha) > 0,\ \mathrm{Re}(\beta) > 0.$$

(f) Prove that

$$\int_0^\infty t^{z-1} \cos t\, dt = \Gamma(z)\cos(\pi z/2), \qquad \forall\ 0 < \mathrm{Re}\, z < 1,$$

$$\int_0^\infty t^{z-1} \sin t\, dt = \Gamma(z)\sin(\pi z/2), \qquad \forall\ -1 < \mathrm{Re}\, z < 1.$$

Deduce from this that

$$\int_0^\infty \frac{\sin x}{x}\, dx = \frac{\pi}{2}, \qquad \int_0^\infty \frac{\sin x}{x^{3/2}}\, dx = \sqrt{2\pi}.$$

(g) Let γ be a version of Hankel's loop contour. This refers to a smooth curve $\gamma = \gamma(t) : \mathbb{R} \to \mathbb{C} \setminus (-\infty, 0]$ which approaches $(-\infty, 0]$ from above as $t \to \infty$ and from below as $t \to -\infty$. Moreover, it encircles $w = 0$ once in a positive sense. An example of such a γ would be with $\varepsilon : \mathbb{R} \to (0,1)$, $\varepsilon(t) \to 0$ as $|t| \to \infty$, $\gamma(t) = t - i\varepsilon(t)$ for $-\infty < t < -1$ and $\gamma(t) = -t + i\varepsilon(t)$ for $1 < t < \infty$ as well as a circular arc $\gamma(t)$ for $-1 \le t \le 1$ encircling $w = 0$ in a positive sense and joining the point $-1 - i\varepsilon(-1)$ to the point $-1 + i\varepsilon(1)$.

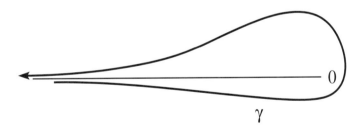

Figure 2.11. A Hankel contour γ

Now prove that for all $z \in \mathbb{C}$,

(2.36)
$$\frac{1}{2\pi i} \int_\gamma e^w w^{-z}\, dw = \frac{1}{\Gamma(z)}$$

as an identity between entire functions. On the left-hand side $w^{-z} = e^{-z\,\mathrm{Log}\, w}$ where $\mathrm{Log}\, w$ is the principal branch of the logarithm.

Problem 2.12. Suppose that $f(z) = \sum_{n=0}^\infty a_n z^{2^n}$ has radius of convergence $R = 1$. Prove that f cannot be analytically continued to any disk centered at any point z_0 with $|z_0| = 1$ (assume that you can analytically continue to a neighborhood of $z = 1$ and substitute $z - aw^2 + bw^3$ where $0 < a < 1$ and $a + b = 1$).

Generalize to other gap series $\sum_{k=0}^{\infty} a_k z^{n_k}$ where $n_{k+1} > \lambda n_k$ for all $k \geq 1$ with $\lambda > 1$ fixed.

Problem 2.13. Suppose $K \subsetneq \partial\mathbb{D}$, $K \neq \emptyset$. Show that for any $\varepsilon > 0$ there exists a polynomial P with $P(0) = 1$ and $|P(z)| < \varepsilon$ on K (Hint: use Runge's theorem).

Problem 2.14. This exercise continues our investigation of the Gamma function.

(a) Prove that there is some constant $A \in \mathbb{C}$ such that

$$(2.37) \qquad \frac{\Gamma'(z)}{\Gamma(z)} = \int_0^1 \left(1 - (1 - t)^{z-1} \right) \frac{dt}{t} + A \qquad \forall \operatorname{Re} z > 0.$$

Deduce from (2.37) that

$$(2.38) \qquad \frac{\Gamma'(z)}{\Gamma(z)} = \sum_{n=0}^{\infty} \left(\frac{1}{n+1} - \frac{1}{n+z} \right) + A,$$

as an identity between meromorphic functions on $\mathbb{C}$.

(b) Derive the following product expansion from (2.38):

$$(2.39) \qquad \frac{1}{\Gamma(z)} = e^{\gamma z} z \prod_{n=1}^{\infty} \left(1 + \frac{z}{n} \right) e^{-\frac{z}{n}},$$

as an identity between entire functions. Here γ is the Euler constant

$$\gamma = \lim_{N \to \infty} \left(1 + \frac{1}{2} + \ldots + \frac{1}{N} - \log N \right).$$

Alternatively, derive (2.39) from Hadamard's theorem; see Theorem 3.33.

(c) Prove *Gauss's formula*: if $z \in \mathbb{C} \setminus \{n : n \leq 0\}$, then

$$\Gamma(z) = \lim_{n \to \infty} \frac{n! \, n^z}{z(z+1)(z+2)\ldots(z+n)}.$$

Problem 2.15. Prove the duplication formula for the Gamma function: $\Gamma(2z) = \pi^{-\frac{1}{2}} 2^{2z-1} \Gamma(z) \Gamma(z + \frac{1}{2})$ for all $z \in \mathbb{C}$.

Problem 2.16. Show that the holomorphic functions on any region form a Fréchet space.

Chapter 3

Harmonic functions

3.1. The Poisson kernel

In the first chapter we encountered the fundamental class of *harmonic functions* on a region. This refers to functions $u \in C^2(\Omega)$ so that $\Delta u = u_{xx} + u_{yy} = 0$. Recall that both real and imaginary parts of analytic functions are of this type. It would be misguided, though, to regard harmonic functions as depending essentially on the notion of analytic function in the plane. Indeed, the Laplace equation $\Delta u = \sum_{j=1}^d \frac{\partial^2 u}{\partial x_j^2} = 0$ makes sense in any dimension, and it appears frequently in mathematics and physics. For example, a conservative field $\vec{E}$, such as the electrostatic field in the absence of charges, satisfies $\mathrm{div}\,\vec{E} = 0$, or in the presence of charges, $\mathrm{div}\,\vec{E} = \rho$ where ρ is the charge density. In the former case the potential function φ associated with $\vec{E}$ (i.e., the voltage) satisfies $\nabla \varphi = \vec{E}$ and thus $\Delta \varphi = 0$. So the potential is harmonic.

If we take a nonconducting surface and place charges unevenly over the surface, then we are specifying a potential function f on the surface. Clearly, an electric field is created inside the surface, and thus also a potential. In mathematical terms, given any open connected set $\Omega \subset \mathbb{R}^d$ with a smooth boundary and a continuous (say) function f on $\partial\Omega$, we expect that there exists a solution to the equation $\Delta \varphi = 0$ in Ω, $\varphi = f$ on $\partial\Omega$. This boundary value problem is called *Dirichlet problem* and is of fundamental importance to science and engineering. Not surprisingly, establishing the existence and uniqueness of a solution to this problem played a decisive role in the development of mathematics from the mid 1800s into the 20th century. Dirichlet himself accepted without proof that the variational problem

$$\inf_{\varphi \in \mathcal{A}} \mathcal{E}(\varphi), \quad \mathcal{E}(\varphi) := \frac{1}{2} \int_\Omega |\nabla\varphi(x)|^2 \, dx$$

has a solution in a "suitable" class $\mathcal{A}$ of admissible functions which at least need to satisfy $\varphi = f$ on $\partial\Omega$. If this infimum is attained by a sufficiently smooth function φ, then it is necessarily harmonic. In fact, if ψ is a C^2 function with compact support in a bounded region Ω, then

(3.1)
$$\begin{aligned}
0 &= \frac{d}{d\varepsilon}\Big|_{\varepsilon=0} \mathcal{E}(\varphi + \varepsilon\psi) = \int_\Omega \nabla\varphi(x) \cdot \nabla\psi(x) \, dx \\
&= - \int_\Omega \Delta\varphi(x) \, \psi(x) \, dx,
\end{aligned}$$

where the last line follows by integration by parts—or equivalently, the divergence theorem. Indeed, one writes

$$\nabla\varphi(x) \cdot \nabla\psi(x) = \mathrm{div}(\psi\nabla\varphi) - \psi\Delta\varphi,$$

and the first term on the right-hand side contributes nothing to the integral over Ω since it vanishes on the boundary. Since ψ was arbitrary, it follows that $\Delta\varphi = 0$. The same argument applies also to solving $\Delta\varphi = g$; indeed, just change the energy to

$$\int_\Omega \Big[\frac{1}{2}|\nabla\varphi(x)|^2 - g(x)\varphi(x)\Big] \, dx.$$

The problem with this approach lies with the assumption that a minimizer exists, which is intimately tied to first clarifying what a "suitable" admissible class $\mathcal{A}$ is. As we now know, the Sobolev space $H^1(\Omega)$ is the correct class with the condition that the trace equals f on $\partial\Omega$. But in order to arrive at this point, one first needs Lebesgue integration (in order to ensure that L^2 is a complete space), then elementary functional analysis (Hilbert spaces, weak topology), and finally also a basic regularity theory to show that φ is in fact a classical C^2 (in fact, more smooth) solution.

There are other, nonvariational ways, of solving the Dirichlet problem. Rather than relying on some form of compactness, they rest on monotonicity arguments. We shall present one such argument, namely Perron's method, in more detail in a later chapter.

For now, we content ourselves with the special case of disks in the plane where we can fall back on the close connection between Fourier series and analytic or harmonic functions. Heuristically speaking, a Fourier series can be viewed as the "boundary values" of a Laurent series

$$\sum_{n=-\infty}^{\infty} a_n z^n.$$

Let us use this observation to derive a solution formula for the Dirichlet problem on the disk: *Given a function f on the boundary of $\mathbb{D}$ find a harmonic function u on $\mathbb{D}$ which attains these boundary values.*

Notice that this problem is formulated too vaguely. In fact, in the history of mathematical analysis the proper interpretation of what we mean by *attaining* the boundary values and what kind of boundedness properties we wish u to satisfy on all of $\mathbb{D}$ played an influential and prominent role.

But for the moment, let us proceed heuristically. Starting with the Fourier series $f(\theta) = \sum_{n\in\mathbb{Z}} \hat{f}(n)e(n\theta)$ with $e(\theta) := e^{2\pi i\theta}$, we observe that one harmonic extension to the interior is given by

$$u(z) = \sum_{n\in\mathbb{Z}} \hat{f}(n)z^n = \sum_{n\in\mathbb{Z}} \hat{f}(n)r^n e(n\theta), \qquad z = re(\theta).$$

This is singular at $z = 0$, though, in case $\hat{f}(n) \neq 0$ for one $n < 0$. Since both z^n and $\overline{z^n}$ are (complex) harmonic, we can avoid the singularity by defining

$$(3.2) \qquad u(z) = \sum_{n=0}^{\infty} \hat{f}(n)z^n + \sum_{n=-\infty}^{-1} \hat{f}(n)\bar{z}^{|n|},$$

which at least formally is a solution of our Dirichlet problem.

Inserting $z = re(\theta)$ and $\hat{f}(n) = \int_0^1 e(-n\varphi)f(\varphi)\,d\varphi$ into (3.2) yields

$$(3.3) \quad u(re(\theta)) = \int_{\mathbb{T}} \sum_{n\in\mathbb{Z}} r^{|n|}e(n(\theta - \varphi))f(\varphi)\,d\varphi =: \int_0^1 P_r(\theta - \varphi)\,f(\varphi)\,d\varphi,$$

where the *Poisson kernel*

$$P_r(\theta) := \sum_{n\in\mathbb{Z}} r^{|n|}e(n\theta) = \frac{1 - r^2}{1 - 2r\cos(2\pi\theta) + r^2},$$

which follows by explicit summation (geometric series). We start the rigorous theory by stating some properties of P_r. We remind the reader that an integral of the form (3.3) is called a *convolution*, and denoted by $*$. The interpretation of $f * g$ is as an average of translates of f with a weight determined by g (or vice versa).

Lemma 3.1. *The function $z = re(\theta) = P_r(\theta)$ is a positive harmonic function on $\mathbb{D}$. It satisfies $\int_0^1 P_r(\theta)\,d\theta = 1$ and for any (complex) Borel measure μ on $\mathbb{T}$,*

$$z = re(\theta) \mapsto (P_r * \mu)(\theta)$$

defines a harmonic function on $\mathbb{D}$.

Proof. These properties are all either evident from the explicit form of the kernel or via the defining series. $\qquad\square$

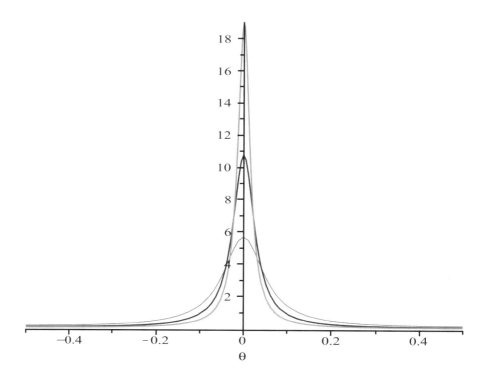

Figure 3.1. The Poisson kernel $P_r(\theta)$ for $r = 0.7, 0.83, 0.9$

The behavior of the Poisson kernel close to the boundary can be captured by means of the following notion.

Definition 3.2. A sequence $\{\Phi_n\}_{n=1}^{\infty} \subset L^{\infty}(\mathbb{T})$ is called an *approximate identity* provided:

A1) $\int_0^1 \Phi_n(\theta)\, d\theta = 1$ for all n,

A2) $\sup_n \int_0^1 |\Phi_n(\theta)|\, d\theta < \infty$,

A3) for all $\delta > 0$ one has $\int_{|x|>\delta} |\Phi_n(\theta)|\, d\theta \to 0$ as $n \to \infty$.

The same definition applies, with obvious modifications, to families of the form $\{\Phi_t\}_{0<t<1}$ (with $n \to \infty$ replaced by $t \to 1^-$).

A standard example is the box kernel

$$\left\{ \frac{1}{2\varepsilon} \chi_{[-\varepsilon,\varepsilon]} \right\}_{0<\varepsilon<\frac{1}{2}}$$

in the limit $\varepsilon \to 0$. Another example is the Fejér kernel from Fourier series. The relevant example for our purposes is of course the Poisson kernel $\{P_r\}_{0<r<1}$. It is easy to see that this family satisfies properties A1)–A3). First, one has $P_r > 0$ and the mean of P_r equals 1, which already implies

A1) and A2). The third property follows from the observation that the denominator of $P_r(\theta)$ is uniformly positive on any region $|\theta| > \delta$. The significance of approximate identities lies with their reproducing properties (as their name suggests).

Lemma 3.3. *For any approximate identity* $\{\Phi_n\}_{n=1}^{\infty}$ *one has:*

    (1) *If* $f \in C(\mathbb{T})$, *then* $\|\Phi_n * f - f\|_\infty \to 0$ *as* $n \to \infty$.

    (2) *If* $f \in L^p(\mathbb{T})$ *where* $1 \le p < \infty$, *then* $\|\Phi_n * f - f\|_p \to 0$ *as* $n \to \infty$.

These statements carry over to approximate identities Φ_t, *with* $0 < t < 1$, *by replacing* $n \to \infty$ *with* $t \to 1$.

Proof. Since $\mathbb{T}$ is compact, f is uniformly continuous. Given $\varepsilon > 0$, let $\delta > 0$ be such that

$$\sup_x \sup_{|y|<\delta} |f(x-y) - f(x)| < \varepsilon.$$

Then by A1)–A3),

$$|(\Phi_n * f)(x) - f(x)| = \left| \int_{\mathbb{T}} (f(x-y) - f(x))\Phi_n(y)\,dy \right|$$

$$\le \sup_{x\in\mathbb{T}} \sup_{|y|<\delta} |f(x-y) - f(x)| \int_{\mathbb{T}} |\Phi_n(t)|\,dt + \int_{|y|\ge\delta} |\Phi_n(y)| 2\|f\|_\infty\,dy,$$

$$< C\varepsilon,$$

provided n is large. To pass to the second line, we spit the integration into $\{|y| < \delta\}$ and $\{|y| \ge \delta\}$. For the second part, fix $f \in L^p$. Let $g \in C(\mathbb{T})$ with $\|f - g\|_p < \varepsilon$. Then

$$\|\Phi_n * f - f\|_p \le \|\Phi_n * (f-g)\|_p + \|f - g\|_p + \|\Phi_n * g - g\|_p$$

$$\le \left(\sup_n \|\Phi_n\|_1 + 1 \right) \|f - g\|_p + \|\Phi_n * g - g\|_\infty,$$

where we have used Young's inequality ($\|f_1 * f_2\|_p \le \|f_1\|_1 \|f_2\|_p$) to obtain the first term on the right-hand side. Using A2), the assumption on g, as well as the first part, finishes the proof. $\qquad\square$

    An immediate consequence is the following simple and fundamental result. It precisely states the unique solvability of the Dirichlet problem on the disk.

Theorem 3.4. *Let* $f \in C(\mathbb{T})$. *The unique harmonic function* u *on* $\mathbb{D}$, *with* $u \in C(\overline{\mathbb{D}})$ *and* $u = f$ *on* $\mathbb{T}$ *is given by* $u(z) = (P_r * f)(\theta)$, $z = re(\theta)$.

Proof. Uniqueness follows from the maximum principle (see Corollary 1.40). Indeed, if there were two distinct solutions, then taking their difference yields a nonzero harmonic function in $\mathbb{D}$ which extends continuously to the closed

unit disk and vanishes on its boundary. But by the maximum principle this
is impossible.

For the existence, we observed before that $u(z) := (P_r * f)(\theta)$ with $|z| < 1$
is harmonic on $\mathbb{D}$. By Lemma 3.3, $\|u(re(\cdot)) - f\|_\infty \to 0$ as $r \to 1^-$. This
implies that we can extend u continuously to $\overline{\mathbb{D}}$ by setting it equal to f
on $\mathbb{T}$. $\qquad\square$

By rescaling, this theorem extends to arbitrary disks. For the sake of
completeness we state this here, together with a useful integral representation of analytic functions in terms of their real or imaginary parts alone
(up to a constant). Note that the Cauchy-Riemann equations imply that an
analytic function on a disk is uniquely determined by the real or imaginary
parts up to constants, so it is no surprise that such a representation should
exist.

Corollary 3.5. *Let u be harmonic on $D(0, R)$ and continuous on the closure
of this disk. Then*

$$(3.4) \quad u(z) = \frac{1}{2\pi} \int_0^{2\pi} \frac{R^2 - r^2}{R^2 - 2rR\cos(\theta - \psi) + r^2} u(Re^{i\psi}) \, d\psi, \quad z = re^{i\theta}.$$

If f is any analytic function in $D(0, R)$ with real part u, then

$$f(z) = \frac{1}{2\pi} \int_0^{2\pi} \frac{\zeta + z}{\zeta - z} u(\zeta) \, d\psi + i \operatorname{Im} f(0)$$

$$(3.5) \qquad = \frac{1}{2\pi i} \oint_{|\zeta|=R} \left(\frac{2}{\zeta - z} - \frac{1}{\zeta} \right) u(\zeta) \, d\zeta + i \operatorname{Im} f(0)$$

$$= \frac{1}{\pi i} \oint_{|\zeta|=R} \frac{1}{\zeta - z} u(\zeta) \, d\zeta - \operatorname{Re} f(0) + i \operatorname{Im} f(0).$$

Proof. Apply Theorem 3.4 to $u(Rz)$ which is harmonic on the unit disk.
Changing variables in the integral yields (3.4). This formula can be written
as

$$u(z) = \frac{1}{2\pi} \int_0^{2\pi} u(Re^{i\psi}) \operatorname{Re} \frac{\zeta + z}{\zeta - z} \, d\psi.$$

Taking the real part outside shows that the integral in (3.5) defines an
analytic function with real part equal to u. So it necessarily equals f up to
a constant. But that constant is $i \operatorname{Im} f(0)$ since the integral is real-valued at
$z = 0$. $\qquad\square$

The second and third lines of (3.5) bear obvious resemblance with the
Cauchy formula for analytic functions. The strange factor of 2 is a result of
integrating only "half" of f, i.e., the real part.

3.2. The Poisson kernel from the probabilistic point of view

In this section, we explore the Poisson kernel as a probability measure on the circle. Let us first investigate this measure from the point of view of conformal invariance. In Proposition 1.32 we identified the automorphism group of the disk, $\mathrm{Aut}(\mathbb{D})$. This is relevant to our current discussion since the class of harmonic functions which are continuous on $\bar{\mathbb{D}}$ is invariant under this group.

The stabilizer of 0 in $\mathrm{Aut}(\mathbb{D})$ are all rotations $z \mapsto e^{i\theta} z$ (these are precisely the automorphisms that leave the origin fixed). Recall that this was a consequence of the Schwarz lemma. Clearly, the only measure on the circle $\mathbb{T}$ which is invariant under all these rotations is the Lebesgue measure, up to a normalization. In other words, there is a unique probability measure on $\mathbb{T}$ (a positive measure of mass 1) which is invariant under all rotations.

In general, *invariant* here means the following: if $F : \mathbb{T} \to \mathbb{T}$ is a homeomorphism, then we say that a (complex) measure μ on $\mathbb{T}$ is invariant under F if and only if $\mu(F^{-1}(A)) = \mu(A)$ for all Borel sets A.

Now suppose we ask about all probability measures which are invariant under the action of $\mathrm{Stab}(z)$ where $z \in \mathbb{D}$ is arbitrary. In other words, we consider all elements in $\mathrm{Aut}(\mathbb{D})$ that leave z fixed. Since

$$(3.6) \qquad \mathrm{Stab}(z) = \Psi^{-1} \circ \mathrm{Stab}(0) \circ \Psi,$$

where $\Psi \in \mathrm{Aut}(\mathbb{D})$ takes $z \mapsto 0$, we deduce that the measure is unique. Not surprisingly it turns out to be given by the Poisson kernel. More precisely, one has the following result.

Proposition 3.6. *Let $z \in \mathbb{D}$. The unique probability measure $\mu = \mu_z$ which is invariant under $\mathrm{Stab}(z) \subset \mathrm{Aut}(\mathbb{D})$ is $P_r(\theta - \theta_0)\, d\theta$ where $z = re^{i\theta_0}$.*

Proof. Let μ be such a measure and pick any $\Phi \in \mathrm{Stab}(z)$. Then

$$\Phi = \Psi^{-1} \circ \widetilde{\Phi} \circ \Psi$$

with $\widetilde{\Phi} \in \mathrm{Stab}(0)$. We require that for all Borel A,

$$\mu(\Phi^{-1} A) = \mu(A),$$

which is the same as

$$\mu(\Psi^{-1} \circ \widetilde{\Phi}^{-1} A) = \mu(\Psi^{-1} A).$$

In other words, $\mu \circ \Psi^{-1}$ is invariant under the action of $\mathrm{Stab}(0)$. As already noted, this implies that this measure is the normalized Lebesgue measure on $\mathbb{T}$.

In terms of integrations one therefore has

$$\int_{\mathbb{T}} f \, d(\mu \circ \Psi^{-1}) = \int_{\mathbb{T}} f(\theta) \, d\theta \quad \forall \, f \in C(\mathbb{T})$$

or, equivalently,

$$(3.7) \qquad \int_{\mathbb{T}} f \, d\mu = \int_{\mathbb{T}} f(\Psi^{-1}(\theta)) \, d\theta \quad \forall \, f \in C(\mathbb{T}).$$

It remains to compute the change of measure in the integral on the right-hand side of (3.7). Restricting

$$\Psi(\zeta) = \frac{\zeta - z}{1 - \bar{z}\zeta}$$

to $\mathbb{T}$ yields

$$e^{i\phi} = \frac{e^{i\theta} - z}{1 - e^{i\theta}\bar{z}}.$$

The task is to find $\frac{d\phi}{d\theta}$. Differentiating

$$e^{i\phi}(1 - e^{i\theta}\bar{z}) = e^{i\theta} - z$$

yields

$$ie^{i\theta} \, d\theta = ie^{i\phi}(1 - e^{i\theta}\bar{z}) \, d\phi - ie^{i\phi}e^{i\theta}\bar{z} \, d\theta$$
$$= i(e^{i\theta} \quad z) \, d\phi - ie^{i\phi}e^{i\theta}\bar{z} \, d\theta$$
$$= i(e^{i\theta} - z) \, d\phi - i\frac{e^{i\theta} - z}{1 - e^{i\theta}\bar{z}}e^{i\theta}\bar{z} \, d\theta.$$

This simplifies to

$$d\phi = \frac{1 - |z|^2}{|1 - e^{-i\theta}z|^2} \, d\theta = P_r(\theta - \theta_0) \, d\theta$$

with $z = re^{i\theta_0}$. This is what we set out to prove. $\square$

The measure $\mu = \mu_z$ identified in Proposition 3.6 can also be characterized geometrically, namely in terms of the Poincaré disk introduced in Chapter 1. Indeed, for any arc $I = [a, b] \subset \mathbb{T}$,

$$(3.8) \qquad \mu(I) = \frac{\varphi}{2\pi},$$

where φ is the angle between two geodesics in the Poincaré disk connecting z to a, b, respectively. To prove this relation, first consider the case $z = 0$ for which it is clear. Then we again use the conjugacy (3.6). On the one hand, the Lebesgue measure gets transformed under the ensuing change of variables to the measure μ in Proposition 3.6. On the other hand, since $\text{Aut}(\mathbb{D})$ is also the group of (orientation preserving) isometries of the Poincaré disk, it follows that the geodesics remain geodesics under the mapping. Finally, by conformality the angle between the geodesics at z is preserved. To summarize, for any interval $I \subset \mathbb{T}$, $\mu(I)$ equals the angle under which it is seen by geodesics rays emanating from z. This is precisely (3.8).

It is interesting to recover the fact that $P_r \to \delta_0$ from this as $r \to 1^-$. To be specific, if $0 \notin [a, b]$, then $\mu_r([a, b]) \to 0$ whereas if $0 \in [a, b]$, then $\mu_r([a, b]) \to 1$ as $r \to 1^-$.

The reader is invited to draw some pictures to illustrate this phenomenon. Let us explore it in terms of formulas using an automorphism that takes r back to 0, i.e., $z \mapsto \frac{z-r}{1-rz}$. The normalization here is such that 1 is fixed, which gives a unique map. By inspection,

$$\lim_{r \to 1^-} \frac{e^{i\theta} - r}{1 - re^{i\theta}} = \begin{cases} -1 & e^{i\theta} \neq 1, \\ 1 & e^{i\theta} = 1. \end{cases}$$

This implies that any arc $I \subset \mathbb{T}$ which does not contain 1 is pushed entirely to -1, whereas any arc which does contain 1 expands to the whole circle $\mathbb{T}$. Using the conformal invariance of (3.8) we arrive at the desired conclusion.

By means of the Riemann mapping theorem, we obtain analogues of the disk results for other bounded simply-connected domains with "nice" boundaries. The latter can mean regular in the sense of Definition 2.29. Indeed, suppose $\Psi : \mathbb{D} \to \Omega$ is such a conformal homeomorphism. Then the unique probability measure on $\partial \Omega$ which is invariant under

$$\mathrm{Stab}(w) \subset \mathrm{Aut}(\Omega)$$

for any fixed $w \in \Omega$ is precisely the pullback of μ_z with $z = \Psi^{-1}(w)$, i.e., $\mu_z \circ \Psi^{-1}$. Since the class of harmonic functions is conformally invariant, it is also this measure which leads to a solution of the Dirichlet problem in Ω. We leave it to the reader to explore this further.

Next, we turn to the construction of the measure defined by the Poisson kernel via random walks, or more precisely, Brownian motion. This section is more of a survey than a detailed presentation and should only be read by someone with a background in basic probability theory. There exists a strong connection between harmonic functions on the one hand, and random walks on the other hand. By the latter we mean sums

$$(3.9) \qquad S_n = \sum_{\ell=1}^{n} X_\ell,$$

where X_ℓ are independent identically distributed (i.i.d.) random variables taking values in $\mathbb{Z}^2$ amongst the four vectors $(0, 1), (1, 0), (-1, 0), (0, -1)$ with equal probability $\frac{1}{4}$. The sums S_n are random variables taking values in $\mathbb{Z}^2$. The sequence $\{S_n\}_{n=1}^{\infty}$ is called the **simple random walk** in the plane.

Now suppose we have a bounded region $\Omega \subset \mathbb{Z}^2$ which contains some square $[-10, 10]^2$, say. A boundary point $p \in \mathbb{Z}^2 \setminus \Omega$ is a point with some nearest neighbor in Ω. We denote the boundary by $\partial\Omega$. Color some points in $\partial\Omega$ red and others blue and define a function

$$u(q) = \mathbb{P}[\text{the walk starting at } q \text{ exits } \Omega \text{ at a blue point}], \quad q \in \Omega.$$

By a *walk starting at* q we just mean the random variables $\{q + S_n\}_{n=1}^{\infty}$, and *exits* means that for some n we have $q + S_n \in \partial\Omega$. First we note that since Ω is bounded, the walk does exit this region with probability 1, in other words, almost surely. On the other hand, by conditioning the walk on the outcome of the first step, we see that

(3.10) $$u(q) = \frac{1}{4} \sum_{q'} u(q'),$$

where the sum is over the four nearest lattice neighbors of q, and $q \in \Omega$ is such that all its nearest neighbors lie in Ω. Denote the subset of all these points in Ω by $\widetilde{\Omega}$. By assumption we have $[-9, 9]^2 \subset \widetilde{\Omega}$. The relation (3.10) means that u is a **discrete harmonic function** on $\widetilde{\Omega}$.

It is natural to take the *scaling limit* of the simple random walk. To find the right scaling, note that $\mathbb{E}S_n = 0$ and $\sqrt{\mathbb{E}|S_n|^2} = \sqrt{n}$ where $|\cdot|$ is the Euclidean length. This shows that there is a square-relation between the "time" n and the distance we expect to travel after that time, which is $\sqrt{n}$. We can also define S_n for continuous time by setting

$$S_t = \theta S_n + (1 - \theta)S_{n+1}, \quad t = \theta n + (1 - \theta)(n + 1), \quad 0 \le \theta \le 1,$$

for all $t \ge 0$. By the preceding we now take a limit

(3.11) $$\delta S_{\delta^{-2}t} \to B_t \qquad \text{as} \quad \delta \to 0,$$

which defines **Brownian motion** rooted at the origin. The limit is to be interpreted in the sense of probability distributions, or as one says *in law*. This means that for every $t > 0$ there exists a probability measure in $\mathbb{R}^2$ so that for every open set $U \subset \mathbb{R}^2$ one has

$$\mathbb{P}[\delta S_{\delta^{-2}t} \in U] \to \nu_t(U) \qquad \text{as} \quad \delta \to 0.$$

This measure (or *distribution*) ν_t then defines the likelihood of finding B_t in any given set. From the central limit theorem one in fact concludes that ν_t is Gaussian (standard normal) with mean zero and variance t, and that the process $\{B_t\}_{t \ge 0}$ is Markovian with stationary Gaussian increments. The almost sure properties of a given Brownian path are well-known. For example, it is Hölder continuous of exponent almost (but not quite) $1/2$.

The continuum analogue of the simple random walk discussion above is easy to guess. Given a bounded domain Ω with C^1 boundary, say, define for a given segment $I \subset \partial\Omega$,

$$(3.12) \qquad u(z) = \mathbb{P}[z + B_t \text{ hits } \partial\Omega \text{ in } I] \quad \forall z \in \Omega.$$

Once again, the Brownian motion almost surely escapes Ω, so $u(z)$ is well-defined. Taking a small disk $D(z, \varepsilon) \subset \Omega$ and conditioning where the Brownian path hits $\partial D(z, \varepsilon)$, we conclude that

$$u(z) = \frac{1}{2\pi\varepsilon} \int_{|z| = \varepsilon} u(\zeta)\, \sigma(d\zeta),$$

where σ is arc-length on $\{|z| = \varepsilon\}$. In other words, u is a harmonic function. Moreover, $u(z)$ as defined in (3.12) is continuous on $\bar{\Omega}$ away from the endpoints of I, and we have $u = 1$ on I and $u = 0$ on $\partial\Omega \setminus I$. This is a special harmonic function, referred to as a **harmonic measure** of $I \subset \partial\Omega$.

From our previous discussion we conclude that in fact $u(z) = \mu_z(I)$. So the Poisson kernel $P_r(\cdot - \theta_0)$ is nothing other than the density of the probability distribution of where a Brownian path starting at $z = re^{i\theta_0}$ hits $\partial\mathbb{D}$.

3.3. Hardy classes of harmonic functions

Next, we wish to reverse this process and understand which classes of harmonic functions on $\mathbb{D}$ assume boundary values on $\mathbb{T}$. Moreover, we need to clarify which boundary values arise naturally in such process and, furthermore, what we mean by "assume". The approach which we shall adopt here is to impose a boundedness assumption on the function in the disk. From this boundedness we shall then deduce existence of the boundary values. Particularly important classes of this type are the following ones, known as the "little" Hardy spaces.

Definition 3.7. For any $1 \le p \le \infty$ define

$$h^p(\mathbb{D}) := \left\{ u : \mathbb{D} \to \mathbb{C} \text{ harmonic } \Big| \sup_{0 < r < 1} \int_0^1 |u(re(\theta))|^p\, d\theta < \infty \right\}$$

with norm

$$\|u\|_p := \sup_{0 < r < 1} \|u(re(\cdot))\|_{L^p(\mathbb{T})}.$$

By the mean-value property, any positive harmonic function belongs to the space $h^1(\mathbb{D})$. Amongst those, the most important example is $P_r(\theta) \in h^1(\mathbb{D})$. Observe that this function has boundary values $P_r \to \delta_0$ (the Dirac mass at $\theta = 0$) as $r \to 1^-$ where the convergence is in the sense of distributions. In what follows, $\mathcal{M}(\mathbb{T})$ denotes the complex-valued Borel measures of finite total variation, and $\mathcal{M}^+(\mathbb{T}) \subset \mathcal{M}(\mathbb{T})$ the positive Borel measures.

In what follows we use the notation $F_r(\theta) := F\big(re(\theta)\big)$.

Theorem 3.8. *There is a one-to-one correspondence between $h^1(\mathbb{D})$ and $\mathcal{M}(\mathbb{T})$ given by $\mu \in \mathcal{M}(\mathbb{T}) \mapsto F_r(\theta) := (P_r * \mu)(\theta)$. Under this correspondence, any $\mu \in \mathcal{M}^+(\mathbb{T})$ relates uniquely to a positive harmonic function. Furthermore,*

$$(3.13) \qquad \|\mu\| = \sup_{0 < r < 1} \|F_r\|_1 = \lim_{r \to 1} \|F_r\|_1,$$

and the following properties hold:

(1) *μ is absolutely continuous with respect to Lebesgue measure ($\mu \ll d\theta$) if and only if $\{F_r\}$ converges in $L^1(\mathbb{T})$. If so, then $d\mu = f\, d\theta$ where $f = L^1$-limit of F_r.*

(2) *The following are equivalent for $1 < p \le \infty$:*

$d\mu = f d\theta \quad \text{with} \quad f \in L^p(\mathbb{T})$

$\Longleftrightarrow \{F_r\}_{0 < r < 1}$ *is L^p-bounded*

$\Longleftrightarrow \{F_r\}$ *converges in L^p if $1 < p < \infty$ and in weak-$*$ sense in L^∞ if $p = \infty$ as $r \to 1$.*

(3) *f is continuous $\Leftrightarrow F$ extends to a continuous function on $\overline{\mathbb{D}} \Leftrightarrow F_r$ converges uniformly as $r \to 1-$.*

This theorem identifies $h^1(\mathbb{D})$ with $\mathcal{M}(\mathbb{T})$, and $h^p(\mathbb{D})$ with $L^p(\mathbb{T})$ for $1 < p \le \infty$. Moreover, $h^\infty(\mathbb{D})$ contains the subclass of harmonic functions that can be extended continuously onto $\overline{\mathbb{D}}$; this subclass is the same as $C(\mathbb{T})$. Before proving the theorem we present two simple lemmas.

Lemma 3.9.

(1) *If $F \in C(\overline{\mathbb{D}})$ and $\triangle F = 0$ in $\mathbb{D}$, then $F_r = P_r * F_1$ for any $0 \le r < 1$.*

(2) *If $\triangle F = 0$ in $\mathbb{D}$, then $F_{rs} = P_r * F_s$ for any $0 \le r, s < 1$.*

(3) *As a function of $r \in (0,1)$ the norms $\|F_r\|_p$ are nondecreasing for any $1 \le p \le \infty$.*

Proof. (1) is a restatement of Theorem 3.4. For (2), rescale the disc $s\mathbb{D}$ to $\mathbb{D}$ and apply the first property. Finally, by Young's inequality,

$$\|F_{rs}\|_p \le \|P_r\|_1 \|F_s\|_p = \|F_s\|_p,$$

as claimed. $\qquad\qquad\qquad\qquad\qquad\qquad\qquad\qquad\qquad\qquad\qquad\qquad\square$

Lemma 3.10. *Let $F \in h^1(\mathbb{D})$. Then there exists a unique Borel measure $\mu \in \mathcal{M}(\mathbb{T})$ such that $F_r = P_r * \mu$. The same conclusion holds for positive harmonic functions in $\mathbb{D}$. In that case, the measure is positive.*

Proof. Since the unit ball of $\mathcal{M}(\mathbb{T})$ is weak-$*$ compact there exists a subsequence $r_j \to 1$ with $F_{r_j} \to \mu$ in weak-$*$ sense to some $\mu \in \mathcal{M}(\mathbb{T})$. Then for any $0 < r < 1$,

$$P_r * \mu = \lim_{j \to \infty} (F_{r_j} * P_r) = \lim_{j \to \infty} F_{rr_j} = F_r,$$

by Lemma 3.9. Let $f \in C(\mathbb{T})$. Then again by Lemma 3.9,

$$\langle F_r, f \rangle = \langle P_r * \mu, f \rangle = \langle \mu, P_r * f \rangle \to \langle \mu, f \rangle$$

as $r \to 1$. This shows that, in the weak-$*$ sense,

$$(3.14) \qquad \mu = \lim_{r \to 1} F_r,$$

which implies uniqueness of μ.

For the second assertion, note that by the mean-value property any positive harmonic function lies in $h^1(\mathbb{D})$. Now apply the first part. $\qquad \square$

Proof of Theorem 3.8. If $\mu \in \mathcal{M}(\mathbb{T})$, then $P_r * \mu \in h^1(\mathbb{D})$. Conversely, given $F \in h^1(\mathbb{D})$ then by Lemma 3.10 there is a unique μ so that $F_r = P_r * \mu$. This gives the one-to-one correspondence. Moreover, (3.14) and Lemma 3.9 show that

$$\|\mu\| \le \limsup_{r \to 1} \|F_r\|_1 = \sup_{0 < r < 1} \|F_r\|_1 = \lim_{r \to 1} \|F_r\|_1 .$$

Since one also has

$$\sup_{0 < r < 1} \|F_r\|_1 \le \sup_{0 < r < 1} \|P_r\|_1 \|\mu\| = \|\mu\| ,$$

(3.13) follows. If $f \in L^1(\mathbb{T})$ and $d\mu = f d\theta$, then Lemma 3.3 shows that $F_r \to f$ in $L^1(\mathbb{T})$. Conversely, if $F_r \to f$ in the sense of $L^1(\mathbb{T})$, then because of (3.14) necessarily $d\mu = f\, d\theta$ which proves the first part. The other parts are equally easy and we skip the details—invoke Lemma 3.3, part (2) for $1 < p < \infty$ and Lemma 3.3 part (1) if $p = \infty$. $\qquad \square$

In passing we remark the following: an important role is played by the kernel $Q_r(\theta)$ which is the *harmonic conjugate* of $P_r(\theta)$. Recall that this means that $P_r(\theta) + iQ_r(\theta)$ is analytic in $z = re(\theta)$ and $Q_0 = 0$. In this case it is easy to find $Q_r(\theta)$ since

$$(3.15) \qquad P_r(\theta) = \text{Re}\left(\frac{1+z}{1-z}\right),$$

and therefore

$$Q_r(\theta) = \text{Im}\left(\frac{1+z}{1-z}\right) = \frac{2r \sin(2\pi\theta)}{1 - 2r\cos(2\pi\theta) + r^2}.$$

Observe that $\{Q_r\}_{0 < r < 1}$ is *not* an approximate identity, since

$$Q_1(\theta) = \cot(\pi\theta)$$

which is not the density of a measure—it behaves like $\frac{1}{\pi\theta}$ close to $\theta = 0$. The Hilbert transform is the map which is formally defined as follows:

$$(3.16) \qquad\qquad f \mapsto u_f \mapsto \widetilde{u}_f \mapsto \widetilde{u}_f|_{\mathbb{T}},$$

where u_f denotes the harmonic extension to $\mathbb{D}$ and $\widetilde{u}_f$ its harmonic conjugate. The map in (3.16) is, for example, defined on the domain L^2, since one can check quite easily that the Fourier multiplier associated with it equals $-i\,\mathrm{sign}(n)$.

From the preceding, Q_1 is the kernel of the Hilbert transform. It is an important object, especially for the role it played in the development of function theory. Similarly famous, the Dirichlet kernel in Fourier series is not an approximate identity and the many efforts in understanding its mapping properties have been of enormous importance in analysis.

To conclude this section, we record an important representation formula for analytic functions in the disk with positive imaginary part (or real part).

Corollary 3.11. *Let f be analytic in $\mathbb{D}$ with $\mathrm{Im}\, f \geq 0$ in $\mathbb{D}$. Then there exists a unique positive finite Borel measure ν on the circle such that*

$$(3.17) \qquad\qquad f(z) = c + i \int_{\mathbb{T}} \frac{1 + ze(\theta)}{1 - ze(\theta)}\, \nu(d\theta),$$

for all $z \in \mathbb{D}$, and a unique constant $c \in \mathbb{R}$.

Proof. We apply Theorem 3.8 to the positive harmonic function $u = \mathrm{Im}\, f$. Thus, $u(re(\theta)) = (P_r * \nu)(\theta)$. In view of (3.15) consider the analytic function

$$g(z) := i \int_{\mathbb{T}} \frac{1 + ze(\theta)}{1 - ze(\theta)}\, \nu(d\theta)$$

in $\mathbb{D}$. By construction, $\mathrm{Im}(f - g) = 0$. By the Cauchy-Riemann equations, we conclude that $f - g$ is a constant, which is necessarily real-valued whence (3.17). $\qquad\qquad\square$

This result goes by the name of *Herglotz representation* in the disk. It is a reflection of the common theme that positivity can play the role of boundedness in theorems of the Riesz representation type.

Let us now formulate the analogous result in the upper half-plane $\mathbb{H}$.

Corollary 3.12. *Let F be analytic in $\mathbb{H}$ with $\mathrm{Im}\, F \geq 0$ in $\mathbb{H}$. Then there exists a unique positive finite Borel measure μ on the line such that*

$$(3.18) \qquad\qquad F(z) = c + mz + \int_{\mathbb{R}} \frac{1 + zt}{t - z}\, \mu(dt)$$

for all $z \in \mathbb{H}$, and unique constants $c \in \mathbb{R}$, $m \geq 0$.

Proof. The map $w = \frac{z-i}{z+i}$ takes $\mathbb{H} \to \mathbb{D}$. Its inverse is $z = i\frac{1+w}{1-w}$, and $z = \infty$ corresponds to $w = 1$. The idea is now of course to apply the previous corollary to $F(z) = f(w)$. Some care needs to be taken, though, since the measure ν in (3.17) can have mass at $\theta = 0$. This corresponds to the mass at infinity in (3.18). Thus,

$$f(w) = c + i \int_{\mathbb{T}} \frac{1 + we(\theta)}{1 - we(\theta)} \, \nu(d\theta)$$

$$= c + mz + i \int_{\mathbb{T}} \frac{1 + \frac{z-i}{z+i}e(\theta)}{1 - \frac{z-i}{z+i}e(\theta)} \, \widetilde{\nu}(d\theta),$$

where $m = \nu(\{0\}) \geq 0$ and $\widetilde{\nu} = \nu - m\delta_0$. This can be further simplified to

$$f(w) = c + mz + i \int_0^1 \frac{z + \tan(\pi\theta)}{z - \cot(\pi\theta)} i \cot(\pi\theta) \, \widetilde{\nu}(d\theta)$$

$$= c + mz + \int_{\mathbb{R}} \frac{1 + zt}{t - z} \, \mu(dt)$$

after transformation of the measure. The uniqueness follows by considering $F(is)$ as $s \to +\infty$ along the reals. Indeed, one first notes that the integral is easily seen to be $o(s)$. This then implies that $m > 0$ if and only if $F(is)$ grows linearly in s. The value of the constant c is determined by setting $z = i$. $\qquad\square$

A function as in the previous corollary is called a *Herglotz function*; in other words, any function holomorphic in the upper half-plane with nonnegative imaginary part. The reader should note the resemblance of (3.18) with the Cauchy formula. The fact that we did not recover the precise Cauchy formula lies with the noncompactness of the domain. We need to take various growth behaviors into account to make the analogy more complete. The following result shows how to truly recover the Cauchy formula.

Lemma 3.13. *Let F be analytic in $\mathbb{H}$ with $\operatorname{Im} F \geq 0$ in $\mathbb{H}$. Assume that*

$$(3.19) \qquad \lim_{s \to +\infty} s|F(is)| < \infty.$$

Then there exists a unique positive finite Borel measure ρ on the line such that

$$(3.20) \qquad F(z) = \int_{\mathbb{R}} \frac{1}{t - z} \, \rho(dt),$$

for all $z \in \mathbb{H}$.

Proof. By the discussion at the end of the previous proof we first see that $m = 0$ in (3.18). Second, computing the imaginary part of $sF(is)$ and applying Fatou to the limit $s \to +\infty$ yields

$$\int t^2 \mu(dt) < \infty.$$

Considering the real part of this same limit yields the relation $c = \int t\mu(dt)$. In conclusion,

$$F(z) = \int_{\mathbb{R}} \left(\frac{1+zt}{t-z} + t \right) \mu(dt) = \int_{\mathbb{R}} \frac{1}{t-z} \rho(dt),$$

with $\rho(dt) = t^2 \mu(dt)$. The uniqueness is a consequence of the uniqueness in the previous corollaries, but can also be seen directly.   □

The Cauchy transform (3.20) can be applied to any complex measure of finite total variation, and the transform then determines the measure uniquely. The Herglotz representation, and (3.20) has many applications. For example, let A be a self-adjoint bounded operator on a Hilbert space $\mathcal{H}$ and consider

$$F(z) = \langle (A-z)^{-1}x, x \rangle, \quad z \in \mathbb{H},$$

where $x \in \mathcal{H}$. The resolvent $(A-z)^{-1}$ exists for any $z \in \mathbb{C} \setminus \mathbb{R}$ because of the self-adjointness. Then F is analytic in the upper half-plane and

$$\operatorname{Im} F(z) = 2 \operatorname{Im} z \| (A-z)^{-1}x \|^2 \geq 0$$

if $z \in \mathbb{H}$. So F is Herglotz and, moreover, $sF(is)$ remains bounded. So we can write

$$\langle (A-z)^{-1}x, x \rangle = \int \frac{1}{t-z} \mu_x(dt),$$

where μ_x is a positive finite Borel measure, called the **spectral measure** associated with A and x. It is of fundamental importance to functional analysis and thus also quantum mechanics, but we shall not develop these topics any further.

3.4. Almost everywhere convergence to the boundary data

For continuous boundary data on the circle, the unique solution of the Dirichlet problem was seen above to approach the data in the uniform sense. For L^p data with finite p, the convergence was in the sense of L^p. However, we shall now see that the pointwise information is not completely lost, provided we are willing to give up a set of measure zero.

More specifically, we turn to the issue of almost everywhere convergence of $P_r * f$ to f as $r \to 1$. The main idea here is to mimic the proof of the Lebesgue differentiation theorem. The essence of the latter is that it involves the interchange of two limits: the one where the size of the balls shrinks to zero on the one hand, and passing to the limit in approximations by continuous functions on the other hand. As is common in analysis, the key to legitimizing such an interchange lies with *uniform control*. For the Lebesgue differentiation theorem, as well as for the more general case of approximate identities, this control is furnished by the Hardy-Littlewood maximal function Mf, which is defined as follows:

$$Mf(x) = \sup_{x \in I \subset \mathbb{T}} \frac{1}{|I|} \int_I |f(y)| \, dy,$$

where $I \subset \mathbb{T}$ is an open interval and $|I|$ is the length of I. The most basic facts concerning this sublinear operator are contained in the following result.

Proposition 3.14. *M is bounded from L^1 to weak L^1, i.e.,*

$$\left| \{ x \in \mathbb{T} \mid Mf(x) > \lambda \} \right| \le \frac{3}{\lambda} \|f\|_1$$

for all $\lambda > 0$. For any $1 < p \le \infty$, M is bounded on L^p.

Proof. Fix some $\lambda > 0$ and any compact

$$(3.21) \qquad\qquad K \subset \{ x \mid Mf(x) > \lambda \}.$$

There exists a finite cover $\{I_j\}_{j=1}^N$ of K by open arcs I_j such that

$$(3.22) \qquad\qquad \int_{I_j} |f(y)| \, dy > \lambda |I_j|$$

for each j. We now pass to a more convenient subcover (this process is known as Wiener's covering lemma): Select an arc of maximal length from $\{I_j\}$; call it J_1. Observe that any I_j such that $I_j \cap J_1 \ne \emptyset$ satisfies $I_j \subset 3 \cdot J_1$ where $3 \cdot J_1$ is the arc with the same center as J_1 and three times the length (if $3 \cdot J_1$ has length larger than 1, then set $3 \cdot J_1 = \mathbb{T}$). Now remove all arcs from $\{I_j\}_{j=1}^N$ that intersect J_1. Let J_2 be one of the remaining ones with maximal length. Continuing in this fashion we obtain arcs $\{J_\ell\}_{\ell=1}^L$ which are pairwise disjoint and such that

$$\bigcup_{j=1}^N I_j \subset \bigcup_{\ell=1}^L 3 \cdot J_\ell.$$

In view of (3.21) and (3.22), therefore,

$$|K| \le \mathrm{mes} \left(\bigcup_{\ell=1}^L 3 \cdot J_\ell \right) \le 3 \sum_{\ell=1}^L |J_\ell|$$

$$\le \frac{3}{\lambda} \sum_{\ell=1}^L \int_{J_\ell} |f(y)| \, dy \le \frac{3}{\lambda} \|f\|_1,$$

as claimed. To prove the L^p statement, one interpolates the weak L^1 bound with the trivial L^∞ bound

$$\|Mf\|_\infty \le \|f\|_\infty,$$

by means of Marcinkiewicz's interpolation theorem (see the appendix). $\square$

We now introduce a class of approximate identities which can be reduced to the box kernels. This refers to the special approximate identity $\left\{ \frac{1}{2\varepsilon} \chi_{[|x|<\varepsilon]} \right\}$ with $0 < \varepsilon < 1/2$.

The importance of this idea is that it allows us to dominate the maximal function associated with an approximate identity by the Hardy-Littlewood maximal function; see Lemma 3.16 below.

Definition 3.15. Let $\{\Phi_n\}_{n=1}^\infty$ be an approximate identity as in Definition 3.2. We say that it is *radially bounded* if there exist functions $\{\Psi_n\}_{n=1}^\infty$ on $\mathbb{T}$ so that the following additional property holds:

A4) $|\Phi_n| \le \Psi_n$, Ψ_n is even and decreasing, i.e., $\Psi_n(x) \le \Psi_n(y)$ for $0 \le y \le x \le \frac{1}{2}$, for all $n \ge 1$. Finally, we require that $\sup_n \|\Psi_n\|_1 < \infty$.

Now for the domination lemma.

Lemma 3.16. *If $\{\Phi_n\}_{n=1}^\infty$ satisfies A4), then for any $f \in L^1(\mathbb{T})$ one has*

$$\sup_n |(\Phi_n * f)(x)| \le Mf(x) \sup_n \|\Psi_n\|_1,$$

for all $x \in \mathbb{T}$.

Proof. It clearly suffices to show the following statement: Let

$$K : [-\frac{1}{2}, \frac{1}{2}] \to \mathbb{R}^+ \cup \{0\}$$

be even and decreasing. Then for any $f \in L^1(\mathbb{T})$,

(3.23) $|(K * f)(x)| \le \|K\|_1 Mf(x).$

Indeed, assume that (3.23) holds. Then

$$\sup_n |(\Phi_n * f)(x)| \le \sup_n (\Psi_n * |f|)(x) \le \sup_n \|\Psi_n\|_1 Mf(x),$$

and the lemma follows. The idea behind (3.23) is to show that K can be written as an average of box kernels, i.e., for some positive measure μ,

(3.24) $K(x) = \int_0^{\frac{1}{2}} \chi_{[-y,y]}(x) \, d\mu(y).$

We leave it to the reader to check that

$$d\mu = -dK + K\left(\frac{1}{2}\right) \delta_{\frac{1}{2}}$$

is a suitable choice. Notice that (3.24) implies that

$$\int_0^1 K(x)\, dx = \int_0^{\frac{1}{2}} 2y\, d\mu(y).$$

Moreover, by (3.24),

$$\left|(K * f)(x)\right| = \left| \int_0^{\frac{1}{2}} \left(\frac{1}{2y} \chi_{[-y,y]} * f \right)(x)\, 2y\, d\mu(y) \right| \leq \int_0^{\frac{1}{2}} Mf(x) 2y\, d\mu(y)$$
$$= Mf(x) \|K\|_1,$$

which is (3.23). □

We can now properly address the question of whether $P_r * f \to f$ in the almost everywhere sense for $f \in L^1(\mathbb{T})$. The idea is as follows: the pointwise convergence is clear from Lemma 3.3 for continuous f. This suggests approximating $f \in L^1$ by a sequence of continuous ones, say $\{g_n\}_{n=1}^\infty$, in the L^1 norm. Evidently, we encounter an interchange of limits here, namely $r \to 1$ and $n \to \infty$. As already mentioned before, the needed uniform control for this interchange is precisely furnished by the Hardy-Littlewood maximal function.

Theorem 3.17. *If $\{\Phi_n\}_{n=1}^\infty$ satisfies A1)–A4), then for any $f \in L^1(\mathbb{T})$ one has $\Phi_n * f \to f$ almost everywhere as $n \to \infty$.*

Proof. Pick $\varepsilon > 0$ and let $g \in C(\mathbb{T})$ with $\|f - g\|_1 < \varepsilon$. By Lemma 3.3, with $h = f - g$ one has, with $|\cdot|$ being Lebesgue measure,

$$\left| \left\{ x \in \mathbb{T} \mid \limsup_{n \to \infty} |(\Phi_n * f)(x) - f(x)| > \sqrt{\varepsilon} \right\} \right|$$
$$\leq \left| \left\{ x \in \mathbb{T} \mid \limsup_{n \to \infty} |(\Phi_n * h)(x)| > \sqrt{\varepsilon}/2 \right\} \right| + \left| \left\{ x \in \mathbb{T} \mid |h(x)| > \sqrt{\varepsilon}/2 \right\} \right|$$
$$\leq \left| \left\{ x \in \mathbb{T} \mid \sup_n |(\Phi_n * h)(x)| > \sqrt{\varepsilon}/2 \right\} \right| + \left| \left\{ x \in \mathbb{T} \mid |h(x)| > \sqrt{\varepsilon}/2 \right\} \right|$$
$$\leq \left| \left\{ x \in \mathbb{T} \mid CMh(x) > \sqrt{\varepsilon}/2 \right\} \right| + \left| \left\{ x \in \mathbb{T} \mid |h(x)| > \sqrt{\varepsilon}/2 \right\} \right|$$
$$\leq C\sqrt{\varepsilon}.$$

To pass to the final inequality we used Proposition 3.14 as well as Markov's inequality (recall $\|h\|_1 < \varepsilon$). □

As a corollary we not only obtain the classical Lebesgue differentiation theorem, but also almost everywhere convergence of the Poisson integrals $P_r * f \to f$ for any $f \in L^1(\mathbb{T})$ as $r \to 1^-$.

In view of Theorem 3.8 it is natural to ask whether a result analogous to Theorem 3.17 holds for **measures** instead of L^1 functions. Since we have already dealt with the case of absolutely continuous measures, it is natural to address this question by means of the Lebesgue decomposition.

The following lemma, which is a general fact from measure theory, treats the singular part.

Lemma 3.18. *If $\mu \in \mathcal{M}(\mathbb{T})$ is a positive measure which is singular with respect to Lebesgue measure m (in symbols, $\mu \perp m$), then for a.e. $\theta \in \mathbb{T}$ with respect to Lebesgue measure we have*

$$\frac{\mu([\theta - \varepsilon, \theta + \varepsilon])}{2\varepsilon} \to 0 \quad \text{as} \quad \varepsilon \to 0.$$

Proof. For every $\lambda \geq 0$ let

$$E(\lambda) := \Big\{ \theta \in \mathbb{T} \mid \limsup_{\varepsilon \to 0} \frac{\mu([\theta - \varepsilon, \theta + \varepsilon])}{2\varepsilon} > \lambda \Big\}.$$

By assumption there exists a Borel set $A \subset \mathbb{T}$ with $|A| = 0$ and such that $\mu(E) = \mu(E \cap A)$ for every Borel set $E \subset \mathbb{T}$. Suppose first that A is compact. Then it follows that $E(0) \subset A$ whence $|E(0)| = 0$ as desired.

In general, A does not need to be compact. But for every $\delta > 0$ there exists K_δ compact such that $\mu(A \setminus K_\delta) < \delta$. Denote by μ_δ the measure μ localized to K_δ. Then by the preceding, for every $\lambda > 0$,

$$E(\lambda) \subset \big\{ \theta \in \mathbb{T} \mid M(\mu_\delta)(\theta) > \lambda \big\}.$$

But by the weak-L^1 estimate for the Hardy-Littlewood maximal function (see Proposition 3.14), one has that the measure of the set on the right-hand side is

$$< \frac{3}{\lambda} \|\mu_\delta\| < \frac{3}{\lambda} \delta.$$

Since $\delta > 0$ was arbitrary, we are done. $\qquad\qquad\qquad\qquad\qquad$ $\square$

Using a Lebesgue decomposition one can now show that $P_r * \mu \to f$ almost everywhere where f is the *density of the absolutely continuous part* of μ. A most important example here is P_r itself! Indeed, its boundary measure is δ_0 and the almost everywhere limit is identically zero.

Proposition 3.19. *Let $\{\Phi_n\}_{n=1}^\infty$ satisfy A1)–A4), and assume that the $\{\Psi_n\}_{n=1}^\infty$ from Definition 3.15 also satisfy*

$$\sup_{\delta < |\theta| < \frac{1}{2}} |\Psi_n(\theta)| \to 0 \text{ as } n \to \infty,$$

for all $\delta > 0$. Under these assumptions one has that for any $\mu \in \mathcal{M}(\mathbb{T})$,

$$\Phi_n * \mu \to f \text{ a.e. as } n \to \infty,$$

where $\mu(d\theta) = f(\theta)\, d\theta + \nu_s(d\theta)$ is the Lebesgue decomposition, i.e., $f \in L^1(\mathbb{T})$ and $\nu_s \perp m$.

We leave the proof of this result to the reader; see Problem 3.4. It follows easily from the preceding results on L^1 functions and singular measures.

Proposition 3.19 shows that we lose a lot of information in the almost everywhere limit; in fact, the entire singular part of the boundary measure. A remarkable fact, known as the F. & M. Riesz theorem, states that there is no such loss in the class $h^1(\mathbb{D}) \cap \mathcal{H}(\mathbb{D})$ (**analytic** functions in $h^1(\mathbb{D})$). These are precisely those functions in $h^1(\mathbb{D})$ whose harmonic conjugate also lies in $h^1(\mathbb{D})$. More precisely, the F. & M. Riesz theorem states that any such function is the Poisson integral of an L^1 function rather than a measure. Another way of expressing this property is as follows: if $\mu \in \mathcal{M}(\mathbb{T})$ satisfies $\hat{\mu}(n) = 0$ for all $n < 0$, then μ is absolutely continuous with respect to Lebesgue measure on $\mathbb{T}$. We now turn to these important results.

3.5. Hardy spaces of analytic functions

In the previous sections, we dealt with functions harmonic in the disk satisfying various boundedness properties. We now study functions

$$F = u + iv \in h^1(\mathbb{D})$$

which are *analytic* in $\mathbb{D}$. This is well-defined since analytic functions are complex-valued harmonic ones. These functions form the class $\mathbb{H}^1(\mathbb{D})$, the "big" Hardy space. We have shown there that $F_r = P_r * \mu$ for some $\mu \in \mathcal{M}(\mathbb{T})$. It is important to note that by analyticity $\hat{\mu}(n) = 0$ if $n < 0$. As already noted, we would like to show that such measures are absolutely continuous. From the example

$$F(z) := \frac{1+z}{1-z} = P_r(\theta) + iQ_r(\theta), \qquad z = re(\theta),$$

one sees an important difference between the analytic and the harmonic cases. Indeed, while $P_r \in h^1(\mathbb{D})$, clearly $F \notin h^1(\mathbb{D})$. The boundary measure associated with P_r is δ_0, whereas F is not associated with any boundary measure in the sense of the previous sections.

Technically speaking, there are a number of ways by which we can approach these results. We shall rely on a class which is more flexible than the harmonic functions, namely the *subharmonic functions*. As we shall see, for such functions we shall be able to exploit algebraic properties of analytic functions that harmonic ones do not have (such as the fact that F^2 is again analytic if F is analytic, which does not hold in the harmonic category).

Definition 3.20. Let $\Omega \subset \mathbb{R}^2$ be a region (i.e., open and connected) and let $f : \Omega \to \mathbb{R} \cup \{-\infty\}$ where we extend the topology to $\mathbb{R} \cup \{-\infty\}$ in the obvious way. We say that f is *subharmonic* if

(1) f is continuous,

(2) for all $z \in \Omega$ there exists $r_z > 0$ so that

$$f(z) \leq \int_0^1 f\big(z + re(\theta)\big)\, d\theta,$$

for all $0 < r < r_z$. We refer to this as the (local) "sub-mean-value property".

It is helpful to keep in mind that in one dimension "harmonic = linear" and "subharmonic = convex". Subharmonic functions derive their name from the fact that they lie below harmonic ones, in the same way that convex functions lie below linear ones. We will make this precise by means of the important *maximum principle* which subharmonic functions obey. We begin by deriving some basic properties of this class.

Lemma 3.21. *Subharmonic functions satisfy the following properties:*

1) *If f and g are subharmonic, then $f \vee g := \max(f, g)$ is subharmonic.*

2) *If $f \in C^2(\Omega)$, then f is subharmonic $\Longleftrightarrow$ $\triangle f \geq 0$ in Ω.*

3) *F analytic implies that $\log|F|$ and $|F|^\alpha$ with $\alpha > 0$ are subharmonic.*

4) *If f is subharmonic and φ is increasing and convex, then $\varphi \circ f$ is subharmonic (we set $\varphi(-\infty) := \lim_{x \to -\infty} \varphi(x)$).*

Proof. 1) is immediate. For 2) we use the following fundamental identity

$$(3.25) \qquad \int_{\mathbb{T}} f(z + re(\theta))\, d\theta - f(z) = \frac{1}{2\pi} \iint_{D(z,r)} \log \frac{r}{|w - z|} \triangle f(w)\, m(dw),$$

where m stands for two-dimensional Lebesgue measure and Jensen's formula (3.25) implies that

$$D(z, r) = \{w \in \mathbb{C} \mid |w - z| < r\}.$$

To prove this, we apply Green's identity

$$(3.26) \qquad \iint_\Omega (F\Delta G - G\Delta F)\, dm = \int_{\partial\Omega} \Big(F \frac{\partial G}{\partial n} - G \frac{\partial F}{\partial n}\Big)\, d\sigma,$$

where Ω has a smooth boundary, say, and $F, G \in C^2(\bar{\Omega})$ with the following choices: $\Omega = D(z, r) \setminus D(z, \varepsilon)$, $F = f$, $G(w) = \log \frac{r}{|w-z|}$. Here $\varepsilon > 0$ is small, and upon passing to the limit $\varepsilon \to 0$, (3.26) implies (3.25).

If $\triangle f \geq 0$, then the sub-mean-value property holds by (3.25). On the other hand, if $\triangle f(z_0) < 0$, then let $r_0 > 0$ be sufficiently small so that $\triangle f < 0$ on $D(z_0, r_0)$. Since $\log \frac{r_0}{|w - z_0|} > 0$ on this disk, Jensen's formula implies that the sub-mean-value property fails.

Next, we verify 4) by means of Jensen's inequality for convex functions:

$$\varphi(f(z)) \leq \varphi\left(\int_{\mathbb{T}} f(z + re(\theta)) \, d\theta\right) \leq \int_{\mathbb{T}} \varphi(f(z + re(\theta)) \, d\theta.$$

The first inequality sign uses that φ is increasing, whereas the second uses convexity of φ (this second inequality is called Jensen's inequality). If F is analytic, then $\log |F|$ is continuous with values in $\mathbb{R} \cup \{-\infty\}$. If $F(z_0) \neq 0$, then $\log |F(z)|$ is harmonic on some disk $D(z_0, r_0)$. Thus, one has the stronger mean-value property on this disk. If $F(z_0) = 0$, then $\log |F(z_0)| = -\infty$, and there is nothing to prove. To see that $|F|^\alpha$ is subharmonic, apply 4) to $\log |F(z)|$ with $\varphi(x) = \exp(\alpha x)$. $\qquad\square$

Now we can derive the aforementioned domination of subharmonic functions by harmonic ones.

Lemma 3.22. *Let Ω be a bounded region. Suppose f is subharmonic on Ω, $f \in C(\bar{\Omega})$ and let u be harmonic on Ω, $u \in C(\bar{\Omega})$. If $f \leq u$ on $\partial\Omega$, then $f \leq u$ on Ω.*

Proof. We can take $u = 0$, so $f \leq 0$ on $\partial\Omega$. Let $M = \max_{\bar{\Omega}} f$ and assume that $M > 0$. Set

$$S = \{z \in \bar{\Omega} \mid f(z) = M\}.$$

Then $S \subset \Omega$ and S is closed in Ω. If $z \in S$, then by the sub-mean-value property there exists $r_z > 0$ so that $D(z, r_z) \subset S$. Hence S is also open. Since Ω is assumed to be connected, one obtains $S = \Omega$. This is a contradiction. $\quad\square$

The following lemma shows that the sub-mean-value property holds on any disk in Ω. The point here is that we upgrade the local sub-mean-value property to a true sub-mean-value property using the largest possible disks.

Lemma 3.23. *Let f be subharmonic in Ω, $z_0 \in \Omega$, $\overline{D(z_0, r)} \subset \Omega$. Then*

$$f(z_0) \leq \int_{\mathbb{T}} f(z_0 + re(\theta)) \, d\theta.$$

Proof. Let $g_n = \max(f, -n)$, where $n \geq 1$. Without loss of generality $z_0 = 0$. Define $u_n(z)$ to be the harmonic extension of g_n restricted to $\partial D(z_0, r)$ where $r > 0$ is as in the statement of the lemma. By the previous lemma,

$$f(0) \leq g_n(0) \leq u_n(0) = \int_{\mathbb{T}} u_n(re(\theta)) \, d\theta;$$

the last equality being the mean-value property of harmonic functions. Since

$$\max_{|z| \leq r} u_n(z) \geq \max_{|z| \leq r} f(z),$$

the monotone convergence theorem for decreasing sequences yields

$$f(0) \le \int_{\mathbb{T}} f(re(\theta)) \, d\theta,$$

as claimed.   □

Corollary 3.24. *If g is subharmonic on $\mathbb{D}$, then for all θ,*

$$g(rse(\theta)) \le (P_r * g_s)(\theta)$$

for any $0 < r, s < 1$.

Proof. If $g > -\infty$ everywhere on $\mathbb{D}$, then this follows from Lemma 3.22. If not, then set $g_n = g \vee n$. Thus

$$g(rse(\theta)) \le g_n(rse(\theta)) \le (P_r * (g_n)_s)(\theta),$$

and consequently,

$$g(rse(\theta)) \le \limsup_{n \longrightarrow \infty}(P_r * (g_n)_s)(\theta) \le (P_r * g_s)(\theta),$$

where the final inequality follows from Fatou's lemma (which can be applied in the "reverse form" here, since the g_n have a uniform upper bound).   □

Note that if $g_s \notin L^1(\mathbb{T})$, then $g \equiv -\infty$ on $D(0,s)$ and so $g \equiv -\infty$ on $D(0,1)$. We now introduce the radial maximal function associated with any function on the disk. It, and the more general *nontangential maximal function*, where the supremum is taken over a cone in $\mathbb{D}$, are of central importance in the analysis of this chapter.

Definition 3.25. Let F be any complex-valued function on $\mathbb{D}$. Then $F^* :$ $\mathbb{T} \to \mathbb{R}$ is defined as

$$F^*(\theta) = \sup_{0<r<1} |F(re(\theta))|.$$

We showed in the previous chapter that any $u \in h^1(\mathbb{D})$ satisfies

$$u^* \le CM\mu$$

where μ is the boundary measure of u, i.e., $u_r = P_r * \mu$. In particular, one has

$$|\{\theta \in \mathbb{T} \mid u^*(\theta) > \lambda\}| \le C\lambda^{-1}\|u\|_1.$$

We shall prove the analogous bound for subharmonic functions which are L^1-bounded.

Proposition 3.26. *Suppose g is subharmonic on $\mathbb{D}, g \ge 0$ and g is L^1-bounded, i.e.,*

$$\|g\|_1 := \sup_{0<r<1} \int_{\mathbb{T}} g(re(\theta)) \, d\theta < \infty.$$

Then

(1) $|\{\theta \in \mathbb{T} \mid g^*(\theta) > \lambda\}| \leq \frac{3}{\lambda}\|g\|_1$ for $\forall \lambda > 0$.

(2) *If g is L^p bounded, i.e.,*

$$\|g\|_p^p := \sup_{0<r<1} \int_{\mathbb{T}} g(re(\theta))^p \, d\theta < \infty,$$

with $1 < p \leq \infty$, then

$$\|g^*\|_{L^p(\mathbb{T})} \leq C_p \|g\|_p.$$

Proof.

(1) Let $g_{r_n} \rightharpoonup \mu \in \mathcal{M}(\mathbb{T})$ in the weak-$*$ sense. Then $\|\mu\| \leq \|g\|_1$ and

$$g_s \longleftarrow g_{r_n s} \leq g_{r_n} * P_s \longrightarrow P_s * \mu.$$

Thus, by Lemma 3.16,

$$g^* \leq \sup_{0<s<1} P_s * \mu \leq M\mu,$$

and the desired bound now follows from Proposition 3.14.

(2) If $\|g\|_p < \infty$, then $\frac{d\mu}{d\theta} \in L^p(\mathbb{T})$ with $\|\frac{d\mu}{d\theta}\|_p \leq \|g\|_p$ and thus

$$g^* \leq CM\left(\frac{d\mu}{d\theta}\right) \in L^p(\mathbb{T}),$$

by Proposition 3.14, as claimed. $\square$

3.6. Riesz theorems

We now present three versions of a theorem due to F. & M. Riesz. It is important to note that the following result fails without analyticity.

Theorem 3.27 (First Version of the F. & M. Riesz Theorem). *Suppose $F \in h^1(\mathbb{D})$ is analytic. Then $F^* \in L^1(\mathbb{T})$.*

Proof. $|F|^{\frac{1}{2}}$ is subharmonic and L^2-bounded. By Proposition 3.26, therefore, $|F|^{\frac{1}{2}*} \in L^2(\mathbb{T})$. But $|F|^{\frac{1}{2}*} = |F^*|^{\frac{1}{2}}$ and thus $F^* \in L^1(\mathbb{T})$. $\square$

Let $F \in h^1(\mathbb{D})$. By Theorem 3.8, $F_r = P_r * \mu$ where $\mu \in \mathcal{M}(\mathbb{T})$ has a Lebesgue decomposition $\mu(d\theta) = f(\theta)\, d\theta + \nu_s(d\theta)$, ν_s singular and $f \in L^1(\mathbb{T})$. By Proposition 3.19 one has $P_r * \mu \to f$ a.e. as $r \to 1$. Thus, $\lim_{r\to 1} F(re(\theta)) = f(\theta)$ exists for a.e. $\theta \in \mathbb{T}$. This justifies the statement of the following theorem.

Theorem 3.28 (Second Version). *Assume $F \in h^1(\mathbb{D})$ and F analytic. Let $f(\theta) = \lim_{r\to 1} F(re(\theta))$. Then $F_r = P_r * f$ for all $0 < r < 1$.*

Proof. We have $F_r \to f$ a.e. and $|F_r| \leq F^* \in L^1$ by the previous theorem. Therefore, $F_r \to f$ in $L^1(\mathbb{T})$ and Theorem 3.8 finishes the proof. $\square$

Theorem 3.29 (Third Version). *Suppose $\mu \in \mathcal{M}(\mathbb{T})$, $\hat{\mu}(n) = 0$ for all $n < 0$. Then μ is absolutely continuous with respect to Lebesgue measure.*

Proof. Since $\hat{\mu}(n) = 0$ for $n \in \mathbb{Z}^-$ one has that $F_r = P_r * \mu$ is analytic on $\mathbb{D}$. By the second version above and the remark preceding it, one concludes that $\mu(d\theta) = f(\theta) \, d\theta$ with $f = \lim_{r \to 1^-} F(re(\theta)) \in L^1(\mathbb{T})$, as claimed. $\square$

The logic of this argument shows that if $\mu \perp m$ (where m is Lebesgue measure), then the harmonic extension u_μ of μ satisfies $u_\mu^* \notin L^1(\mathbb{T})$. It is possible to give a more quantitative version of this fact. Indeed, suppose that μ is a positive measure. Then for some absolute constant C,

$$(3.27) \qquad\qquad C^{-1} M\mu < u_\mu^* < CM\mu,$$

where the upper bound is Lemma 3.16 (applied to the Poisson kernel) and the lower bound follows from the assumption $\mu \geq 0$ and the fact that the Poisson kernel dominates the box kernel. See Problem 3.5 for a related result.

The F. & M. Riesz theorem raises the following question: Given a function $f \in L^1(\mathbb{T})$, how can one decide if

$$P_r * f + iQ_r * f \in h^1(\mathbb{D}) \ ?$$

We know that necessarily $u_f^* = (P_r * f)^* \in L^1(\mathbb{T})$. A theorem by Burkholder, Gundy, and Silverstein states that this is also sufficient (they proved this for the *nontangential* maximal function). It is important to note the difference from (3.27), i.e., that this is *not* the same as the Hardy-Littlewood maximal function satisfying $Mf \in L^1(\mathbb{T})$ due to possible cancellation in f. In fact, it is known that

$$(3.28) \qquad\qquad Mf \in L^1(\mathbb{T}) \iff |f| \log(2 + |f|) \in L^1.$$

We conclude this chapter with another theorem due to the Riesz brothers, which can be seen as a generalization of the uniqueness theorem for analytic functions. In fact, it says that if an analytic function F on the disk does not have too wild growth as one approaches the boundary (expressed through the L^1-boundedness condition), then the boundary values are well-defined and cannot vanish on a set of positive measure (unless F vanishes identically).

Theorem 3.30 (Second F. & M. Riesz Theorem). *Let F be analytic on $\mathbb{D}$ and L^1-bounded, i.e., $F \in h^1(\mathbb{D})$. Assume $F \not\equiv 0$ and set $f = \lim_{r \to 1^-} F_r$. Then $\log|f| \in L^1(\mathbb{T})$. In particular, f does not vanish on a set of positive measure.*

Proof. The idea is that if $F(0) \neq 0$, then

$$\int_{\mathbb{T}} \log |f(\theta)| \, d\theta \geq \log |F(0)| > -\infty.$$

Let $\log_+(x) := \max(\log x, 0)$ for $x > 0$. Since $\log_+ |f| \leq |f| \in L^1(\mathbb{T})$ by Theorem 3.27, we should be done. Some care needs to be taken, though, as F attains the boundary values f only in the almost everywhere sense. This issue can easily be handled by means of Fatou's lemma. First, $F^* \in L^1(\mathbb{T})$, so $\log_+ |F_r| \leq F^*$ implies that $\log_+ |f| \in L^1(\mathbb{T})$ by Lebesgue dominated convergence. Second, by subharmonicity,

$$\int_{\mathbb{T}} \log |F_r(\theta)| \, d\theta \geq \log |F(0)|,$$

so that

$$\int_{\mathbb{T}} \log |f(\theta)| \, d\theta = \int_{\mathbb{T}} \lim_{r \to 1} \log |F_r(\theta)| \, d\theta$$

$$\geq \limsup_{r \to 1} \int_{\mathbb{T}} \log |F_r(\theta)| \, d\theta \geq \log |F(0)|.$$

If $F(0) \neq 0$, then we are done. If $F(0) = 0$, then choose another point $z_0 \in \mathbb{D}$ for which $F(z_0) \neq 0$. Now one either repeats the previous argument with the Poisson kernel instead of the sub-mean-value property, or one composes F with an automorphism of the unit disk that moves 0 to z_0. Then the previous argument applies. □

Theorem 3.30 generalizes the following fact from complex analysis, which is proved by Schwarz reflection and Riemann mapping: Let F be analytic in Ω and continuous up to $\Gamma \subset \partial\Omega$ which is an open Lipschitz arc. If $F = 0$ on Γ, then $F \equiv 0$ in Ω.

3.7. Entire functions of finite order

Suppose F is analytic in some domain Ω, and fix $z_0 \in \Omega$. If F does not vanish identically, then its zeros form a discrete set in Ω. It is natural to ask about a quantitative way to bound the number of zeros of f which fall into a disk $D \subset \Omega$. The answer is provided by *Jensen's formula* which is nothing other than (3.25) applied to $f = \log |F|$. Since

$$\Delta f = 2\pi \sum_{\zeta : F(\zeta) = 0} \delta_\zeta$$

we deduce that

$$(3.29) \quad \int_0^1 \log |F(z_0 + re(\theta))| \, d\theta - \log |F(z_0)|$$

$$= \sum_{|\zeta - z_0| < r \, : \, F(\zeta) = 0} \log \left(\frac{r}{|z_0 - \zeta|} \right),$$

where the zeros are counted with multiplicity. This holds for any disk $D = D(z_0, r) \subset \Omega$ for which $F(z_0) \neq 0$. If F is meromorphic and nonconstant, then we instead have

$$\int_0^1 \log |F(z_0 + re(\theta))| \, d\theta - \log |F(z_0)| = \sum_{|\zeta - z_0| < r \, : \, F(\zeta) = 0} \log \left(\frac{r}{|z_0 - \zeta|} \right)$$

$$- \sum_{|\zeta - z_0| < r \, : \, F(\zeta) = \infty} \log \left(\frac{r}{|z_0 - \zeta|} \right).$$

In other words, we obtain a difference between zeros and poles. For analytic functions we deduce the quantitative bound on the number of zeros in disks:

$$(3.30) \quad \#\{|\zeta - z_0| < r/2 \, : \, F(\zeta) = 0\} \log 2$$

$$\leq \int_0^1 \log |F(z_0 + re(\theta))| \, d\theta - \log |F(z_0)|.$$

Now suppose that F is entire. Then we can use formula (3.29) to relate the number of zeros in disks with increasing radii to the growth of the entire function at infinity. We begin with the basic notion of finite order.

Definition 3.31. An entire function F is of **finite order** provided:

$$(3.31) \quad |F(z)| \leq A e^{B|z|^\rho} \qquad \forall \, z \in \mathbb{C},$$

for some constants A, B and $\rho \geq 0$. The infimum of all possible ρ is called the *order* of F.

It is easy to give examples: For any polynomial $P(z)$, the function $e^{P(z)}$ is of this type, with order equal to the degree of P. To obtain a fractional order, consider $\frac{\sin(\sqrt{z})}{\sqrt{z}}$. It is entire of order $\frac{1}{2}$. Below we will give many more examples, in fact of arbitrary order, based on their Taylor series. A function which is not of this type is e^{e^z}.

But first we will derive bounds on the zeros with the goal of improving on Weierstrass' product formula for entire functions; cf. (2.27). The following result gives quantitative control on the distribution of the zeros of entire functions of finite order.

Corollary 3.32. *Let F be entire of order $\rho \geq 0$ and not identically zero. Then for any $\varepsilon > 0$ one has*

$$\#\{\zeta \in D(0, R) \mid F(\zeta) = 0\} \leq C(\varepsilon) R^{\rho + \varepsilon},$$

for all $R \geq 1$. In particular,

$$\sum_{\zeta:F(\zeta)=0} |\zeta|^{-b} < \infty,$$

for any $b > \rho$.

Proof. Assume for simplicity that $F(0) = 1$. Otherwise, pick a nearby point where $F \neq 0$ and normalize. By (3.30) we have

$$\#\{|\zeta - z_0| \leq R : F(\zeta) = 0\} \leq C(\varepsilon) R^{\rho+\varepsilon},$$

for all $R \geq 1$, as claimed. In particular,

$$\sum_{R/2<|\zeta|<R:F(\zeta)=0} |\zeta|^{-b} < C(\varepsilon) R^{\rho+\varepsilon-b}.$$

Summing this over $R = 2^j$ concludes the proof. $\qquad\square$

In the previous chapter we saw that entire functions admit a product representation (2.27) which involved a nonvanishing factor of the form e^g, with g entire. The class of entire functions satisfies the more precise *Hadamard factorization theorem*, in which g is a polynomial; not surprising given (3.31). In addition, one has control of the canonical factors; see (2.28).

Theorem 3.33. *Let $f \in \mathcal{H}(\mathbb{C})$ with order at most $\rho \geq 0$. Let k be the largest integer with $k \leq \rho$. Then*

(3.32)
$$f(z) = e^{P(z)} z^\nu \prod_{\zeta \in \mathbb{C}^*:f(\zeta)=0} E_k(z/\zeta),$$

where P is a polynomial of degree at most k and $\nu \geq 0$ is the order of vanishing of f at $z = 0$.

Proof. Since

$$\log E_k(z) = \log(1-z) + z + \frac{1}{2}z^2 + \ldots + \frac{1}{k}z^k = O(z^{k+1}),$$

it follows from Corollary 3.32 that the Weierstrass representation converges with canonical factors E_k. It remains to show that the entire nonvanishing factor e^g is in fact of the form e^P with a polynomial P, as in (3.32).

One way to proceed is to show that the product of the canonical factors is an entire function of order at most k, and that the same also holds for f divided by this product. Evidently, e^g then needs to be of the desired form e^P with P as above. However, rather than following this somewhat laborious route, we will use a shortcut that produces the entire product representation (3.32) in one fell swoop. The idea is again to pass to the logarithms and work with sums instead. By taking $k+1$ derivatives of $\log f$ we shall then be able to deduce the various finiteness statements.

But we need a tool for that, and it will come in the form of a Poisson integral representation of $\log f$ as given by Corollary 3.5. Indeed, assume first that f does not vanish in $|z| \leq R$. Then $\log f$ is analytic and we obtain from (3.5)

$$(3.33) \quad \log f(z) = \frac{1}{\pi i} \oint_{|\zeta|=R} \frac{1}{\zeta - z} \log |f(\zeta)| \, d\zeta - \log |f(0)| + i \operatorname{Im} \log f(0).$$

To treat the general case we assume without loss of generality that $f(0) \neq 0$ (otherwise just replace f with $z^{-\nu} f(z)$). Denote the zeros of f by $\{\zeta_n\}_n$, listed with multiplicity. Let R be such that $f(z) \neq 0$ on $|z| = R$. The product

$$\varphi(z) := \prod_{|\zeta_n| < R} \frac{R^2 - \bar{\zeta}_n z}{R(z - \zeta_n)}$$

is analytic in $|z| \leq R$ and vanishes where f does with the same order. Moreover, $|\varphi(z)| = 1$ on $|z| = R$. So we can apply (3.33) to f/φ to conclude that

(3.34)

$$\log f(z) = \frac{1}{\pi i} \oint_{|\zeta|=R} \frac{1}{\zeta - z} \log |f(\zeta)| \, d\zeta + \sum_{|\zeta_n| < R} \log \frac{R^2 - \bar{\zeta}_n z}{R(z - \zeta_n)} + \text{const.}$$

Let $p = k + 1 > \rho$ and differentiate the previous line p times:

$$\frac{d^p}{dz^p} \log f(z) = \frac{1}{\pi i} \oint_{|\zeta|=R} \frac{p!}{(\zeta - z)^{p+1}} \log |f(\zeta)| \, d\zeta - \sum_{|\zeta_n| < R} \frac{(p-1)! \, \bar{\zeta}_n^p}{(R^2 - \bar{\zeta}_n z)^p}$$

$$- \sum_{|\zeta_n| < R} \frac{(p-1)!}{(\zeta_n - z)^p}.$$

The main terms are the ones on the left-hand side and the final sum. Indeed,

$$\left| \frac{d^p}{dz^p} \log f(z) + \sum_{|\zeta_n| < R} \frac{(p-1)!}{(\zeta_n - z)^p} \right|$$

$$\leq \frac{2Rp!}{(R - |z|)^{p+1}} \max_{|z|=R} \log |f(z)| + \frac{(p-1)!}{(R - |z|)^p} \#\{n \mid |\zeta_n| \leq R\}.$$

By (3.31) and Corollary 3.32 we conclude that for fixed z the right-hand side here vanishes in the limit $R \to \infty$. In other words,

$$(3.35) \qquad\qquad \frac{d^p}{dz^p} \log f(z) = - \sum_{n=1}^{\infty} \frac{(p-1)!}{(\zeta_n - z)^p}.$$

In order to integrate this equation from 0 to z we first introduce cuts from each zero ζ_n to ∞ along parallel lines in such a way that z does not lie on any of these cuts. The resulting ambiguity is eliminated by the exponentiation required in the end. Integrating (3.35) p times along a curve which does not intersect any of these cuts yields the following:

$$\log f(z) - P(z) = \sum_{n=1}^{\infty} \left[\log \left(1 - \frac{z}{\zeta_n} \right) + \frac{z}{\zeta_n} + \frac{z^2}{2\zeta_n^2} + \ldots + \frac{z^p}{p\zeta_n^p} \right].$$

The convergence of the series is automatic given the convergence of (3.35) but of course also follows from Corollary 3.32 as discussed in the first part of the proof. The polynomial P has degree $p - 1 = k$ or less. $\square$

This important theorem has numerous applications. For example, we leave it to the reader to check that an entire function with nonintegral order must have infinitely many zeros. In addition, we invite the reader to revisit the example $f(z) = \sin(\pi z)$ that was presented after Theorem 2.27. For the sake of illustration, let us consider the example $f(z) = \frac{\sin \sqrt{z}}{\sqrt{z}}$ which is entire of order $\frac{1}{2}$. It vanishes at precisely $z = n^2 \pi^2$ with n a positive integer. So by Hadamard with $\rho = \frac{1}{2}$ and $k = 0$ we therefore write

$$\frac{\sin \sqrt{z}}{\sqrt{z}} = \prod_{n=1}^{\infty} \left(1 - \frac{z}{n^2 \pi^2} \right).$$

The prefactor e^C with constant C is equal to 1 as can be seen by setting $z = 0$ in this identity. Replacing z with $\pi^2 z^2$ leads to our previous example,

$$\sin(\pi z) = \pi z \prod_{n=1}^{\infty} \left(1 - \frac{z^2}{n^2} \right).$$

We conclude our discussion of entire functions of finite order with an analysis of the decay of their Taylor coefficients. We define

$$M_f(r) := \sup_{|z|=r} |f(z)|.$$

Proposition 3.34. *Let $f(z) = \sum_{n=0}^{\infty} a_n z^n$ be entire. If $M_f(r) < e^{Ar^\rho}$ for all large r and some fixed $A, \rho > 0$, then*

(3.36) $$|a_n| < \left(\frac{eA\rho}{n} \right)^{\frac{n}{\rho}} \quad \forall \, n \geq n_0.$$

Conversely, if (3.36) holds, then

(3.37) $$M_f(r) \leq e^{(A+\varepsilon)r^\rho},$$

for all large r.

Proof. By Cauchy's estimate,

$$|a_n| \leq \frac{M_f(r)}{r^n} \leq e^{Ar^\rho - n \log r} \quad \forall \, r \geq r_0.$$

Optimizing in r yields (3.36) for large n. "Optimizing" just refers to finding the minimum of the exponent which is attained at $A\rho r^\rho - n = 0$.

For the converse, we can assume that $f(0) = 0$ and that (3.36) holds for all $n \geq 1$. Indeed, (3.37) is unchanged under addition of a polynomial to f. Thus,

$$|f(z)| \leq \sum_{n=1}^{\infty} \left(\frac{eA\rho}{n}\right)^{\frac{n}{\rho}} r^n \leq \sum_{n=1}^{\infty} \left(\frac{eAr^\rho}{n/\rho}\right)^{\frac{n}{\rho}}.$$

Let $m \leq n/\rho$ be the largest integer with this property. Then

$$\left(\frac{eA\rho r^\rho}{n}\right)^{\frac{n}{\rho}} \leq \left(\frac{eAr^\rho}{m}\right)^{m+1},$$

$$|f(z)| \leq \sum_{n=1}^{\infty} \left(\frac{eAr^\rho}{m}\right)^{m+1}.$$

Now use the Stirling formula

$$m! \sim \left(m/e\right)^m \sqrt{2\pi m} \quad m \to \infty,$$

and the bound

$$\sqrt{2\pi m} < C\left(\frac{A+\varepsilon}{A}\right)^{m+1},$$

to conclude that

$$
\begin{aligned}
(3.38) \qquad |f(z)| &\leq C \sum_{n=1}^{\infty} \frac{e^m}{m^m}(Ar^\rho)^{m+1} \leq C \sum_{n=1}^{\infty} \frac{((A+\varepsilon/2)r^\rho)^{m+1}}{m!} \\
&\leq C(A+\varepsilon/2)r^\rho \, e^{(A+\varepsilon/2)r^\rho} \leq Ce^{(A+\varepsilon)r^\rho},
\end{aligned}
$$

as claimed. $\qquad\qquad\qquad\qquad\qquad\qquad\qquad\qquad\qquad\qquad\qquad\quad\square$

Proposition 3.34 allows us to generate many examples of entire functions of given order. Indeed, for any given $\rho > 0$ the Taylor series

$$f(z) = \sum_{n=0}^{\infty} \left(\frac{eA\rho}{n}\right)^{\frac{n}{\rho}} z^n$$

is entire and has order ρ. The function

$$f(z) = \sum_{n=0}^{\infty} e^{-n^2} z^n$$

is of order zero. As an exercise, we as the reader to deduce from Proposition 3.34 that the order of an entire function does not change under differentiation. See Problem 3.14.

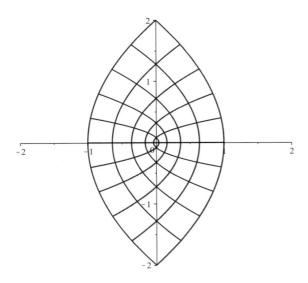

Figure 3.2. The function $w = z^2$, $-1 \leq \mathrm{Re}\, z \leq 1$, $0 \leq \mathrm{Im}\, z \leq 1$

3.8. A gallery of conformal plots

In this final section we display a few images generated by mapping rectangular grids of some finite size via conformal maps into the complex plane. For example, Figure 3.2 is obtained by taking a few lines $x = \mathrm{const}$, $y = \mathrm{const}$ inside the rectangle $-1 < x < 1$, $0 < y < 1$ and mapping them as follows:

$$x + iy \mapsto (x + iy)^2 = x^2 - y^2 + 2ixy.$$

For example, the top edge of the rectangle is mapped onto the parabola on the left-hand side of Figure 3.2. The edge $1 + iy$, $0 \leq y \leq 1$ is mapped on the parabolic arc connecting $2i \to 1$. The real segment $1 \to -1$ is taken on to the interval $[0, 1]$ traversed twice, and the left edge $-1 + iy$ finally becomes the arc $1 \to -2i$.

We may interpret Figure 3.2 also in terms of the inverse map, the square root in this case. If we consider the branch of the root defined on the plane $\mathbb{C} \setminus [0, \infty)$, then the curves shown here are examples of level curves $u = \mathrm{const}$, and $v = \mathrm{const}$, respectively, where $u + iv$ represents the root. In the development of complex analysis in the 19th century pictures such as these played a decisive role because of their close connection with fluids and electrical fields, which were also regarded as manifestation of "electrical fluids" in a medium known as *the ether*. The images in this chapter were computed by using Maple®. In Figures 3.4, 3.6 the displayed area has been truncated due to the large values attained by z^{-2}.

In fact, we can regard the level curves of the harmonic function u as the flow lines of a fluid (or the electrical field lines), whereas the level curves of

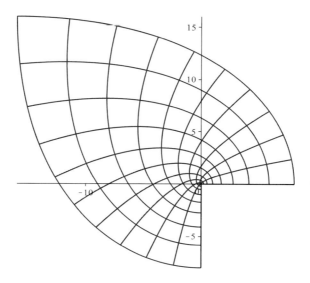

Figure 3.3. The function $w = z^3, \quad 0 \le \operatorname{Re} z \le 2, 0 \le \operatorname{Im} z \le 2$

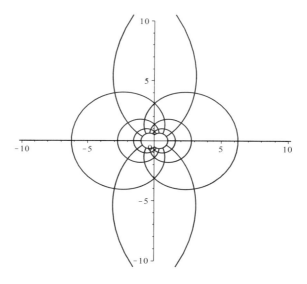

Figure 3.4. The function $w = z^{-2}, \quad -1 \le \operatorname{Re} z \le 1, 0 \le \operatorname{Im} z \le 1$

the harmonic conjugate v then represent the lines of equal potential (i.e., voltage). The harmonicity of these functions is a direct consequence of the fact that *in absence of electrical sources* the electrical field $\vec{E}$ satisfies $\operatorname{div}\vec{E} = 0$ (in the language of fluids, this represents *incompressibility*). So if $\vec{E} = \nabla\phi$, a consequence of the fact that the "electrical fluid" is irrotational, i.e., $\operatorname{curl}\vec{E} = 0$, then $\operatorname{div}\nabla\phi = \Delta\phi = 0$. In other words, the potential ϕ is harmonic. Of particular importance are **singularities** which basically means that we lose the perpendicular family of smooth curves (loss of conformality). Physically, this is most significant as it represents sinks or sources, such as electrical charges. In terms of "real fluids", what we have said above applies to *irrotational, incompressible* flows (curl$\vec{u} = 0$, div$\vec{u} = 0$) since they correspond to harmonic functions.

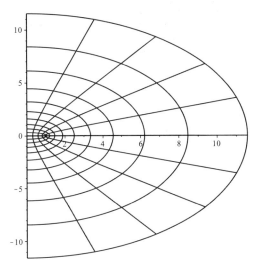

Figure 3.5.   The function $w = \cos(z)$, $-\pi/2 \leq \operatorname{Re} z \leq \pi/2$, $0 \leq \operatorname{Im} z \leq \pi$

This visualization of fields and flows played a decisive role in Riemann's introduction of the surfaces named after him, since it turns out to make perfect sense to carry out the same type of analysis on surfaces in $\mathbb{R}^3$. Locally this amounts to introducing *isothermal coordinates*, which means that we can always find coordinates locally such that the metric on the surface becomes $ds^2 = \lambda^2(dx^2 + dy^2)$ where $\lambda \neq 0$ is a smooth function (see Chapter 4 for the details).

This implies something rather profound, namely that in isothermal coordinates (x, y) we can give meaning to harmonic and analytic functions: *they are precisely those that satisfy the standard Laplace or Cauchy-Riemann equations in the plane.* In other words, we can carry out complex analysis on curved surfaces in $\mathbb{R}^3$ or for that matter "abstract" surfaces without an ambient space. At this point the reader might find it helpful to consider Problem 3.3 below, which makes the passage from a perpendicular grid of level curves of harmonic functions to a conformal map explicit.

Passing from the local analysis to the global one leads us to many new phenomena. For example, when can we find *global isothermal coordinates*?

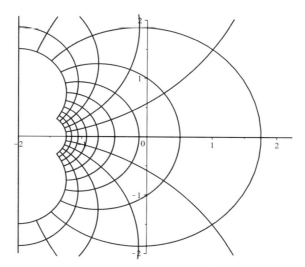

Figure 3.6. The function $w = \frac{2z-1}{2-z}$, $\quad -2 \le \operatorname{Re} z \le 2, 0 \le \operatorname{Im} z \le 2$

Physically speaking, it is precisely the *global geometry* which forces the presence of sources and sinks. We shall encounter the close relation between geometry-topology on the one hand and analysis on the other hand in such results as the Riemann-Roch theorem. See the notes to this chapter for more information.

Since the stereographic projection is conformal, one obtains rectangular grids on the Riemann sphere, too. Often the resulting images are more transparent.

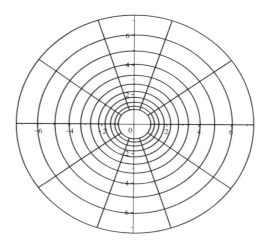

Figure 3.7. The function $w = e^z$, $0 \le \operatorname{Re} z \le 2, 0 \le \operatorname{Im} z \le 2\pi$

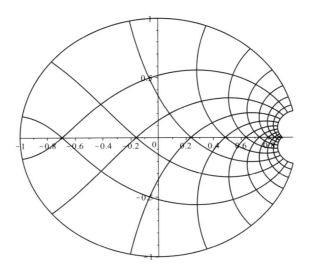

Figure 3.8. The function $w = \frac{z^2-i}{z^2+i}$, $0 \le \operatorname{Re} z \le 3$, $0 \le \operatorname{Im} z \le 3$

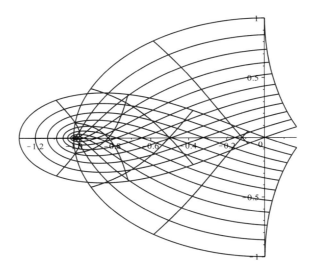

Figure 3.9. The function $w = \frac{z^3-i}{z^3+i}$, $-1 \le \operatorname{Re} z \le 1$, $0 \le \operatorname{Im} z \le \frac{1}{2}$

Notes

Standard references on harmonic functions on the disk and the Poisson kernel are the classic book by Hoffman [**43**], as well as those by Garnett [**31**], and Koosis [**52**]. Harmonic functions play a fundamental role also in higher dimensions, and notions such as the mean-value property, the maximum principle, as well as the Poisson kernel, carry over to $\mathbb{R}^d$ for $d > 2$; see for example the elliptic PDE text [**40**].

Our coverage of probabilistic aspects involving Brownian motion is a tiny sketch at best. If we scale Brownian motion, i.e., λB_t with $\lambda > 0$ then we obtain another Brownian motion, namely $B_{\lambda^2 t}$. In other words, up to a time change, Brownian motion is scaling invariant. Rotations of course leave B_t unchanged. Since conformal maps are locally nothing other than rotations composed with dilations, we expect that Brownian motion is conformally invariant—up to a time change. This is indeed the case.

Especially over the past 15 years the influence of complex analysis in probability theory has been enormous, lead by the developments centering around the SLE revolution. See for example the books by Lawler [57] and for a modern introduction to random walk in general, see Lawler and Limic [58]. Another beautiful introduction to this circle of ideas is the lecture course by Werner [87]. For a detailed study of harmonic measure see the monograph [32].

For further material on entire functions of finite order we refer the reader to [80] and [60]. For (3.28) see for example [65, Volume 1, Problem 7.6]. One way to approach this inequality is via the Calderón-Zygmund decomposition of measures.

For space reasons, we do not systematically develop H^p spaces on the upper half-plane. These can be found in many places, such as Hoffman [43] and Levin [60].

Another omission in this text is **Nevanlinna theory** of meromorphic functions, which has had a major impact in the development of complex function theory. It is closely related to some of the formulas in this chapter such as Jensen's formula and (3.34). Nevanlinna theory explores the distribution of values of meromorphic functions in the plane. There are two basic theorems, the first one being a rephrasing of Jensen's formula. It relates the value distribution of meromorphic functions in a disk $\{|z| < r\}$ to the growth of the meromorphic function.

The physical imagery derived from fluids and electrostatics which motivated Riemann alluded to in the final section of this chapter is made explicit in Felix Klein's book [51]. Riemann apparently used this intuition to address the mathematical problem (which played a central role in 19th century mathematics) of computing various algebraic integrals such as elliptic and hyperelliptic ones. We will keep this point of view in mind as we present Riemann surfaces in later chapters. For example, we discuss isothermal coordinates which lie at the foundation of Riemann surfaces in Chapter 4. It should therefore also not come as a surprise to the reader that harmonic and meromorphic functions on a Riemann surface play a central role to the entire theory, and we will expend considerable effort in the second half of the book in the construction of such functions as well as their differentials.

The images in this chapter were computed by using Maple®.

3.9. Problems

Problem 3.1. Let $f(z) = \sum_{n=0}^{\infty} a_n z^n$ have radius of convergence $R = 1$. Problems (a)–(c) further explore the connection between the behavior of the series and the function f at the boundary. They are completely elementary but a bit tricky.

(a) Suppose $a_n \in \mathbb{R}$ for all $n \geq 0$ and $s_n = a_0 + a_1 + \ldots + a_n \to \infty$ as $n \to \infty$. Prove that $f(z)$ cannot be analytically continued to any neighborhood of $z = 1$. Is it meaningful to call $z = 1$ a pole of f? Does the same conclusion hold if all a_n are real and $|s_n| \to \infty$ as $n \to \infty$?

(b) Suppose $\sum_{n=0}^{\infty} a_n = s$. Show that then $f(z) \to s$ as $z \to 1$ inside the region $z \in K_\alpha \cap \mathbb{D}$, $0 < \alpha < \pi$ arbitrary but fixed. Here K_α is a cone with tip at $z = 1$, symmetric about the x-axis, opening angle α, and with $(-\infty, 1) \subset K_\alpha$ (this type of convergence $z \to 1$ is called "nontangential convergence"). Note that $z = 1$ can be replaced by any $z \in \partial\mathbb{D}$.

(c) Now assume that $n a_n \to 0$ as $n \to \infty$. If $f(z) \to s$ as $z \to 1$ nontangentially, then prove that $\sum_{n=0}^{\infty} a_n = s$. Note again that $z = 1$ can be replaced by any $z \in \partial\mathbb{D}$.

Problem 3.2. (a) Let $0 \leq r_1 < r_2 \leq \infty$ and suppose that u is a real-valued harmonic function on the annulus $\mathcal{A} = \{z \in \mathbb{C} : r_1 < |z| < r_2\}$. Prove that there exists some unique $k \in \mathbb{R}$ and $f \in \mathcal{H}(\mathcal{A})$ such that

$$u(z) = k \log|z| + \operatorname{Re} f(z) \qquad \forall\, z \in \mathcal{A}.$$

Next, assume that $r_1 = 0$. Prove that if u is bounded on $\mathcal{A}$, then $k = 0$ and u extends to a harmonic function throughout $|z| < r_2$.

(b) Suppose $\Omega \subset \mathbb{C}$ is open and simply-connected. Let $z_0 \in \Omega$ and suppose that $u \in \Omega \setminus \{z_0\} \to \mathbb{R}$ is harmonic such that

$$u(z) - \log|z - z_0|$$

remains bounded as $z \to z_0$. Show that there exists $f \in \mathcal{H}(\Omega)$ such that $f(z_0) = 0$, $u(z) = \log|f(z)|$, and f is one-to-one on some disk around z_0.

Problem 3.3. Suppose that u, v are harmonic in Ω so that ∇u and ∇v never vanish in Ω (we call this *nondegenerate*). If $f = u + iv$ is conformal (i.e., $f \in \mathcal{H}(\Omega)$), then we know that the level curves $u = \text{const}$ and $v = \text{const}$ in Ω are perpendicular to each other (why?). This exercise addresses the converse:

(a) Suppose v, w are harmonic and nondegenerate in Ω such that the level curves of v and w coincide in Ω. How are v and w related?

(b) Suppose u, v are harmonic and nondegenerate in Ω, and assume their level curves are perpendicular throughout Ω. Furthermore, assume that $|\nabla u(z_0)| = |\nabla v(z_0)|$ at *one point* $z_0 \in \Omega$. Prove that either $u + iv$ or $u - iv$ is conformal in Ω.

Problem 3.4. Prove Proposition 3.19. *Hint:* Invoke the Lebesgue decomposition and the results preceding that proposition.

Problem 3.5. Show that

(3.39) $$|\{\theta \in \mathbb{T} \mid u_\mu^*(\theta) \geq \lambda\}| \geq \frac{C}{\lambda}\|\mu\|,$$

for $\mu \perp m$, where μ is a positive measure.

Problem 3.6. This problem establishes further properties of subharmonic functions. We denote $u : \Omega \to [-\infty, \infty)$ *subharmonic* by $u \in \mathfrak{sh}(\Omega)$. Establish the following properties:

(i) Maximum principle: if Ω is bounded and $u \in \mathfrak{sh}(\Omega)$, then

$$\sup_{\zeta \in \partial\Omega} \limsup_{\substack{z \to \zeta \\ z \in \Omega}} u(z) \leq M < \infty \Longrightarrow u(z) \leq M \quad \forall\, z \in \Omega,$$

with equality being attained on the right-hand side for some $z \in \Omega$ if and only if $u = $ const.

(ii) Let $u \in \mathfrak{sh}(\Omega)$ on Ω and suppose h is harmonic on some open disk K compactly contained in Ω and $h \in C(\bar{K})$. Further, assume that $u \leq h$ on ∂K. Show that $u \leq h$ on K. Furthermore, if $u = h$ at some point in K, then $u = h$ on K (this explains the name subharmonic).

(iii) This is a converse of (ii): suppose $u : \Omega \to [-\infty, \infty)$ is continuous so that for every disk K with $\bar{K} \subset \Omega$ the *harmonic majorization property* holds: if $h \in C(\bar{K})$ is harmonic on K and satisfies $u \leq h$ on ∂K, then $u \leq h$ on K. Prove that u is subharmonic.

(iv) Suppose $u \in \mathfrak{sh}(\Omega)$. Prove that for any $z_0 \in \Omega$ and any $0 < r_1 < r_2 < \text{dist}(z_0, \partial\Omega)$,

$$-\infty < \frac{1}{2\pi}\int_0^{2\pi} u(z_0 + r_1 e^{i\theta})\, d\theta \leq \frac{1}{2\pi}\int_0^{2\pi} u(z_0 + r_2 e^{i\theta})\, d\theta$$

and

$$\lim_{r \to 0+} \frac{1}{2\pi}\int_0^{2\pi} u(z_0 + r e^{i\theta})\, d\theta = u(z_0),$$

as well as

$$\int_0^{2\pi} |u(z_0 + r e^{i\theta})|\, d\theta < \infty,$$

for any $0 < r < \text{dist}(z_0, \partial\Omega)$.

(v) Show that in $C(\Omega)$ the harmonic functions are precisely those that satisfy the *mean-value property*. Use this to prove that the limit of any sequence $\{u_n\}_{n=1}^\infty$ of harmonic functions on Ω which converges uniformly on every compact subset of Ω is again harmonic.

(vi) Show that every subharmonic function is the decreasing limit of smooth subharmonic functions. Use convolution with a radial, smooth, non-negative bump function and obtain the decreasing limit from the sub-mean-value property.

Problem 3.7. This problem explores the important topic of maximum principles on unbounded domains; cf. Corollary 1.30. For more, see Levin's book [**60**] as well as Titchmarsh [**80**]. Results of this type go by the name of *Phragmen-Lindelöf principles*.

(a) Let $\lambda \geq 1$ and let $\mathcal{S}$ be the sector

$$\mathcal{S} := \left\{ re^{i\theta} \,\Big|\, 0 < r < \infty, \ |\theta| < \frac{\pi}{2\lambda} \right\}.$$

Let $u \in \mathfrak{sh}(\mathcal{S}) \cap C(\bar{\mathcal{S}})$ satisfy $u \leq M$ on $\partial \mathcal{S}$ and $u(z) < |z|^\rho$ in $\mathcal{S}$ where $\rho < \lambda$. Prove that $u \leq M$ on $\mathcal{S}$.

(b) Let $u \in \mathfrak{sh}(\Omega)$ where Ω is a bounded domain. Further, suppose $E := \{z_n\}_{n=1}^\infty \subset \partial \Omega$ has the property that

$$\limsup_{z \to \partial \Omega \setminus E} u(z) \leq M.$$

Prove that $u \leq M$ in Ω.

Problem 3.8. The problem presents Hadamard's three lines lemma, and its analogue in terms of circles.

Suppose f is holomorphic and bounded on a vertical strip $a \leq \operatorname{Re} z \leq b$. Show that the logarithm of $M(x) = \sup_y |f(x+iy)|$ is a convex function on $[a, b]$. Formulate and prove the analogous statement for circles (use a conformal transformation).

Problem 3.9. Let u be subharmonic on a domain $\Omega \subset \mathbb{C}$.

(a) Prove that

$$\langle u, \Delta \phi \rangle \geq 0 \quad \forall \, \phi \in \mathbb{C}_{\text{comp}}^\infty(\Omega), \ \phi \geq 0,$$

where $\langle \cdot, \cdot \rangle$ denotes the standard $L^2(\Omega)$ pairing, and deduce from it that there exists a unique positive Borel measure (called the Riesz measure) on Ω such that

$$\langle u, \Delta \phi \rangle = \iint_\Omega \phi(x)\,\mu(dx),$$

for all $\phi \in \mathbb{C}_{\text{comp}}^\infty(\Omega)$ (from this identity, $\mu(K) < \infty$ for all compact $K \subset \Omega$). In other words, even if a subharmonic function is not C^2 its distributional Laplacian is no worse than a measure. Find μ for $u = \log|f|$ where $f \in \mathcal{H}(\Omega)$.

(b) Show that with μ as in (a) and for any $\Omega_1 \subset \Omega$ compactly contained,

$$(3.40) \qquad u(z) = \iint_{\Omega_1} \log|z - \zeta|\, \mu(d\zeta) + h(z),$$

where h is harmonic on Ω_1. This is "Riesz's representation of subharmonic functions". Interpret its meaning for $u = \log|f|$ with $f \in \mathcal{H}(\Omega)$. Show that, conversely, any nonnegative Borel measure μ which is finite on compact sets of Ω defines a subharmonic function u via (3.40) (with $h = 0$) provided the integral on the right-hand side is continuous with values in $[-\infty, \infty)$. Give an example of a μ where u is not continuous. But show that (3.40) is always upper semicontinuous (usc), i.e.,

$$u(z_0) \geq \limsup_{z \to z_0} u(z),$$

for all $z_0 \in \Omega$. Check that upper semicontinuous functions always attain their supremum on compact sets. In fact, the theory of subharmonic functions which we have developed so far applies to the wider class of upper semicontinuous functions satisfying the sub-mean-value property. See Levin's book for more on this.

(c) With u and μ as in (a), show that

$$(3.41) \qquad \int_0^1 u(z + re(\theta))\, d\theta - u(z) = \int_0^r \frac{\mu(D(z,t))}{t}\, dt,$$

for all $D(z, r) \subset \Omega$. Note that generalizes Jensen's formula; cf. (3.25) and (3.29). In other words, μ measures the extent to which the mean-value property fails and really is a *sub*-mean-value property. Now find an estimate for $\mu(K)$ where $K \subset \Omega$ is compact in terms of the *pointwise size* of u. Finally, write (3.41) down explicitly for $u = \log|f|$ with $f \in \mathcal{H}(\Omega)$.

Problem 3.10. This problem introduces the important Harnack inequality and principle for harmonic functions.

(a) Let $P_r(\phi) = \frac{1-r^2}{1-2r\cos\phi+r^2}$ be the Poisson kernel. Show that for any $0 < r < 1$,

$$(3.42) \qquad \frac{1-r}{1+r} \leq P_r(\phi) \leq \frac{1+r}{1-r},$$

and deduce from this that for any *nonnegative* harmonic function u on $\mathbb{D}$ one has

$$\sup_{|z| \leq r} u(z) \leq C(r) \inf_{|z| \leq r} u(z),$$

where $C(r) < \infty$ for $0 < r < 1$. What is the optimal constant $C(r)$? Now show that for any Ω and K compactly contained in Ω one has the inequality

$$\sup_{z \in K} u(z) \leq C(K, \Omega) \inf_{z \in K} u(z),$$

for nonnegative harmonic functions u on Ω. Now prove that if $u : \mathbb{R}^2 \to \mathbb{R}$ is harmonic, and bounded from one side (thus, $u \leq M$ in Ω for some finite constant M or $u \geq M$), then u is constant.

(b) Suppose $u_1 \leq u_2 \leq u_3 \leq \ldots$ are harmonic functions in Ω. Let $u = \sup_n u_n$. Then either $u \equiv \infty$ or u is harmonic in Ω.

Problem 3.11. Let $u \in \mathfrak{sh}(\mathbb{D})$. Show that the following two properties are equivalent:

(i) u has a harmonic majorant on $\mathbb{D}$, i.e., there exists $h : \mathbb{D} \to \mathbb{R}$ harmonic such that $u \leq h$ on $\mathbb{D}$.

(ii) $\sup_{0 < r < 1} \int_0^1 u(re(\theta)) \, d\theta < \infty$ where $e(\theta) = e^{2\pi i \theta}$.

We say that h_0 is a *least harmonic majorant* of u if and only if h_0 is a harmonic majorant of u on $\mathbb{D}$ and if $h \geq h_0$ for every other harmonic majorant h of u.

Prove that if u has a harmonic majorant on $\mathbb{D}$, then it has a least harmonic majorant. Given an example of a $u \in \mathfrak{sh}(\mathbb{D})$ that has no harmonic majorant.

Problem 3.12. Let $f \in \mathcal{H}(\mathbb{D})$, $f \not\equiv 0$. Then prove that the following two properties are equivalent (here $\log_+ x = \max(0, \log x)$):

(i) $\log_+ |f|$ has a harmonic majorant in $\mathbb{D}$.

(ii) $f = \frac{g}{h}$ where $g, h \in \mathcal{H}(\mathbb{D})$ with $|g| \leq 1$, $0 < |h| \leq 1$ in $\mathbb{D}$.

Problem 3.13. You should compare this to Problem 2.1.

(a) Suppose $\mathcal{Z} = \{z_n\}_{n=0}^\infty \subset \mathbb{D} \setminus \{0\}$ satisfies

$$\sum_{n=0}^\infty (1 - |z_n|) < \infty.$$

Prove that

$$B(z) = \prod_{n=0}^\infty \frac{|z_n|}{z_n} \frac{z_n - z}{1 - \bar{z}_n z}$$

converges uniformly on every $D(0, r)$ with $0 < r < 1$ to a holomorphic function $B \in \mathcal{H}(\mathbb{D})$ with $|B(z)| \leq 1$ for all $|z| < 1$. It vanishes exactly at the z_n (with the order of the zero being equal to the multiplicity of z_n in $\mathcal{Z}$).

(b) We know that $\lim_{r \to 1-} B(re^{i\theta})$ exists for almost every θ (after all, $B \in h^\infty(\mathbb{D})$ so Chapter 3 applies). Denote these boundary values by $B(e^{i\theta})$. Prove that $|B(e^{i\theta})| = 1$ for almost every θ.

Problem 3.14. Deduce from Proposition 3.34 that the order of an entire function does not change under differentiation.

Chapter 4

Riemann surfaces: definitions, examples, basic properties

In this chapter we introduce rigorously the concept of a Riemann surface. Historically, this idea arose naturally in the 19th century in an attempt to understand "multi-valued" analytic functions. The prime examples here are the logarithm, as well as algebraic functions. By the latter we mean the analytic continuations of the roots of a polynomial equation $P(w, z) = 0$ relative to w. We will defer the details of this algebraic construction to the following chapter. This chapter mostly presents various basic examples (such as elliptic functions) and basic general geometric-topological properties which Riemann surfaces possess.

4.1. The basic definitions

We begin with the abstract Riemann surface. Needless to say, the historical development was the exact opposite: examples first and then—after more than sixty years of "naive" but no less successful usage of the concept of a Riemann surface—H. Weyl gave the following definition.

Definition 4.1. A *Riemann surface* is a two-dimensional, connected, Hausdorff topological manifold M with a countable base for the topology and with conformal transition maps between charts. That is, there exists a family of open sets $\{U_\alpha\}_{\alpha \in \mathcal{A}}$ covering M and homeomorphisms $\phi_\alpha : U_\alpha \to V_\alpha$ where

$V_\alpha \subset \mathbb{C}$ is some open set so that

$$\phi_\alpha \circ \phi_\beta^{-1} \; : \; \phi_\beta(U_\alpha \cap U_\beta) \to \phi_\alpha(U_\alpha \cap U_\beta)$$

is biholomorphic (in other words, a conformal homeomorphism). We refer to each (U_α, ϕ_α) as a *chart* and to the collection of all charts as an *atlas* of M.

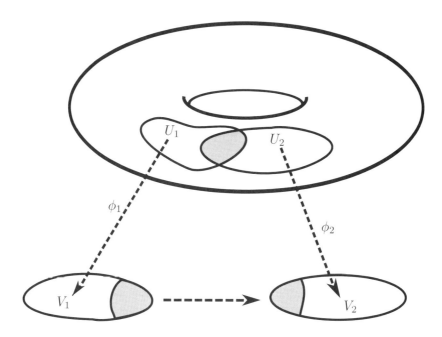

Figure 4.1. Charts and analytic transition maps

Connectivity is a convenient assumption to include. For example, one obtains the uniqueness theorem this way. There is also nothing lost, since we may consider the connected components.

The countability axiom can be dispensed with as it can be shown to follow from the other axioms (this is called Rado's theorem, preceded by the important Poincaré-Volterra theorem), but in all applications it is easy to check directly. Two atlases $\mathcal{A}_1, \mathcal{A}_2$ of M are called equivalent if $\mathcal{A}_1 \cup \mathcal{A}_2$ is an atlas of M. An equivalence class of atlases of M is called a *conformal structure* and a *maximal atlas* of M is the union of all atlases in a conformal structure. We shall often write (U, z) for a chart indicating the fact that $p \mapsto z(p)$ takes U into the complex plane. Moreover, a *parametric disk* is a set $D \subset U$ where (U, z) is a chart with $z(D)$ a Euclidean disk in $\mathbb{C}$. We shall always assume that $\overline{z(D)} \subset z(U)$. By a parametric disk D *centered* at $p \in M$ we mean that (U, z) is a chart with $p \in U$, $z(p) = 0$, and $D = z^{-1}(D(0, r))$ for some $r > 0$.

Throughout this text, we say that the Riemann surface M is an *extension* of the Riemann surface N if $N \subset M$ as an open subset and if the conformal structure of M restricted to N is exactly the conformal structure that N carried to begin with. Note that it follows immediately from the definition that any homeomorphic image of one Riemann surface is another Riemann surface in a natural way: the conformal structure is pushed forward to the target by the homeomorphism.

Definition 4.2. A continuous map $f : M \to N$ between Riemann surfaces is said to be *analytic* if it is analytic in charts, i.e., if $p \in M$ is arbitrary and $p \in U_\alpha$, $f(p) \in V_\beta$ where (U_α, z_α) is a chart of M and (V_β, w_β) is a chart of N, respectively, then $w_\beta \circ f \circ z_\alpha^{-1}$ is analytic where it is defined. We say that f is a *conformal isomorphism* if f is an analytic homeomorphism. If $N = \mathbb{C}$, then one says that f is holomorphic; if $N = \mathbb{C}_\infty$, f is called meromorphic.

We remark that if f is an analytic homeomorphism then the inverse mapping f^{-1} is also analytic. This follows from the fact that this same property holds for maps between open sets in the plane $\mathbb{C}$. It is clear that the meromorphic functions on a Riemann surface form a field. One refers to this field as the *function field*[1] of a surface M.

4.2. Examples and constructions of Riemann surfaces

In this section we discuss a number of examples of Riemann surfaces, some of which will play a formative role in the development of the theory. The first three examples are very basic, and serve to illustrate the main ideas in as simple a context as possible. Examples 4)–7), on the other hand, are more involved and should perhaps only be read after more theory and experience have been acquired. This being said, Examples 4)–7) played a formative role in the development of the theory of Riemann surface. In fact, they each can be seen as an entry point to either the entire theory or a large part of it.

The be specific, Example 4) shows how we may carry out complex analysis on orientable smooth two-dimensional manifolds, such as imbedded compact surfaces in $\mathbb{R}^3$. This insight played a key role during the early stages of Riemann surfaces as it provided a tangible connection with intuitive geometry. The main computational device in this context, which refers to a coordinate-based approach, is the introduction of *isothermal coordinates*.

Example 5) shows how the topological notion of a covering space (see the appendix) arises naturally in Riemann surface theory. In fact, *every non-simply-connected* Riemann surface is obtained from a simply-connected

---

[1] At least when M is compact, this terminology is commonly used in algebraic geometry.

one by taking the quotient relative to the group of deck transformations. We shall prove this statement in the final chapter of this book which covers the *uniformization theorem*. This is one of the more beautiful and central aspects of the theory; it reveals that up to conformal isomorphisms there are only three simply-connected surfaces: the disk, the plane, and the Riemann sphere.

Example 6) discusses *smooth projective algebraic curves*. These are given by algebraic equations $P(w, z) = 0$ where P is a polynomial. The nonsingular curves are the ones for which the implicit function theorem permits to solve for either z or w. One of the key classical theorems which we establish in this book is that *every compact Riemann surface is obtained from an algebraic equation*. This result has clear connections with Galois theory, in the sense that the polynomial $P(w, z)$ is obtained by thinking in terms of the symmetric polynomials involving roots.

Finally, Example 7) discusses how we may "grow" a Riemann surface from an analytic "germ" (which is nothing other than a convergent power series around a point) by means of all possible analytic continuations along chains of disks, see Figure 2.6. This is precisely where Riemann's surfaces meet Weierstrass' *analytisches Gebilde*. We recall in Example 7) what this means. The classical Poincaré-Volterra theorem states that we may obtain at most countably many distinct power series above a fixed base point $z_0 \in \mathbb{C}$ by means of all possibly analytic continuations from a fixed germ at z_0.

In the notes the reader will find more historical comments as well as contemporary references which explain the course of events in detail.

1) *Any open region* $\Omega \subset \mathbb{C}$: Here, a single chart suffices, namely (Ω, z) with z being the identity map on Ω. The associated conformal structure consists of all (U, ϕ) with $U \subset \Omega$ open and $\phi : U \to \mathbb{C}$ biholomorphic. Notice that an alternative, nonequivalent conformal structure is $(\Omega, \bar{z})$ where $\bar{z}$ is the complex conjugation map.

2) *The Riemann sphere* $S^2 \subset \mathbb{R}^3$, *which can be described in three, conformally equivalent, ways*: S^2 (the standard 2-sphere), $\mathbb{C}_\infty$ (the complex plane compactified by a point at infinity), and $\mathbb{C}P^1$ (the complex projective line).

2a) We define a conformal structure on S^2 via two charts

$$(S^2 \setminus (0, 0, 1), \phi_+), \quad (S^2 \setminus (0, 0, -1), \phi_-)$$

where $\phi_\pm$ are the stereographic projections

$$\phi_+(x_1, x_2, x_3) = \frac{x_1 + ix_2}{1 - x_3}, \quad \phi_-(x_1, x_2, x_3) = \frac{x_1 - ix_2}{1 + x_3}$$

from the north, and south pole, respectively; see Figure 1.1 of Chapter 1. If

$$p = (x_1, x_2, x_3) \in S^2$$

with $x_3 \neq \pm 1$, then

$$\phi_+(p)\phi_-(p) = 1.$$

This shows that the transition map between the two charts is $z \mapsto \frac{1}{z}$ from $\mathbb{C}^* \to \mathbb{C}^*$.

2b) The one-point compactification of $\mathbb{C}$ denoted by $\mathbb{C}_\infty := \mathbb{C} \cup \{\infty\}$. The neighborhood base of ∞ in $\mathbb{C}_\infty$ is given by the complements of all compact sets of $\mathbb{C}$. Again there are two charts, namely

$$(\mathbb{C}, z), \quad (\mathbb{C}_\infty \setminus \{0\}, \frac{1}{z})$$

in the obvious sense. The transition map is again given by $z \mapsto \frac{1}{z}$.

2c) The one-dimensional complex projective space

$$\mathbb{C}P^1 := \left\{ (z, w) \mid (z, w) \in \mathbb{C}^2 \setminus \{(0,0)\} \right\} / \sim$$

where the equivalence relation is $(z_1, w_1) \sim (z_2, w_2)$ if and only if

$$z_2 = \lambda z_1, \ w_2 = \lambda w_1$$

for some $\lambda \in \mathbb{C}^*$. The equivalence class of (z, w) is denoted by $[z : w]$. Our charts are (U_1, ϕ_1) and (U_2, ϕ_2) where

$$U_1 := \{[z : w] \in \mathbb{C}P^1 \mid w \neq 0\}, \quad \phi_1([z : w]) = \frac{z}{w},$$
$$U_2 := \{[z : w] \in \mathbb{C}P^1 \mid z \neq 0\}, \quad \phi_2([z : w]) = \frac{w}{z}.$$

Here, too, the transition map is $z \mapsto \frac{1}{z}$.

To go between $\mathbb{C}P^1$ and $\mathbb{C}_\infty$ we take $[z_1 : z_2] \mapsto \frac{z_1}{z_2}$ where the point at infinity is given by $z_2 = 0$. The stereographic projection takes S^2 onto $\mathbb{C}_\infty$, the north pole being sent to the point at infinity. See also Theorem 4.4.

In the previous chapters, we classified all analytic homeomorphisms of the Riemann sphere: they are exactly the Möbius transforms, in other words $\mathrm{PSL}(2, \mathbb{C})$. We also saw that any such analytic homeomorphism is conformal with a conformal inverse.

3) *Any polyhedral surface $S \subset \mathbb{R}^3$ carries the structure of a Riemann surface*: Such a surface S is defined to be a compact topological manifold which can be written as the finite union of *faces* $\{f_i\}$, *edges* $\{e_j\}$, and *vertices* $\{v_k\}$. Any f_i is assumed to be an open subset of a plane in $\mathbb{R}^3$ with line segments as edges (in other words, a planar open polygon), an edge is an open line segment and a vertex a point in $\mathbb{R}^3$, with the obvious relations between them (the boundaries of faces in $\mathbb{R}^3$ are finite unions of edges and

vertices and the endpoints of the edges are vertices; an edge is where two faces meet etc.).

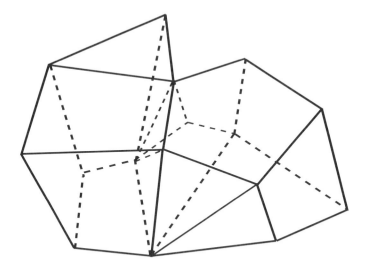

Figure 4.2. Polyhedra are Riemann surfaces

To define a conformal structure on such a polyhedral surface, proceed as follows: each f_i defines a chart (f_i, ϕ_i) where ϕ_i is a Euclidean motion (affine isometry) that takes f_i into $\mathbb{C} = \mathbb{R}^2 \subset \mathbb{R}^3$ where we identify $\mathbb{R}^2$ with the (x_1, x_2)-plane of $\mathbb{R}^3$, say. Each edge e_j defines a chart as follows: let f_{i_1} and f_{i_2} be the two unique faces that meet in e_j. Then $(f_{i_1} \cup f_{i_2} \cup e_j, \phi_j)$ is a chart where ϕ_j is a map that folds $f_{i_1} \cup f_{i_2} \cup e_j$ at the edge so that it becomes piece of a plane, and then maps that plane isometrically into $\mathbb{R}^2$. Finally, at a vertex v_k we define a chart as follows: for the sake of illustration, suppose three faces meet at v_k, say $f_{i_1}, f_{i_2}, f_{i_3}$ with respective angles α_1, α_2, and α_3. Let $\gamma > 0$ be defined so that

$$(4.1) \qquad\qquad \gamma \sum \alpha_i = 2\pi,$$

and let the chart map these faces together with their edges meeting at v into the plane in such a way that angles get dilated by γ. It is easy to see that this defines a conformal structure (for example, at a vertex, the transition maps are z^γ where γ is as in (4.1)). Note that z^γ is analytic in any sector of opening angle less than 2π and with vertex at the origin.

Note that the complex structure which turns the polyhedral surface into a Riemannian one is completely different from the Euclidean structure inherited from the ambient space.

4) *Any smooth, compact, orientable two-dimensional submanifold of $\mathbb{R}^3$ carries the structure of a Riemann surface. In other words, any smooth*

orientable compact surface in $\mathbb{R}^3$ *admits a conformal structure.* There are a number of different ways of thinking about this. One approach is to note that any such surface is homeomorphic to a polyhedral one as in the previous example. In fact, topologically it is equivalent to a sphere with a finite number of handles attached; see the appendix. A conformal structure on the original surface is then obtained by pulling the one on the polygonal surface back.

The condition of orientability is essential: the tangent spaces of any Riemann surface are canonically complex vector spaces of dimension one (follows from conformal change of charts) and the multiplication by i in the tangent space defines the positive orientation. In particular, the Möbius strip does not admit the structure of a Riemann surface. The following lemma makes this precise.

Lemma 4.3. *Let M be a Riemann surface. Every tangent space T_pM is in a natural way a complex vector space. In particular, M is orientable and thus carries a volume form. Moreover, if $f : M \to N$ is a C^1 map between Riemann surfaces, then f is analytic if and only if $Df(p)$ is complex linear as a map $T_pM \to T_{f(p)}N$ for each $p \in M$.*

Proof. First note that $\sphericalangle(\vec{v}, \vec{w})$ is well-defined in T_pM. We can measure this angle in any chart—because of conformality of the transition maps this does not depend on the choice of chart. The sign of the angle is also well-defined because of the orientation on M. Now let R be a rotation in T_pM by $\frac{\pi}{2}$ in the positive sense. Then we define

$$i\vec{v} := R\vec{v}.$$

It is clear that this turns each T_pM into a complex one-dimensional vector space. To fix an orientation on M, define (v, iv) with $v \in T_pM$, $v \neq 0$, as the positive orientation. Since $f : U \to \mathbb{R}^2$ with $f \in C^1(U)$, $U \subset \mathbb{C}$ open is holomorphic if and only if Df is complex linear, we see via charts that the same property lifts to the Riemann surface case. $\square$

Classically, the observation is simply that a conformal change of coordinates always preserves orientation: As we say in Chapter 1 a conformal map has the property that its (real) differential is a rotation followed by a dilation and thus preserves orientation. Another way of seeing this is that if f is conformal, then $\det(df) = |f'|^2 > 0$ by the Cauchy-Riemann equations whence the (real) differential df preserves orientation.

Historically speaking, the realization that we may carry out complex analysis on orientable two-dimensional surfaces in $\mathbb{R}^3$ (which is another way of saying that they are Riemann surfaces) was the beginning of the entire story. The classical approach involves *isothermal coordinates* to which we now turn. Start from a local surface given by a parametrization $\vec{x} = \vec{x}(u, v)$, where the function $\vec{x} = (x_1, x_2, x_3)$ is smooth with maximal rank, and $(u, v) \subset \Omega \subset \mathbb{R}^2$, is some region in the plane. Then the metric in the tangent space is given by

$$
\text{(4.2)} \quad
\begin{aligned}
ds^2 &= E \, du^2 + 2F \, du dv + G \, dv^2, \\
E(u, v) &= \langle \vec{x}_u(u, v), \vec{x}_u(u, v) \rangle, \ F = \langle \vec{x}_u, \vec{x}_v \rangle, \ G = \langle \vec{x}_v, \vec{x}_v \rangle,
\end{aligned}
$$

with $\langle \cdot, \cdot \rangle$ being the standard Euclidean inner product in $\mathbb{R}^3$. For example, the length of a curve $\vec{\gamma}(t) = \vec{x}(u(t), v(t))$, $a \le t \le b$, is given by

$$
L(\vec{\gamma})
$$
$$
= \int_a^b \sqrt{E(u(t), v(t)) \, \dot{u}^2(t) + 2F(u(t), v(t)) \, \dot{u}(t) \, \dot{v}(t) + G(u(t), v(t)) \, \dot{v}(t)^2} \, dt.
$$

In a similar fashion we compute angles and areas on the surface in these local coordinates. By positive definiteness of the metric, $W^2 := EG - F^2 > 0$.

Motivated by conformal maps in the plane, we ask if we may change coordinates $u = u(x, y)$, $v = v(x, y)$ such that the metric becomes

$$
ds^2 = \mu^2(dx^2 + dy^2)
$$

with $\mu = \mu(x, y) > 0$ smooth. Such coordinates are called **isothermal**. To find the differential equations for x, y as functions of u, v, we factor the metric into linear terms:

$$
ds^2 = (\omega_1 \, du + \omega_2 \, dv)(\bar{\omega}_1 \, du + \bar{\omega}_2 \, dv) = \mu(dx + idy) \, \mu(dx - idy),
$$

which implies that we need to solve for

$$
\text{(4.3)} \quad
\begin{aligned}
\omega_1 \, du + \omega_2 \, dv &= e^{i\alpha} \mu(dx + idy), \\
\bar{\omega}_1 \, du + \bar{\omega}_2 \, dv &= e^{-i\alpha} \mu(dx - idy).
\end{aligned}
$$

where $\alpha \in \mathbb{R}$. The conditions for ω_1, ω_2 are

$$
E = |\omega_1|^2, \quad F = \operatorname{Re}(\omega_1 \bar{\omega}_2), \quad G = |\omega_2|^2
$$

with solutions

$$
\omega_1 = \zeta \sqrt{E}, \quad \omega_2 = \zeta \, \frac{F \pm iW}{\sqrt{E}}, \quad |\zeta| = 1.
$$

The choice of ζ then needs to be such that, with $\sigma = \frac{\zeta}{\mu}$,

$$
\sigma \, (\omega_1 \, du + \omega_2 \, dv) = dx + idy = (x_u \, du + x_v \, dv) + i(y_u \, du + y_v \, dv)
$$

is a total differential. This means that

$$
\sigma \, \omega_1 = x_u + iy_u, \quad \sigma \, \omega_2 = x_v + iy_v,
$$

or, eliminating the integrating factor σ,

$$\omega_2(x_u + iy_u) = \omega_1(x_v + iy_v) \quad \text{or} \quad E(x_v + iy_v) = (F + iW)(x_u + iy_u).$$

Solving for y_u, y_v yields

(4.4) $$y_u = \frac{F x_u - E x_v}{W}, \quad y_v = \frac{G x_u - F x_v}{W}$$

which, upon equating mixed partials, finally gives the following partial differential equation for $x = x(u, v)$:

(4.5) $$\frac{\partial}{\partial v} \frac{F x_u - E x_v}{\sqrt{EG - F^2}} + \frac{\partial}{\partial u} \frac{F x_v - G x_u}{\sqrt{EG - F^2}} = 0.$$

Similarly, we obtain for $y = y(u, v)$,

(4.6) $$\frac{\partial}{\partial v} \frac{F y_u - E y_v}{\sqrt{EG - F^2}} + \frac{\partial}{\partial u} \frac{F y_v - G y_u}{\sqrt{EG - F^2}} = 0.$$

Any reader familiar with the Laplace-Beltrami operator on a manifold will recognize (4.5), (4.6) to be precisely of this form (up to a sign); in fact, on a d-dimensional manifold with coordinates $(\xi^1, \xi^2, \ldots, \xi^d)$ the Laplacian equation takes the form

(4.7) $$\Delta f = \frac{\partial}{\partial \xi^i} \left(\sqrt{g} \, g^{ij} \frac{\partial f}{\partial \xi^j} \right) = 0,$$

where $\{g^{ij}\}_{i,j=1}^d = \{g_{ij}\}^{-1}$ is the dual metric and $g = \det(g_{ij})$ the determinant of the metric (but we shall make no use of this fact).

Let us now *assume* that $x = x(u, v)$ is a smooth nondegenerate solution of (4.5), i.e., $dx \neq 0$, on some open set. Then we compute $y = y(u, v)$ from (4.4). This is possible since (4.5) is precisely the integrability condition which guarantees the existence of y. We leave it to reader to check that y is then a solution of (4.6), as well as that the map $(u, v) \mapsto (x, y)$ has maximal rank. In other words, it is a local diffeomorphism.

Now suppose that we had already started with a conformal metric, i.e., $F = 0$ and $E = G$. Then we see that (4.5), (4.6) turn into

$$x_{uu} + x_{vv} = 0, \quad y_{uu} + y_{vv} = 0.$$

In other words, x, y are harmonic in the (u, v)-coordinates. Moreover, (4.4) becomes the standard Cauchy-Riemann system

$$y_u = -x_v, \quad y_v = x_u.$$

This shows us the following: if we were to use the isothermal coordinates (x, y) constructed above to express *any other isothermal coordinates* (ξ, η) as functions of (x, y), then necessarily $\xi + i\eta$ or $\xi - i\eta$ would be **conformal mappings in the plane** relative to $z = x + iy$. In particular, if we choose the isothermal coordinates in agreement with a global orientation, this implies that the changes in coordinates are always analytic.

Or to say this differently, on **any surface** in $\mathbb{R}^3$, at least locally, we may give meaning to analytic and conformal maps. This is a remarkable insight since the entire **local** theory, as developed, for example, in the first three chapters of this book carries over to the surfaces in $\mathbb{R}^3$. "Local" here refers to any description of analytic functions in a small neighborhood of any point. Moreover, orthogonal families of level curves such as those in Section 3.8—which should be interpreted as flow lines of incompressible fluids and their associated equipotential curves—now equally make sense on such surfaces.

Note that we really did not make any use of the ambient space and our analysis carries over to abstract manifolds. So if we accept that we can always find a nondegenerate solution of (4.5), then it is clear that all orientable two-dimensional manifolds admit a Riemann surface structure. Indeed, orientability means precisely that we may choose our isothermal coordinates in agreement with the global sense of orientation. Therefore, they form an atlas on the surface.

However, we have yet to settle the existence question relating to the PDE (4.5). In other words, how can we be sure that there always exists a nondegenerate harmonic function near any point on a surface? If the metric is analytic, i.e., E, F, G are analytic functions of (u, v), then we may for example appeal to the Cauchy-Kowalewskaya theorem which gives many analytic nontrivial solutions. If the metric is not analytic, then we may still solve the elliptic equation (4.5) by other means such as through a variational principle or through the standard weak-solutions approach to elliptic equations (Hilbert space methods). Later we shall rigorously treat a related existence problem in the context of the Hodge theorem; see Chapter 6. For this reason we do not dwell on the existence problem any further.

5) *Covers and universal covers, and their quotients.* This refers to a large class of fundamental objects. We will treat this topic in more detail both, later in this chapter, as well as in Chapters 5 and 8. For the purposes of this list of examples, we limit ourselves to an introduction. We refer the reader to the appendix for the definition of a covering space and its relation to the fundamental group π_1.

$\mathbb{C} \backslash \{0\}$ is covered by the plane $\mathbb{C}$ with covering map $z \mapsto e^z$. On each open horizontal strip of width 2π the map is a bijection. Denote by Γ the subgroup of all Möbius transforms generated by the translation $\gamma : z \mapsto z + 2\pi i$. Then the quotient $\mathbb{C}/\Gamma$ defined by identifying two points of $\mathbb{C}$ if and only if they are mapped onto each other by an element of Γ, is conformally equivalent to $\mathbb{C} \backslash \{0\}$. Hence $\mathbb{C}$ covers $\mathbb{C} \backslash \{0\}$.

Moreover, Γ is precisely the group of deck transformations. This group is isomorphic to $\mathbb{Z}$, which happens to be the fundamental group $\pi_1(\mathbb{C} \setminus \{0\})$. This is no accident, but a *general fact*.

These observations can and should be interpreted in the context of the inverse of the covering map, i.e., the complex logarithm. Thus, we can view $\mathbb{C}$ as the Riemann surface of $\log z$, visualized, however, more easily by means of the usual "infinite helix" sitting above $\mathbb{C} \setminus \{0\}$.

This example suggests something much more general: any subgroup $\Gamma \subset \mathrm{Aut}(\mathbb{C})$ which is "discrete" in a suitable sense leads to a Riemann surface $\mathbb{C}/\Gamma$ covered by $\mathbb{C}$. The *discreteness* here of course refers to the property that we cannot allow arbitrarily close points to be identified under Γ (the technical term is *properly discontinuous group action*). Recall from Chapter 2 that $\mathrm{Aut}(\mathbb{C}) = \{az + b \ : \ a \neq 0\}$; see Proposition 2.10. We leave it to the reader to explore which subgroups have this property. It turns out that the only Riemann surfaces covered by $\mathbb{C}$ are the punctured plane which we just analyzed (which is the same as the twice punctured sphere), as well as tori of genus one (corresponding to subgroups Γ with two generators). We will discuss this latter case in detail later on in this chapter; it is the same as the classical theory of elliptic functions.

Now suppose we remove *two points* from $\mathbb{C}$. Thus, consider the Riemann surface $S := \mathbb{C} \setminus \{0, 1\}$; what is its universal cover? A remarkable theorem of Picard from 1879 states that S is covered by the disk; in other words, there exists a surjection $\pi : \mathbb{D} \to \mathbb{C} \setminus \{0, 1\}$. We shall prove this result later in this chapter. An immediate application of this fact is the little Picard theorem (see Theorem 4.18): *Every entire function which omits two values is constant.* The exponential function shows that Picard's theorem is sharp: an entire function may omit one value (which for the exponential is 0). Later in this chapter we present a standard construction based on the geometry of the Poincaré disk, and the Riemann mapping theorem, to identify the disk as the universal cover of $\mathbb{C}$ with two or more points removed.

6) *Riemann surfaces defined as smooth (projective) algebraic curves*: Let $P(w, z)$ be an irreducible polynomial such that $dP \neq 0$ on

$$S := \{(z, w) \in \mathbb{C}^2 \mid P(z, w) = 0\}.$$

In other words, $(\partial_z P, \partial_w P)(z, w) \neq (0, 0)$ when $P(z, w) = 0$ (such P are called *nonsingular*). By the implicit function theorem, $S \subset \mathbb{C}^2$ is a Riemann surface embedded in $\mathbb{C}^2$, called an affine *algebraic curve*. To define the complex structure on S, one can use either z or w as local coordinates depending on whether $\partial_z P \neq 0$ or $\partial_w P \neq 0$ on that neighborhood. The irreducibility of P implies that S is connected. By construction, any function of the form $\frac{f(z)}{g(w)}$ or $\frac{f(w)}{g(z)}$ where f, g are meromorphic on $\mathbb{C}$ and g is not identically zero, is a meromorphic function on S.

The Riemann sphere is obtained from the complex plane by compactification. Here, too, we wish to compactify the affine algebraic curve S. As in Example 2) above, we may carry out a projective construction.

To be specific, pass to the homogeneous version of P; thus, let $\nu \geq 1$ be the minimal integer for which

$$(4.8) \qquad\qquad u^\nu P(z/u, w/u) =: Q(z, w, u)$$

has no negative powers of u. Then

$$(4.9) \qquad\qquad \widetilde{S} := \{[z : w : u] \in \mathbb{C}P^2 \mid Q(z, w, u) = 0\}$$

is well-defined. Assuming that Q is nonsingular, i.e., $dQ \neq 0$ on $\widetilde{S}$, it follows just as before that $\widetilde{S}$ is a Riemann surface which is compact as a closed subset of the compact space $\mathbb{C}P^2$. $\widetilde{S}$ is called a *smooth projective algebraic curve*, whereas $S = \widetilde{S} \cap \{[z : w : 1] : (z, w) \in \mathbb{C}^2\}$ is called the *affine part* of $\widetilde{S}$. To be more precise, we use the three charts

$$\{[1 : w : u] \mid (w, u) \in \mathbb{C}^2\}, \; \{[z : w : 1] \mid (z, w) \in \mathbb{C}^2\}, \; \{[z : 1 : u] \mid (z, u) \in \mathbb{C}^2\}$$

to cover $\mathbb{C}P^2$. Differentiating the homogeneity equation $Q(\lambda z, \lambda w, \lambda u) = \lambda^\nu Q(z, w, u)$ in λ at $\lambda = 1$ one obtains Euler's relation

$$dQ(z, w, u)(z, w, u) := Q_z(z, w, u)z + Q_w(z, w, u)w + Q_u(z, w, u)u$$
$$= \nu Q(z, w, u).$$

In particular, on $\widetilde{S}$ we infer that $dQ(z, w, u)(z, w, u) = 0$. If we set any one of the coordinates equal to 1, then the polynomial in the two remaining variables is nonsingular in the affine sense (see above); otherwise, we violate $dQ \neq 0$ on $\widetilde{S}$. This allows us to define complex structures on $\widetilde{S}$ over each of the three projective charts which are of course compatible with each other. The meromorphic functions

$$\frac{f(z)}{g(w)} \quad \text{and} \quad \frac{f(w)}{g(z)}$$

extend to meromorphic functions on $\widetilde{S}$ provided f, g are rational. Being compact, $\widetilde{S}$ has finite genus.

An example of the affine part of a curve of genus $g \geq 1$ is given by

$$(4.10) \qquad\qquad w^2 - \prod_{j=1}^N (z - z_j) = 0$$

where $\{z_j\}_{j=1}^N \subset \mathbb{C}$ are distinct and $N = 2g + 1$ or $N = 2g + 2$. For any $z_0 \in \mathbb{C} \setminus \{z_j\}_{j=1}^N$ one has local coordinates

$$w(z) = \pm\sqrt{\prod_{j=1}^N (z - z_j)}$$

where the two signs correspond precisely to the two "sheets" locally near z_0; note that the square root is analytic. Near any z_ℓ, $1 \le \ell \le N$ one sets $z := z_\ell + \zeta^2$ so that

$$w(\zeta) = \zeta\sqrt{\prod_{j=1,\, j\neq\ell}^N (z_\ell - z_j + \zeta^2)}$$

where the ambiguity of the choice of sign can be absorbed into ζ (the square root is again analytic). It is clear that the transition maps between the charts are holomorphic. The reader will easily verify that the projective version of (4.10) with $N \ge 2$, i.e.,

$$Q(z, w, u) := w^2 u^{N-2} - \prod_{j=1}^N (z - u z_j),$$

is nonsingular for $N = 2, 3$ but **singular** when $N \ge 4$. Indeed, if $N \ge 4$ one has $dQ = 0$ "at the point at infinity" of $\widetilde{S}$ (which means for all points $u = 0$). Indeed, let $N \ge 3$. Then $u = 0$ means that

$$\widetilde{S} \cap \{[z : w : 0] \in \mathbb{C}P^2\} = \{[0 : w : 0] \in \mathbb{C}P^2\}.$$

On the other hand, on $\widetilde{S}$,

$$dQ(z, w, 0) = w^2 \, du \neq 0$$

for $N = 3$, but $dQ = 0$ for $N = 4$.

Returning to the affine curve, one refers to the z_j as *branch points*, since the natural projection $w \mapsto z$, which is a covering map on $\mathbb{C}_\infty \setminus \{z_j\}_{j=1}^N$, ceases to be a covering map near each z_j. Rather, one refers to this case as a *branched covering map* and any algebraic curve is a *branched cover* of the Riemann sphere. The specific algebraic curves we just considered are called **elliptic curves** if $g = 1$ or **hyper-elliptic curves** if $g > 1$. We shall return to these important examples in the following chapters, where the reader will also find figures illustrating how the genus is determined through cuts in the extended complex plane.

A most remarkable fact in the theory of Riemann surfaces is this: *any compact Riemann surface is conformally equivalent to an algebraic curve defined by some irreducible polynomial $P \in \mathbb{C}[z, w]$; see Chapter 5. For that construction, we no longer assume that P is nonsingular and therefore proceed differently with our construction of the Riemann surface of P; it is defined via all possible analytic continuations of a locally defined analytic solution $w = w(z)$ of $P(z, w(z)) = 0$.

If we accept this fact for now, then we are presented with a basic question which provided a major impetus in the development of complex function theory as well as analysis as a whole: *How do we find any nontrivial global meromorphic functions on a hyper-elliptic curve, or for that matter, any Riemann surface?*

The aforementioned vanishing $dQ = 0$ at infinity (i.e., $u = 0$) where Q is the homogeneous version of (4.10) provided $N \geq 4$, precludes us from using the naive construction $f(z)/g(w)$ and $f(w)/g(z)$. Recall that $N \geq 4$ means that the genus of the curve satisfies $g > 1$. In the *nonsingular* case we could simply use these functions. But this only makes sense if we may solve for one variable in terms of the other. This precisely fails in the singular case.

However, the reader should not be misled into thinking of $u = 0$ as being a genuine singularity, or there being some sort of a "problem" with this Riemann surface. This would be absurd, since the behavior of (4.10) at $z = \infty$ is clearly that of $w^2 - z^N = 0$ which does not present any problem whatsoever: if N is even, then there is no branching at $z = \infty$, otherwise there is. In Chapter 5 we shall develop the "affine construction" of the Riemann surfaces systematically, which is based on analytic continuation.

A much more serious mystery surrounding the question on the existence of meromorphic functions has to do with the abundance of Riemann surfaces that **a priori** have nothing to do with concrete algebraic or analytical expressions, as evidenced by the classes 3) and 4), above, of surfaces. In fact, a branched cover of S^2 of any genus *can be constructed by purely topological methods*. For any reader versed in basic algebraic topology, one possible construction proceeds as follows: fix three distinct points $p_1, p_2, p_3 \in S^2$. Then $\pi_1(S^2 \setminus \{p_1, p_2, p_3\})$ is isomorphic to the free group with two generators, F_2. Construct a homomorphism $\pi_1(S^2 \setminus \{p_1, p_2, p_3\}) \to \mathbb{Z}/k\mathbb{Z}$ where k is odd. Gluing small disks into the sphere around p_1, p_2, p_3 then shows that the Euler characteristic is $3 - k = 2(1 - g)$. From this sketch it is evident that the branched cover which we have constructed is in fact a compact Riemann surface.

As we shall see in our development of Hodge theory in later chapters, one does need a fair amount of 20th century mathematics to answer this problem of the 19th century, namely Hilbert spaces applied to existence problems in potential theory. In this respect, there are some similarities to the resolution of the Dirichlet problem and the "naive" usage of the Dirichlet principle in the 19th century; see the introduction to Chapter 3. We shall also see that the resolution of this question lies at the heart of much of the classical Riemann surface theory.

7) *Riemann surfaces defined via analytic continuation of an analytic germ*: Let $\mathcal{P}$ be the set of all power series

$$\sum_{n=0}^{\infty} a_n \, (z - z_0)^n$$

around some point $z_0 \in C$ and with radius of convergence $0 < r_0 \leq \infty$. We denote elements of $\mathcal{P}$ by $y(z_0, r_0)(z)$ or simply by $y(z_0, r_0)$. We say that $y(z_1, r_1)$ is a *direct continuation* of $y(z_0, r_0)$ if $|z_1 - z_0| < r_0$ and $y(z_0, r_0)(z) = y(z_1, r_1)(z)$ for all z in the intersections of the respective disks of convergence, i.e.,

$$|z - z_0| < r_0, \quad |z - z_1| < r_1.$$

By the uniqueness theorem from Chapter 1 (see Proposition 1.26), for every $|z_1 - z_0| < r_0$ there exists exactly one direct continuation of $y(z_0, r_0)$. We say that $y(\zeta, \rho)$ can be joined to $y(z_0, r_0)$ by a *chain* if there exist finitely many elements $y(z_k, r_k) \in \mathcal{P}$, $0 \leq k \leq N$ so that $z_n = \zeta$, $r_N = \rho$ and such that $y(z_{k+1}, r_{k+1})$ is a direct continuation of $y(z_k, r_k)$ for each $0 \leq k < N$ (see Figure 2.6). This establishes an equivalence relation in $\mathcal{P}$. The equivalence classes are called *analytic functions*. This is Weierstrass' notion of *analytisches Gebilde*.

Every analytic function is completely determined by a single power series $y(z_0, r_0)$. Denote by $S(a)$ all distinct power series in $z - a$ which are equivalent to $y(z_0, r_0)$. The theorem of Poincaré-Volterra asserts that this set is countable. See the notes for more history of this theorem.

A typical example of this process would be $f(z) = \log z$, some branch of the logarithm, defined on the disk $\{|z-1| < 1\}$. We can analytically continue this branch to some neighborhood of any point other than the origin. In this way, we obtain the full complex logarithm. In Chapter 5 we will see that one can put a complex structure on an equivalence class of power series as defined above which renders it a Riemann surface.

4.3. Functions on Riemann surfaces

We already defined analytic functions between Riemann surfaces and also introduced the concept of a conformal isomorphism. Note that any conformal isomorphism has a conformal inverse. In Example 1) above, the Riemann surfaces with conformal structures induced by (Ω, z) and $(\Omega, \bar{z})$, respectively, do not have equivalent conformal structures but are conformally isomorphic (via $z \mapsto \bar{z}$). For the sake of completeness, we now demonstrate the conformal equivalence of the three models of the Riemann sphere. As usual,

$$\mathrm{PSL}(2, \mathbb{C}) = \mathrm{SL}(2, \mathbb{C})/\{\pm \mathrm{Id}\}.$$

Theorem 4.4. *The Riemann surfaces $S^2, \mathbb{C}_\infty$, and $\mathbb{C}P^1$ are conformally isomorphic. Furthermore, the group of automorphisms of these surfaces is $\mathrm{PSL}(2, \mathbb{C})$.*

Proof. As already noted before, the maps are straightforward: stereographic projection takes S^2 onto $\mathbb{C}_\infty$, and the quotient $[z_1 : z_2] \mapsto \frac{z_1}{z_2}$ equates $\mathbb{C}P^1$ with $\mathbb{C}_\infty$. The analyticity of these maps is immediate from the definition of the complex structures on these Riemann surfaces. In fact, those structures are defined precisely with these identifications in mind.

As for the automorphism group, each

$$A = \begin{bmatrix} a & b \\ c & d \end{bmatrix} \in \mathrm{SL}(2, \mathbb{C})$$

defines an automorphism of $\mathbb{C}P^1$ via the Möbius transformation

$$[z : w] \mapsto [az + bw : cz + dw].$$

Note that A and $-A$ define the same map. On the other hand, if f is an automorphism of $\mathbb{C}_\infty$, then composing with a Möbius transformation we may assume that $f(\infty) = \infty$. Indeed, the Möbius transformations act transitively on $\mathbb{C}P^1$. Hence restricting f to $\mathbb{C}$ yields a map from $\mathrm{Aut}(\mathbb{C})$ which is of the form $f(z) = az + b$ by Proposition 2.10, and we are done. $\square$

We now state the uniqueness and open mapping theorems for analytic functions on Riemann surfaces. These are of course the analogues of the "local" theorems we encountered in the first two chapters of the book. In this section, M, N will denote Riemann surfaces.

Theorem 4.5 (Uniqueness theorem). *Let $f, g : M \to N$ be analytic mappings. Then either $f = g$ identically, or $\{p \in M \mid f(p) = g(p)\}$ is discrete in M.*

Proof. Define

$$A := \{p \in M \mid \text{locally at } p, \ f \text{ and } g \text{ are identically equal}\},$$

$$B := \{p \in M \mid \text{locally at } p, \ f \text{ and } g \text{ agree only on a discrete set}\}.$$

As usual, "locally" means in a chart of a maximal atlas. It is clear that both A and B are open subsets of M. We claim that $M = A \cup B$ which then finishes the proof since M is connected. If $p \in M$ is such that $f(p) \neq g(p)$, then by continuity $p \in B$. Suppose, on the other hand, that $f(p) = g(p)$. If

$\{f = g\}$ is not discrete, then we apply the standard uniqueness theorem in charts to conclude that $f = g$ locally around p. □

As an obvious corollary, note that for any analytic map $f : M \to N$ each "level set" $\{f \in M \mid f(p) = q\}$ with $q \in N$ fixed, is either discrete or all of M (and thus f is constant). In particular, if M is compact and f is not constant, then $\{p \in M \mid f(p) = q\}$ is *finite*.

Theorem 4.6 (Open mapping theorem). *Let $f : M \to N$ be an analytic map. If f is not constant, then $f(M)$ is an open subset of N. More generally, f takes open subsets of M to open subsets of N.*

Proof. By the uniqueness theorem, if f is locally constant around any point, then f is globally constant. Hence we can apply the usual open mapping theorem (see Proposition 1.27) in every chart to conclude that $f(M) \subset N$ is open. □

Corollary 4.7. *Let M be a compact Riemann surface and $f : M \to N$ an analytic nonconstant map. Then f is onto and N is compact.*

Proof. First, $f(M)$ is closed, since it is a compact set and since N is a Hausdorff space. Second, $f(M)$ is open by Theorem 4.6. By connectivity of N it follows that $f(M) = N$ as claimed. □

Recall from Definition 4.2 that the *holomorphic* functions on a Riemann surface M, denoted by $\mathcal{H}(M)$, are defined as all analytic $f : M \to \mathbb{C}$. The *meromorphic* functions on M, denoted by $\mathcal{M}(M)$, are defined as all analytic $f : M \to \mathbb{C}_\infty$.

In view of the preceding, the following statements are immediate.

Corollary 4.8. *Let M be a Riemann surface. Then the following properties hold:*

i) if M is compact, then every holomorphic function on M is constant.

ii) Every nonconstant meromorphic function on a compact Riemann surface is onto $\mathbb{C}_\infty$.

iii) If f is a nonconstant holomorphic function on a Riemann surface M, then $|f|$ attains neither a local maximum nor a positive local minimum on M.

To illustrate what we have accomplished so far, let us give a "topological proof" of Liouville's theorem: assume that $f \in \mathcal{H}(\mathbb{C}) \cap L^\infty(\mathbb{C})$. Then $f(1/z)$ has a removable singularity at $z = 0$. In other words, $f \in \mathcal{H}(\mathbb{C}_\infty)$ and is therefore constant. The analytical ingredient in this proof consists of the uniqueness and open mapping theorems as well as the removability theorem: the first two are reduced to the same properties in charts which then require power series expansions. But instead of using expansions that converge on all of $\mathbb{C}$ and Cauchy's estimate we relied on connectivity to pass from a local property to a global one.

It is a good exercise at this point to verify the following assertion: the meromorphic functions on $\Omega \subset \mathbb{C}$ in the sense of standard complex analysis coincide exactly with $\mathcal{M}(\Omega) \setminus \{\infty\}$ in the sense of Definition 4.2 up to the function which is constant equal to infinity. In particular,

$$\mathcal{M}(\mathbb{C}_\infty) = \Big\{ \frac{P}{Q} \mid P, Q \in \mathbb{C}[z], \ Q \not\equiv 0 \Big\} \cup \{\infty\}.$$

In other words, the meromorphic functions on $\mathbb{C}_\infty$ up to the function which is constant equal to ∞, are exactly the rational functions.

Note that we may prescribe the location of the finitely many zeros and poles of any meromorphic function $f \in \mathcal{M}(\mathbb{C}P^1)$ arbitrarily provided the combined order of the zeros exactly equals the combined order of the poles and provided the set of zeros is distinct from the set of poles.

4.4. Degree and genus

We shall now use the "normal form" from Chapter 1 (see Proposition 1.27) to define the valency of an analytic map.

Definition 4.9. Let $f : M \to N$ be an analytic and nonconstant map between Riemann surfaces. Then the *valency* of f at $p \in M$, denoted by $\nu_f(p)$, is defined to be the unique positive integer n with the property that in charts (U, ϕ) around p (with $\phi(p) = 0$) and (V, ψ) around $f(p)$ (with $\psi(f(p)) = 0$) we have $(\psi \circ f \circ \phi^{-1})(z) = (zh(z))^n$ where $h(0) \neq 0$. If M is compact, then the degree of f at $q \in N$ is defined as

$$\deg_f(q) := \sum_{p : f(p) = q} \nu_f(p)$$

which is a positive integer.

Locally around any point $p \in M$ with valency $\nu_f(p) = n \geq 1$ the map f is n-to-one; in fact, every point q' close to but not equal to $q = f(p)$ has exactly n pre-images close to p.

Let $f = \frac{P}{Q}$ be a nonconstant rational function on $\mathbb{C}_\infty$ represented by a reduced fraction (i.e., P and Q are relatively prime). Then for every $q \in \mathbb{C}_\infty$, the reader will easily verify that $\deg_f(q) = \max(\deg(Q), \deg(P))$ where the degree of P, Q is in the sense of polynomials. It is a general fact that $\deg_f(q)$ does not depend on $q \in N$.

Lemma 4.10. *Let $f : M \to N$ be an analytic and nonconstant map between two compact Riemann surfaces M and N. Then $\deg_f(q)$ does not depend on q. It is called the* degree of f *and is denoted by $\deg(f)$. The isomorphisms*

*from M to N are precisely those nonconstant analytic maps f from M to N
with $\deg(f) = 1$.*

Proof. We recall that, by Corollary 4.7, if M is a compact Riemann surface
and $f : M \to N$ is as in the statement, then N is compact and $f(M) = N$.
We shall prove that $\deg_f(q)$ is locally constant. Let $f(p) = q$ and suppose
that $\nu_f(p) = 1$. As remarked before, f is then an isomorphism from a
neighborhood of p onto a neighborhood of q. If, on the other hand, $n =
\nu_f(p) > 1$, then each q' close but not equal to q has exactly n pre-images
$\{p'_j\}_{j=1}^n$ and $\nu_f(p'_j) = 1$ at each $1 \leq j \leq n$. This proves that $\deg_f(q)$ is
locally constant and therefore globally constant by connectivity of N. The
statement concerning isomorphisms is evident. $\square$

We remark that this notion of degree coincides with the one associated
with general differentiable manifolds; see the appendix. Let us now prove the
Riemann-Hurwitz formula for *branched covers*. The latter notion refers to
any analytic nonconstant map $f : M \to N$ from a compact Riemann surface
M onto another compact Riemann surface N. If necessary, the reader might
wish to review the Euler characteristic and the genus on compact surfaces;
see the appendix.

Theorem 4.11 (Riemann-Hurwitz formula). *Let $f : M \to N$ be an analytic nonconstant map between compact Riemann surfaces. Define the* total
branching number *to be*

$$B := \sum_{p \in M} (\nu_f(p) - 1).$$

Then

(4.11) $$g_M - 1 = \deg(f)(g_N - 1) + \frac{1}{2}B$$

*where g_M and g_N are the genera of M and N, respectively. In particular,
B is always an even nonnegative integer.*

Proof. Denote by $\mathcal{B}$ the set of all $p \in M$ with $\nu_f(p) > 1$ (the branch points).
We shall now use a theorem of Radó which asserts that every Riemann
surface admits a triangulation (see Chapter 6, in particular, Problem 6.5).
Thus let $\mathcal{T}$ be a triangulation of N such that all $f(p)$, $p \in \mathcal{B}$ are vertices
of $\mathcal{T}$. Lift $\mathcal{T}$ to a triangulation $\widetilde{\mathcal{T}}$ on M. If $\mathcal{T}$ has V vertices, E edges
and F faces, then $\widetilde{\mathcal{T}}$ has $nV - B$ vertices, nE edges, and nF faces where
$n = \deg(f)$. Therefore, by the Euler-Poincaré formula (A.1),

$$2(1 - g_N) = V - E + F,$$
$$2(1 - g_M) = nV - B - nE + nF = 2n(1 - g_N) - B,$$

as claimed. $\square$

The Riemann-Hurwitz formula is very useful in the computations of genera of various Riemann surfaces, such as for the algebraic curves defined in Example 6) of Section 4.2. We shall apply it on several occasions in the remainder of this text.

4.5. Riemann surfaces as quotients

Many Riemann surfaces M are generated as quotients of other surfaces N modulo an equivalence relation, i.e., $M = N/\sim$. We have already encountered several instances of this. A common way of defining the equivalence relation is via the action of a subgroup $G < \mathrm{Aut}(N)$. In this case, $q_1 \sim q_2$ in N if and only if there exists some $g \in G$ with $gq_1 = q_2$. Let us state a theorem to this effect where $N = \mathbb{C}_\infty$. Examples will follow immediately after the theorem.

Recall that a covering map is a local homeomorphism. For example, $\exp : \mathbb{C} \to \mathbb{C}^*$ is a covering map, as is $z^n : \mathbb{C}^* \to \mathbb{C}^*$ for each $n \geq 1$. Note that if $n \geq 2$, then the latter example does not extend to a covering map $\mathbb{C} \to \mathbb{C}$; rather, we encounter a branch point at zero and this extension is then referred to as a *branched cover*. Since we have defined the notion of branched cover only for compact surfaces we consider z^n as a map $\mathbb{C}P^1 \to \mathbb{C}P^1$.

Theorem 4.12. *Let $\Omega \subset \mathbb{C}_\infty$ and $G < \mathrm{Aut}(\mathbb{C}_\infty)$ with the property that*

- *$g(\Omega) \subset \Omega$ for all $g \in G$,*
- *for all $g \in G$, $g \neq \mathrm{id}$, all fixed points of g in $\mathbb{C}_\infty$ lie outside of Ω,*
- *for all $K \subset \Omega$ compact, the cardinality of $\{g \in G \mid g(K) \cap K \neq \emptyset\}$ is finite.*

Under these assumptions, the natural projection $\pi : \Omega \to \Omega/G$ is a covering map which turns Ω/G canonically into a Riemann surface.

Proof. By definition, the topology on Ω/G is the coarsest one that makes π continuous. In this case, π is also open; indeed, for every open set $A \subset \Omega$,

$$\pi^{-1}(\pi(A)) = \bigcup_{g \in G} g(A)$$

is open since $g(A)$ is open. Next, let us verify that the topology is Hausdorff. Suppose $\pi(z_1) \neq \pi(z_2)$ and define for all $n \geq 1$,

$$A_n := \left\{ z \in \Omega \mid |z - z_1| < \frac{r}{n} \right\} \subset \Omega,$$

$$B_n := \left\{ z \in \Omega \mid |z - z_2| < \frac{r}{n} \right\} \subset \Omega,$$

where $r > 0$ is sufficiently small. Define $K := \overline{A}_1 \cup \overline{B}_1$ and suppose that $\pi(A_n) \cap \pi(B_n) \neq \emptyset$ for all $n \geq 1$. Then for some $a_n \in A_n$ and $g_n \in G$ we have

$$g_n(a_n) \in B_n \qquad \forall\, n \geq 1.$$

Since, in particular, $g_n(K) \cap K \neq \emptyset$, we see that there are only finitely many possibilities for g_n and one of them therefore occurs infinitely often. Let us say that $g_n = g \in G$ for infinitely many n. Passing to the limit $n \to \infty$ implies that $g(z_1) = z_2$ or $\pi(z_1) = \pi(z_2)$, a contradiction. For all $z \in \Omega$ we can find a small pre-compact open neighborhood of z denoted by $K_z \subset \Omega$, so that

$$(4.12) \qquad g(\overline{K_z}) \cap \overline{K_z} = \emptyset \qquad \forall\, g \in G,\ g \neq \mathrm{id}.$$

Note that at this point we require all three assumptions in the statement of the theorem. Then $\pi : K_z \to K_z$ is the identity and therefore we can use the K_z as charts. Note that the transition maps are given by $g \in \mathrm{Aut}(\mathbb{C}_\infty)$, which are Möbius transformations, and are therefore holomorphic. Finally, $\pi^{-1}(K_z) = \bigcup_{g \in G} g^{-1}(K_z)$ with pairwise disjoint open sets $g^{-1}(K_z)$. The disjointness follows from (4.12) and we are done. $\qquad \square$

We remark that any group G as in the theorem is necessarily *discrete* in the topological sense. First, we remark that $G < \mathrm{Aut}(\mathbb{C}) = \mathrm{PSL}(2, \mathbb{C})$ carries the natural topology; second, if G is not discrete, then the third requirement in the theorem will fail (since we can find group elements in G as close to the identity as we wish). There are many natural examples to which this theorem applies. In what follows, we use $\langle g_1, g_2, \ldots, g_k \rangle$ to denote the group generated by these k elements and, as usual, $\mathbb{H}$ is the upper half-plane.

1) The punctured plane and disk: the cylinder $\mathbb{C}/\langle z \mapsto z + 1 \rangle$ satisfies $\mathbb{C}/\langle z \mapsto z + 1 \rangle \simeq \mathbb{C}^*$ where the isomorphism is given by the exponential map $e^{2\pi i z}$. Here $\Omega = \mathbb{C}$, and $G = \langle z \mapsto z + 1 \rangle$. Similarly, $\mathbb{H}/\langle z \mapsto z + 1 \rangle \simeq \mathbb{D}^*$.

2) The tori: Let $\omega_1, \omega_2 \in \mathbb{C}^*$ be linearly independent over $\mathbb{R}$. Then

$$\mathbb{C}/\langle z \mapsto z + \omega_1, z \mapsto z + \omega_2 \rangle$$

is a Riemann surface. It is the same as $\mathbb{C}/\Lambda$ with the lattice

$$(4.13) \qquad \Lambda = \{ n\omega_1 + m\omega_2 \mid n, m \in \mathbb{Z} \}.$$

In Figure 4.3 the lattice is generated by any distinct pair of vectors from $\{\omega_1, \omega_2, \omega_3\}$, showing that a pair of generators, or *basis*, is not unique. Furthermore, up to conformal equivalence of $\mathbb{C}/\Lambda$ we may always assume that $\omega_1 = 1$ and $\omega_2 = \tau$ where $\mathrm{Im}(\tau) > 0$.

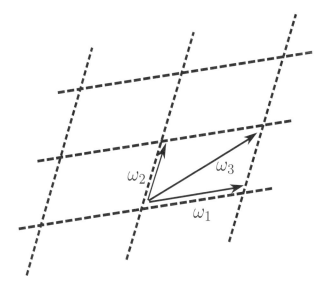

Figure 4.3. A lattice in $\mathbb{C}$

We may identify the surfaces

$$\mathbb{C}^*/\langle z \mapsto \lambda z\rangle \simeq \mathbb{C}/\langle z \mapsto z+1, z \mapsto z + \frac{1}{2\pi i}\log\lambda\rangle$$

where $\lambda > 1$. The surface on the left-hand side naturally has the doughnut or inner-tube shape that one associates with a torus of genus 1. The same exponential map induces the isomorphism in this case as in 1). A natural question is to determine the *space of all conformal equivalence classes of tori*. For this, see Section 4.8.

3) The annuli: consider $\mathbb{H}/\langle z \mapsto \lambda z\rangle$ with $\lambda > 1$. Then $\log z$ maps this quotient onto

$$\{w \in \mathbb{C} : 0 < \operatorname{Im} w < \pi, \, 0 \le \operatorname{Re} w \le \log\lambda\}$$

with the sides $\operatorname{Re} w = 0, \operatorname{Re} w = \log\lambda$ identified. Next, send this via the conformal map

$$w \mapsto \exp\left(2\pi i \frac{w}{\log\lambda}\right)$$

onto the annulus $\Delta_r := \{r < |z| < 1\}$ where $\log r = -\frac{2\pi^2}{\log\lambda}$.

It is well-known that there is no conformal isomorphism between Δ_r and Δ_s if $0 \le r < s < 1$. The reader is invited to try to establish this by elementary means, although this is perhaps somewhat tricky. Hence the space of conformal equivalence classes of annuli $\{z \in \mathbb{C}^* : r_1 < |z| < r_2\}$ with $0 < r_1 < r_2$ is the same as all $\frac{r_2}{r_1}$, i.e., $(1, \infty)$.

It is simple to prove the nonequivalence for the special case $r = 0$. Thus, assume φ is a conformal homeomorphism from $\Delta_0 = \mathbb{D}^*$ onto Δ_r for some $r > 0$. Then $z = 0$ is a removable singularity of φ since it remains uniformly bounded as we approach this point. Moreover, $\varphi'(0) \neq 0$ since otherwise φ would be n-to-1 near $z = 0$ for some $n \geq 2$. So near $z = 0$ the extended map φ is an isomorphism.

Clearly, $w_0 := \varphi(0) \in \bar{\Delta}_r$. If $\varphi(0) \in \Delta_r$, then $\varphi(0) = \varphi(z_0)$ for some $z_0 \in \mathbb{D}^*$. But this is impossible since then a neighborhood of w_0 would be hit both by a neighborhood of 0 and by one of z_0, respectively.

On the other hand, if $w_0 \in \partial \Delta_r$, then we obtain a contradiction by the maximum principle applied to either φ or $\frac{1}{\varphi}$; depending on whether $|w_0| = 1$ or $|w_0| = r$, respectively.

Problem 8.7 in Chapter 8 treats the general case within the context of the uniformization theorem.

This list of examples is relevant for a number of reasons. First, we remark that we have exhausted all possible examples with $\Omega = \mathbb{C}$. Indeed, we leave it to the reader to verify that all nontrivial discrete subgroups of $\text{Aut}(\mathbb{C})$ *that have no fixed point* are either $\langle z \mapsto z + \omega \rangle$ with $\omega \neq 0$, or $\langle z \mapsto z + \omega_1, z \mapsto z + \omega_2 \rangle$ with $\omega_1 \neq 0, \omega_2/\omega_1 \notin \mathbb{R}$ (see Problem 4.1). Second, $\mathbb{C}^*, \mathbb{D}^*, \Delta_r$ and $\mathbb{C}/\Lambda$ where Λ is a lattice, is a complete list of Riemann surfaces (up to conformal equivalence, of course) whose fundamental group is nontrivial and abelian. See the notes to this chapter for references.

Theorem 4.12 leaves open the case where the action does exhibit fixed points. If this is so, the map $\pi : \Omega \to \Omega/G$ may or may not induce the structure of a Riemann surface on Ω/G. Problem 5.8 provides a tool by which one may obtain a Riemann surface in the presence of fixed points.

4.6. Elliptic functions

Throughout this section, we let

$$M = \mathbb{C}/\langle z \mapsto z + \omega_1, z \mapsto z + \omega_2 \rangle$$

be the torus of Example 2 from the above list. As usual, we refer to the group by which we quotient as the lattice Λ. We first remark that $\omega_1' := a\omega_1 + b\omega_2$, $\omega_2' := c\omega_1 + d\omega_2$ is another basis of the same lattice if and only if $a, b, c, d \in \mathbb{Z}$ and $ad - bc = \pm 1$. Indeed, since ω_1', ω_2' are in the lattice, it follows that the coefficients a, b, c, d are integers. If they are a basis, then we may express ω_1, ω_2 via the inverse transformation, which must also have integer coefficients and thus an integral determinant. So the determinant of the original transformation must have been ± 1 as claimed.

Thus, in Figure 4.3 we can pass to other bases as well as other **fundamental regions**.

Definition 4.13. A fundamental region is any closed connected set $P \subset \mathbb{C}$ with the property that:

    i) every point in $\mathbb{C}$ is congruent modulo Λ to some point of P,

    ii) no pair of points from the interior of P are congruent.

In Figure 4.3 the parallelogram spanned by ω_1, ω_2 is one such fundamental region, whereas the parallelogram spanned by ω_1, ω_3 is another. A natural choice of such a region is given by the *Dirichlet polygon* (see Problem 4.5).

Let us now turn to the study of meromorphic functions on the torus M. By definition

$$(4.14) \qquad \mathcal{M}(M) = \{f \in \mathcal{M}(\mathbb{C}) \mid f(z) = f(z + \omega_1) = f(z + \omega_2)\}$$

where we ignore the function constant and equal to ∞. For the purists, we remark that (4.14) is not an alternative definition but rather a description. These functions are called *doubly-periodic* or *elliptic functions*. First, since M is compact the only holomorphic functions are the constants. Next, we claim that any nonconstant function $f \in \mathcal{M}(M)$ satisfies $\deg(f) \geq 2$. Indeed, suppose $\deg(f) = 1$. Then in the notation of the Riemann-Hurwitz theorem above, $B = 0$ and therefore $1 = g_M = g_{S^2} = 0$, a contradiction. The reader should check that we can arrive at the same conclusion by verifying that

$$(4.15) \qquad \oint_{\partial P} f(z)\, dz = 0$$

which implies that the sum of the residues inside P is zero. Here P is a fundamental region so that f has neither zeros nor poles on its boundary. To obtain a contradiction from (4.15) note that a function f of degree 1 would need to have a unique simple pole in P, for which the integral (4.15) would then give a vanishing residue.

An interesting question concerns the existence of elliptic functions of minimal degree, viz. $\deg(f) = 2$. From the Riemann-Hurwitz formula, any elliptic function f with $\deg(f) = 2$ satisfies $B = 4$ and therefore has exactly four branch points each with valency 2. We shall now present the classical Weierstrass function $\wp$ which is of this type. As we shall see later in this section, all elliptic functions can be expressed in terms of this one function; see Proposition 4.16.

Throughout this section, we shall use meromorphic functions both in terms of the compact surface M, as well as on the plane $\mathbb{C}$. In other words, we invoke the identification (4.14). This should not cause any confusion as it will be clear from the context in which sense we are viewing functions.

In the following proposition we use the term *group of periods* of a function f. This just refers to all $\omega \in \mathbb{C}$ with the property that $f(z+\omega) = f(z)$. It is clear that the periods form a group.

Proposition 4.14. *Let Λ be as in (4.13) and set $\Lambda^* := \Lambda \setminus \{0\}$. For any integer $n \geq 3$, the series*

$$(4.16) \qquad f(z) = \sum_{w \in \Lambda} (z+w)^{-n}$$

defines a function $f \in \mathcal{M}(M)$ with $\deg(f) = n$. Furthermore, the Weierstrass function

$$(4.17) \qquad \wp(z) := \frac{1}{z^2} + \sum_{w \in \Lambda^*} \left[(z+w)^{-2} - w^{-2} \right],$$

is an even elliptic function of degree two with Λ as its group of periods. The poles of $\wp$ are precisely the points in Λ and they are all of order 2.

Proof. If $n \geq 3$, then we claim that

$$f(z) = \sum_{w \in \Lambda} (z+w)^{-n}$$

converges absolutely and uniformly on every compact set $K \subset \mathbb{C} \setminus \Lambda$. It suffices to prove this on the closure of any fundamental region. There exists $C > 0$ such that

$$C^{-1}(|x|+|y|) \leq |x\omega_1 + y\omega_2| \leq C(|x|+|y|)$$

for all $x, y \in \mathbb{R}$. Hence when $z \in \{x\omega_1 + y\omega_2 \mid 0 \leq x, y \leq 1\}$, then

$$|z + (k_1\omega_1 + k_2\omega_2)| \geq C^{-1}(|k_1|+|k_2|) - |z| \geq (2C)^{-1}(|k_1|+|k_2|)$$

provided $|k_1| + |k_2|$ is sufficiently large. Since

$$\sum_{|k_1|+|k_2|>0} |k_1\omega_1 + k_2\omega_2|^{-n} < \infty$$

as long as $n > 2$, we conclude $f \in \mathcal{H}(\mathbb{C} \setminus \Lambda)$. Since

$$f(z) = f(z+\omega_1) = f(z+\omega_2)$$

for all $z \in \mathbb{C} \setminus \Lambda$, it is clear that $f \in \mathcal{M}(M)$. The degree of (4.16) is determined by noting that inside a fundamental region the series has a unique pole of order n.

For the second part, we note that

$$\left| (z+w)^{-2} - w^{-2} \right| \leq \frac{|z||z+2w|}{|w|^2|z+w|^2} \leq \frac{C|z|}{|w|^3}$$

provided $|w| > 2|z|$ so that the series defining $\wp$ converges absolutely and uniformly on compact subsets of $\mathbb{C} \setminus \Lambda$. Clearly, $\wp(z)$ is an even function of z. For the periodicity of $\wp$, note that

$$\wp'(z) = -2 \sum_{w \in \Lambda} (z+w)^{-3}$$

is periodic relative to the lattice Λ. Thus, for every $w \in \Lambda$,

$$\wp(z+w) - \wp(z) = C(w) \quad \forall\, z \in \mathbb{C}$$

with some constant $C(w)$. Expanding around $z = 0$ yields $C(w) = 0$ as desired. Alternatively, one may note that

$$\wp(\omega_1/2) - \wp(-\omega_1/2) = 0$$

whence $C(w) = 0$. $\qquad\qquad\qquad\qquad\qquad\qquad\qquad\qquad\qquad\qquad\qquad\qquad\qquad$ $\square$

Likewise, one shows that

$$\wp'(z) = -2 \sum_{w \in \Lambda} (z+w)^{-3}$$

is an elliptic function with poles of order 3 at all points in Λ.

Another way of obtaining the function $\wp$ is as follows: let σ be defined as the Weierstrass product

(4.18) $$\sigma(z) := z \prod_{w \in \Lambda^*} E_2(z/w)$$

with canonical factors E_2 as in Chapter 2 (see (2.28)). Thus σ is entire with simple zeros precisely at the points of Λ. Consider the logarithmic derivative of σ, i.e.,

$$\zeta(z) = \frac{\sigma'(z)}{\sigma(z)} = \frac{1}{z} + \sum_{w \in \Lambda^*} \left[\frac{1}{z-w} + \frac{1}{w} + \frac{z}{w^2} \right].$$

By inspection, $\wp = -\zeta'$. In particular, $\zeta'(z+w) = \zeta'(z)$ for all $w \in \Lambda$. Integrating, we obtain

$$\zeta(z+w) - \zeta(z) = C(\omega)$$

where the latter represents some constant. In particular,

$$\zeta(z + \omega_j) - \zeta(z) = \eta_j, \qquad j = 1, 2$$

or, in other words,

$$\frac{\sigma'(z+\omega_j)}{\sigma(z+\omega_j)} - \frac{\sigma'(z)}{\sigma(z)} = \eta_j, \qquad j = 1, 2.$$

Integrating this relation implies that

(4.19) $$\sigma(z + \omega_j) = \sigma(z)\, e^{z\,\eta_j + \theta_j}$$

where θ_j is some complex constant. We may read off from (4.18) that $\sigma(z)$ is an odd function. Setting $z = -\omega_j/2$ in (4.19) and using the fact that $\sigma(\omega_j/2) \neq 0$ shows that

$$(4.20) \qquad \sigma(z + \omega_j) = -\sigma(z)\,e^{\eta_j(z+\omega_j/2)}.$$

We shall make use of this relation in the construction of meromorphic functions on the tori (see Theorem 4.17 below).

The Weierstrass $\wp$ function has many remarkable properties, the most basic of which is the following differential equation.

Lemma 4.15. *With $\wp$ as before, one has*

$$(4.21) \qquad (\wp'(z))^2 = 4(\wp(z) - e_1)(\wp(z) - e_2)(\wp(z) - e_3)$$

where $e_1 = \wp(\omega_1/2)$, $e_2 = \wp(\omega_2/2)$, and $e_3 = \wp((\omega_1 + \omega_2)/2)$ are pairwise distinct. Furthermore, one has $e_1 + e_2 + e_3 = 0$ so that (4.21) can be written in the form

$$(4.22) \qquad (\wp'(z))^2 = 4(\wp(z))^3 - g_2\wp(z) - g_3$$

with constants $g_2 = -4(e_1e_2 + e_1e_3 + e_2e_3)$ and $g_3 = 4e_1e_2e_3$.

Proof. In this proof it will be convenient to view the underlying torus as given by

$$S = \{x\omega_1 + y\omega_2 \mid -1/2 \leq x, y < 1/2\}.$$

By inspection,

$$\wp'(z) = -2\sum_{z \in \Lambda}(z + w)^{-3}$$

is an odd function in $\mathcal{M}(M)$. Since it has a pole of order 3 at $z = 0$ but no other poles in the parallelogram S, it follows that $\wp'(z)$ is of degree 3. Thus,

$$\wp'(\omega_1/2) = -\wp'(-\omega_1/2) = -\wp'(\omega_1/2) = 0.$$

Similarly, $\wp'(\omega_2/2) = \wp'((\omega_1 + \omega_2)/2) = 0$. In other words, the three points

$$\frac{1}{2}\omega_1, \quad \frac{1}{2}\omega_2, \quad \frac{1}{2}(\omega_1 + \omega_2)$$

are the three zeros of $\wp'$, each simple, and thus also the unique points where $\wp$ has valency 2 apart from $z = 0$. The e_j are distinct, for otherwise $\wp$ would assume such a value four times in contradiction to its degree being 2.

Denoting the right-hand side of (4.21) by $F(z)$, this implies that

$$\frac{(\wp'(z))^2}{F(z)} \in \mathcal{H}(M)$$

and therefore equals a constant. Considering the expansion of $\wp'(z)$ and $F(z)$, respectively, around $z = 0$ shows that the value of this constant equals 1, as claimed. The final statement follows by observing from the Laurent series around zero that

$$(\wp'(z))^2 - 4(\wp(z))^3 + g_2\wp(z),$$

with g_2 as above, is analytic and therefore equals a constant. $\square$

The values e_1, e_2, e_3 are of great importance. Later in this chapter we will study the ratio

$$\lambda = \frac{e_3 - e_2}{e_1 - e_2}$$

as a function of ω_1, ω_2. It can be easily seen to be a function of ω_1/ω_2, and as such is known as the *modular function*.

The previous proof shows that 0, $\omega_1/2$, $\omega_2/2$, and $(\omega_1 + \omega_2)/2$ are precisely the branch points of $\wp$ in the fundamental region S. We are now able to establish the following property of $\wp$.

Proposition 4.16. *Every $f \in \mathcal{M}(M)$ is a rational function of $\wp$ and $\wp'$. If f is even, then it is a rational function of $\wp$ alone.*

Proof. Suppose that f is nonconstant and even. Then for all but finitely many values of $w \in \mathbb{C}_\infty$, the equation $f(z) - w = 0$ has only simple zeros (since there are only finitely many zeros of f'). Pick two such $w \subset \mathbb{C}$ and denote them by c, d. Moreover, we can ensure that the zeros of $f - c$ and $f - d$ are distinct from the branch points of $\wp$. Thus, since f is even and with $2n = \deg(f)$, one has:

$$\{z \in M \ : \ f(z) - c = 0\} = \{a_j, -a_j\}_{j=1}^n,$$
$$\{z \in M \ : \ f(z) - d = 0\} = \{b_j, -b_j\}_{j=1}^n.$$

The elliptic functions

$$g(z) := \frac{f(z) - c}{f(z) - d}$$

and

$$h(z) := \prod_{j=1}^n \frac{\wp(z) - \wp(a_j)}{\wp(z) - \wp(b_j)}$$

have the same zeros and poles which are all simple. It follows that $g = \alpha h$ for some $\alpha \neq 0$. Solving this relation for f yields the desired conclusion.

If f is odd, then $f/\wp'$ is even so $f = \wp' R(\wp)$ where R is rational. Finally, if f is any elliptic function, then

$$f(z) = \frac{1}{2}\big(f(z) + f(-z)\big) + \frac{1}{2}\big(f(z) - f(-z)\big)$$

is a decomposition into even/odd elliptic functions whence

$$f(z) = R_1(\wp) + \wp' R_2(\wp)$$

with rational R_1, R_2, as claimed. $\square$

For another result along these lines see Problem 4.10. It is interesting to compare the previous result for the tori to a similar one for the simply-periodic functions, i.e., functions on the surface $\mathbb{C}/\langle z \mapsto z+1 \rangle \simeq \mathbb{C}^*$. These can be represented via Fourier series, i.e, infinite expansions in the basis $e^{2\pi i z}$ which plays the role of $\wp$ in this case. Observe the distinction between the *infinite expansions* for the cylinder on the one hand, and the finite ones for tori, on the other hand. This is of course rooted in the fact that the tori are compact whereas $\mathbb{C}^*$ is not.

We conclude our discussion of elliptic functions by turning to the following natural question: given disjoint finite sets of distinct points $\{z_j\}$ and $\{\zeta_k\}$ in M as well as positive integers n_j for z_j and ν_k for ζ_k, respectively, is there an elliptic function with precisely these zeros and poles and of the given orders? We remark that for the case of $\mathbb{C}_\infty$ the answer was affirmative if and only if the constancy of the degree was not violated, i.e.,

$$(4.23) \qquad \sum_j n_j = \sum_k \nu_k.$$

For the tori, however, there is a new obstruction:

$$(4.24) \qquad \sum_j n_j z_j = \sum_k \nu_k \zeta_k \quad (\text{mod } \Lambda).$$

To obtain this relation, we first observe that by the residue theorem one has

$$(4.25) \qquad \frac{1}{2\pi i} \oint_{\partial P} z \frac{f'(z)}{f(z)}\, dz = \sum_j n_j z_j - \sum_k \nu_k \zeta_k$$

where ∂P is the boundary of a fundamental region P as in Figure 4.3 so that no zero or pole of f lies on that boundary. Second, comparing parallel sides of the fundamental region and using the periodicity shows that the left-hand side in (4.25) is of the form $n_1 \omega_1 + n_2 \omega_2$ with $n_1, n_2 \in \mathbb{Z}$ and thus equals 0 in Λ.

Indeed, consider the edges in ∂P given by $\gamma_1(t) := \{t\omega_1 \mid 0 \le t \le 1\}$ and $\gamma_2(t) := \{\omega_2 + (1-t)\omega_1 \mid 0 \le t \le 1\}$, respectively. Note that we have already reversed the orientation of the second relative to the first edge. Using the

ω_2-periodicity of $\frac{f'(z)}{f(z)}$ we infer that

$$\int_{\gamma_1} z \frac{f'(z)}{f(z)}\, dz + \int_{\gamma_2} z \frac{f'(z)}{f(z)}\, dz$$

$$= -\omega_2 \int_{\gamma_1} \frac{f'(z)}{f(z)}\, dz = -\omega_2 \int_{\gamma_1} d \log f(z).$$

The branch of the logarithm here is irrelevant, since the arbitrary constant is differentiated away. Recall that by assumption $f \neq 0$ on the edge along which we are integrating. Using periodicity, we see that f takes the same value at the endpoints of the edge γ_1. In conclusion

$$\omega_2 \frac{1}{2\pi i} \int_{\gamma_1} d \log f(z) \in \omega_2 \mathbb{Z}$$

as desired. The other edge pair gives an element of $\omega_1 \mathbb{Z}$, whence (4.24).

It is a remarkable fact that (4.23) and (4.24) are also *sufficient* for the existence of an elliptic function with precisely these given sets of zeros and poles. Notice that these two conditions can only hold simultaneously if the total degree is two or more.

Theorem 4.17. *Suppose (4.23) and (4.24) hold. Then there exists an elliptic function which has precisely these zeros and poles with the given orders. This function is unique up to a nonzero complex multiplicative constant.*

Proof. Listing the points z_j and ζ_k with their respective multiplicities, we obtain sequences z'_j and ζ'_k of the same length, say n. Shifting by a lattice element if needed, one has

(4.26)
$$\sum_{j=1}^{n} z'_j = \sum_{k=1}^{n} \zeta'_k.$$

Now set

$$f(z) = \prod_{j=1}^{n} \frac{\sigma(z - z'_j)}{\sigma(z - \zeta'_j)}$$

where σ has been defined in (4.18). The function f has the desired zeros and poles. It remains to check the periodicity. This, however, follows immediately from (4.20) and (4.26). $\square$

The reader may be wondering why *elliptic functions* are so-called. Thus, let $0 < a < b$ and suppose we wish to compute the arc-length of a section of the ellipse

$$\frac{x^2}{a^2} + \frac{y^2}{b^2} = 1.$$

Setting $x = a \cos \theta$, $y = b \sin \theta$ where $0 \leq \theta_0 < \theta < \theta_1 \leq \pi$, say, we are thus lead to the integral

$$\int_{\theta_1}^{\theta_0} \sqrt{a^2 \sin^2 \theta + b^2 \cos^2 \theta} \, d\theta = \int_{t_0}^{t_1} \frac{\sqrt{a^2 t^2 + b^2 (1 - t^2)}}{\sqrt{1 - t^2}} \, dt$$

(4.27)
$$= b \int_{t_0}^{t_1} \frac{\sqrt{1 - k^2 t^2}}{\sqrt{1 - t^2}} \, dt$$

$$= b \int_{t_0}^{t_1} \frac{dt}{\sqrt{(1 - k^2 t^2)(1 - t^2)}} - bk^2 \int_{t_0}^{t_1} \frac{t^2 \, dt}{\sqrt{(1 - k^2 t^2)(1 - t^2)}}$$

where we substituted $t = \sin \theta$ and with $k^2 = 1 - a^2/b^2$. In the 19th century evaluating or approximating integrals such as those—aptly named *elliptic integrals*, and classified by Legendre—was intensely researched by Abel, Legendre, Dirichlet, Monge, Dupin, Gauss, Weierstrass, Jacobi, Riemann, just to name a few. The reason for this lies with the perhaps not so surprising fact that many concrete problems in mechanics and geometry involve integrals of this type.

Just to give another example, consider the pendulum equation (with normalized constants) $\ddot{\theta} + \frac{1}{2} \sin \theta = 0$ where θ is the angle between the pendulum and a vertical. The conserved energy is $\dot{\theta}^2 - \cos \theta = E$, which leads to the solution

$$t = t_0 \pm \int \frac{d\theta}{\sqrt{E + \cos \theta}}$$

(4.28)
$$= t_0 \mp \int \frac{du}{\sqrt{(E + u)(1 - u^2)}}.$$

The integrals in (4.27) and (4.28) are examples of expressions of the form

(4.29)
$$\int \sqrt{R(t)} \, dt$$

where $R(t)$ is a rational function. Another rather famous problem which leads to such integrals is the problem of finding the geodesics on a generic triaxial ellipsoid, which occupied many mathematicians and which was eventually solved by Jacobi.

The absolutely remarkable, as well as "abstract", realization that emerged in the 19th century was that the integrals (4.29) are best viewed in the complex domain and, in fact, of the Riemann surface associated with the rational function $R(t)$. What this exactly means will become more transparent in the next chapter. However, let us emphasize at this point that the revolution was to view the endpoints of integration as a function of the integral, rather than the other way around; indeed, the endpoints do not lie in the complex plane as was of course the rule for the longest time, but on possibly different sheets of the surface defined by the integral.

To be more specific, let us solve (4.22) as follows: integrating

$$\frac{d\wp(z)}{\sqrt{4(\wp(z))^3 - g_2\wp(z) - g_3}} = dz$$

where we choose some branch of the root, yields

(4.30)
$$z - z_0 = \int_{\wp(z_0)}^{\wp(z)} \frac{d\zeta}{\sqrt{4\zeta^3 - g_2\zeta - g_3}}.$$

In other words, the Weierstrass function $\wp$ is the inverse of an elliptic integral. The integration path in (4.30) needs to be chosen to avoid the zeros and poles of $\wp'$, and the branch of the root is determined by $\wp'$.

The reader may wish to compare what we have just observed to the fact that

$$\int_{w_0}^{w} \frac{d\zeta}{\sqrt{1 - \zeta^2}} = z - z_0$$

is satisfied by $w = \sin z$ (the restrictions on the path and the choice of branch again being determined appropriately). In other words, we obtain a periodic function with one period, whereas in the more complicated elliptic integral (4.30) we obtain two periods.

In more modern terminology, these integrals need to be viewed as those of differential forms on Riemann surfaces such as the hyper-elliptic ones (see Section 5.6 and Section 6.7). There are two algebraic equations implicit in (4.27) and (4.28):

$$w^2 - (1 - k^2z^2)(1 - z^2) = 0, \quad w^2 - (E + z)(1 - z^2) = 0$$

where $0 < k < 1$, and $-1 < E < 1$. The latter condition means that the pendulum performs the usual motion as in a grandfather clock since $\dot{\theta}$ needs to vanish at the highest points of the pendulum. These equations are closely related from the point of view of Riemann surfaces: indeed, while the first one exhibits four distinct branch points in $\mathbb{C}P^1$, namely $\pm k^{-1}$ and ± 1, the second one exhibits three distinct ones in $\mathbb{C}$, namely $-E, \pm 1$, as well as one at infinity. So they in fact determine isomorphic compact Riemann surfaces which we shall identify in Chapter 5 as a torus. The reader familiar with the Schwarz-Christoffel formula from conformal mapping (see for example (2.30)) may recognize a connection with the elliptic integrals of this section. See Problem 4.14 for more on this topic.

4.7. Covering the plane with two or more points removed

We now provide the details of a construction to which we had alluded in Example 5 of Section 4.2. To be specific, we shall present the standard "geometric" procedure by which the covering map $\pi : \mathbb{D} \to \mathbb{C} \setminus \{p_1, p_2\}$ may be obtained. Here p_1, p_2 are distinct points. This then leads naturally to the "little" and "big" Picard theorems, which are fundamental results of classical function theory.

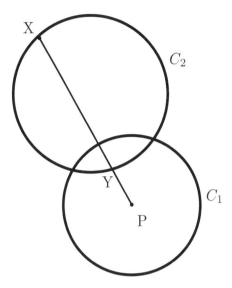

Figure 4.4. Reflection of one circle about another

The construction takes place in the Poincaré disk that we encountered in Chapter 1. We may assume that $p_1 = 0, p_2 = 1$. The main analytical tools we shall rely on are the Riemann mapping theorem and the Schwarz reflection principle (see Problem 2.6). As for the latter, recall from Chapter 1 the reflection about a circle.

Figure 4.4 shows the circle C_2 being reflected about C_1. The configuration is such that C_2 does not pass through the center of C_1, and that it intersects C_1 at a right angle. Since every point of C_1 is fixed, the two intersection points are fixed. Since the angle of intersection is also invariant, we see that C_2 gets mapped onto itself. However, the two arcs of C_2 relative to C_1 are interchanged: the one inside of C_1 is mapped onto the one outside and vice versa.

To construct the map, we start with a triangle Δ_0 inside the unit circle consisting of circular arcs that intersect the unit circle at right angles. In other words, a geodesic triangle in the Poincaré disk with vertices "at infinity" (which means that the interior angles are 0). Now reflect Δ_0 across each of its sides. The result are three more triangles with circular arcs intersecting the unit circle at right angles. Figure 4.5 shows how the unit disk is partitioned by triangles as a result of iterating these reflections indefinitely. To obtain the sought after covering map, we start from the Riemann mapping theorem from Chapter 2 which gives us a conformal isomorphism

$f : \Delta_0 \to \mathbb{H}$, the upper half-plane. We may also achieve that the three vertices of Δ_0 get mapped onto $0, 1, \infty$, respectively. Moreover, the map extends as a homeomorphism to the boundary; see Theorem 2.30. Thus, the three circular arcs of Δ_0 get mapped to the intervals $[-\infty, 0], [0, 1], [1, \infty]$, respectively. By the Schwarz reflection principle (see Problem 2.6) the map f extends analytically to the region obtained by reflecting Δ_0 across each of its sides as just explained above. In this way we obtain a conformal map onto $\mathbb{C} \setminus \{0, 1\}$ which is defined on the entire disk. By construction, it is a local isomorphism and a covering map.

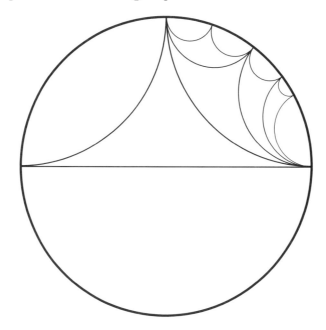

Figure 4.5. Successive reflection of triangles across their sides

If we remove three or more points (but finitely many) from $\mathbb{C}$, then we may apply the same procedure but starting with a polygon instead of a triangle.

The little Picard theorem is an immediate corollary.

Theorem 4.18. *Every entire function which omits two values is constant.*

Proof. Indeed, if f is such a function, we may assume that it takes its values in $\mathbb{C} \setminus \{0, 1\}$. But then we can lift f to the universal cover of $\mathbb{C} \setminus \{0, 1\}$ to obtain an entire function F into $\mathbb{D}$. By Liouville's theorem, F is constant. □

For the relation between the map constructed here and the modular group, we refer the reader to Section 4.8. Another corollary is the following compactness theorem due to Montel. It uses the notion of a *normal family* that we encountered in Chapter 2. Let us recall it: we say that $\mathcal{F} \subset \mathcal{H}(\Omega)$ is **normal** if and only if for every compact $K \subset \Omega$ every sequence in $\mathcal{F}$ has a subsequence which converges uniformly on K. We also allow uniform convergence to ∞. Since we can always pass to finite subcovers of open covers of compact sets we deduce that normality is a *local property*.

Theorem 4.19. *Any family of functions $\mathcal{F}$ in $\mathcal{H}(\Omega)$ which omits the same two distinct values in $\mathbb{C}$ is a normal family.*

Proof. Let $\mathcal{F}$ omit the distinct values $a, b \in \mathbb{C}$. First, passing to $\frac{f-a}{b-a}$ if needed, we may assume that $a = 0$ and $b = 1$. This allows us to pass to the universal cover of $\mathbb{C} \setminus \{0, 1\}$ as before. We may lift $\mathcal{F}$ to another family $\widetilde{\mathcal{F}} \subset \mathcal{H}(\Omega)$, each element of which takes its values in the unit disk. In particular, this family is bounded, and therefore normal. However, it is not immediate that $\mathcal{F}$ inherits the normality. To be specific, let $\{f_n\}_{n=1}^{\infty} \subset \mathcal{F}$ be any sequence and fix some $z_0 \in \Omega$. Passing to a subsequence, we may assume that $f_n(z_0) \to w_\infty \in \mathbb{C}_\infty$. Clearly, the issue is now to distinguish the "degenerate cases" $w_\infty \in \{0, 1, \infty\}$ from the others. Let us start with the latter.

Case 1: $w_\infty \notin \{0, 1, \infty\}$. By normality of $\widetilde{\mathcal{F}}$ we can assume that the lifted sequence converges: $\widetilde{f}_n \to \widetilde{f}_\infty$. Clearly, $|\widetilde{f}_\infty| \leq 1$. If equality is attained here anywhere in Ω, then $\widetilde{f}_\infty$ is a constant of absolute value 1. But then $|\widetilde{f}_n(z_0)| \to 1$ which implies that $f_n(z_0) \to w_\infty \in \{0, 1, \infty\}$—a contradiction. So we see that $|\widetilde{f}_\infty| < 1$ everywhere in Ω. Thus, on any compact $K \subset \Omega$ one has $|\widetilde{f}_n| \leq \gamma(K) < 1$ for all large n where $\gamma(K)$ is some constant. But now we may pass back down from the cover to the twice punctured plane $\mathbb{C} \setminus \{0, 1\}$ to conclude that

$$\sup_K |f_n| \leq M < \infty \quad \text{for all large } n.$$

By the "little Montel theorem" (see Proposition 2.22), we may pass to a uniformly convergent subsequence of $\{f_n\}$ as desired.

Case 2: $w_\infty = 1$. Since f_n misses 0, and we may assume that Ω is simply-connected (a disk, in fact) we may define the square root $g_n = \sqrt{f_n}$. We pick the branch for which $g_n(z_0) \to -1$ as $n \to \infty$. But then g_n misses $0, 1$ and Case 1 applies. Normality of g_n implies that of $f_n = g_n^2$.

Case 3: $w_\infty = 0$. In that case define $g_n = 1 - f_n$, which again misses $0, 1$, and for which we obtain a modified w_∞, denoted by $\widetilde{w}_\infty = 1 - w_\infty = 1$. So the previous case applies.

Case 4: Finally, suppose $w_\infty = \infty$. Then let $g_n = 1/f_n$ which is analytic and misses $0, 1$. Moreover, we obtain a new limit $\widetilde{w}_\infty = 0$ for this modified sequence, and so Case 3 applies. Thus, $\{g_n\}_{n=1}^{\infty}$ is a normal family whence $g_n \to g_\infty$ on a given compact set $K \subset \Omega$. By Lemma 2.20 we further see that $g_\infty \equiv 0$. Indeed, none of the g_n vanishes on Ω and $g_\infty(z_0) = 0$. Thus, we must have $g_\infty = 0$ everywhere. But this means that $f_n \to \infty$ uniformly in compact sets and we are done. $\qquad\square$

Montel's theorem 4.19 is referred to as *fundamental normality test*. Note that this fails for families which omit one value:

$$\mathcal{F} = \{e^{nz} \mid n \in \mathbb{Z}\} \subset \mathcal{H}(\mathbb{C})$$

omits 0 but is not normal. By passing to the Riemann sphere, one can establish similar results for meromorphic functions. One then obtains a normality test for functions which omit three values. As an application of the fundamental normality test, we now prove **Picard's big theorem** which is a substantial strengthening of the Casorati-Weierstrass principle (see Proposition 2.6).

Theorem 4.20. *If f has an isolated essential singularity at z_0, then in any small neighborhood of z_0 the function f attains every complex value infinitely often, with one possible exception.*

Proof. The idea is of course to "zoom into" z_0. By the normality test we may pass to a limit and thus conclude that z_0 is either removable or a pole.

To be specific, let $z_0 = 0$ and define $f_n(z) = f(2^{-n}z)$ for an integer $n \geq 1$. We take n so large that f_n is analytic on $0 < |z| < 2$. Then $f_{n_k}(z) \to F(z)$ uniformly on $1/2 \leq |z| \leq 1$ where either F is analytic or $F \equiv \infty$. In the former case, we infer from the maximum principle that f is bounded near $z = 0$, which is therefore removable. In the latter case, $z = 0$ is a pole. $\qquad\square$

4.8. Groups of Möbius transforms

Automorphism groups of regions Ω in the complex plane, or for that matter of any Riemann surface, are natural objects to study. By automorphism group of course we mean all conformal homeomorphisms from some Riemann surface to itself. Prominent examples are $\mathrm{Aut}(\mathbb{D})$ (see Proposition 1.32) or $\mathrm{Aut}(\mathbb{H}) = \mathrm{PSL}(2, \mathbb{R})$, which are subgroups of $\mathrm{PSL}(2, \mathbb{C})$, the group of all fractional linear transformations. Example 5) from Section 4.2, as well as all of Section 4.5, show the importance of subgroups of $\mathrm{Aut}(\Omega)$ which are free of fixed-points and act *properly discontinuously* on Ω (see, however, Problem 5.8 for a construction in the presence of fixed points).

Let us determine the possible fixed points of elements in $\mathrm{Aut}(\mathbb{D})$. Problem 4.2 shows that this group is precisely given by maps

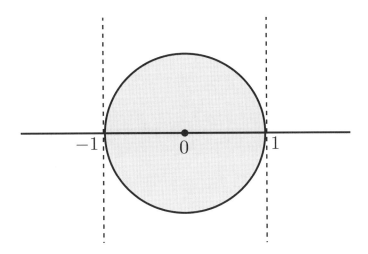

Figure 4.6. SU(1, 1) and fixed points in Aut($\mathbb{D}$)

$$(4.31) \qquad z \mapsto \frac{az + \bar{b}}{bz + \bar{a}}, \qquad a, b \in \mathbb{C}, \quad |a|^2 - |b|^2 = 1.$$

Thus, $|a| \geq 1$. If $|a| = 1$, then $b = 0$ and the map is a rotation about the origin which has precisely two fixed points, $0, \infty$ (unless it is the identity). Figure 4.6 shows the relevant geometry in the a plane. The unit circle is shaded to indicate it needs to be excluded. So let us assume that $|a| > 1$ which means $b \neq 0$. Then the fixed points are given by

$$(4.32) \qquad \zeta_\pm := \frac{i \operatorname{Im} a \pm \sqrt{(\operatorname{Re} a)^2 - 1}}{b}.$$

Note that $|\zeta_+ \zeta_-| = 1$. These points coincide precisely if $|\operatorname{Re} a| = 1$, which also means that
$$|b| = |\operatorname{Im} a|.$$
We may assume that $\operatorname{Im} a > 0$ (since the sign is factored out in (4.31)) and set
$$b = ie^{-i\varphi} \operatorname{Im} a.$$

Thus, $\zeta_\pm = e^{i\varphi}$ is the unique fixed point on the unit circle (the so-called *parabolic case*, cf. Problem 4.3). Next, suppose we are in

Case 1: $|\operatorname{Re} a| > 1$. Then the root in (4.32) is real-valued and $|\zeta_+ \zeta_-| = 1$ implies that $|\zeta_\pm|^2 = 1$. We have a pair of distinct fixed points on the unit circle. Moreover,
$$|\zeta_+ - \zeta_-| = 2\frac{\sqrt{(\operatorname{Re} a)^2 - 1}}{\sqrt{|a|^2 - 1}}$$

which can be anything in the interval $(0, 2]$. The endpoint 2 here means that $\zeta_+ = -\zeta_-$, which happens if and only if $a > 1$ or $a < -1$.

Case 2: $|\operatorname{Re} a| < 1$. Then $\operatorname{Im} a \neq 0$ and one checks by direct calculation that $|\zeta_-| < 1$ if $\operatorname{Im} a > 0$, and $|\zeta_+| < 1$ if $\operatorname{Im} a < 0$, respectively. In other words, if $|\operatorname{Re} a| < 1$, then we always have a fixed point inside of the unit disk, which is not allowed for the purposes of Theorem 4.12.

Conversely, suppose we are given two distinct points $\zeta_\pm$ on the unit circle. One wants to find $a, b \in \mathbb{C}$ so that $\zeta_\pm$ are the fixed points of (4.31). By the above analysis, the condition $|\operatorname{Re} a| > 1$ needs to be true. Setting

$$b = re^{i\varphi} = e^{i\varphi}\sqrt{|a|^2 - 1},$$

and taking into account (4.32), we are first lead to finding $\varphi \in \mathbb{R}$ so that $e^{i\varphi}(\zeta_+ - \zeta_-)$ is real-valued. Then we have

$$e^{i\varphi}\zeta_\pm = \pm\beta + i\alpha$$

with

$$\alpha, \beta \in \mathbb{R}, \quad \alpha^2 + \beta^2 = 1.$$

In fact, one has

$$\alpha = \frac{\operatorname{Im} a}{\sqrt{|a|^2 - 1}}, \quad \beta = \frac{\sqrt{(\operatorname{Re} a)^2 - 1}}{\sqrt{|a|^2 - 1}}.$$

A special case arises when $\alpha = 0, \beta = 1$. In that case, $\zeta_\pm = \pm e^{-i\varphi}$. We again read off from (4.32) that

$$a > 1, \quad b = e^{i\varphi}\sqrt{a^2 - 1}$$

is the 1-parameter subgroup of maps which fix the points $\pm e^{-i\varphi}$ on the unit circle. The case $a = 1, b = 0$ is special, since it corresponds to the identity.

When $|\beta| < 1$, then again from (4.32) one sees that the 1-parameter subgroup which fixes $\zeta_\pm$ is determined by the hyperbola

(4.33) $$\xi^2 - \frac{\beta^2}{1 - \beta^2}\eta^2 = 1, \quad a = \xi + i\eta, \ \xi \geq 1.$$

The reader may want to sketch the location of these hyperbolas in Figure 4.6. The value of b is determined by $b = e^{i\varphi}\sqrt{|a|^2 - 1}$. Moreover, the pair (a, b) is uniquely determined by specifying a point on the hyperbola (4.33); but $(-a, -b)$ generates the same element in $\operatorname{Aut}(\mathbb{D})$.

To the partition of $\mathbb{D}$ generated from one geodesic triangle by successive reflections as in Figure 4.5, we can now associate the subgroup of $\operatorname{Aut}(\mathbb{D})$ that leaves that partition invariant. It is exactly the subgroup that takes the vertices of one geodesic triangle of the partition onto the vertices of another such triangle. Suppose we wish to keep two vertices fixed. As we have just seen there is a 1-parameter subgroup of $\operatorname{Aut}(\mathbb{D})$ that fixes these two points; the one-dimensional freedom corresponding exactly to sending the third vertex to an arbitrary point on the circle, with the exception of the two fixed points. By construction, we are sending that vertex to its reflection across the circular arc whose endpoints are fixed. Similarly, fixing only one point leaves us with two degrees of freedom in $\mathrm{Aut}(\mathbb{D})$ which we use to move the other two vertices.

By means of a fractional linear transformation, we may move our observations about $\mathbb{D}$ to the upper half-plane $\mathbb{H}$. Let us now introduce a special subgroup of $\mathrm{Aut}(\mathbb{H})$, namely $\mathrm{PSL}(2, \mathbb{Z}) \subset \mathrm{PSL}(2, \mathbb{R})$, the so-called **modular group**. We already encountered this subgroup in Section 4.6, where we noted that it is precisely the one which transforms any basis of a lattice Λ into another basis of the same lattice, and which, moreover, preserves the orientation. The role of fractional linear transformations is not immediately apparent here. It arises by the usual change of coordinates associated with an oriented basis (ω_1, ω_2), viz. $z \mapsto \omega_2^{-1} z$. This sends the basis into $(\tau, 1)$ where $\tau = \frac{\omega_1}{\omega_2}$ and the orientation is such that $\mathrm{Im}\, \tau > 0$. So if we pass from a basis (ω_1, ω_2) in Λ to another one, $(\omega_1', \omega_2') := (a\omega_1 + b\omega_2, c\omega_1 + d\omega_2)$, then τ transforms according to

$$(4.34) \qquad \tau' = \frac{a\omega_1 + b\omega_2}{c\omega_1 + d\omega_2} = \frac{a\tau + b}{c\tau + d}.$$

This shows that any two lattices Λ, Λ' whose normalized representations $(\tau, 1)$ and $(\tau', 1)$ are related by (4.34) are conformally equivalent.

Problem 4.9 asks the reader to verify that the converse holds, too. We are thus lead to the problem of understanding the action of $\mathrm{PSL}(2, \mathbb{Z})$ on $\mathbb{H}$. Note that elements of the modular group may have fixed points and thus $\mathbb{H}/\mathrm{PSL}(2, \mathbb{Z})$ is not a Riemann surface (cf. Theorem 4.12); for example, $\begin{bmatrix} 1 & -2 \\ 1 & -1 \end{bmatrix}$ has $1 \pm i$ as fixed points. Using the notation of the theorem, fixed points in Ω of maps in the group G create singularities of Ω/G. This will become clear to the reader after drawing the pictures associated with elliptic fixed points as in Problem 4.3. Nevertheless, this quotient exists as a topological space, in fact, a Hausdorff one provided the action is properly discontinuous—which it is for the modular group.

Examples of maps in $\mathrm{PSL}(2, \mathbb{Z})$ are $z \mapsto -\frac{1}{z}$ and $z \mapsto z + 1$. We shall now show that these maps, which we call S, T, respectively, generate the whole modular group.

Lemma 4.21. *The modular group is generated by S and T.*

Proof. The underlying procedure, which is a form of the Euclidean algorithm, is best demonstrated by means of an example. First, if $Uz = az + b$ lies in the modular group, then we need $a = 1$ and thus $U = T^b$. Consider $Uz = \frac{7z+5}{4z+3}$. We first replace z with $z - 1$. This makes the constant in the

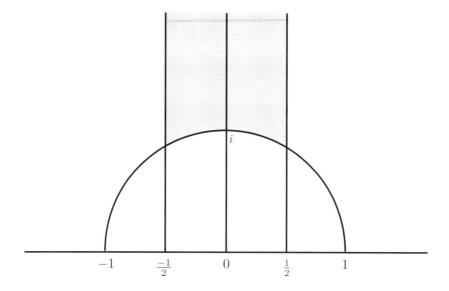

Figure 4.7. The fundamental domain of the modular group

denominator the smallest in absolute value:

$$UT^{-1}z = \frac{7z - 2}{4z - 1}.$$

Next, compose with S:

$$UT^{-1}Sz = \frac{2z + 7}{z + 4}.$$

Translate again to make the constant in the denominator as small as possible:

$$UT^{-1}ST^{-4}z = \frac{2z - 1}{z}.$$

Finally,

$$UT^{-1}ST^{-4}ST^{-2}z = z$$

and we are done.

We leave it to the reader (see Problem 4.16) to show that this algorithm *always* produces the identity in a finite number of steps. The essential ingredient is of course that the determinant is 1 to begin with, and always remains so. Otherwise, we would end up with a transformation of the form $w = nz + m$ with $n, m \in \mathbb{Z}$ but $n \neq 1$ being the determinant we started with.   □

We can now easily describe the fundamental region of the modular group.

Proposition 4.22. *The fundamental region is the one shown in Figure 4.7, i.e., it is bounded by* $\operatorname{Re} z = \pm\frac{1}{2}$, *and the unit circle. In particular, the modular group acts properly discontinuously on* $\mathbb{H}$.

Proof. The map S is the composition of a reflection about the imaginary axis, and an inversion on the unit circle ($z \mapsto 1/\bar{z}$). The shaded region Ω is symmetric with respect to the former, and the latter maps Ω onto a geodesic triangle with one vertex at 0 and with the circular arc remaining fixed. The action of the translations T is clear. It follows that all images of Ω under the modular group tile $\mathbb{H}$ as in Figure 4.7.

It remains to show that no two points in the interior of Ω are mapped onto each other. Thus, let $w = \frac{az+b}{cz+d}$ be *unimodular*, i.e., an element of the modular group.

(1) $c = 0$. Then $w = z + b$ is a translation by an integer and the interior of Ω is mapped outside of itself.

(2) $c = \pm 1$. Then $|w - ac| = 1/|z + d|$ where $a, d \in \mathbb{Z}$. But for $z \in \Omega \backslash \partial\Omega$ we have $|z + d| > 1$ and thus $|w - a| < 1$ whence $w \notin \Omega$.

(3) $|c| \geq 2$. Then $|w - a/c| = 1/(c^2|z + d/c|)$. Now $\operatorname{Im} z > 1/2$ implies

$$1/(c^2|z + d/c|) < 2/c^2 \leq 1/2,$$

which means that $w \notin \Omega$.

This covers all cases and we are done. $\square$

Problem 4.9 asks the reader to apply these observations to the problem of classifying conformally inequivalent tori.

Definition 4.23. A group of Möbius transformations which acts properly discontinuously on a disk and leaves the boundary circle invariant is called a *Fuchsian group*.

The modular group is an example of a Fuchsian group. These groups are of fundamental importance in the classification of Riemann surfaces (see Sections 8.6 and 8.7). Problem 4.6 shows the properly discontinuous action is equivalent to the group being discrete in the natural topology on matrices. Problem 4.7 introduces some elementary geometric properties of Fuchsian groups, namely the existence of a fundamental region, which tessellates the underlying disk under the action of the group. Furthermore, we may choose the boundary to consist of geodesic arcs.

Section 4.6 studied meromorphic functions on tori, whereas here we have been concerned with the symmetries of the tori. We conclude this chapter by exploring a connection between these two points of view. Returning to Lemma 4.15, consider the ratio as a function of the pair (ω_1, ω_2),

$$\lambda := \frac{e_3 - e_2}{e_1 - e_2},$$

which is well-defined and never vanishes since the finite complex numbers e_j are distinct. Inspection of the defining series (4.17) and the definition of e_j in terms of $\omega_1/2, \omega_2/2, (\omega_1 + \omega_2)/2$ shows that λ is in fact a function of $\tau = \frac{\omega_1}{\omega_2}$, analytic in the upper half-plane. Moreover, $\lambda(\tau)$ never assumes the values 0 or 1.

If we replace the basis (ω_1, ω_2) with another one (ω_1', ω_2') by means of a unimodular transformation, then $\wp$ does not change in view of the series expansion (4.17). From the *differential equation* (4.21) we infer therefore that the three points e_j can be at most permuted. If the unimodular transformation satisfies

$$(4.35) \qquad \begin{bmatrix} a & b \\ c & d \end{bmatrix} = \begin{bmatrix} 1 & 0 \\ 0 & 1 \end{bmatrix} \quad \mod 2,$$

then $\frac{1}{2}\omega_j' \equiv \frac{1}{2}\omega_j$ in the lattice for $j = 1, 2$. Thus, the e_j are fixed under such a transformation whence

$$\lambda\left(\frac{a\tau + b}{c\tau + d}\right) = \lambda(\tau)$$

under maps in the subgroup (4.35) known as the *congruence subgroup modulo* 2. In other words, λ is invariant under this subgroup and therefore an example of an *automorphic function* relative to this subgroup (also known as *elliptic modular function*). By direct calculation we find that the entire modular group reduces to the group of six transformations modulo 2:

$$(4.36) \qquad \left\{ \begin{bmatrix} 1 & 0 \\ 0 & 1 \end{bmatrix}, \begin{bmatrix} 1 & 1 \\ 0 & 1 \end{bmatrix}, \begin{bmatrix} 0 & 1 \\ 1 & 0 \end{bmatrix}, \begin{bmatrix} 0 & 1 \\ 1 & 1 \end{bmatrix}, \begin{bmatrix} 1 & 0 \\ 1 & 1 \end{bmatrix}, \begin{bmatrix} 1 & 1 \\ 1 & 0 \end{bmatrix} \right\}.$$

From Lemma 4.21 or otherwise one concludes that this group is generated by the second and third matrices in this list. The second matrix interchanges e_1, e_3 and takes τ to $\tau + 1$. Thus,

$$(4.37) \qquad \lambda(\tau + 1) = \frac{1}{\lambda(\tau)}.$$

Similarly, from the third matrix which corresponds to $z \mapsto -\frac{1}{z}$, we obtain the function equation

$$(4.38) \qquad \lambda\left(-\frac{1}{\tau}\right) = 1 - \lambda(\tau).$$

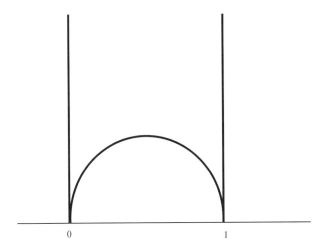

Figure 4.8. The geodesic triangle associated to λ

As far as the action on λ is concerned (meaning the right-hand sides of these relations), the full group in (4.36) generates the so-called *anharmonic group*

$$\Big\{\lambda,\ \frac{1}{1-\lambda},\ \frac{\lambda-1}{\lambda},\ \frac{1}{\lambda},\ \frac{\lambda}{\lambda-1},\ 1-\lambda\Big\}.$$

We leave it to the reader to work out the left-hand sides of the corresponding functional equations. For example, combining (4.37) and (4.38) yields the expression

$$(4.39)\qquad\qquad \lambda\Big(1-\frac{1}{\tau}\Big)=\frac{1}{1-\lambda(\tau)}.$$

Proposition 4.24. *The modular function λ takes the geodesic triangle in $\mathbb{H}$ with vertices $0,1,\infty$ (see Figure 4.8) bijectively onto the upper half-plane. It is continuous on the closure of this triangle and the boundary is mapped to the real axis. The points $0,1,\infty$ are mapped onto $0,\infty,1$, respectively.*

Proof. We may assume that $\omega_1=\tau$ and $\omega_2=1$. Then from (4.17) we conclude that

$$(4.40)\qquad
\begin{aligned}
e_1-e_2 &= \sum_{n,m\in\mathbb{Z}}\Big[\big((n+\tfrac{1}{2})\tau+m\big)^{-2}-\big(n\tau+m+\tfrac{1}{2}\big)^{-2}\Big],\\
e_3-e_2 &= \sum_{n,m\in\mathbb{Z}}\Big[\big((n+\tfrac{1}{2})\tau+m+\tfrac{1}{2}\big)^{-2}-\big(n\tau+m+\tfrac{1}{2}\big)^{-2}\Big].
\end{aligned}$$

These sums are absolutely and uniformly convergent in any region of the form $\operatorname{Im}\tau>\delta>0$. Moreover, we may freely shift n,m by any fixed integer amount without changing anything. The sums are even in τ, thus, they remain the same if we replace τ with $-\tau$. In particular, on $\operatorname{Re} \tau = 0$ these expression are purely real-valued, and so is $\lambda(\tau)$. From (4.37) it follows that the same holds on $\operatorname{Re} \tau = 1$. Similarly, $\tau \mapsto \frac{\tau}{1+\tau}$ takes the upper half-plane to itself and $\operatorname{Re} \tau = 0, \operatorname{Im} \tau > 0$ onto the circular arc in Figure 4.8, and one checks that

$$\lambda\left(\frac{\tau}{1+\tau}\right) = 1 - \frac{1}{\lambda(\tau)},$$

so that the circular arc is indeed mapped onto the real axis again. So care, however, is needed in dealing with the points $0, 1, \infty$ with regard to the series (4.40) (the first two cannot be plugged into these series since it is illegitimate to evaluate them for real τ, whereas ∞ involves an interchange of limits).

Recall (2.24), i.e.,

$$\frac{\pi^2}{\sin^2(\pi z)} = \sum_{n \in \mathbb{Z}} (z-n)^{-2} \qquad \forall\, z \in \mathbb{C} \setminus \mathbb{Z}.$$

Thus,

(4.41)
$$
\begin{aligned}
e_1 - e_2 &= \pi^2 \sum_{n \in \mathbb{Z}} \left[\frac{1}{\sin^2((n+\frac{1}{2})\tau\pi)} - \frac{1}{\cos^2(n\tau\pi)} \right], \\
e_3 - e_2 &= \pi^2 \sum_{n \in \mathbb{Z}} \left[\frac{1}{\cos^2((n+1/2)\tau\pi)} - \frac{1}{\cos^2(n\tau\pi)} \right],
\end{aligned}
$$

and we read off from $n = 0$ that both of these sums converge to $-\pi^2$ as $\operatorname{Im} \tau \to \infty$. This settles the claim that $\lambda(\tau) \to 1$ as $\operatorname{Im} \tau \to \infty$. But by the functional equations for λ the limits $\tau \to 0$ and $\tau \to 1$ along the vertical direction now also follow. This settles all the claims apart from the bijection onto the upper half-plane. The latter follows by means of the argument principle and we leave this to the reader (see Problem 4.11). $\square$

By the proposition, the modular function λ furnishes us with an explicit Riemann map from the geodesic triangle in Figure 4.8 to the upper half-plane. Moreover, if we reflect this map across the imaginary axis by means of Schwarz reflection, then we obtain a map which is a bijection from the union of the two geodesic triangles $\Delta(-1, 0, \infty) \cup \Delta(0, 1, \infty)$ onto $\mathbb{C} \setminus \{0, 1\}$. We have thus carried out an explicit construction of the map which we encountered in Section 4.7 (in the upper-half plane instead of the Poincaré disk, which, however, makes no difference).

Notes

This chapter sets the stage for the remainder of this textbook. Of particular importance is the question about nonconstant global meromorphic functions on any given Riemann surface. As we pointed out by means of the hyper-elliptic curves (which furnish examples of branched cover of the Riemann sphere of genus at least 2), the answer to this question is far from obvious. To appreciate the difficulty, note that branched covers of S^2 of any genus can be constructed by elementary topology, without any reference to complex variables. There is no obvious way of placing a meromorphic function on such an object. We shall devote a substantial part of the remainder of this text to this very question. It naturally leads into Hodge theory, which we develop to the extent needed in this text in Chapter 6.

Radó's countability theorem, which we mentioned after the definition of Riemann surfaces, has an interesting history. Its precursor is the Poincaré-Volterra theorem. This result says that we can only generate countably many different power series with center $z = a$ by all possible analytic continuations from a given one at $z = a$. See Example 7) in Section 4.2 above. For a fascinating account of the history of this result, see the papers [**45**] and [**82**]. These articles further explain the wider context in which the Poincaré-Volterra theorem developed. For example, Poincaré himself regarded Riemann surfaces as more of a heuristic geometric device, invaluable for building intuition and for experimentation, but not rigorous and acceptable for proofs. For rigorous verification he regarded Weierstrass' theory based on power series as the only safe and acceptable method. The paper by Majstrenko [**62**] carries out such a Weierstrassian approach to the Poincaré-Volterra theorem. Today of course this seems strange, but the modern reader needs to keep in mind that the rigorous development of Riemann surfaces and of the concept of a manifold only occurred in the 20th century. See pages 185–190 in Forster's book [**29**] for a modern formulation and proof of both the Poincaré-Volterra and Radó theorems.

Isothermal coordinates, which played a central role in Example 4) of Section 4.2, have been investigated and used in differential geometry since Gauss, who constructed them for analytic metrics. For those metrics we may solve the PDEs (4.5), (4.6), by means of power series; in other words, we can invoke the Cauchy-Kovalevskaya theorem (see Folland's book [**27**], for example). A beautiful timeless paper on the construction of isothermal coordinates for much more general metrics is the one by S. S. Chern [**11**].

Example 6) of Section 4.2 barely scratches the surface. For concrete examples of algebraic curves such as the Fermat curve, rational curves, and conics, cubics, see Walker's book [**85**].

This chapter also has the purpose to place some classical topics such as elliptic functions and the Picard theorems into a more geometric context, rather than including them in Chapter 2, say. Sometimes these results are presented from a purely computational point of view (which is perhaps how they were discovered), without reference to their basic and simple geometrical underpinnings. At least to the author's mind this leads to a substantial loss of transparency.

The classical point of view of Riemann surfaces, which is connected with the practical problem of computing or integrals involving algebraic functions, is beautifully represented in Hancock's timeless book [**41**], as well as Felix Klein's wonderful exposition [**51**]. See, in particular, Article 153 in [**41**] where part of Dirichlet's obituary for Jacobi is reproduced. Dirichlet explicitly writes there that Abel and Jacobi had the fruitful and most important idea to view the integration limits as

function of the elliptic integral rather than the other way around. While sources
such as these are mostly forgotten today, they not only reveal the concrete moti-
vations often deriving from practical problems in mechanics or geometry, but also
present calculations and geometrical arguments which ultimately lead to the modern abstractions.

At least to the author's mind much of the "antiquated" material in [**41, 51**]
has not lost any of its value. It would seem that the student of today, who is,
more often than not, forced to absorb mathematics in the reverse historical order
(for example, by learning complex line bundles and Serre duality without ever being
asked to compute an integral of some algebraic function), would greatly benefit from
occasionally returning to the concrete foundations on which the abstract machinery
was built.

It was mentioned in this chapter that $\mathbb{C}^*, \mathbb{D}^*, \Delta_r$ and $\mathbb{C}/\Lambda$ where Λ is a lattice,
is a complete list of Riemann surfaces whose fundamental group is nontrivial and
abelian. For details about this assertion, see Chapter 8 as well as [**23**], Chapter IV.6.

For more on the fundamental normality test (FNT), and its version for meromorphic functions which involves omitting three values, see Schiff [**74**]. The relation
between constancy of entire functions omitting two values and the FNT, which is
also formulated in terms of omission of two values, is not accidental. The *Bloch
principle* is a general manifestation of this relation; see loc. cit.

Fuchsian and Kleinian groups comprise a large body of mathematics, not to
mention modular and automorphic functions. The problems below introduce the
reader to some easy results on Fuchsian groups, which will play an essential role in
the uniformization theorem; see Chapter 8. Some of the problems below introduce
geometric concepts relevant to the study of these groups, and ask the reader to
verify certain simple properties. An excellent introduction to this topic is the book
by Katok [**50**]. See also Ford's classical but timeless book [**28**].

4.9. Problems

Problem 4.1. Show that all nontrivial discrete subgroups of $\mathrm{Aut}(\mathbb{C})$ *that
have no fixed point* are either $\langle z \mapsto z + \omega \rangle$ with $\omega \neq 0$, or $\langle z \mapsto z + \omega_1, z \mapsto
z + \omega_2 \rangle$ with $\omega_1 \neq 0, \omega_2/\omega_1 \notin \mathbb{R}$.

Problem 4.2. This exercise revisits fractional linear transformations.

(a) Prove that

$$G = \left\{ \begin{bmatrix} a & \bar{b} \\ b & \bar{a} \end{bmatrix} \ : \ a, b \in \mathbb{C}, \ |a|^2 - |b|^2 = 1 \right\}$$

is a subgroup of $\mathrm{SL}(2, \mathbb{C})$ (it is known as $\mathrm{SU}(1, 1)$). Establish the group
isomorphism $G/\{\pm I\} \simeq \mathrm{Aut}(\mathbb{D})$ in two ways: (i) by showing that each
element of G defines a fractional linear transformation which maps $\mathbb{D}$ onto

$\mathbb{D}$; and conversely, that every such fractional linear transformation arises in this way uniquely up to the signs of a, b. (ii) By showing that the map

$$(4.42) \qquad e^{2i\theta} \frac{z - z_0}{1 - \bar{z}_0 z} \mapsto \begin{bmatrix} \dfrac{e^{i\theta}}{\sqrt{1-|z_0|^2}} & \dfrac{-z_0 e^{i\theta}}{\sqrt{1-|z_0|^2}} \\[2mm] -\dfrac{\bar{z}_0 e^{-i\theta}}{\sqrt{1-|z_0|^2}} & \dfrac{e^{-i\theta}}{\sqrt{1-|z_0|^2}} \end{bmatrix}$$

leads to an explicit isomorphism.

(b) We have established in the text that $\mathrm{Aut}(\mathbb{C}_\infty)$ is the group of all fractional linear transformations, i.e.,

$$\mathrm{Aut}(\mathbb{C}_\infty) = \mathrm{PSL}(2, \mathbb{C}) = \mathrm{SL}(2, \mathbb{C})/\{\pm\mathrm{id}\}$$

and that each such transformation induces a conformal homeomorphism of S^2 (indeed, the stereographic projection is conformal). The purpose of this exercise is to identify the subgroup G_{rig} of those transformations in $\mathrm{Aut}(\mathbb{C}_\infty)$ which are *isometries* (in other words, rigid motions) of S^2 (viewing $\mathbb{C}_\infty$ as the Riemann sphere S^2). Prove that

$$G_{\mathrm{rig}} \simeq \mathrm{SO}(3) \simeq \mathrm{SU}(2)/\{\pm I\}$$

where

$$\mathrm{SU}(2) = \left\{ \begin{bmatrix} a & -\bar{b} \\ b & \bar{a} \end{bmatrix} : a, b \in \mathbb{C}, \ |a|^2 + |b|^2 = 1 \right\}.$$

Find the fractional linear transformation which corresponds to a rotation of S^2 of angle $\frac{\pi}{2}$ about the x_1-axis. For the latter recall how we defined the stereographic projection.

(c) Show that the quaternions can be viewed as the four-dimensional real-vector space spanned by the basis

$$e_1 = \begin{bmatrix} 1 & 0 \\ 0 & 1 \end{bmatrix}, \quad e_2 = \begin{bmatrix} i & 0 \\ 0 & -i \end{bmatrix}, \quad e_3 = \begin{bmatrix} 0 & -1 \\ 1 & 0 \end{bmatrix}, \quad e_4 = \begin{bmatrix} 0 & i \\ i & 0 \end{bmatrix},$$

and with the algebra structure being defined via the matrix products of the e_j's (typically, one writes $1, i, j, k$ instead of e_1, e_2, e_3, e_4). Show that in this representation the unit quaternions are nothing but $\mathrm{SU}(2)$ and exhibit a homomorphism Q of the unit quaternions onto the group $\mathrm{SO}(3)$ so that $\ker(Q) = \{\pm 1\}$.

Which rotation does the unit quaternion $\xi_1 + \xi_2 i + \xi_3 j + \xi_4 k$ represent (i.e., what are the axis and angle of rotation)?

Problem 4.3. Show that all Möbius transforms with two distinct fixed points $z_1, z_2 \in \mathbb{C}_\infty$ are of the form

$$(4.43) \qquad \frac{w - z_1}{w - z_2} = K \frac{z - z_1}{z - z_2},$$

where $K \in \mathbb{C} \setminus \{0\}$ is a complex parameter. For the case where $K > 0$ (called *hyperbolic*) demonstrate the action of such a map by means of the family of circles passing through the points z_1, z_2, as well as by means of the orthogonal family of circles.

Do the same when $K = e^{i\theta}$ (called *elliptic*). If K does not fall into either of these classes we call the map *loxodromic*; these maps are compositions of a hyperbolic and an elliptic transformation (with the same pair of fixed points).

The *parabolic* maps are the ones with a unique fixed point, such as translations. Draw figures that demonstrate the action of such maps.

To which of these classes do the maps

$$w = \frac{z}{2z - 1}, \quad w = \frac{2z}{3z - 1}, \quad w = \frac{3z - 4}{z - 1}, \quad w = \frac{z}{2 - z}$$

belong? If $w = \frac{az+b}{cz+d}$ with $ad - bc = 1$, give a criterion in terms of $a + d$ which determines the class. Explain the relation between eigenvalues and eigenvectors of the matrix $\begin{bmatrix} a & b \\ c & d \end{bmatrix}$ on the one hand, and fixed points $w = z$ on the other hand.

Problem 4.4. This problem combines the analysis of fixed points of transformations in $\mathrm{Aut}(\mathbb{D})$ as presented at the beginning of Section 4.8 with the classification given in the previous problem. Show that the maps with one fixed point inside $\mathbb{D}$ are elliptic, those with a unique fixed point on the unit circle are parabolic, and those with two on the circle are hyperbolic. Reformulate also for the upper half-plane, that is, for $\mathrm{Aut}(\mathbb{H})$.

Problem 4.5. Let $\Lambda \subset \mathbb{C}$ be the lattice (i.e., the discrete subgroup) generated by ω_1, ω_2 which are independent over $\mathbb{R}$. Show that the *Dirichlet polygon*

$$\{z \in \mathbb{C} : |z| \leq |z - \omega| \quad \forall\, \omega \in \Lambda\}$$

is a fundamental region.

Problem 4.6. Let $G < \mathrm{PSL}(2, \mathbb{C})$ be a **Fuchsian** group; see Definition 4.23.

- Prove that a Fuchsian group G operating on the upper half-plane $\mathbb{H}$ is the same as a *discrete subgroup* of $\mathrm{PSL}(2, \mathbb{R})$. The topology here is natural one on 2×2 matrices.
- Show further that this discreteness is the same as each point having a locally finite orbit. This means that for every $z \in \mathbb{H}$ the set $\{gz \mid g \in G\}$ interests any compact subset of $\mathbb{H}$ in only finitely many points.

Problem 4.7. Prove the following properties of Fuchsian groups.

- Show that we may assume that the invariant circle is the real line.

- Show that each transformation in G either has a fixed point in $\mathbb{H}$, which is then necessarily elliptic, or a unique one on the line, which is parabolic, or two fixed points on the line which are the hyperbolic. Thus, there can be no loxodromic fixed points (why?).

- Show that G possesses a fundamental region, and that the boundary of any such region consists of a finite or infinite number of congruent curves.

- What can you say about fixed points of maps in G relative to any fundamental region?

- Give several distinct examples of Fuchsian groups (with the line as fixed circle) and of associated fundamental regions. Do these regions always necessarily lie above the real axis?

- Show that we may always select a fundamental region in such a way that the boundary consists entirely of circular arcs whose centers lie on the real axis.

We remark that **Kleinian groups** are those without a fixed circle.

Problem 4.8. Show that the tori $\mathbb{C}/\Lambda_1$ and $\mathbb{C}/\Lambda_2$ for lattices Λ_j, each generated by two $\mathbb{R}$-independent translations, are conformally equivalent if and only if Λ_1 and Λ_2 are conjugate subgroups in $\mathrm{Aut}(\mathbb{C})$.

Problem 4.9. Show that the classes of tori under conformal equivalence can be naturally identified with the Hausdorff space $\mathbb{H}/\mathrm{PSL}(2, \mathbb{Z})$. As usual, by torus we mean $\mathbb{C}/\Lambda$ where Λ is the group generated by two nontrivial translations $z \mapsto z + \omega_j$, $j = 1, 2$, with $\omega_1/\omega_2 \notin \mathbb{R}$.

In particular, we see that each lattice is represented by $\tau = \omega_1/\omega_2$ belonging to the closure of the shaded region shown in Figure 4.7. Show that this representation is unique if we include the portion of the boundary given by $\mathrm{Re}\, z = \frac{1}{2}$ and $|z| = 1$ restricted to $0 \leq \mathrm{Re}\, z \leq \frac{1}{2}$. Show further that to each τ in that region corresponds a choice of two, four, or six bases. Explain the special role of i and $(\pm 1 + i\sqrt{3})/2$.

Problem 4.10. Let $M = \mathbb{C}/\Lambda$ where Λ is the lattice generated by the vectors $\omega_1, \omega_2 \in \mathbb{C}^*$ with $\frac{\omega_1}{\omega_2} \notin \mathbb{R}$. As usual $\wp$ denotes the Weierstrass function on M. Suppose that $f \in \mathcal{M}(M)$ has degree two. Prove that there exists

$$A = \begin{bmatrix} a & b \\ c & d \end{bmatrix} \in \mathrm{SL}(2, \mathbb{C})$$

and $w \in \mathbb{C}$ such that

$$f(z) = \frac{a\wp(z - w) + b}{c\wp(z - w) + d}.$$

Problem 4.11. Finish the proof of Proposition 4.24, i.e., use the argument principle to prove that λ takes the region in Figure 4.8 bijectively onto the upper half-plane. Also, show that the map is monotone along the boundary.

Problem 4.12. Suppose N is a Riemann surface, and let N_1 be a compact manifold with boundary so that $N \subset N_1$ and the closure of N in N_1 is N_1. Thus, for every $p \in \partial N$ there exists a neighborhood U of p in N_1 and a map $\phi : U \to \mathbb{R}_+^2$ such that ϕ takes U homeomorphically onto $\mathbb{D} \cap \{\operatorname{Im} z \geq 0\}$. Moreover, we demand that the transition maps between such charts are conformal on $\operatorname{Im} z > 0$. Prove that then $N_1 \subset M$ where M is a Riemann surface. In other words, N can be extended to a strictly larger Riemann surface.

Problem 4.13. Let M be a compact Riemann surface and suppose $S \subset M$ is discrete. Assume $f : M \setminus S \to \mathbb{C}$ is analytic and nonconstant. Show that the image of $M \setminus S$ under f is dense in $\mathbb{C}$.

Problem 4.14. Prove that the special case of the Schwarz-Christoffel formula (2.30) takes the upper half-plane onto a rectangle. Explain how this fits together with the doubly-periodic elliptic integrals discussed in this chapter.

Problem 4.15. Let M, N be compact Riemann surfaces and suppose

$$\Phi : M \setminus \mathcal{S} \to N \setminus \mathcal{S}'$$

is an isomorphism where $\mathcal{S}, \mathcal{S}'$ are finite sets. Show that Φ extends to an isomorphism from $M \to N$.

Problem 4.16. Provide the details for the general case in Lemma 4.21.

Chapter 5

Analytic continuation, covering surfaces, and algebraic functions

5.1. Analytic continuation

This chapter takes us back to the origins of Riemann surfaces as a way of "explaining" multi-valued functions arising through analytic continuation. As an example, consider the polynomial equation

$$(5.1) \qquad\qquad w^4 - 2w^2 + 1 - z = 0.$$

A special solution is given by $(z, w) = (1, \sqrt{2})$ and near $z = 1$ this gives rise to the function $w_1(z) = \sqrt{1 + \sqrt{z}}$ which solves (5.1); the convention here is that $\sqrt{z} > 0$ if $z > 0$. However, there are other solutions, namely $(z, w) = (1, -\sqrt{2})$ leading to $w_2(z) = -\sqrt{1 + \sqrt{z}}$ as well as $(z, w) = (1, 0)$. The latter formally corresponds to the functions $w(z) = \pm\sqrt{1 - \sqrt{z}}$ which are not analytic near $z = 0$. Thus, $(1, 0)$ is referred to as a branch point and it is characterized as a point obstruction to analytic continuation. The purpose of this chapter is to put this example, as well as all such algebraic equations, on a solid foundation in the context of Riemann surfaces.

Some of the material in this chapter might seem overly "abstract" due to the cumbersome definitions we will have to work through. The reader should therefore always try to capture the simple geometric ideas underlying these notions. To begin with, we define *function elements* or *germs* and their analytic continuations. There is a natural equivalence relation on these function elements leading to the notion of a *complete analytic function*.

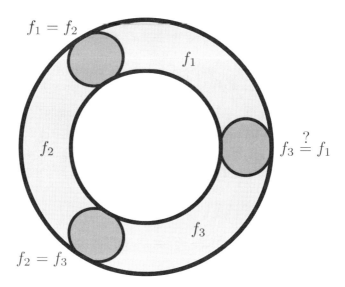

Figure 5.1. Failure of transitivity

Definition 5.1. Let M, N be fixed Riemann surfaces. A *function element* is a pair (f, D) where $D \subset M$ is a connected, open nonempty subset of M and $f : D \to N$ is analytic. We say that two function elements (f_1, D_1) and (f_2, D_2) are *direct analytic continuations* of each other if

$$D_1 \cap D_2 \neq \emptyset, \qquad f_1 = f_2 \ \text{ on } \ D_1 \cap D_2.$$

Note that by the uniqueness theorem on Riemann surfaces there is at most one f_2 that makes (f_2, D_2) a direct analytic continuation of (f_1, D_1). This relation, denoted by $\simeq$, is reflexive and symmetric but not transitive; cf. Figure 5.1. On the other hand, it gives rise to an equivalence relation, denoted by $\sim$, in the following canonical way:

Definition 5.2. We say that two function elements (f, D) and $(g, \widetilde{D})$ are *analytic continuations* of each other if there exist function elements (f_j, D_j), $0 \leq j \leq J$ such that $(f_0, D_0) = (f, D)$, $(f_J, D_J) = (g, \widetilde{D})$, and $(f_j, D_j) \simeq (f_{j+1}, D_{j+1})$ for each $0 \leq j < J$.

The *complete analytic function* of (f, D) is the equivalence class $[(f, D)]_\sim$ of this function element under $\sim$. In this chapter, we denote a complete analytic function by the letter $\mathcal{A}$.

Our main goal for now is to analyze the complete analytic function in more detail. But before doing so, we need to clarify the process of analytic continuation on a Riemann surface some more. In particular, we wish to prove an analogue of the monodromy theorem, Theorem 2.19, for Riemann

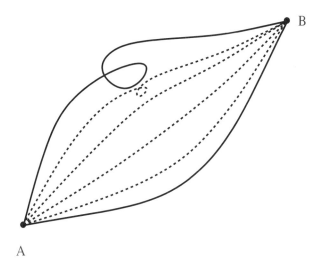

Figure 5.2. A homotopy with fixed endpoints

surfaces. To begin with, we remark that the notion of analytic continuation from Definition 5.2 agrees with analytic continuation along paths.

Lemma 5.3. *Two function elements (f, D) and $(\widetilde{f}, \widetilde{D})$ are analytic continuations of each other in the sense of Definition 5.2 if and only if there exists a continuous path $\gamma : [0, 1] \to M$ connecting a point of D to one of $\widetilde{D}$ with the following property: there exists a partition*

$$0 = t_0 < t_1 < \ldots < t_m = 1$$

so that for each $0 \le i < m$, $\gamma([t_i, t_{i+1}])$ belongs to a single parametric disk of M and analytic continuation relative to each of these local coordinates in the sense of Definition 2.17 leads (necessarily uniquely) from f defined around $\gamma(0)$ to $\widetilde{f}$ defined around $\gamma(1)$.

Proof. This is an immediate consequence of the path-connectedness of M and the uniqueness theorem on Riemann surfaces. If there is such a path γ, then we let the (f_j, D_j) in Definition 5.2 be given by evaluating the analytically continued function along a sufficiently fine net of points on γ. Conversely, connecting points from the sets D_j by continuous paths and partitioning the path into sufficiently many intervals shows that $\widetilde{f}$ is obtained from f via continuation in local coordinates. $\qquad\square$

As a corollary, we now state the monodromy theorem.

Corollary 5.4. *Let $H : [0, 1]^2 \to M$ be a homotopy with fixed endpoints A and B (see Figure 5.2). Suppose (f, D) is a function element with $A \in D$ which can be analytically continued along each path $H(\cdot, s)$ of the homotopy*

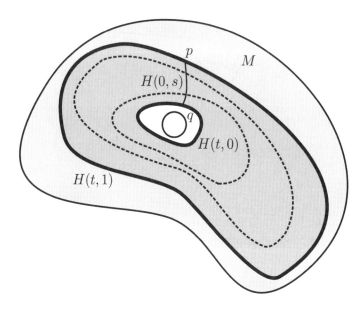

Figure 5.3. A homotopy of closed curves

leading to a function element (g_s, D_s) with $B \in D_s$, $0 \le s \le 1$. Then $g_0 = g_1$ on $D_0 \cap D_1$. If H does not fix endpoints but each path $H(\cdot, s)$ is a closed curve, then the following holds: suppose (f_0, D_0) is a function element with $H(0,0) \in D_0$ which can be analytically continued along $H(0, s)$ yielding function elements (f_s, D_s) with $H(0, s) \in D_s$, $0 \le s \le 1$. Assume further that each (f_s, D_s) can be analytically continued along $H(\cdot, s)$ yielding $(g_s, \widetilde{D}_s)$. If $f_0 = g_0$ on $D_0 \cap \widetilde{D}_0$, then $f_1 = g_1$ on $D_1 \cap \widetilde{D}_1$.

Proof. We begin with the fixed endpoint case. By the previous lemma, analytic continuation can be carried out in local coordinates. More precisely, we can cover each path by parametric disks and analytically continue locally in each of these disks. We can use the same disks as long as we move the parameter s at most by a small amount. But then the analytic continuation does not depend on s since it has the same property in local coordinates. For the closed curves version, we argue analogously, covering by parametric disks and changing s by at most a small quantity. Figure 5.3 explains the meaning of the monodromy statement for closed curves. The short arc connecting p and q is $H(0, s)$ and we are assuming that we are allowed to analytically continue f_s along all curves $t \mapsto H(t, s)$. Observe that if we come back to the same function at p, then we have to come back to the same function at q (see Figure 5.3 for a depiction of such a homotopy). $\square$

The monodromy theorem of course implies that on *simply-connected* Riemann surfaces M any function element (f, D) that can be analytically continued *everywhere on* M defines a global analytic function on M. Another way of arriving at the same conclusion is furnished by the following "sheaf-theoretic" device that can be a useful tool. The logic is as follows: if on a simply-connected Riemann surface we can always glue function elements together locally, then this can also be done globally.

Lemma 5.5. *Suppose M is a simply-connected Riemann surface and*

$$\{D_\alpha \subset M \, : \, \alpha \in A\}$$

is a collection of domains (connected, open). Assume further that these sets form an open cover $M = \bigcup_{\alpha \in A} D_\alpha$ such that for each $\alpha \in A$ there is a family F_α of analytic functions $f : D_\alpha \to N$, where N is some other Riemann surface, with the following properties: if $f \in F_\alpha$ and $p \in D_\alpha \cap D_\beta$, then there is some $g \in F_\beta$ so that $f = g$ near p. Then given $\gamma \in A$ and some $f \in F_\gamma$ there exists an analytic function $\psi_\gamma : M \to N$ so that $\psi_\gamma = f$ on D_γ.

Proof. Let

$$\mathcal{U} := \{(p, f) \, | \, p \in D_\alpha, \, f \in F_\alpha, \, \alpha \in A\}/\sim$$

where $(p, f) \sim (q, g)$ if and only if $p = q$ and $f = g$ in a neighborhood of p. Let $[p, f]$ denote the equivalence class of (p, f). As usual, $\pi([p, f]) := p$. For each $f \in F_\alpha$, let

$$D'_{\alpha, f} := \{[p, f] \, | \, p \in D_\alpha\}.$$

Clearly, $\pi : D'_{\alpha, f} \to D_\alpha$ is bijective. We define a topology on $\mathcal{U}$ as follows: $\Omega \subset D'_{\alpha, f}$ is open if and only if $\pi(\Omega) \subset D_\alpha$ is open. An arbitrary $\Omega \subset \mathcal{U}$ is open if and only if $\Omega \cap D'_{\alpha, f}$ is open for each $\alpha, f \in F_\alpha$. This does indeed define open sets in $\mathcal{U}$: since $\pi(D'_{\alpha, f} \cap D'_{\beta, g})$ is the union of connected components of $D_\alpha \cap D_\beta$ by the uniqueness theorem (if it is not empty), it is open in M as needed. With this topology, $\mathcal{U}$ is a Hausdorff space since M is Hausdorff (we use this if the base points differ) and because of the uniqueness theorem (which we use if the base points coincide). Note that by construction, we have made the fibers indexed by the functions in F_α discrete in the topology of $\mathcal{U}$.

The main point is now to realize that if $\widetilde{M}$ is a connected component of $\mathcal{U}$, then $\pi : \widetilde{M} \to M$ is onto and in fact is a covering map. Let us check that it is onto. First, we claim that $\pi(\widetilde{M}) \subset M$ is open. Thus, let $[p, f] \in \widetilde{M}$ and pick D_α with $p \in D_\alpha$ and $f \in F_\alpha$. Clearly, $D'_{\alpha, f} \cap \widetilde{M} \neq \emptyset$ and since D_α, and thus also $D'_{\alpha, f}$, is open and connected the connected component $\widetilde{M}$ has to contain $D'_{\alpha, f}$ entirely. Therefore, $D_\alpha \subset \pi(\widetilde{M})$ as claimed.

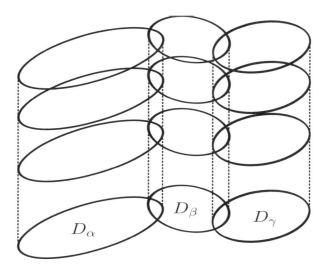

Figure 5.4. Local gluing and simple connectivity implies global gluing

Next, we need to check that $M \setminus \pi(\widetilde{M})$ is open. Let $p \in M \setminus \pi(\widetilde{M})$ and pick D_β so that $p \in D_\beta$. If $D_\beta \cap \pi(\widetilde{M}) = \emptyset$, then we are done. Otherwise, let $q \in D_\beta \cap \pi(\widetilde{M})$ and pick D_α containing q and some $f \in F_\alpha$ with $D'_{\alpha,f} \subset \widetilde{M}$ (we are using the same "nonempty intersection implies containment" argument as above). But now we can find $g \in F_\beta$ with the property that $f = g$ on a component of $D_\alpha \cap D_\beta$. As before, this implies that $\widetilde{M}$ would have to contain $D'_{\beta,g}$ which is a contradiction.

To see that $\pi : \widetilde{M} \to M$ is a covering map, one verifies that

$$\pi^{-1}(D_\alpha) = \bigcup_{f \in F_\alpha} D'_{\alpha,f}.$$

The sets on the right-hand side are disjoint and in fact they are the connected components of $\pi^{-1}(D_\alpha)$.

Since M is simply-connected, $\widetilde{M}$ is homeomorphic to M (see the appendix). We thus infer the existence of a globally defined analytic function which agrees with some $f \in F_\alpha$ on each D_α. By picking the connected component that contains any given $D'_{\alpha,f}$ one can fix the "sheet" locally on a given D_α. $\qquad\square$

The reader should try to apply this proof to the case where $M = \mathbb{C}^*$, D_α are all possible disks in $\mathbb{C}^*$, and F_α all possible branches of the logarithm on the disk D_α. What are all possible $\widetilde{M}$ here, and is π still a covering map?

Arguments as in the previous lemma are powerful and allow one to base the theory of analytic continuations, and thus the constructions of the following section, entirely on the theory of covering spaces (for example, the monodromy theorem then becomes the well-known invariance of lifts under homotopies). Instead of using indirect arguments based on these "sheaves", the author has chosen to follow the more direct traditional approach based on analytic continuation along curves.

5.2. The unramified Riemann surface of an analytic germ

Heuristically, we can regard the complete analytic function from Definition 5.2 as an analytic function F defined on a new Riemann surface $\widetilde{M}$ as follows: writing

$$[(f, D)]_{\sim} = \{(f_{\alpha}, D_{\alpha}) \mid \alpha \in \mathcal{A}\},$$

we regard each D_{α} as distinct from any other D_{β} with $\beta \neq \alpha$, even if $D_{\alpha} = D_{\beta}$. We slightly abuse notation in this section by denoting the complete analytic function as well as the index set by $\mathcal{A}$. Next, define $f = f_{\alpha}$ on D_{α}. Finally, identify $p \in D_{\alpha}$ with $q \in D_{\beta}$ if and only if (i) $p = q$ when considered as points in M and (ii) $f_{\alpha} = f_{\beta}$ near p. In other words, we let the functions label the points and only identify if we have local agreement. This is precisely the "naive" way in which we picture the Riemann surfaces of $\log z$, $\sqrt{z}$, etc.

In the following lemma, we prove that this construction does indeed give rise to a Riemann surface $\widetilde{M}$ and a function defined on it. Throughout, M, N will be fixed Riemann surfaces and any function element and complete analytic function will be defined relative to them.

Lemma 5.6. *Any complete analytic function $\mathcal{A}$ as defined above satisfies the following properties:*

(a) Given a complete analytic function $\mathcal{A}$ and $p \in M$, we define an equivalence relation $\sim_p$ on function elements in

$$\{(f, D) \in \mathcal{A} \mid p \in D\}$$

as follows:

$$(f_0, D_0) \sim_p (f_1, D_1) \iff f_0 = f_1 \quad near \ p.$$

We define $[f, p]$ to be the equivalence class of (f, D), $p \in D$ under $\sim_p$ and call this a germ. *Then the germ $[f, p]$ uniquely determines three objects: the point p, the value $f(p)$, and the complete analytic function $\mathcal{A}$.*

(b) Let $[f_0, p_0]$ be a germ and let $\mathcal{A} = \mathcal{A}(f_0, p_0)$ be the associated complete analytic function. Define

$$\mathcal{RS}(M, N, f_0, p_0) = \{[f, p] \mid p \in D, \ (f, D) \in \mathcal{A}\}$$

and endow this set with a topology as follows: the base for the topology is

$$[f, D] = \{[f, p] \mid p \in D\}, \quad (f, D) \in \mathcal{A}.$$

With this topology, $\mathcal{R}S(M, N, f_0, p_0)$ is a two-dimensional, arcwise connected, Hausdorff manifold with a countable base for the topology.

(c) On $\mathcal{R}S(M, N, f_0, p_0)$ there are two natural maps: the first is the canonical map $\pi : \mathcal{R}S(M, N, f_0, p_0) \to M$ defined by $\pi([f, p]) = p$. The second is the analytic continuation of (f_0, p_0), denoted by F, and defined as $F([f, p]) = f(p)$. The map π is a local homeomorphism and thus defines a complex structure on $\mathcal{R}S(M, N, f_0, p_0)$ which renders π a local conformal isomorphism. Hence $\mathcal{R}S = \mathcal{R}S(M, N, f_0, p_0)$ is a Riemann surface, called the unramified Riemann surface *of the germ $[f_0, p_0]$ and F is an analytic function $\mathcal{R}S \to N$.*

Proof. (a) It is clear that the germ determines p as well as the Taylor series at p.

(b) M is arcwise connected and $\mathcal{R}S(M, N, f_0, p_0)$ is obtained by analytic continuation along curves—so it, too, is arcwise connected. If two points $[f, p]$ and $[g, q]$ in $\mathcal{R}S(M, N, f_0, p_0)$ satisfy $p \neq q$, then invoke the property that the base M is a Hausdorff space. If $p = q$, then the germs are distinct and can thus be separated by open connected neighborhoods via the uniqueness theorem. For the countable base, use that M satisfies this and check that only countably many paths are needed to analytically continue a germ.

(c) The statements regarding π and F are tautologically true by construction. $\qquad\square$

The map π in part (c) does not need to be onto. Indeed, suppose some analytic function $f \in \mathcal{H}(\mathbb{D})$ cannot be analytically continued to any larger region than $\mathbb{D}$. In that case, $\mathcal{R}S(\mathbb{C}, \mathbb{C}, f, 0) = \mathbb{D}$, $\pi(z) = z$ and $F = f$. As another example, consider the function elements given by $\log z$ or $z^{\frac{1}{n}}$ with integer $n > 1$ on a neighborhood of $z = 1$. Then we cannot analytically continue into $z = 0$ which leads us to the notion of a "branch point" of the Riemann surface constructed in the previous lemma. We remark that these two classes of examples (logarithms and roots) are representative of all possible types of branch points and that in the case of the roots there is a way to adjoin the branch point to $\mathcal{R}S(M, N, f_0, p_0)$ and to make it "essentially disappear" (see the following section).

Definition 5.7. Let (U, ϕ) be a chart at $p_1 \in M$ with $\phi(p_1) = 0$, $\phi(U) = \mathbb{D}$. Let $[f, p] \in \mathcal{R}S(M, N, f_0, p_0)$ with $p \in U \setminus \{p_1\}$. If $[f, p]$ can be analytically continued along every path in $U \setminus \{p_1\}$ but not into p_1 itself, then we say that

$\mathcal{RS}(U, N, f, p)$ represents a *branch point* of $\mathcal{RS} = \mathcal{RS}(M, N, f_0, p_0)$ rooted at p_1.

By a *branch point* $\mathfrak{p}_1$ rooted at $p_1 \in M$ we mean an equivalence class as follows: suppose $\mathcal{RS}(U, N, f, p)$ and $\mathcal{RS}(V, N, g, q)$ each represent a branch point of $\mathcal{RS}$ rooted at p_1. We say that they are equivalent if there is another such $\mathcal{RS}(W, N, h, r)$ with

$$\mathcal{RS}(W, N, h, r) \subset \mathcal{RS}(U, N, f, p) \cap \mathcal{RS}(V, N, g, q).$$

The reader should convince himself or herself that $\mathcal{RS}(U, N, f, p)$ is not necessarily the same as $\pi^{-1}(U)$ (it can be smaller; see Figure 5.6). This is why we need to distinguish between $\mathfrak{p}_1$ and its root p_1 in M. We now define the *branching number* at a branch point.

Definition 5.8. Let $p_1 \in M$ be the root of some branch point $\mathfrak{p}_1$ and pick a representative $\mathcal{RS}(U, N, f, p)$ from the equivalence class of surfaces representing this branch point $\mathfrak{p}_1$ as explained above. Let $\phi(U) = \mathbb{D}$, $\phi(p_1) = 0$ be a chart and let $\alpha(t) = \phi^{-1}(\phi(p)e^{2\pi i t})$ be a closed loop in U around p_1. Then we let $[f_n, p]$ be the germ obtained by analytic continuation of $[f, p]$ along $\alpha^n = \alpha \circ \ldots \circ \alpha$ (n-fold composition), $n \geq 1$. We define the *branching number* at $\mathfrak{p}_1$ to be

$$(5.2) \qquad B(\mathfrak{p}_1) := \begin{cases} \infty & \text{if } [f_n, p] \neq [f, p] \quad \forall\, n \geq 1, \\ \min\{n \geq 1 \mid [f_n, p] = [f, p]\} - 1 & \text{otherwise.} \end{cases}$$

If $B(\mathfrak{p}_1) = \infty$, then we say that $\mathfrak{p}_1$ is a *logarithmic* branch point.

The reason for subtracting 1 in the second line of (5.2) lies with branching number 0: in that case one returns to the same function after one loop. In other words, there is no branching associated to branching number 0. Figure 5.5 is a schematic view of a branch point with branching number equal to two. We now need to check that these notions are well-defined. In what follows, we shall freely use the simple fact that the winding number characterizes equivalence classes of homotopic loops in $\mathbb{D}^*$.

Lemma 5.9. *The branch number introduced in the previous definition is well-defined, i.e., it does not depend on the representative $\mathcal{RS}(U, N, f, p)$. Further, if $\mathcal{RS}(U, N, f, p)$ is a representative of the branch point $\mathfrak{p}_1$ rooted at p_1, then the following holds: let γ be a closed loop in $U \setminus \{p_1\}$. Then $[f, p]$ is invariant under analytic continuation along γ if and only if*

$$B(\mathfrak{p}_1) + 1 \quad \text{divides the winding number} \quad n(\phi \circ \gamma; 0).$$

Proof. Suppose $\mathcal{RS}(U, N, f, p)$ and $\mathcal{RS}(V, N, g, q)$ are equivalent in the sense of Definition 5.7. Then there exists $\mathcal{RS}(W, N, h, r)$ with

$$\mathcal{RS}(W, N, h, r) \subset \mathcal{RS}(U, N, f, p) \cap \mathcal{RS}(V, N, g, q).$$

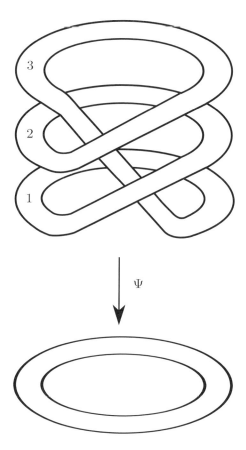

Figure 5.5. A schematic depiction of a uniformizing chart at a branch point with branching number 2

In particular, the germ $[h, r]$ is an analytic continuation of $[f, p]$ as well as $[g, q]$ along paths in $U \setminus \{p\}$ and $V \setminus \{q\}$, respectively. Let α be the closed loop from Definition 5.8 for U, β be the one for V, and γ the one for W. Since the winding number classifies homotopy classes of closed curves in the punctured disk, we see that $\alpha \sim_{U^*} \gamma$ in the sense of homotopy relative to $U^* := U \setminus \{p_1\}$, as well as $\beta \sim_{V^*} \gamma$ relative to $V^* := V \setminus \{p_1\}$. By the closed-curve version of the monodromy theorem (see Corollary 5.4), we conclude that $[f, p]$ and $[h, r]$ yield the same number in (5.2) and by the same token, also $[g, q]$ and $[h, r]$ do. It therefore follows that $B(\mathfrak{p}_1)$ is well-defined on the equivalence class defining the branch point.

For the final statement, suppose $n_0 := B(\mathfrak{p}_1) + 1$ does not divide $n(\phi \circ \gamma; 0)$. Then

$$n(\phi \circ \gamma; 0) = k n_0 + r_0, \qquad 0 < r_0 < n_0.$$

Since a loop of winding number kn_0 brings $[f, p]$ back to itself, this implies that there exists a loop of winding number r_0 which does so, too. But this contradicts (5.2) and we are done. □

5.3. The ramified Riemann surface of an analytic germ

We now show that at each branch point $\mathfrak{p}_1$ of $\mathcal{RS}$ with $B(\mathfrak{p}_1) < \infty$ and for every representative $\mathcal{RS}(U) = \mathcal{RS}(U, N, f, p)$ of $\mathfrak{p}_1$ there exists a chart Ψ defined globally on $\mathcal{RS}(U)$ (known as *uniformizing variable*) which maps $\mathcal{RS}(U)$ biholomorphically onto $\mathbb{D}^*$. The construction is natural and proceeds as follows:

Lemma 5.10. *With $\mathcal{RS}(U, N, f, p)$ representing a branch point, let*

$$\phi : U \to \mathbb{D}$$

be a chart that takes $p_1 \mapsto 0$. Pick a path γ that connects $[f, p]$ with an arbitrary $[g, q] \in \mathcal{RS}(U)$, and pick a branch ρ_0 of the nth root $z^{\frac{1}{n}}$ locally around $z_0 = \phi(p)$; $n := B(\mathfrak{p}_1) + 1$. Now continue the germ $[\rho_0, z_0]$ analytically along the path $\phi \circ \pi \circ \gamma$ to a germ $[\rho_\gamma, z]$ where $z = \phi(q)$. Define

$$\Psi([g, q]) = \rho_\gamma(z).$$

The map Ψ, once ρ_0 has been selected, is well-defined. Moreover, Ψ is analytic, and a homeomorphism onto $\mathbb{D}^*$.

Proof. First, we check that the choice of γ does not affect Ψ. Let $\widetilde{\gamma}$ be another path connecting $[f, p]$ with $[g, q] \in \mathcal{RS}(U)$. As usual, $\widetilde{\gamma}^-$ is the reversed path and $\gamma\widetilde{\gamma}^-$ is the composition. By construction, analytically continuing $[f, p]$ along $\pi \circ \gamma\widetilde{\gamma}^-$ then leads back to $[f, p]$. This implies that $\phi \circ \pi \circ \gamma\widetilde{\gamma}^-$ has winding number around zero which is divisible by n (for otherwise we could obtain a smaller integer in (5.2) by division). Therefore, $[\rho_0, z_0]$ is invariant under analytic continuation along $\phi \circ \pi \circ \gamma\widetilde{\gamma}^-$; in other words, $\rho_\gamma(z) = \rho_{\widetilde{\gamma}}(z)$ as was to be shown. This also shows that Ψ is analytic since π is a local homeomorphism as well as an analytic map. Ψ is onto $\mathbb{D}^*$ by our standing assumption that analytic continuation can be performed freely in U^*. Finally, we need to check that Ψ is one-to-one. Suppose $\Psi([g_1, q_1]) = \Psi([g_2, q_2])$. Then $\Psi([g_1, q_1])^n = \Psi([g_2, q_2])^n$ which means that $\phi(q_1) = \phi(q_2)$ and thus $q_1 = q_2$. By construction, $\Psi([g_j, q_j]) = \rho_{\gamma_j}(z)$ where $z = \phi(q_1)$. Since Ψ was obtained as the analytic continuation of a branch of $z^{\frac{1}{n}}$ along $\phi \circ \pi \circ \gamma$, it follows that

$$n(\phi \circ \pi \circ \gamma_1\gamma_2^- \,; 0) = kn, \quad k \in \mathbb{Z}.$$

But then $[g_1, q_1] = [g_2, q_2]$ by (5.2) and we are done. □

The most fundamental example in this context is given by the roots, which give rise to the Riemann surfaces

$$\mathcal{RS}(\mathbb{C}, \mathbb{C}, z^{\frac{1}{n}}, 1),$$

for which one has $\Psi^{-1}(z) = z^n$. Obviously, in that case $(\Psi^{-1}(z))^{\frac{1}{n}} = (z^n)^{\frac{1}{n}} = z$ for all $z \in \mathbb{D}^*$. The point of our discussion here is that locally at a branch point with finite branching number $n-1$ *any* unramified Riemann surface behaves the same as the nth root. And, moreover, adjoining the branch point $\mathfrak{p}_1$ to the unramified surface yields another Riemann surface with a chart around $\mathfrak{p}_1$ that maps a neighborhood biholomorphically onto $\mathbb{D}$. This is relevant from the point of view of analytically continuing the global function F into a branch point by means of the chart Ψ. This can indeed be done, at least in the algebraic case to which we now turn.

Definition 5.11. Given an unramified Riemann surface $\mathcal{RS}$, we define the *ramified Riemann surface* by adjoining all algebraic branch points to $\mathcal{RS}$. The latter are defined as being precisely those branch points with finite branching number so that F (relative to the uniformizing variable Ψ) has a removable singularity at zero, i.e., $F \circ \Psi^{-1} : \mathbb{D}^* \to N$ extends to an analytic function $\mathbb{D} \to N$.

An example of a nonalgebraic branch point with finite branching number is

$$\mathcal{RS}(\mathbb{C}_\infty, \mathbb{C}_\infty, \exp(z^{\frac{1}{2}}), 1).$$

Note that $z = 0$ is the root of an algebraic branch point (set $z = \zeta^2$ which yields e^ζ) whereas $z = \infty$ is not algebraic since $z = \zeta^{-2}$ with ζ near zero leads to $e^{\zeta^{-1}}$ which has an essential singularity at $\zeta = 0$.

We can now state precisely how to define the ramified Riemann surface.

Lemma 5.12. *Let $\mathcal{P}_{\text{al}}$ be the set of algebraic branch points of $\mathcal{RS}(M, N, f_0, p_0)$ and define*

$$\widetilde{\mathcal{RS}} = \widetilde{\mathcal{RS}}(M, N, f_0, p_0) := \mathcal{RS}(M, N, f_0, p_0) \cup \mathcal{P}_{\text{al}}.$$

Then $\widetilde{\mathcal{RS}}$ is canonically a Riemann surface to which π and F have analytic continuations $\widetilde{\pi} : \widetilde{\mathcal{RS}} \to M$, and $\widetilde{F} : \widetilde{\mathcal{RS}} \to N$, respectively. We call $\widetilde{\mathcal{RS}}$ the ramified Riemann surface *(or just Riemann surface), and $\widetilde{F}$ the complete analytic function of the germ $[f_0, p_0]$. At each $\mathfrak{p} \in \mathcal{P}_{\text{al}}$ the branching number $B(\mathfrak{p}) = \nu(\widetilde{\pi}, \mathfrak{p}) - 1$ where ν is the valency as defined earlier (see Definition 5.8).*

Proof. This is an immediate consequence of the preceding results and definitions, in particular, of Lemma 5.10. $\qquad\square$

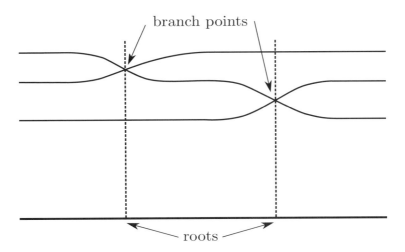

Figure 5.6.   Three sheets

We shall discuss numerous examples throughout this chapter. At this point, we invite the reader to picture the ramified Riemann surface of $\sqrt{z}$ over $M = S^2$. Identify 0 with the north pole and ∞ with the south pole, respectively. We then place a cut from one pole to another as required by analytic continuation. Two copies of these cut spheres are then glued together along the cuts representing the fact that we pass from one sheet to another as we cross the cut. However, the resulting surface is just another sphere: to see this, we deform the cut sphere until it becomes a hemisphere; glue two such hemispheres together along their equators gives a complete sphere.

The term "complete analytic function" had been introduced previously for the collection of all function elements obtained via analytic continuation from a given one (see Example 7) in Section 4.2. However, from now on we shall use this term exclusively in the new sense. Next, we turn to the special case where the Riemann surface is compact.

Lemma 5.13. *If $\widetilde{\mathcal{RS}} = \widetilde{\mathcal{RS}}(M, N, f_0, p_0)$ is compact, then M is compact. Moreover, there can only be finitely many branch points in $\mathcal{RS}$; we denote the set of their projections onto M by $\mathcal{B}$ and define $\mathcal{P} := \widetilde{\pi}^{-1}(\mathcal{B})$. The map $\widetilde{\pi}_1 : \widetilde{\mathcal{RS}} \setminus \mathcal{P} \to M \setminus \mathcal{B}$ (the restriction of $\widetilde{\pi}$ to $\widetilde{\mathcal{RS}} \setminus \mathcal{P}$) is a covering map and the number of pre-images of this restricted map is constant; this is called the number of sheets of $\widetilde{\mathcal{RS}}$ and it equals the degree of $\widetilde{\pi}$. Finally, the following Riemann-Hurwitz type relation holds:*

$$(5.3) \qquad g_{\widetilde{\mathcal{RS}}} = 1 + S(g_M - 1) + \frac{1}{2}\sum_{\mathfrak{p}} B(\mathfrak{p}),$$

where $g_{\widetilde{\mathcal{RS}}}, g_M$ are the respective genera, S is the number of sheets of $\widetilde{\mathcal{RS}}$, and the sum runs over the branch points $\mathfrak{p}$ in $\mathcal{RS}$ with $B(\mathfrak{p})$ being their respective branching numbers.

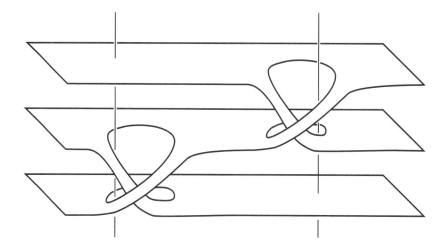

Figure 5.7. A three-dimensional rendition of the previous figure

Proof. It is clear from the compactness of $\widetilde{\mathcal{RS}}$ that there can be only finitely many branch points. Note that $\mathcal{RS}\backslash\mathcal{P} = \widetilde{\mathcal{RS}}\backslash\mathcal{P}$ and $\widetilde{\pi}_1 : \mathcal{RS}\backslash\mathcal{P} \to M\backslash\mathcal{B}$ is a local homeomorphism which is also proper; i.e., the pre-images of compact sets in $M \setminus \mathcal{B}$ are compact. This then easily implies that $\widetilde{\pi}$ restricted to $\widetilde{\mathcal{RS}} \setminus \mathcal{P}$ is a covering map. Figures 5.6 and 5.7 are a schematic depiction of a three-sheeted surface with two (finite) branch points. Observe that $\mathcal{RS} \neq \widetilde{\mathcal{RS}} \setminus \mathcal{P}$ in that case due to the fact that there are unbranched sheets covering the roots of branch points. It is clear that the cardinality of the fibers equals the degree of $\widetilde{\pi}$. Finally, the Riemann-Hurwitz relation follows from the general Riemann-Hurwitz formula (4.11) applied to $\widetilde{\pi}$. $\square$

We remark that $\widetilde{\pi}$ is what one calls a **branched covering map**.

5.4. Algebraic germs and functions

So far, our exposition has been general in the sense that no particular kind of function element was specified to begin with. This will now change as we turn to a more systematic development of the ramified Riemann surfaces of **algebraic functions**. For example, consider the ramified Riemann surface $\widetilde{\mathcal{RS}}$ of $\sqrt{(z - z_1) \cdots (z - z_m)}$ where $z_j \in \mathbb{C}$ are distinct points (it is easy to see that $\widetilde{\mathcal{RS}}$ is compact; see below). In our notation, we are looking at

$$\widetilde{\mathcal{RS}}(\mathbb{C}_\infty, \mathbb{C}_\infty, \sqrt{(z - z_1) \cdots (z - z_m)}, z_0), \qquad z_0 \neq z_j \quad \forall\, 1 \leq j \leq m$$

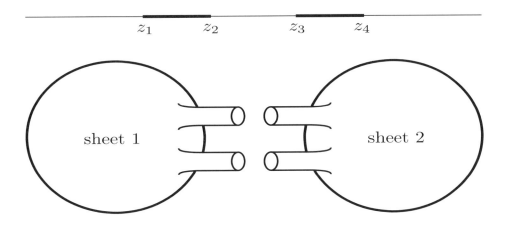

$$z_1 \qquad z_2 \qquad\qquad z_3 \qquad z_4$$

Figure 5.8. The case $m = 2$ with genus 1

and with one of the two branches of the square root fixed at z_0. What is the genus of $\widetilde{\mathcal{RS}}$? If m is even, then $\mathcal{RS}$ has $M = m$ branch points, and if m is odd, then it has $M = m+1$ branch points (the point at ∞ is a branch point in that case). In all cases, the branching numbers are one. The number of sheets is $S = 2$. Hence in view of (5.3),

$$g_{\widetilde{\mathcal{RS}}} = \frac{M}{2} - 1.$$

In other words, the Riemann surface is a sphere with $\frac{M}{2} - 1$ handles attached. This can also be seen directly, by cutting the Riemann sphere along $[z_1, z_2]$, $[z_3, z_4], \ldots, [z_{m-1}, z_m]$ (if m is even). Then the surface consists of two copies of the Riemann sphere glued together along these edges which results in genus $\frac{m}{2} - 1$ as claimed.

The reason for this cutting is of course to allow for the transition from one sheet to the other as we continue analytically along a small loop centered at one of the z_j. Observe that we skipped the cut $[z_2, z_3]$ above since analytic continuation along a loop surrounding the pair z_1, z_2 but encircling none of the other branch points does not change the sheet.

If m is odd, then we also need to introduce a cut from z_m to ∞. For the case of $m = 2$ it is possible to make all of this explicit. Indeed, setting $z = \frac{1}{2}(\zeta + \zeta^{-1})$ (this is the *Jukowski map* from Problem 1.10) yields

$$(5.4) \qquad\qquad \sqrt{(z-1)(z+1)} = \frac{1}{2}(\zeta - \zeta^{-1})$$

where we have made a choice of branch of the square root.

Since the right-hand side of (5.4) is analytic as a map from $\mathbb{C}_\infty$ to itself, we see immediately that the Riemann surface of the left-hand side is the Riemann sphere; cf. Figure 5.9. Moreover, in the ζ plane, the two sheets of

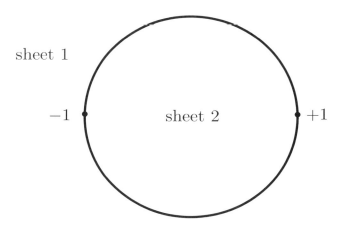

Figure 5.9. The Riemann surface of $\sqrt{z^2 - 1}$ via the Jukowski map as a global uniformizing map

the Riemann surface of $\sqrt{z^2 - 1}$ correspond precisely to the regions $\{|\zeta| < 1\}$ and $\{|\zeta| > 1\}$, respectively. Recall that $\zeta \mapsto z$ is a conformal isomorphism from each of these regions onto $\mathbb{C} \setminus [-1, 1]$ with $\{|z| = 1\}$ mapped onto $[-1, 1]$. More precisely, $z = \pm 1$ are mapped onto ± 1, respectively, whereas each point $z \in (-1, 1)$ is represented exactly twice in the form $z = \cos(\theta)$, $0 < |\theta| < \pi$. Moreover, $z'(\zeta) = \frac{1}{2}(1 - \zeta^{-2}) = 0$ exactly at $\zeta = \pm 1$ and $\zeta''(\zeta) \neq 0$ at these points, which corresponds precisely to the simple branch points rooted at $z = \pm 1$.

This example serves to illustrate the uniformizing charts from Lemma 5.10: at a branch point the ramified Riemann surface looks like every other point in the plane. Finally, note that the map $\zeta \mapsto \zeta^{-1}$ switches these two sheets and also changes the sign in (5.4) which needs to happen given the two different signs of the square root. Clearly, the genus is zero; see also Figure 5.10.

Another example of an algebraic function is furnished by the ramified Riemann surface generated by any root of $P(x, z) = w^3 - 3w - z = 0$ relative to the w variable.

It is natural that the branch points are given precisely by the failure of the implicit function theorem. In other words, by all those pairs (z, w) for which

$$P(w, z) = 0, \quad \partial_w P(w, z) = 0.$$

This means that $w = \pm 1$ and $z = \mp 2$. Since $\partial_w^2 P(w, z) \neq 0$ at these points we conclude that the branching number equals 1 there, whereas at $z = \infty$ the branching number equals 2. Finally, the number of sheets is three, so that the surface looks schematically like the one in Figures 5.6 and 5.7. Finally, the genus $g_{\widetilde{\mathcal{RS}}} = 0$ from (5.3).

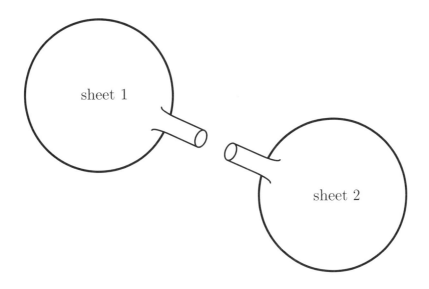

Figure 5.10. The two sheets form a Riemann sphere for $m = 1$

For the remainder of this section, $M = N = \mathbb{C}P^1$ are fixed; in particular, analytic functions are allowed to take the value ∞. To develop the theory, we need to start with some definitions.

Definition 5.14. An analytic germ $[f_0, z_0]$ is called *algebraic* if there is a polynomial $P \in \mathbb{C}[w, z]$ of positive degree so that $P(f_0(z), z) = 0$ identically for all z close to z_0. The complete analytic function

$$\widetilde{F} : \widetilde{\mathcal{R}S} = \widetilde{\mathcal{R}S}(\mathbb{C}P^1, \mathbb{C}P^1, f_0, z_0) \to \mathbb{C}P^1$$

generated by $[f_0, z_0]$ is called an *algebraic function*.

The following lemma develops some of the basic properties of algebraic functions. In particular, we show that all branch points of an algebraic function are algebraic and that $\widetilde{\mathcal{R}S}$ is compact. We will view polynomials $P(w, z)$ as elements of $\mathbb{C}(z)[w]$, where the field $\mathbb{C}(z)$ is the one of all rational functions in z. This allows us to use the Euclidean algorithm, resultants, discriminants, etc. By $P(w, z)$ being irreducible we mean in this ring $\mathbb{C}(z)[w]$.

Lemma 5.15. *Let P and $\widetilde{\mathcal{R}S}$ be as in the previous definition. Then one has the following properties:*

(a) $P(f(z), z) = 0$ for all $[f, z] \in \widetilde{\mathcal{R}S}$. In fact, the same holds true with some irreducible factor of P.

(b) There is the following version of the implicit function theorem: Let $P(w, z) \in \mathbb{C}[w, z]$ satisfy $P(w_1, z_1) = 0$, $P_w(w_1, z_1) \neq 0$. Then there is a

unique analytic germ $[f_1, z_1]$ with $P(f_1(z), z) = 0$ locally around z_1 and with $f_1(z_1) = w_1$.

(c) If $P(w, z) = \sum_{j=0}^n a_j(z)w^j \in \mathbb{C}[w, z]$ is irreducible and satisfies $a_n \not\equiv 0$, then up to finitely many z the polynomial $w \mapsto P(w, z)$ has exactly n simple roots.

(d) Given an algebraic germ $[f_0, z_0]$, there are finitely many points

$$\{\zeta_j\}_{j=1}^J \in \mathbb{C}P^1$$

(called "critical points") such that $[f_0, z_0]$ can be analytically continued along every path in $\mathbb{C}P^1 \setminus \{\zeta_1, \ldots, \zeta_J\}$. If the unramified Riemann surface

$$\mathcal{RS}(\mathbb{C}P^1, \mathbb{C}P^1, f_0, z_0)$$

has a branch point at $\mathfrak{p}$, then $\mathfrak{p}$ has to be rooted over one of the ζ_j. Furthermore, $\#\pi^{-1}(z)$ is constant on $\mathbb{C}P^1 \setminus \{\zeta_1, \ldots, \zeta_J\}$ and no larger than the degree of $P(w, z)$ in w.

(e) All branch points of the unramified Riemann surface

$$\mathcal{RS}(\mathbb{C}P^1, \mathbb{C}P^1, f_0, z_0)$$

generated by an algebraic germ are necessarily algebraic. In particular, the ramified Riemann surface of an algebraic germ is compact.

Proof. (a) Since $[f, z]$ is obtained from $[f_0, z_0]$ via analytic continuation, we conclude from the uniqueness theorem that $P(f(z), z) = 0$ for all

$$[f, z] \in \widetilde{\mathcal{RS}}.$$

To pass to an irreducible factor, we will need to use the resultant (see the appendix): given two relatively prime polynomials $P, Q \in \mathbb{C}[w, z]$, there exist $A, B \in \mathbb{C}[w, z]$ such that

(5.5) $A(z, w)P(w, z) + B(z, w)Q(w, z) = R(z) \in \mathbb{C}[z]$

is a *nonzero* polynomial in z alone; it is called the *resultant* of P and Q.

To conclude the proof of (a), let $P_0(z, w)$ be an irreducible factor of P for which $P_0(f_0(z), z) = 0$ near z_0. Such a factor exists by the uniqueness theorem; see Proposition 1.26.

Suppose $P_1(w, z)$ is another irreducible polynomial with the same property, which is not a scalar multiple of P_0. Then by (5.5) we have

$$0 = A(f_0(z), z)P_0(f_0(z), z) + B(f_0(z), z)P_1(f_0(z), z) = R(z)$$

for all z near z_0. But then the polynomial $R(z)$ vanishes identically, which is a contradiction.

(b) First, there exist $\varepsilon > 0$ and $\delta > 0$ such that

$$P(w, z) \neq 0 \quad \forall |z - z_1| < \delta, \; |w - w_1| = \varepsilon.$$

Next, from the residue theorem,

$$\frac{1}{2\pi i} \oint_{|w - w_1| = \varepsilon} \frac{P_w(w, z)}{P(w, z)} \, dw = 1 \quad \forall |z - z_1| < \delta$$

and one infers from this that $P(w, z) = 0$ has a unique zero

$$w = f_1(z) \in \mathbb{D}(w_1, \varepsilon) \quad \forall |z - z_1| < \delta.$$

Finally, write

$$f_1(z) = \frac{1}{2\pi i} \oint_{|w - w_1| = \varepsilon} w \frac{P_w(w, z)}{P(w, z)} \, dw,$$

again from the residue theorem, which allows one to conclude that $f_1(z)$ is analytic in $\mathbb{D}(z_1, \delta)$. The reader familiar with the Weierstrass preparation theorem will recognize this argument from the proof of that result (see Problem 5.2).

(c) This follows from the (a) and (b) by considering the *discriminant* of P, which is defined to be the resultant of $P(w, z)$ and $P_w(w, z)$. Thus, we write

$$A(w, z)P(w, z) + B(w, z)P_w(w, z) = R(z) \in \mathbb{C}[z]$$

where $R \neq 0$. Apart from the finitely many zeros of $R(z)$, we conclude that $P(w, z) = 0$ implies $P_w(w, z) \neq 0$.

(d) This is a consequence of (b) and (c). The constancy of the cardinality of $\pi^{-1}(z)$ follows from the fact that this cardinality equals the degree of $\tilde{\pi}$. It is clear that there can be no more sheets than the degree of P in w specifies (there could be fewer sheets, though, but as we shall see, only if P is reducible).

(e) Let $\mathfrak{p}$ be a branch point of $\mathcal{R}S(\mathbb{C}P^1, \mathbb{C}P^1, f_0, z_0)$. If $\mathfrak{p}$ is rooted over ∞, then consider instead $f_0(\zeta + z^{-1})$ where ζ is not the root of any branch point. So let us assume that $\mathfrak{p}$ is rooted over some point $z_1 \in \mathbb{C}$. We need to show that relative to the uniformizing chart Ψ from Lemma 5.10 the analytic function F has a removable singularity or a pole at z_1. For this it suffices to show that any solution $f(z)$ of $P(f(z), z) = 0$ can grow at most like $|z - z_1|^{-k}$ as $z \to z_1$ for some $k \geq 0$ (indeed, the role of Ψ is merely to remove "multi-valued" issues but does not affect the polynomial growth as $z \to z_1$ other than by changing the power k). This follows easily from the fact that

$$\sum_{j=0}^{n} a_j(z)(f(z))^j = 0.$$

Indeed, suppose $a_n(z_1) \neq 0$. Then let $|a_n(z)| > \delta > 0$ for all $|z - z_1| < r_0$ with r_0 small. Fix such a z. Since

$$f(z) = -a_n(z)^{-1} \sum_{j=0}^{n-1} a_j(z)(f(z))^{j-(n-1)},$$

either $|f(z)| \leq 1$ or $|f(z)| \leq \delta^{-1} \sum_{j=0}^{n-1} |a_j(z)|$. If, on the other hand, $a_n(z_1) = 0$, then $a_n(z) = (z - z_1)^{\ell} b_n(z)$ where $b_n(z_1) \neq 0$. Thus $|b_n(z)| > \delta$ for all $|z - z_1| < r_0$. From this we conclude that

$$|f(z)(z - z_1)^{\ell}| \leq \delta^{-1} \sum_{j=0}^{n-1} |a_j(z)||z - z_1|^{\ell(n-1-j)} |f(z)(z - z_1)^{\ell}|^{j-(n-1)}.$$

As before, this implies that $f(z)(z - z_1)^{\ell}$ remains bounded and we have shown that all branch points are indeed algebraic. Finally, since $\mathbb{C}P^1$ is compact, due to Lemma 5.10 it follows that the ramified surface $\widetilde{\mathcal{RS}}$ can be covered by finitely many compact sets. This of course implies that $\widetilde{\mathcal{RS}}$ is itself compact and we are done. $\square$

Lemma 5.15 is not just of theoretical value, but also has practical implications. Let us sketch how to "build" the ramified Riemann surface of some irreducible polynomial equation $P(w, z) = 0$ which we solve for w. Suppose the degree of P in w is $n \geq 1$. Let $D(z) := R(P, P_w)$ be the *discriminant* of P (i.e., the resultant of P and P_w). We remove all critical points $\mathcal{C} \subset \mathbb{C}_\infty$ which are defined to be all zeros of D and ∞ from $\mathbb{C}_\infty$. It is clear that for all $z_0 \in \mathbb{C}_\infty \setminus \mathcal{C}$ there are n analytic functions $w_j(z)$ defined near z_0 so that $P(w_j(z), z) = 0$ for $1 \leq j \leq n$ and such that all $w_j(z)$ are distinct.

Locally at each finite critical point ζ the following happens: there is a neighborhood of ζ, say U, so that on U at least one of the zeros w_j ceases to be analytic due to the fact that $P(\cdot, \zeta) = 0$ has at least one multiple root. But in view of Lemma 5.10 we see that locally around ζ there is always a representation of the form

$$w_j(z) = \sum_{k=0}^{\infty} a_{jk}(z - \zeta)^{\frac{k}{\nu_j}}$$

with some $\nu_j \geq 1$. Such series are called **Puiseux series**.

If $\nu_j = 1$, then w_j is of course analytic, whereas in all other cases it is analytic as a function of η which is defined via the *uniformizing change of variables* $z = \zeta + \eta^{\nu_j}$. This is precisely the meaning of Lemma 5.10. It may seem clear from this example that the number of sheets needs to be precisely n. However, this requires some work as the reader will see below. For related examples see the problems of this chapter.

For an explicit example of a Puiseux series, consider the irreducible polynomial

$$P(w, z) = w^4 - 2w^2 + 1 - z$$

and solve for w locally around $(w, z) = (1, 0)$. This leads to

$$w(z) = \sqrt{1 + \sqrt{z}} = \sum_{n=0}^{\infty} \binom{\frac{1}{2}}{n} z^{\frac{n}{2}},$$

which converges in $|z| < 1$.

5.5. Algebraic equations generated by compact surfaces

We now turn to the following remarkable result which is in some sense a converse of what we have done so far. More precisely, we will show how to *generate an algebraic equation from a nonconstant meromorphic function on any compact Riemann surface.*

Proposition 5.16. *Let $z = z(p)$ be a meromorphic function of degree $n \geq 1$ on a compact Riemann surface M. If $f : M \to \mathbb{C}P^1$ is any other nonconstant meromorphic function, then f satisfies an algebraic equation*

$$(5.6) \qquad f^n + \sigma_1(z) f^{n-1} + \sigma_2(z) f^{n-2} + \ldots + \sigma_{n-1}(z) f + \sigma_n(z) = 0$$

of degree n, where the functions $\sigma_j(z)$ are rational functions in z. In particular, if $[f_0, z_0]$ is any holomorphic germ, and if the ramified Riemann surface

$$\widetilde{\mathcal{RS}}(\mathbb{C}P^1, \mathbb{C}P^1, f_0, z_0)$$

is compact, then $[f_0, z_0]$ is algebraic.

Proof. To prove the theorem we proceed as follows: remove from $\mathbb{C}_\infty$ the point ∞, as well as the image $z(p)$ of any branch point of the map

$$p \mapsto z(p)$$

(recall that a branch point of an analytic function is defined as having valency strictly bigger than one). Denote these finitely many points as $\mathcal{C} := \{z_j\}_{j=0}^J$.

We refer to them as "critical points". If $z \in \mathbb{C}_\infty \setminus \mathcal{C}$, then let

$$\{p_1(z), \ldots, p_n(z)\}$$

be the n pre-images under $z(p)$ in arbitrary order and define

$$\sigma_j(z) := \sum_{1 \leq \nu_1 < \nu_2 < \ldots < \nu_j \leq n} f(p_{\nu_1}(z)) \cdot \ldots \cdot f(p_{\nu_j}(z))$$

with $\sigma_0 = 1$. Thus, the σ_j are the elementary symmetric functions in $f(p_1), \ldots, f(p_n)$ and they satisfy

$$(5.7) \qquad \sum_{j=0}^{n} w^j \sigma_{n-j}(z) = \prod_{\ell=1}^{n} (w - f(p_\ell(z))).$$

By Lemma 5.5, each $p_j(z)$ is a holomorphic function on any simply-connected subdomain of $\mathbb{C} \setminus \mathcal{C}$ (possibly after a renumbering of the branches). This implies that σ_j is meromorphic on any such domain. Furthermore, analytic continuation of σ_j along a small loop surrounding an arbitrary point of $\mathcal{C}$ takes σ_j back to itself, as the different branches of p_j can only be permuted; however, σ_j is invariant under such a permutation.

This implies that σ_j has isolated singularities at the points of $\mathcal{C}$ and since f is meromorphic these singularities can be at worst poles. In conclusion, σ_j is meromorphic on $\mathbb{C}_\infty$ and therefore rational as claimed. Note that (5.6) holds by construction. For the final statement, let

$$\tilde{\pi} : \widetilde{\mathcal{RS}}(\mathbb{C}P^1, \mathbb{C}P^1, f_0, z_0) \to \mathbb{C}P^1$$

be the meromorphic function $z(p)$ from the first part. Thus, (f, p) is algebraic as desired. $\qquad\square$

As an example, take $M = \mathbb{C}P^1$ and choose coordinates $[\zeta : 1]$, $\zeta \in \mathbb{C}$ on M with the point at infinity removed. Further, let $z(\zeta) = \zeta^n$ and $f(\zeta) = \zeta^m$ where $n, m \geq 1$ are integers. Clearly, these functions are meromorphic on $\mathbb{C}P^1$ with poles at infinity of order n, m, respectively. The construction in the previous proof yields (see (5.7)),

$$(5.8) \qquad P(w, z) = \prod_{\ell=1}^{n} (w - f(p_\ell(z))) = \prod_{\ell=1}^{n} \left(w - z^{\frac{\ell m}{n}} \right).$$

If m and n are relatively prime, then this product equals $P(w, z) = w^n - z^m$. We claim that this is irreducible. Suppose that

$$P(w, z) = \prod_k P_k(w, z)$$

where P_k have positive degrees. Then $P(w, 1) = w^n - 1 = \prod_k P_k(w, 1)$. On the other hand, we have the factorization into cyclotomic polynomials (see the algebra section of the appendix)

$$w^n - 1 = \prod_{d \mid n} \chi_d(w), \quad \chi_d(w) = \prod_{\gcd(d_1, d) = 1} (w - \zeta_d^{d_1})$$

and ζ_d is a primitive d^{th} root of unity. The χ_d are known to be irreducible and they are of degree $\phi(d)$, where ϕ is the Euler totient function (see the appendix).

Thus, each $P_k(w, 1)$ is a product of cyclotomic factors (we can assume that each $P_k(w, 1)$ has highest coefficient equal to 1). Consequently, for each k one has

$$(5.9) \qquad P_k(w, z) = \prod_{d \in \mathcal{D}_k} \prod_{\gcd(d_1, d) = 1} \left(w - z^{\frac{m}{n}} \zeta_d^{d_1} \right),$$

where the outer product runs over some divisors $d | n$. But the power of z in such a product equals

$$\left(z^{\frac{m}{n}} \right)^{\sum_{d \in \mathcal{D}_k} \phi(d)} = z^{\frac{m\ell}{n}}.$$

If $\mathcal{D}_k$ does not contain all divisors, then $\ell < n$. But then $\frac{m\ell}{n}$ is not an integer and thus (5.9) is not a polynomial. From this contradiction we indeed conclude that $P(w, z) = w^n - z^m$ is irreducible.

On the other hand, assume that $d = \gcd(m, n) \geq 2$. Then

$$P(w, z) = (w^{\frac{n}{d}} - z^{\frac{m}{d}}) Q(w, z), \qquad Q \in \mathbb{C}[w, z],$$

and so $P(w, z)$ is reducible.

Suppose the polynomial $P(w, z)$ as given by (5.6) (after multiplying through with a polynomial in z to remove any denominators of the coefficients) is reducible. By Lemma 5.15 we can then replace $P(w, z)$ by an irreducible factor. In other words, we obtain the following result.

Corollary 5.17. *Let $z = z(p)$ be a meromorphic function of degree $n \geq 1$ on a compact Riemann surface M. If $f : M \to \mathbb{C}P^1$ is any other nonconstant meromorphic function, then f satisfies an algebraic equation*

$$P(f(p), z(p)) = 0 \quad \forall \, p \in M,$$

where $P(w, z) \in \mathbb{C}[w, z]$ is irreducible.

Note, however, that this corollary is of limited value. Indeed, we might obtain trivial $P(w, z)$ such as $P(w, z) = w - z$ or $P(w, z) = w - z^n$ which is the case if we choose $f(p) = z(p)^n$ in Proposition 5.16. On the other hand, in the example above (cf. (5.8)), we saw that to the given meromorphic function $z(\zeta) = \zeta^n$ we can always find another (in fact many) meromorphic functions such that the polynomial in (5.6) is irreducible and of degree n. That this can be done *in general* is not a simple matter and plays a decisive role in Theorem 5.20 below.

Proposition 5.16 is a fundamental statement in the theory of algebraic functions. It raises a number of questions. For example:

- Which Riemann surfaces carry nontrivial meromorphic functions?
- Furthermore, what degrees (in the sense of *how low of a degree*) can a nontrivial meromorphic function achieve on a given surface?

These questions can be restated as follows: how can we realize a given compact Riemann surface M as a branched cover of S^2, and which restrictions exist for the number of sheets of such a cover? The Riemann-Hurwitz formula provides one such obstruction, albeit a rather weak one. A much more useful tool will later be given in terms of the Riemann-Roch theorem. Let us first observe the trivial fact that for M to admit a meromorphic function of degree one, it is necessary and sufficient that $M \simeq S^2$ in the sense of conformal isomorphism. We shall see later (in Chapter 7) that in fact every compact simply-connected Riemann surface is isomorphic to S^2.

Before pursuing these matters any further, let us first derive a simple but no less important corollary from Proposition 5.16. It will allow us to determine the number of sheets of the Riemann surface determined by an irreducible polynomial.

Corollary 5.18. *Let $P \in \mathbb{C}[w, z]$ be irreducible and suppose $\deg_w(P) = n$. Then the ramified Riemann surface $\widetilde{R}$ generated by some germ $[f_0, z_0]$ with $P(f_0(z), z) = 0$ locally at z_0 has n sheets and satisfies*

$$\widetilde{R} = \widetilde{\mathcal{R}S}(\mathbb{C}_\infty, \mathbb{C}_\infty, f_1, z_1)$$

for every germ $[f_1, z_1]$ with $P(f_1(z), z) = 0$ for all z near z_1.

Proof. If the number of sheets were $m < n$, then by Proposition 5.16 we could find a polynomial Q of degree m with the property that $Q(f_0(z), z) = 0$ for z near z_0. But then Q would necessarily need to be a factor of P which is impossible. $\square$

In other words, the ramified Riemann surface of a germ satisfying an irreducible polynomial equation contains all germs satisfying this equation.

Let us now clarify the connection between the smooth, affine or projective, algebraic curves which were introduced in the previous chapter, and the ramified Riemann surfaces of an algebraic germ which we just constructed. In particular, the reader needs to recall the notion of nonsingular polynomials as well as the homogenization of a polynomial (see (4.8) and (4.9)).

Lemma 5.19. *Let $P \in \mathbb{C}[w, z]$ be an irreducible polynomial so that its homogenization Q is nonsingular. Then the smooth projective algebraic curve $\widetilde{S}$ defined by Q (see (4.9)), is isomorphic to the Riemann surface $\widetilde{R} := \widetilde{\mathcal{R}S}(\mathbb{C}P^1, \mathbb{C}P^1, f_0, z_0)$ of any algebraic germ $[f_0, z_0]$ defined by P. In particular, $\widetilde{\mathcal{R}S}$ can be embedded into $\mathbb{C}P^2$.*

Proof. We will need the following fact (see Problem 4.15): *Let M, N be compact Riemann surfaces and suppose $\Phi : M \backslash \mathcal{C} \to N \backslash \mathcal{C}'$ is an isomorphism where $\mathcal{C}, \mathcal{C}'$ are finite sets. Then Φ extends to an isomorphism $\widetilde{\Phi} : M \to N$.*

Remove from $\widetilde{R}$ all points "at infinity", more precisely, all germs rooted at $z = \infty$. In other words, we consider

$$M := \widetilde{\mathcal{R}\mathcal{S}}(\mathbb{C}, \mathbb{C}_\infty, f_0, z_0)$$

for an arbitrary germ $[f_0, z_0]$ of P with $z_0 \in \mathbb{C}$. Similarly, remove from $\widetilde{S}$ the line at infinity, i.e.,

$$N := \widetilde{S} \setminus L_\infty, \qquad L_\infty := \{[z : w : 0] \mid (z, w) \in \mathbb{C}^2\}.$$

Thus, consider the affine curve S instead of the projective one $\widetilde{S}$. The reader should convince himself or herself that $\widetilde{S} \cap L_\infty$ is always finite. By the aforementioned fact concerning isomorphisms, it will suffice to show that $M \simeq N$. We will accomplish this by showing that we can identify M and N as sets, and also use the same charts on them.

First, locally at all noncritical points (z_1, w_1), which are defined via

$$P(w_1, z_1) = 0, \quad \partial_w P(w_1, z_1) \neq 0.$$

one has $n = \deg_w(P)$ branches $w_j(z)$ defined and analytic near z_1. These branches define n charts on both M and N on neighborhoods which we can identify provided they are chosen small enough (so that there is no overlapping of values); indeed, we just map the germ $[f, z]$ on M onto the pair $(f(z), z) \in N$.

Next, consider any critical point (w_1, z_1). Since P is nonsingular, one has

$$\partial_z P(w_1, z_1) \neq 0,$$

which implies that there exists an analytic function $Z_1(w)$ defined near $w = w_1$ and an analytic and nonvanishing function Q near (z_1, w_1) so that

$$P(w, z) = (z - Z_1(w))Q(w, z)$$

locally around (z_1, w_1). This follows either from Lemma 5.15 or the Weierstrass preparation theorem (see Problem 5.2). Now suppose that

$$\partial_w^j P(w_1, z_1) = 0$$

for all $0 \leq j < \ell$ but

$$\partial_w^\ell P(w_1, z_1) \neq 0$$

for some $\ell \geq 2$.

This is equivalent to

$$\frac{d^j Z}{dw^j}(w_1) = 0 \quad \forall\, 0 \leq j < \ell, \qquad \frac{d^\ell Z}{dw^\ell}(w_1) \neq 0.$$

Thus, the branching number of the branch point of M at (z_1, w_1) is $\ell - 1 \geq 1$ and a uniformizing chart as in Lemma 5.10 is given by $z = Z_1(w)$ provided $w = f(z)$ with $[f, z]$ a germ from the Riemann surface representing the branch point $(z \neq z_1)$. On the other hand, by definition $z = Z_1(w)$ is a chart on N near w_1. Hence this again allows one to identify M and N near (z_1, w_1) with the same chart and we are done. $\qquad\square$

Proposition 5.16 raises the following natural question: *Is M conformally equivalent to the Riemann surface associated with the algebraic equation* (5.6) *over* $\mathbb{C}P^1$? For this to hold (5.6) needs to be irreducible in $\mathbb{C}(z)[w]$. We shall see later, as an application of the Riemann-Roch theorem, that we can in fact find f for a given z such that (5.6) is irreducible. This will then allow us to obtain an affirmative answer to our question, which has a remarkable consequence: **any compact Riemann surface which carries a nonconstant meromorphic function is isomorphic to the Riemann surface associated to some irreducible polynomial $P(w, z)$.** Since we shall see later that in fact every Riemann surface carries a nonconstant meromorphic function, we can now state the following truly remarkable conclusion.

Theorem 5.20. *Every compact Riemann surface M is the ramified Riemann surface of some algebraic germ.*

Proof. As already explained, the proof hinges on two facts:

- *every Riemann surface carries a nonconstant meromorphic function $z : M \to \mathbb{C}P^1$.*

- *given a nonconstant meromorphic function z on M, we can find another meromorphic function f on M such that* (5.6) *is irreducible.*

We will prove these two facts in Chapters 6 (see Corollary 6.29), and 7 (see Proposition 7.23). Assuming their validity for the moment, we can easily finish the argument by going back to the proof of Proposition 5.16.

Indeed, let $P(w, z)$ be the irreducible polynomial associated with (5.6) and let $\widetilde{\mathcal{RS}}$ be the ramified Riemann surface of $P(w, z)$. In view of Corollary 5.18, $\widetilde{\mathcal{RS}}$ has exactly $n = \deg(z)$ sheets. For any $z_0 \in \mathbb{C}P^1 \backslash \mathcal{C}$ there are n distinct pre-images $\{p_j(z_0)\}_{j=1}^n$ with the property that locally around these points $p \mapsto z$ is an isomorphism onto some neighborhood of z_0. Moreover, these neighborhoods are also isomorphic to neighborhoods of $\widetilde{\mathcal{RS}}$.

To see this, note that each $f(p_j(z))$ is analytic close to z_0 and therefore an unbranched function element from $\widetilde{\mathcal{RS}}$. But since $\widetilde{\mathcal{RS}}$ has n sheets this implies that the germs $\{[f \circ p_j, z_0]\}_{j=1}^n$ are distinct and in fact parametrize neighborhoods on distinct sheets. This in turn defines isomorphisms between each of these neighborhoods of the points $p_j(z_0)$ on M: map $[f \circ p_j, z]$ onto $p_j(z)$ for all z close to z_0.

Now connect the points of $\mathcal{C}$ by a piecewise linear path γ so that the set

$$\Omega := \mathbb{C}_\infty \backslash \gamma$$

is simply-connected. By Lemma 5.5 these local isomorphisms extend to global ones between those sheets of $\widetilde{\mathcal{R}S}$ that cover Ω via the canonical projection $\widetilde{\pi} : \widetilde{\mathcal{R}S} \to \mathbb{C}_\infty$ as well as the respective components of M which cover Ω via the map z. It remains to check that over each critical point $\widetilde{\mathcal{R}S}$ is branched in exactly the same way as M. More precisely, one needs to verify that at each critical point $z_0 \in \mathcal{C}$ there is a one-to-one correspondence between the branch points of M and $\widetilde{\mathcal{R}S}$, respectively, with equal branching numbers (recall that we can have unbranched sheets over a given root, see Figure 5.6).

However, this is clear from the fact that the germs are given by $f \circ p_j$ and thus inherit the branching numbers from the map z: suppose analytic continuation of the germ $[f \circ p_j, z_1]$ with a fixed $z_1 = z_0 + \varepsilon e^{i\theta_0}$ close to z_0 along the loop $\rho := z_0 + \varepsilon e^{i\theta}$, $\theta_0 \leq \theta \leq \theta_0 + 2\pi$ yields the germ $[f \circ p_k, z_1]$ with $j \neq k$. Since we verified before that these germs are distinct, it follows that the lift of ρ to M under the branched cover z which starts at p_j must end at p_k. But this means precisely that there is the desired one-to-one correspondence between the branch points which preserves the branching number. $\qquad\square$

In other words, **any compact Riemann surface is obtained by analytic continuation of a suitable algebraic germ**! Note that the proof gives an "explicit" conformal isomorphism:

$$p \mapsto (z(p), f(p))$$

where z and f are the meromorphic functions from the proof. On first sight, this might be somewhat confusing because of an inherent ambiguity. For example, let us return to our two meromorphic functions $z(\zeta) = \zeta^n$ and $f(\zeta) = \zeta^m$ on $\mathbb{C}P^1$ (cf. (5.8)), with $\gcd(n,m) = 1$. Then they generate the irreducible polynomial $P(w,z) = w^n - z^m$ and we see that the Riemann surface associated with this polynomial is the same as the of the nth root. This has n sheets, but $n \geq 1$ *was arbitrary*, given by the degree of the meromorphic function z. But there is no contradiction, since that surface — irrespective of n — is conformally equivalent to $\mathbb{C}P^1$.

The reader should visualize this by taking n copies of S^2, slicing each of them along a circular arc connecting the north and south poles, deforming each cut spheres into a spherical wedge of opening angle $\frac{2\pi}{n}$, and then by gluing the cuts together as dictated by the analytic continuations of the nth root. The result is just another sphere.

As the surface of the logarithm shows, Theorem 5.20 fails in the non-compact case. Another example is given by

$$\widetilde{\mathcal{R}S}(\mathbb{C}_\infty, \mathbb{C}_\infty, \exp(z^{\frac{1}{2}}), 1).$$

It is clearly not algebraic and, in fact, is not compact since the branch point at $z = \infty$ is not part of the ramified Riemann surface.

The existence of a meromorphic function on an (abstract) Riemann surface is a highly nontrivial issue; indeed, even though we can of course define such functions locally on every chart, the challenge lies with the *extension of such a function beyond the chart*; in other words, in the problem of gluing together the functions defined on different charts.

In the realm of smooth manifolds, we can of course resort to partitions of unity. However, by the uniqueness theorem this would take us outside of the analytic category and is therefore completely impossible here.

5.6. Some compact surfaces and their associated polynomials

As already noted before, the case $n = 1$ of Proposition 5.16 means precisely that $z : M \to \mathbb{C}P^1$ is an isomorphism and we recover the result that all meromorphic functions on $\mathbb{C}P^1$ are rational. The first interesting case is $n = 2$, and any compact M of genus $g > 1$ carrying such a meromorphic function $z(p)$ is called *hyper-elliptic*, whereas the genus 1 case is typically referred to as *elliptic* (it will follow from the Riemann-Roch theorem that every compact surface of genus 1 carries a meromorphic function of degree two).

Suppose now that $n = 2$ in Proposition 5.16. To proceed we quote a result that we shall prove in Chapter 6 (see Corollary 6.29): *Let $p, q \in M$ be two distinct points on a Riemann surface M. Then there exists $f \in \mathcal{M}(M)$ with $f(p) = 0$ and $f(q) = 1$.*

It is customary to refer to this property as follows: *the function field on M separates points.* Apply this fact with $\{p, q\} = z^{-1}(z_0)$ where z_0 is not a critical value of z (we have equality here rather than inclusion since degree equals 2). By the previous section, f satisfies an equation of the form

$$(5.10) \qquad f^2 + \sigma_1(z)f + \sigma_2(z) = 0$$

with rational σ_1, σ_2. This equation needs to be irreducible. Indeed, otherwise f is a rational function of z which would contradict the fact that f takes different values at p and q. Replacing f by $f + \sigma_1/2$ shows that the Riemann surface generated by (5.10) is the same as that generated by

$$f^2 + \sigma_3(z) = 0, \qquad \sigma_3 := \sigma_2 + \sigma_1^2/4.$$

By irreducibility, σ_3 is not the square of a rational function. Let $\sigma_3 = \frac{P}{Q}$ where P, Q are, without loss of generality, relatively prime monic polynomials. By the proof of Theorem 5.20, we see that M is isomorphic to the Riemann surface generated by $\sqrt{\frac{P}{Q}}$.

A moment's reflection shows that this surface is isomorphic to the Riemann surface of $\sqrt{PQ}$, and moreover, we can assume that each linear factor in PQ appears only to the first power. In other words, we infer that every elliptic or hyper-elliptic Riemann surface is isomorphic to one of the examples which we already encountered above, viz.

$$\widetilde{\mathcal{RS}}(\mathbb{C}P^1, \mathbb{C}P^1, \sqrt{(z-z_1) \cdot \ldots \cdot (z-z_m)}, z_0)$$

where $\{z_j\}_{j=0}^m$ are all distinct. Let us now examine the elliptic surfaces more closely.

Corollary 5.21. *Suppose M is a compact surface of genus one. Then M is isomorphic to the set of zeros in $\mathbb{C}P^2$ of a cubic polynomial*

$$(5.11) \quad E_\zeta := \{[z:w:u] \in \mathbb{C}P^2 \,|\, Q_\zeta(z,w,u) := w^2 u - z(z-u)(z-\zeta u) = 0\}$$

where $\zeta \in \mathbb{C} \setminus \{0,1\}$. In other words, M can be embedded into $\mathbb{C}P^2$.

For the particular case of tori $\mathbb{C}/\Gamma$ with $\Gamma := \langle z \mapsto z + \omega_1, z \mapsto z + \omega_2 \rangle$ and ω_1, ω_2 independent over $\mathbb{R}$, this embedding is given explicitly in terms of the Weierstrass function $\wp$ associated with the lattice Γ:

$$(5.12) \qquad \Psi \,:\, z \in \mathbb{C}/\Gamma \mapsto \begin{cases} [\wp(z) : \wp'(z) : 1] & z \neq 0, \\ [0:1:0] & z = 0. \end{cases}$$

Proof. We need to refer to the aforementioned fact (see Chapter 7, Corollary 7.18) that every genus 1 compact surface can be realized as a two-sheeted branched cover of S^2 (in other words, it carries a meromorphic function of degree two). Note that for the case of tori this is nothing but the existence of the Weierstrass $\wp$ function. By our previous discussion, M is therefore isomorphic to the Riemann surface of $\sqrt{\prod_{j=1}^m (z - z_j)}$ with either $m = 3$ or $m = 4$ and distinct z_j. In the latter case, the surface does not branch at $z = \infty$, whereas it does in the former. Since these two cases are conformally equivalent, it suffices to consider $m = 3$.

Composing with a Möbius transform which moves z_0, z_1 to $0, 1$, respectively, and fixes ∞, we now arrive at the the cubic polynomial

$$P_\zeta := w^2 - z(z-1)(z-\zeta) = 0, \qquad \zeta \in \mathbb{C} \setminus \{0,1\}.$$

Not only is P_ζ nonsingular, but so is its homogenization Q_ζ from (5.11). We leave this to the reader to check. Hence applying Lemma 5.19, we see that M is isomorphic to both the Riemann surface of P_ζ from this chapter as well as the algebraic curve E_ζ as defined in the previous chapter.

Finally, for the torus we proved in Chapter 4 that the Weierstrass function satisfies the differential equation

$$(\wp'(z))^2 = 4(\wp(z) - e_1)(\wp(z) - e_2)(\wp(z) - e_3).$$

In other words, $z \mapsto (\wp(z), \wp'(z))$ maps the torus into the set of zeros (where E stands for "elliptic curve")

$$E := \{(\zeta, \eta) \in \mathbb{C}_\infty^2 \; : \; \eta^2 - 4(\zeta - e_1)(\zeta - e_2)(\zeta - e_3) = 0\}.$$

We need to "projectivize" this in the usual way, which yields (5.12). The choice of $[0 : 1 : 0]$ for $z = 0$ is the only possible one as can be seen from the Laurent expansion of $\wp$ and $\wp'$ at $z = 0$. The reader will easily verify that this map is a homeomorphism between the torus and the projective version of E. Since the latter is in a canonical way the Riemann surface of the irreducible polynomial $\eta^2 - 4(\zeta - e_1)(\zeta - e_2)(\zeta - e_3)$, we have obtained the desired isomorphism.

Historically, the inverse to the map

$$\Phi : z \mapsto (\zeta, \eta) := (\wp(z), \wp'(z))$$

was given by the "elliptic integral"

$$(5.13) \qquad z(p) = \int_\infty^p \frac{d\zeta}{\eta} = \int_\infty^p \frac{d\zeta}{\sqrt{4\zeta^3 - g_2\zeta - g_3}}$$

where $p \in E$ and the latter is viewed as the Riemann surface of

$$\eta^2 - 4(\zeta - e_1)(\zeta - e_2)(\zeta - e_3) =: \eta^2 - (4\zeta^3 - g_2\zeta - g_3).$$

The integration proceeds along any path that avoids the branch points. The branch of the square root in (5.13) is determined by analytic continuation along that path.

Clearly, the integral in (5.13) is invariant under homotopies, but the path is determined only up to integral linear combinations of the homology basis a, b (see Figure 5.11). The dashed line on b means that we are entering the other sheet. The torus is shown because E is topologically equivalent to one. However, such an integral linear combination changes $z(p)$ only by

$$(5.14) \qquad m \oint_a \frac{d\zeta}{\eta} + n \oint_b \frac{d\zeta}{\eta} = m\omega_1 + n\omega_2$$

with $n, m \in \mathbb{Z}$. We leave the evaluation of the integrals to the reader (see Problem 5.1). Consequently, $z(p)$ is well-defined as an element of the torus $\mathbb{C}/\Gamma$. Finally, since $\Phi : z \mapsto (\wp(z), \wp'(z))$ is clearly onto, we can write a path connecting ∞ to p as $\Phi \circ \gamma$ where $\gamma : [0, 1] \to \mathbb{C}/\Gamma$ is a path connecting 0 to z_0. But then

$$z(p) = \int_0^1 \frac{d(\wp \circ \gamma)}{\wp'(\gamma)} = \int_0^1 \gamma'(t)\, dt = \gamma(1) = z_0,$$

which shows that $p \mapsto z(p)$ is indeed the inverse to Φ. $\qquad\qquad\square$

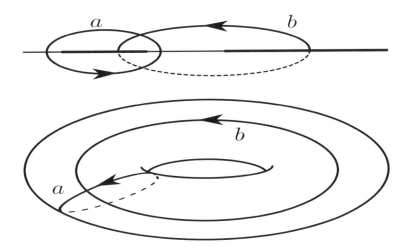

Figure 5.11. The homology basis for E

Elliptic curves have many remarkable properties, of which we just mention the following one: *the three distinct points $\{\Psi(z_j)\}_{j=1}^3$ are collinear if and only if $z_1 + z_2 + z_3 = 0$.* In other words,

$$(5.15) \qquad \det \begin{bmatrix} \wp(z_1) & \wp'(z_1) & 1 \\ \wp(z_2) & \wp'(z_2) & 1 \\ \wp(z_3) & \wp'(z_3) & 1 \end{bmatrix} = 0 \Leftrightarrow z_1 + z_2 + z_3 = 0,$$

where the final equality is to be understood modulo Γ. This result of course also raises a number of questions, for example: *does any compact Riemann surface of higher genus admit an embedding into some projective space $\mathbb{C}P^d$?* In fact, the answer is "yes" with $d = 3$ (see the notes at the end of the chapter).

To conclude this section, let us now return full circle to the beginning of this chapter and construct the ramified Riemann surface defined by the germ $[\sqrt{1 + \sqrt{z}}, 1]$. The convention regarding the square root shall be $\sqrt{x} > 0$ for $x > 0$.

This not only serves to illustrate the concepts which we have introduced here, but should also hopefully help in building some intuition for the more mechanical aspects of analytic continuation, algebraic germs, and the surfaces which they generate.

The aforementioned germ gives rise to the unique irreducible monomial $P(w, z) = (w^2 - 1)^2 - z$. The system $P = 0, \partial_w P = 0$ has solutions

$$(w, z) \in \{(0, 1), (1, 0), (-1, 0)\}.$$

Note that $\partial_w^2 P(w, z) \neq 0$ as well as $\partial_z P(w, z) \neq 0$ at each of these points.

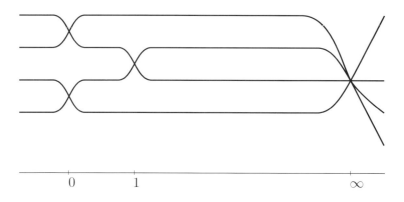

Figure 5.12. The sheets of $\sqrt{1+\sqrt{z}}$

Thus, any branch point associated with them has branching number 1. Moreover, if $z = 0$, then necessarily $w = \pm 1$, whereas $z = 1$ yields $w = 0$ as well as $w = \pm\sqrt{2}$. Finally, $z = \infty$ is a branch point and analytic continuation around a large circle (more precisely, any loop encircling both $z = 0$ and $z = 1$ once) permutes the four sheets cyclically.

For this reason, the sheets look schematically as shown in Figure 5.12 (the two sheets which branch over $z = 1$ cannot branch again over $z = 0$ since this would contradict the aforementioned cyclic permutation property at $z = \infty$). Let us now analyze the four sheets and their permutation properties more carefully.

This is most easily done by introducing cuts from the branch points to infinity; cf. Figure 5.13. First, on the simply-connected region

$$\Omega := \mathbb{C} \setminus (-\infty, 0]$$

there exist four branches $f_j(z)$, $0 \le j \le 3$ uniquely determined by the asymptotic equalities

$$f_0(x) \sim x^{\frac{1}{4}}, \ f_1(x) \sim ix^{\frac{1}{4}}, \ f_2(x) \sim -x^{\frac{1}{4}}, \ f_3(x) \sim -ix^{\frac{1}{4}}$$

as $x \to \infty$. The enumeration here has been chosen so that analytic continuation along any circle containing $z = 0$ and $z = 1$ with positive orientation induces the cyclic permutation

$$f_0 \mapsto f_1 \mapsto f_2 \mapsto f_3 \mapsto f_0.$$

Next, for all $x > 1$ there are the explicit expressions

$$f_0(x) = \sqrt{1+\sqrt{x}}, \quad f_2(x) = -\sqrt{1+\sqrt{x}},$$
$$f_1(x) = i\sqrt{\sqrt{x}-1}, \quad f_3(x) = -i\sqrt{\sqrt{x}-1}.$$

Analytic continuation to Ω yields

$$f_1(i0+) = f_3(i0-) = f_2(0) = -1, \quad f_1(i0-) = f_3(i0+) = f_0(0) = 1.$$

Recall that by our convention, $\sqrt{z}$ is analytic on Ω with $\sqrt{x} > 0$ if $x > 0$. Analytic continuation around the loop $z(\theta) = 1 + \varepsilon^2 e^{i\theta}$, $0 \leq \theta \leq 2\pi$, with $\varepsilon > 0$ small leaves f_0 and f_2 invariant, whereas f_1 and f_3 are interchanged. Similarly, analytic continuation around $z(\theta) = \varepsilon^2 e^{i\theta}$ (starting with $\theta > 0$ small) takes f_0 into f_3 and f_2 into f_1. This implies that the *monodromy group* of this Riemann surface is generated by the permutations $(12)(03)$ and (13).

The formal definition of the monodromy group is as follows: for any $c \in \pi_1(\mathbb{C} \setminus \{0,1\})$ let $\mu(c) \in S_4$ (the group of permutations on four symbols) be defined as the permutation of the four sheets which is induced by analytic continuation along the closed loop c. For this we assume that c has its base point somewhere in Ω and we pick the four germs defined on each branch over that base point for analytic continuation. Note that μ is well-defined by the monodromy theorem.

This refers to the fact that c is really a representative of an equivalence class of loops which are all homotopic in $\mathbb{C} \setminus \{0,1\}$. The map

$$\mu : \pi_1(\mathbb{C} \setminus \{0,1\}) \to S_4$$

is a group homomorphism and the monodromy group is the image $\mu(\pi_1)$. For example, $(13)(12)(03) = (0123)$ which is precisely the cyclic permutation at $z = \infty$. The genus g of this Riemann surface is given by the Riemann-Hurwitz formula as

$$g - 1 = 4(-1) + \frac{1}{2}(1 + 1 + 1 + 3) = -4 + 3 = -1$$

which implies that $g = 0$.

5.7. ODEs with meromorphic coefficients

Judging from the previous sections, the reader might be under the impression that Riemann surfaces arise "in nature" mostly in the study of algebraic equations. This is wholly erroneous, since differential equations provide an equally important as well as natural setting for their construction.

Indeed, a large body of classical work is devoted to the analysis of the solutions to linear equations of the form

(5.16) $$Y'(z) = A(z)Y(z), \quad Y(z_0) = Y_0$$

where A is an $n \times n$-matrix, meromorphic in some domain $\Omega \subset \mathbb{C}$, and $z_0 \in \Omega$ is not a singularity of $A(z)$. Any scalar linear ordinary differential equation of the form

(5.17) $y^{(n)}(z) + a_{n-1}(z)y^{(n-1)}(z) + \ldots + a_1(z)y'(z) + a_0(z)y(z) = 0$

is reduced to (5.16) by setting

$$Y = \left(y^{(n-1)}, y^{(n-2)}, \ldots, y'(z), y(z)\right)^t.$$

If A is analytic on a simply-connected domain Ω, then a standard existence and uniqueness theorem states that (5.16) possesses a unique solution which is analytic on Ω. This can be proved in a number of ways, for example by expanding A into a power series around any point $z_1 \in \Omega$ and then showing that we may solve for Y locally near z_1 in terms of a power series as well. In terms of formal power series this is fairly immediate, just from the system of equations (setting $z_1 = 0$ for simplicity)

(5.18)
$$A(z) = \sum_{n=0}^{\infty} A_n z^n, \quad Y(z) = \sum_{n=0}^{\infty} Y_n z^n,$$
$$(n+1)Y_{n+1} = \sum_{m+\ell=n} A_\ell Y_m.$$

Here A_n, Y_n are constant. We may solve this with Y_0 being the only free parameter. Inserting the Cauchy estimates $|A_\ell| \le C^{\ell+1}$ into the recursion in (5.18) one then obtains similar estimates for Y_n which proves that the series for $Y(z)$ converges locally near 0. To extend this existence result for disks to Ω, one just glues the functions together using Lemma 5.5.

Suppose, however, that A has a pole at $z_0 \in \Omega$. Then it is of course natural to ask about the analytic continuation of a solution obtained in a disk near z_0 (but not containing z_0) along a loop centered at z_0. Many new phenomena may appear in this process which go beyond the level of this text, such as *Stokes lines*. Generally speaking, one distinguishes between *regular singular points* and *irregular singular points* z_0. The former being precisely those points at which the coefficients a_j in (5.17) exhibit at most a pole of order $n - j$ for each $0 \le j \le n - 1$; in that case we say that (5.17) is of the *Fuchsian type*. These singularities are special since the solutions near such points may be constructed in terms of power series, the branching powers $(z - z_0)^\alpha$, and logarithms $\log(z - z_0)$. We shall observe this property in the ensuing analysis of the Bessel equation. *Irregular singularities* display much more complicated behavior and we shall not deal with them here.

Rather than investigating Fuchsian equations in general, we have chosen here instead to study the **Bessel equation** in some detail. The goal is not to bore the reader with tedious calculations, but rather to exhibit some of the main features that might arise in the analysis of Fuchsian equations.

We proceed through a number of steps, each of which investigates a particular aspect of Bessel functions. First, we define the Bessel functions J_n for integer index by means of their generating function in (5.19). We then derive an integral representation, followed by the differential equation satisfied by these functions (the Bessel equation). In the further "steps" appearing below we obtain all possible solutions of the Bessel equation (leading the solutions Y_n linearly independent from J_n) as well as derive various of their properties (power series expansions, nature of possible singularities, further integral representations, noninteger indices). The reader will easily identify the Riemann surfaces which are naturally associated with the solutions. They are only of the simplest kind, such as logarithmic ones.

Thus, we define the *Bessel functions $J_n(z)$* with $n \in \mathbb{Z}$, $z \in \mathbb{C}$ as the coefficients in the Laurent expansion

$$(5.19) \qquad \exp\left(\frac{z}{2}(\zeta - \zeta^{-1})\right) = \sum_{n=-\infty}^{\infty} J_n(z)\zeta^n, \quad 0 < |\zeta| < \infty.$$

Step A: *We conclude from the generating function (5.19) that for each $n \in \mathbb{Z}$ the function $J_n(z)$ is entire and satisfies*

$$(5.20) \qquad J_n(z) = \frac{1}{\pi} \int_0^\pi \cos(n\theta - z\sin\theta)\, d\theta$$

as an identity between entire functions. Moreover, $J_{-n} = (-1)^n J_n$.

Proof. The generating function is entire in ζ so the coefficients $J_n(z)$ are, too. Moreover, by the formula for computing Laurent coefficients,

$$\begin{aligned}
J_n(z) &= \frac{1}{2\pi i} \oint \exp\left(\frac{z}{2}(\zeta - \zeta^{-1})\right) \frac{d\zeta}{\zeta^{n+1}} \\
&= \frac{1}{2\pi} \int_0^{2\pi} \exp(-in\theta + zi\sin\theta)\, d\theta \\
&= \frac{1}{2\pi} \int_0^{2\pi} \cos(n\theta - z\sin\theta)\, d\theta \\
&= \frac{1}{\pi} \int_0^\pi \cos(n\theta - z\sin\theta)\, d\theta
\end{aligned}$$

as claimed. Changing n to $-n$ and substituting $\theta + \pi$ for θ proves that $J_{-n} = (-1)^n J_n$. $\qquad\square$

Step B: *Using (5.20) we now prove that for each $n \in \mathbb{Z}$, $w = J_n(z)$ satisfies* Bessel's equation

$$(5.21) \qquad z^2 w''(z) + z w'(z) + (z^2 - n^2) w(z) = 0.$$

This equation, which arises frequently in both mathematics and physics, is the main reason why Bessel functions appear frequently in engineering and the sciences.

Proof. Differentiate (5.20) under the integral sign:

$$J_n'(z) = \frac{1}{\pi} \int_0^\pi \sin\theta \sin(n\theta - z\sin\theta)\, d\theta$$

$$= \frac{1}{\pi} \int_0^\pi (n - z\cos\theta)\cos\theta \cos(n\theta - z\sin\theta)\, d\theta,$$

where we integrated by parts to get the second line. Differentiating the first line again in z yields,

$$J_n''(z) = -\frac{1}{\pi} \int_0^\pi \sin^2\theta \cos(n\theta - z\sin\theta)\, d\theta,$$

so that

$$z^2 J_n''(z) + z J_n'(z) + (z^2 - n^2) J_n(z)$$

$$= \frac{n}{\pi} \int_0^\pi (z\cos\theta - n)\cos(n\theta - z\sin\theta)\, d\theta$$

$$= -\frac{n}{\pi} \int_0^\pi \frac{d}{d\theta}\sin(n\theta - z\sin\theta)\, d\theta = 0,$$

and we are done. $\qquad\square$

To proceed, let $\mathbb{C}^* := \mathbb{C} \setminus \{0\}$ and we now allow $n = \nu \in \mathbb{C}$ in (5.21).

Step C: *For any $z_0 \in \mathbb{C}^*$ as well as $w_0, w_1 \in \mathbb{C}$ arbitrary there exists a unique function $w(z)$ defined and analytic locally around $z = z_0$ with the property that $w(z_0) = w_0$, $w'(z_0) = w_1$ and so that (5.21) holds on the domain of w. We refer to such a solution as a* local solution *around z_0. Any local solution around an arbitrary $z_0 \in \mathbb{C}^*$ can be analytically continued to any simply-connected domain $\Omega \subset \mathbb{C}^*$ containing z_0. Moreover, for any simply-connected domain $\Omega \subset \mathbb{C}^*$ there exist two linearly independent solutions $W_0, W_1 \in \mathcal{H}(\Omega)$ of (5.21) so that any local solution w around an arbitrary $z_0 \in \Omega$ is a linear combination of W_0, W_1 (such a pair is referred to as a* fundamental system *of solutions on Ω).*

Given a local solution $w(z)$ around an arbitrary $z_0 \in \mathbb{C}^*$, we set $f(\zeta) = w(e^\zeta)$ which is defined and analytic around any ζ_0 with $e^{\zeta_0} = z_0$. We shall derive a differential equation for f and use it to argue that f can be analytically continued to an entire function (in the language of Riemann surfaces this shows that e^ζ uniformizes the Riemann surface of any local solution of Bessel's equation; loosely speaking, the "worst" singularity that a solution of Bessel's equation can have at $z = 0$ is logarithmic).

Proof. We make the power series ansatz $w(z) = \sum_{n=0}^{\infty} a_n (z - z_0)^n$ with $z_0 \neq 0$. The coefficients a_0, a_1 are determined by the initial conditions $w(0)$ and $w'(0)$. Plugging this into the Bessel equation, which we rewrite as

$$[(z - z_0)^2 + 2z_0(z - z_0) + z_0^2]w''(z) + [(z - z_0) + z_0]w'(z)$$
$$+ [(z - z_0)^2 + 2z_0(z - z_0) + z_0^2 - n^2]w(z) = 0$$

yields a recursion relation for the coefficients a_n. Crude estimates show that the solutions a_n of this recursion grow at most exponentially in n, so the power series will converge in some small disk around z_0, as desired.

Observe that the two solutions w_1, w_2 with $w_1(z_0) = w_2'(z_0) = 1$ and $w_1'(z_0) = w_2(z_0) = 0$ generate all solutions in a small disk around z_0: simply set

$$w(z) = w(z_0)w_1(z) + w'(z_0)w_2(z).$$

By the monodromy theorem this can be analytically continued (uniquely) to any simply-connected region $G \subset \mathbb{C} \setminus \{0\}$. Hence w_1, w_2 are a fundamental system in all of G. At $z_0 = 0$ it is no longer possible to solve the Bessel equation for general initial data, and we can in general not continue analytically into the origin.

As for the final part, set $f(\zeta) = w(e^\zeta)$. Then locally around ζ_0 the function f satisfies the ordinary differential equation

$$\frac{d^2}{d\zeta^2} f + (e^{2\zeta} - n^2) f = 0$$

which admits (by power series) analytic solutions around *every* point. Hence, again by the monodromy theorem, $f(\zeta)$ can be continued to the entire plane as an entire function. $\square$

Step D: *Using either* (5.19) *or* (5.20) *we note that the power series expansion of* $J_n(z)$ *around zero is*

(5.22)
$$J_n(z) = (z/2)^n \sum_{k=0}^{\infty} \frac{(-1)^k (z/2)^{2k}}{k!(n + k)!}$$

provided $n \geq 0$. *For negative integers we use the relation* $J_{-n} = (-1)^n J_n$ *to obtain the power series of* J_n *for* $n < 0$.

Proof. From (5.19),

$$\sum_{\ell=0}^{\infty} \frac{1}{\ell!} \left(\frac{z}{2}\right)^{\ell} (\zeta - \zeta^{-1})^{\ell} = \sum_{\ell=0}^{\infty} \frac{1}{\ell!} \left(\frac{z}{2}\right)^{\ell} \sum_{k=0}^{\ell} \binom{\ell}{k} (-1)^{\ell-k} \zeta^{2k-\ell}$$

$$= \sum_{\ell=0}^{\infty} \left(\frac{z}{2}\right)^{\ell} \sum_{k=0}^{\ell} \frac{(-1)^{\ell-k}}{k!(\ell-k)!} \zeta^{2k-\ell} = \sum_{k=0}^{\infty} \sum_{\ell=0}^{\infty} \left(\frac{z}{2}\right)^{\ell+k} \frac{(-1)^{\ell}}{k!\ell!} \zeta^{k-\ell}$$

$$= \sum_{n \in \mathbb{Z}} \left[\sum_{k=0}^{\infty} \sum_{\ell=0}^{\infty} \chi_{[k-\ell=n]} \left(\frac{z}{2}\right)^{\ell+k} \frac{(-1)^{\ell}}{k!\ell!} \right] \zeta^n = \sum_{n=-\infty}^{\infty} J_n(z) \zeta^n$$

which gives the desired result.   □

Step E: *Suppose the formal power series $w_n(z) = \sum_{k=0}^{\infty} a_{k,n} z^k$ satisfies the ordinary differential equation (5.21) with some fixed integer $n \geq 0$. Then w_n is a multiple of J_n. In particular, J_n is the only solution of (5.21) (up to multiples) which is analytic around $z = 0$.*

Proof. One derives a recursion relation for the coefficients $a_{k,n}$ which then shows that up to a multiplicative constant the formal power series equals (5.22), i.e., w_n is a multiple of J_n. This is rather mechanical, and we leave this to the reader as Problem 5.9.   □

Step F: *We next set out to find a fundamental system of solutions of Bessel's equation (5.21) with $n = 0$ on $G = \mathbb{C} \setminus (-\infty, 0]$, using from Step C that the worst singularity at $z = 0$ of any solution of (5.21) is logarithmic. We also investigate general $n \geq 0$.*

Proof. The idea is to seek a solution of the form

$$\widetilde{J}_0(z) = J_0(z) \log z + \sum_{n=0}^{\infty} b_n z^n.$$

Observe that if $w(z)$ is a solution of the Bessel equation with $n = 0$, and which is analytic around 0, then $\widetilde{w}(z) := w(z) \log z$ satisfies

$$z^2 \widetilde{w}''(z) + z\widetilde{w}'(z) + z^2 \widetilde{w}(z) = 2zw'(z).$$

The right-hand side is analytic around 0, vanishes at $z = 0$, and is even. Hence, one can uniquely solve for b_n; thus, $b_0 = 0$, and all b_n with n odd vanish. In fact, the patient reader will verify that

$$\widetilde{J}_0(z) = J_0(z) \log z - \sum_{n=1}^{\infty} \frac{(-1)^n}{(n!)^2} \left(\frac{z}{2}\right)^{2n} \left[1 + \frac{1}{2} + \frac{1}{3} + \ldots + \frac{1}{n}\right]$$

(the usual notation for this function is Y_0 which is the same as $\widetilde{J}_0$ up to some normalizations; after all, we can multiply by any nonzero scalar and add any multiple of J_0). A similar procedure works for all other J_n, $n \geq 1$.

The reader is invited to check that J_ν and $J_{-\nu}$ with $\nu \in \mathbb{C} \setminus \mathbb{Z}$ (as defined in part (f)) are linearly independent and thus a fundamental system for these ν. A fundamental system for $n \in \mathbb{Z}$ is then given by the limit (by L'Hôpital's rule)

$$J_n(z), \qquad Y_n(z) := \lim_{\nu \to n} \frac{J_\nu(z) \cos(\nu\pi) - J_{-\nu}(z)}{\sin(\nu\pi)}.$$

The reader is invited to compute this for $\nu = 0$ and compare the result with $\widetilde{J}_0$ above. □

Step G: *We now use (5.22) to define J_ν for $\nu \in \mathbb{C}$ by the formula*

$$\text{(5.23)} \qquad J_\nu(z) = (z/2)^\nu \sum_{k=0}^{\infty} \frac{(-1)^k (z/2)^{2k}}{k!\, \Gamma(\nu + k + 1)},$$

where we select the principal branch of $z^\nu = e^{\nu \operatorname{Log} z}$ for definiteness (with $\operatorname{Log} z$ being the branch of the logarithm defined on the plane cut along $(-\infty, 0]$). Hence we view (5.23) as an element of $\mathcal{H}(\mathbb{C} \setminus (-\infty, 0])$. In particular,

$$J_{\frac{1}{2}}(z) = \left(\frac{2}{\pi z}\right)^{\frac{1}{2}} \sin z,$$

$$J_{\frac{3}{2}}(z) = \left(\frac{2}{\pi z}\right)^{\frac{1}{2}} \left(\frac{\sin z}{z} - \cos z\right).$$

The representation (5.23) agrees with the previous definition for all integer ν, including negative ones. The function J_ν defined in this fashion solves (5.21) with n replaced by $\nu \in \mathbb{C}$, and this property fails if we were to define J_ν by replacing n with $\nu \in \mathbb{C}$ in (5.20) (which explains why we used the power-series instead). For any $\nu \in \mathbb{C}$, the function $J_\nu(e^\zeta)$ is entire in ζ.

Proof. Verifying the formulas for $J_{\frac{1}{2}}$ and $J_{\frac{3}{2}}$ requires nothing but the identity

$$\Gamma(1/2) = \sqrt{\pi}$$

and a comparison with the power series of $\cos(z)$ and $\sin(z)$. The fact that the definition of J_ν agrees with the previous one for nonnegative integers ν is evident. For the negative ones, use that $\frac{1}{\Gamma(z)} = 0$ at all $z \in \mathbb{Z}_0^-$. The reason that (5.20) does not yield a solution for noninteger ν is the integration by parts that was required for that purpose: we pick up nonzero boundary terms when ν is not an integer. □

Step H: *Next, we establish that for all $\nu \in \mathbb{C}$ with $\mathrm{Re}\,\nu > -\frac{1}{2}$ there is the representation*

$$J_\nu(z) = \frac{(z/2)^\nu}{\Gamma(\nu + \frac{1}{2})\sqrt{\pi}} \int_{-1}^{1} e^{izt}(1 - t^2)^{\nu - \frac{1}{2}}\, dt$$
$$= \frac{(z/2)^\nu}{\Gamma(\nu + \frac{1}{2})\sqrt{\pi}} \int_{0}^{\pi} \cos(z \cos \theta) \sin^{2\nu} \theta\, d\theta.$$

We can also check directly that these integral representations satisfy the Bessel equation (5.21) with $n = \nu$.

Proof. This is proved by expanding the exponential into a power series and then by showing that you get the same series as in (5.23). Hence,

$$\frac{(z/2)^\nu}{\Gamma(\nu + \frac{1}{2})\sqrt{\pi}} \int_{-1}^{1} e^{izt}(1 - t^2)^{\nu - \frac{1}{2}}\, dt$$
$$= \sum_{n=0}^{\infty} \frac{(z/2)^\nu}{\Gamma(\nu + \frac{1}{2})\sqrt{\pi}} \int_{-1}^{1} \frac{(izt)^n}{n!}(1 - t^2)^{\nu - \frac{1}{2}}\, dt$$
$$= \sum_{n=0}^{\infty} \frac{(iz)^{2n}}{(2n)!} \frac{(z/2)^\nu}{\Gamma(\nu + \frac{1}{2})\sqrt{\pi}} 2 \int_{0}^{1} t^{2n}(1 - t^2)^{\nu - \frac{1}{2}}\, dt$$
$$= \sum_{n=0}^{\infty} \frac{(z/2)^\nu}{\Gamma(\nu + \frac{1}{2})\sqrt{\pi}} \frac{(iz)^{2n}}{(2n)!} \int_{0}^{1} u^{n - \frac{1}{2}}(1 - u)^{\nu - \frac{1}{2}}\, du$$
$$= \sum_{n=0}^{\infty} \frac{(z/2)^\nu}{\Gamma(\nu + \frac{1}{2})\sqrt{\pi}} \frac{(-1)^n z^{2n}}{(2n)!} \frac{\Gamma(\nu + \frac{1}{2})\Gamma(n + \frac{1}{2})}{\Gamma(n + \nu + 1)}$$
$$= (z/2)^\nu \sum_{n=0}^{\infty} \frac{(-1)^n (z/2)^{2n}}{n!\, \Gamma(n + \nu + 1)},$$

where we used that

$$\Gamma(n + 1/2) = \frac{(2n)!}{2^{2n} n!}\sqrt{\pi}$$

(invoke the functional equation of Γ as well as $\Gamma(1/2) = \sqrt{\pi}$). The interchange of summation and integration is justified as follows: putting absolute values inside everything (by the same argument) yields a convergent power series that converges for every $z \in \mathbb{C}$. To verify Bessel's equation, differentiate under the integral sign (we skip this somewhat mechanical calculation; see Problem 5.9). $\square$

Step I: *Using (5.23) we show that for any $\nu \in \mathbb{C}$,*

$$
\begin{aligned}
J_\nu(z) &= \frac{(z/2)^\nu}{2\pi i} \int_\gamma \exp\left(w - \frac{z^2}{4w}\right) \frac{dw}{w^{\nu+1}} \\
&= \frac{1}{2\pi i} \int_\gamma \exp\left(\frac{z}{2}(\zeta - \zeta^{-1})\right) \frac{d\zeta}{\zeta^{\nu+1}},
\end{aligned}
$$

(5.24)

where γ is a Hankel contour (see (2.36)). In both cases the powers involving ν are principal branches. Equation (5.24) is reminiscent of our starting point (5.19). Indeed, for $\nu = n \in \mathbb{Z}$ the representation (5.24) is nothing but the integral computing the nth Laurent coefficient of (5.19). Note that the power $\zeta^{\nu+1}$ in the denominator is single-valued if and only if $\nu \in \mathbb{Z}$.

Finally, we deduce from (5.24) that

(5.25)
$$
J_\nu(z) = \frac{1}{2\pi i} \int_{\widetilde{\gamma}} e^{z \sinh \tau - \nu\tau}\, d\tau
$$

where $\widetilde{\gamma} = \operatorname{Log} \gamma$ is the (principal) logarithm of a Hankel contour γ (see Figure 2.11).

Proof. By (2.36),

$$
\frac{1}{\Gamma(\nu + k + 1)} = \frac{1}{2\pi i} \int_\gamma e^w w^{-(\nu+k+1)}\, dw,
$$

so that

$$
\begin{aligned}
J_\nu(z) &= \frac{1}{2\pi i} \int_\gamma e^w (z/2)^\nu \sum_{k=0}^\infty \frac{(-1)^k (z/2)^{2k}}{k!} w^{-(\nu+k+1)}\, dw \\
&= \frac{(z/2)^\nu}{2\pi i} \int_\gamma \exp\left(w - \frac{z^2}{4w}\right) \frac{dw}{w^{\nu+1}} \\
&= \frac{1}{2\pi i} \int_\gamma \exp\left(\frac{z}{2}(\zeta - \zeta^{-1})\right) \frac{d\zeta}{\zeta^{\nu+1}},
\end{aligned}
$$

where we substituted $\frac{z}{2}\zeta = w$ to pass to the last line. This proves (5.24). Finally, to pass to (5.25) substitute $\zeta = e^\tau$ in the second line of (5.24). $\square$

Step J: *Finally, we use (5.25) to prove the recursion relation of the* Bessel functions

$$
\begin{aligned}
J_{\nu-1}(z) + J_{\nu+1}(z) &= (2\nu/z)J_\nu(z), \\
J_{\nu-1}(z) - J_{\nu+1}(z) &= 2J_\nu'(z),
\end{aligned}
$$

and from these that

$$
\begin{aligned}
J_{\nu+1}(z) &= (\nu/z)J_\nu(z) - J_\nu'(z), \\
J_{\nu-1}(z) &= (\nu/z)J_\nu(z) + J_\nu'(z).
\end{aligned}
$$

In particular, $J_0'(z) = -J_1(z)$.

Proof. From (5.25),

$$J_{\nu-1}(z) + J_{\nu+1}(z) = \frac{1}{2\pi i} \int_{\tilde{\gamma}} e^{z \sinh \tau - \nu \tau} 2 \cosh \tau \, d\tau$$

$$= \frac{2\nu}{z} \frac{1}{2\pi i} \int_{\tilde{\gamma}} e^{z \sinh \tau - \nu \tau} \, d\tau = \frac{2\nu}{z} J_\nu(z),$$

as well as

$$J_{\nu-1}(z) - J_{\nu+1}(z) = \frac{1}{2\pi i} \int_{\tilde{\gamma}} e^{z \sinh \tau - \nu \tau} 2 \sinh \tau \, d\tau = 2 J_\nu'(z).$$

The second set of identities follows by adding and subtracting the two lines of the first one. $\square$

Notes

The goal of this chapter is to put the intuitive way of approaching Riemann surfaces, i.e., by "looking at all possible analytic continuations" on a firm footing. Especially for algebraic functions this is a powerful, albeit perhaps cumbersome, way of obtaining the full Riemann surface associated with such an object. From a practical point of view, the author hopes that the reader will develop some intuition for these surfaces by working out examples such as those in Problem 5.6 below. For more examples of arguments involving "sheaves", as mentioned right before Section 5.2, see [29]. Needless to say, in practice one does not think in terms of all the different equivalence relations which we introduced in the first three sections. Nevertheless, in a rigorous text such as this there is no alternative to making these concepts, which are sometimes left "hanging in the air", precise.

For the proof of (5.15), as well as how to use this fact to put a group structure on an elliptic curve (and many other properties of these curves) we refer the reader to [21] and Chapter 3 of [47]. For answers to the question about embedding mentioned right after (5.15), see Chapter 7 or Jost's book [48].

The most important theorem of this chapter is Theorem 5.20 which equates compact Riemann surfaces (a geometric object) with an algebraic object, namely a polynomial $P(w, z)$. Historically, it is fair to say that Galois theory played a decisive role in much of the thinking of the 19th century, and this theorem is no exception. Indeed, Proposition 5.16 shows clearly how roots and their symmetries enter into the construction of meromorphic functions on Riemann surfaces — concepts which originate in Galois theory. For much more on this theme see Alekseev's wonderful exposition [4], which is based on lectures delivered by V. I. Arnold on Abel's theorem.

The proof of Theorem 5.20 given here is evidently not complete. Starting with the next chapter we will spend considerable effort on providing the missing analytical backbone, which is found in the construction of nontrivial meromorphic functions.

Linear differential equations with analytic or meromorphic coefficients constitute a rich area in which singularities of the coefficients are classified as either *regular* or *irregular* depending on the behavior of a fundamental system near these points. For more on the classical theory of Fuchsian equations, see Ahlfors [1] and Hartman [42]. This theory has produced interesting unresolved questions tied up with the monodromy group associated with such equations (such as the hypergeometric one), which continue to be addressed at the research level. Of particular importance here is the Riemann-Hilbert problem. We refer the reader to Kostov's survey [53], Chapter 7 entitled *Differential equations with irregular singularities* in Varadarajan's book [83], as well as the research papers by Costin, Costin [13], Beukers, Heckman [9], Fuchs, Meiri, Sarnak [30].

5.8. Problems

Problem 5.1. Fill in the missing details in Corollary 5.21. First check that Φ is indeed a homeomorphism from $\mathbb{C}/\Gamma$ onto E. Second, verify that the integrals (5.14) are correct.

Problem 5.2. Prove the Weierstrass preparation theorem: suppose $f(w, z)$ is analytic in both variables[1] and such that $f(w, z) \neq 0$ for all

$$|w - w_0| = r_0 > 0 \quad \text{and} \quad |z - z_0| < r_1.$$

Then there exists a polynomial

$$P(w, z) = \sum_{j=0}^{n} a_j(z) w^j$$

with a_j analytic on $|z - z_0| < r_1$ so that

$$f(w, z) = P(w, z) g(w, z)$$

with g analytic and nonvanishing on $D(z_0, r_1) \times D(w_0, r_0)$. Moreover, all solutions of $P(\cdot, z) = 0$ lie inside of $D(w_0, r_0)$ for all $z \in D(z_0, r_1)$.

In particular, show the following: if $\partial_w^\ell f(w_0, z_0) = 0$ for all $0 \leq \ell < n$, but $\partial_w^n f(w_0, z_0) \neq 0$, then there exist $r_0, r_1 > 0$ so that the conditions of the preparation theorem hold.

Hint: Observe that

$$b_p(z) := \frac{1}{2\pi i} \oint_{|w - w_0| = r_0} w^p \frac{\partial_w f(w, z)}{f(w, z)} \, dw$$

is analytic in $D(z_0, r_1)$ for all integers $p \geq 0$. Now define

$$P(w, z) := \prod_{j=1}^{n} (w - w_j(z)), \qquad f(z, w_j(z)) = 0, \ |w_j(z) - w_0| < r_0.$$

---

[1]This means that f is jointly continuous and analytic in each variable.

Since the coefficients of $P(w, z)$ are polynomials in the $b_p(z)$ they are also analytic. Moreover, $f(w, z)/P(w, z)$ has removable singularities at each of the $w_j(z)$ and is therefore analytic and nonvanishing.

Problem 5.3. Picture the unramified Riemann surfaces

$$(5.26) \qquad \mathcal{RS}(\mathbb{C}, \mathbb{C}, \log z, 1), \qquad \mathcal{RS}(\mathbb{C}, \mathbb{C}, z^{\frac{1}{n}}, 1),$$

$n \geq 2$. Prove that they cover $\mathbb{C}^*$. Compute the fundamental groups $\pi_1(\mathcal{RS})$ of these surfaces and prove that

$$\mathcal{RS}(\mathbb{C}, \mathbb{C}, \log z, 1) \simeq \mathbb{C},$$

$$\mathcal{RS}(\mathbb{C}, \mathbb{C}, z^{\frac{1}{n}}, 1) \simeq \mathbb{C}^*, \quad n \geq 2,$$

in the sense of conformal isomorphisms. Show that each of the surfaces in (5.26) has a branch point rooted at zero.

Problem 5.4. Let $A(z)$ be an $n \times n$ matrix so that each entry $A_{ij}(z)$ is a polynomial in z. Let the eigenvalues be denoted by $\lambda_j(z)$, $1 \leq j \leq n$. Prove that around each point z_0 at which $\lambda_j(z_0)$ is a simple eigenvalue, $\lambda_j(z)$ is an analytic function of z. Furthermore, if z_1 is a point at which $\lambda_j(z_1)$ has multiplicity k, then there is a local representation of the form

$$\lambda_j(z) = \sum_{n=0}^{\infty} a_n (z - z_1)^{\frac{n}{\ell}}$$

with some $1 \leq \ell \leq k$ (this is called a Puiseaux series). Now assume that $A(z)$ is Hermitian for all $z \in \mathbb{R}$. Prove that each λ_j is *analytic* on a neighborhood of $\mathbb{R}$. In other words, if $z_1 \in \mathbb{R}$, then the Puiseux series is actually a power series. Check these statements by means of the examples

$$A(z) = \begin{bmatrix} 0 & z \\ 1 & 0 \end{bmatrix}, \qquad A(z) = \begin{bmatrix} 0 & z \\ z & 0 \end{bmatrix}.$$

Problem 5.5. Prove Proposition 4.16 by means of Proposition 5.16.

Problem 5.6. For each of the following algebraic functions, you are asked to understand their Riemann surfaces by answering each of the following questions: Where are the branch points on the surface (be sure to check infinity)? How many sheets does it have? How are these sheets permuted under analytic continuation along closed curves which avoid the (roots of the) branch points? What is its genus? You should also try to obtain a sketch or at least some geometric intuition of the Riemann surface:

$$w = \sqrt[4]{\sqrt{z} - 1}, \quad w = \sqrt[3]{2\sqrt{z} + z + 1}, \quad w^3 - 3w - z = 0,$$

$$w = \sqrt[3]{z^2 - 1}, \quad w = \sqrt{z^2 + 16} - 5, \quad w = \sqrt{\sqrt{z^2 + 16} - 5}.$$

For the final example, analyze its Riemann surface by means of the two distinct set of cuts connecting the branch points to infinity, as depicted in Figure 5.13.

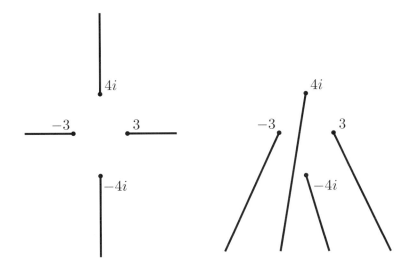

Figure 5.13. The set of cuts for $\sqrt{\sqrt{z^2 + 16} - 5}$

Problem 5.7. Let f be holomorphic on a simply-connected Riemann surface M, and assume that f never vanishes. Then there exists F holomorphic on M such that $f = e^F$. Show that harmonic functions on M have conjugate harmonic functions; see Definition 1.35.

Problem 5.8. This problem provides a tool for the construction of Riemann surfaces by quotients in case Theorem 4.12 does not apply due to fixed points. Let M be a Riemann surface, Γ a discrete group of automorphisms acting on M so that the action of Γ on M is proper. This means that if $\{p_n\}_{n=1}^{\infty}$ is a sequence in M and $\{\gamma_n\}_{n=1}^{\infty}$ is a sequence in Γ so that the p_n belong to some compact subset of M, and the γ_n are pairwise distinct, then $\gamma_n p_n$ "tends to infinity in M" (which expresses that the sequence of these points eventually leaves any given compact set).

(a) Prove that in this setting the quotient M/Γ carries the structure of a Riemann surface induced by the projection $\pi : M \to M/\Gamma$.

(b) Let $M = \mathbb{D}$ be the disk and $\Gamma = \mathbb{Z}/n\mathbb{Z} =: \mathbb{Z}_n$. Exhibit a natural proper action of Γ on M such that the map $z \mapsto z^n$ induces an isomorphism $\mathbb{D}/\mathbb{Z}_n \simeq \mathbb{D}$.

Problem 5.9. Prove Step E in Section 5.7 above. Provide the missing details in the proof of Step H. Rewrite the Bessel equation near $z = \infty$.

Decide whether the Bessel equation is of Fuchsian type at ∞, i.e., whether $z = \infty$ is a regular or irregular singularity of the Bessel equation.

Problem 5.10. Determine two linearly independent solutions of the equation

$$z^2(z+1)w''(z) - z^2w'(z) + w(z) = 0$$

near $z = 0$ and one near $z = -1$.

Chapter 6

Differential forms on Riemann surfaces

In this chapter we begin to develop function theory on Riemann surfaces. Stated quite generally, the main challenge is to understand **global objects** on these surfaces such as holomorphic or meromorphic 1-forms and their integration theory. The latter of course requires taking the topology of the compact (say) surface into account, which is quite different from the "local theory" of the first two chapters. But there, too, we encountered the role that topology plays, namely through the properties of loops (cf. simple connectivity).

Before turning to these global questions we first need to see which concepts from basic complex analysis carry over to Riemannian surfaces. This is tantamount to selecting the coordinate-invariant notions. For example, a Laurent series does not have meaning on a Riemann surface, but as we shall see, the residue does. The fact that residues have a coordinate independent meaning further demonstrates their fundamental importance.

6.1. Holomorphic and meromorphic differentials

We already observed in Chapter 4 that every Riemann surface is orientable as a smooth two-dimensional manifold. As a smooth manifold, M carries k-forms for each $0 \leq k \leq 2$. We allow these forms to be complex-valued and denote the respective spaces by

$$\Omega^0(M; \mathbb{C}), \quad \Omega^1(M; \mathbb{C}), \quad \Omega^2(M; \mathbb{C}).$$

By definition, $\Omega^0(M;\mathbb{C})$ consists of C^∞ functions on M, whereas because of orientability $\Omega^2(M;\mathbb{C})$ contains a 2-form denoted by vol which never vanishes; hence, every other element in $\Omega^2(M;\mathbb{C})$ is of the form $f$vol where $f \in \Omega^0(M;\mathbb{C})$. This leaves $\Omega^1(M;\mathbb{C})$ as the only really interesting object. By definition, each $\omega \in \Omega^1(M;\mathbb{C})$ defines a *real-linear* functional ω_p on T_pM. We will be particularly interested in those that are complex linear. We start with a basic observation from linear algebra which already appeared in Chapter 1. We restate it here for the convenience of the reader.

Lemma 6.1. *If $T : V \to W$ is a $\mathbb{R}$-linear map between complex vector spaces, then there is a unique representation $T = T_1 + T_2$ where T_1 is complex linear and T_2 complex anti-linear. The latter property means that $T_2(\lambda\vec{v}) = \bar{\lambda}T_2(\vec{v})$.*

Proof. Uniqueness follows since a $\mathbb{C}$-linear map which is simultaneously $\mathbb{C}$-anti linear vanishes identically. For existence, set

$$T_1 = \frac{1}{2}(T - iTi), \qquad T_2 = \frac{1}{2}(T + iTi).$$

Then $T_1 i = iT_1$ and $T_2 i = -iT_2$, $T = T_1 + T_2$, as desired. $\square$

As an application, consider the following four complex-valued maps on $U \subset \mathbb{R}^2$ where U is any open set: $\pi_1, \pi_2, z, \bar{z}$ which are defined as follows:

$$\pi_1(x,y) = x, \ \pi_2(x,y) = y, \ z(x,y) = x + iy, \ \bar{z} = x - iy.$$

Identifying the tangent space of U with $\mathbb{R}^2$ at every point the differentials of each of these maps correspond to the following constant matrices

$$d\pi_1 = \begin{bmatrix} 1 & 0 \\ 0 & 0 \end{bmatrix}, \ d\pi_2 = \begin{bmatrix} 0 & 1 \\ 0 & 0 \end{bmatrix}, \ dz = \begin{bmatrix} 1 & 0 \\ 0 & 1 \end{bmatrix}, \ d\bar{z} = \begin{bmatrix} 1 & 0 \\ 0 & -1 \end{bmatrix}.$$

Let us now write $\omega \in \Omega^1(M;\mathbb{C})$ in local coordinates

$$\omega = a\,dx + b\,dy = \frac{1}{2}(a - ib)\,dz + \frac{1}{2}(a + ib)\,d\bar{z} = u\,dz + v\,d\bar{z}.$$

Of course, this is exactly the decomposition of Lemma 6.1 in each tangent space.

We single out the special case $\omega = df$ with $f \in \Omega^0(M;\mathbb{C})$ (we already encountered this form in Chapter 1). Then

$$df = \partial_z f\,dz + \partial_{\bar{z}} f\,d\bar{z},$$

$$\partial_z f = \frac{1}{2}(\partial_x f - i\partial_y f), \quad \partial_{\bar{z}} f = \frac{1}{2}(\partial_x f + i\partial_y f).$$

If $f \in \mathcal{H}(M)$, then df needs to be complex linear. In other words, f satisfies the Cauchy-Riemann equations $\partial_{\bar{z}} f = 0$. In this notation, it is easy to give a one-line proof of Cauchy's theorem: Let $f \in \mathcal{H}(U)$ where $U \subset \mathbb{C}$ is a domain with piecewise C^1 boundary and $f \in C^1(\bar{U})$. Then

$$\int_{\partial U} f \, dz = \int_U d(f \, dz) = \int_U \partial_{\bar{z}} f \, d\bar{z} \wedge dz = 0.$$

We leave it to the reader the verify the chain rules,

$$\partial_z(g \circ f) = (\partial_w g) \circ f \, \partial_z f + (\partial_{\bar{w}} g) \circ f \, \partial_z \bar{f},$$
$$\partial_{\bar{z}}(g \circ f) = (\partial_w g) \circ f \, \partial_{\bar{z}} f + (\partial_{\bar{w}} g) \circ f \, \partial_{\bar{z}} \bar{f},$$

as well as the representation of the Laplacian $\Delta = 4 \frac{\partial^2}{\partial z \partial \bar{z}}$.

Definition 6.2. The *holomorphic differentials* on a Riemann surface M, denoted by $\mathcal{H}\Omega^1(M)$, are precisely those $\omega \in \Omega^1(M; \mathbb{C})$ so that $\omega = u \, dz$ in arbitrary local coordinates with u holomorphic. The *meromorphic differentials*, denoted by $\mathcal{M}\Omega^1(M)$, are all $\omega \in \mathcal{H}\Omega^1(M \setminus \mathcal{S}; \mathbb{C})$ where $\mathcal{S} \subset M$ is discrete and so that in local coordinates around an arbitrary point of M one has $\omega = u \, dz$ where u is meromorphic. The points of $\mathcal{S}$ will be called *poles* of ω.

It is clear that these notions as well-defined: if $z = z(\zeta)$ is a change of coordinates, then

$$u(z) \, dz = u(z(\zeta)) \, z'(\zeta) \, d\zeta.$$

Note that we are assuming here that those points of $\mathcal{S}$ which are removable singularities of u have been removed. Obvious examples of holomorphic and meromorphic differentials, respectively, are given by df where $f \in \mathcal{H}(M)$ or $f \in \mathcal{M}(M)$.

6.2. Integrating differentials and residues

The only meaningful objects to integrate along curves on surfaces are 1-forms. We *cannot integrate functions along curves*, as we did in local complex analysis, we can only integrate functions against a volume form.

It is convenient to introduce the following terminology, where M, N are Riemann surfaces.

Definition 6.3. We say that $N \subset M$ is a **Stokes region** if $\bar{N}$ is compact and ∂N (the boundary of N in M) is piecewise C^1. This means that ∂N is the finite union of curves $\gamma_j : [0,1] \to M$ which are C^1 on the closed interval $[0,1]$.

The importance of a Stokes region lies with the fact that Stokes' theorem applies to it. Holomorphic 1-forms enjoy the following basic properties. Proposition 6.4 generalizes Cauchy's theorem.

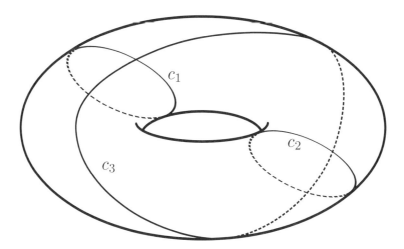

Figure 6.1. c_1 and c_2 are homologous to each other, but not to c_3

Proposition 6.4. *Suppose* $\omega \in \mathcal{H}\Omega^1(M)$. *Then* $d\omega = 0$. *Thus,* $\int_{\partial N} \omega = 0$ *for every Stokes region* $N \subset M$. *For any closed curve* γ *the integral* $\oint_\gamma \omega$ *only depends on the homology class of* γ.

In particular, $\oint_\gamma \omega = \oint_\eta \omega$ *if* γ *and* η *are homotopic closed curves. Finally, if* c *is a curve with initial point* p *and endpoint* q, *then*

(6.1)
$$\int_c \omega = f_1(q) - f_0,$$

where $df_0 = \omega$ *locally around* p *and* f_1 *is obtained via analytic continuation of* f_0 *along* c. *In particular,* $df_1 = \omega$ *locally around* q.

Proof. Since $\omega = u\, dz$ in a chart, one has

$$d\omega = \partial_{\bar{z}} u\, d\bar{z} \wedge dz = 0$$

as claimed. So by Stokes' theorem we conclude that

$$\int_{\partial N} \omega = \int_N d\omega = 0.$$

If γ and η are homologous, then by definition $\gamma - \eta = \partial N$ for some Stokes region N. By the previous property $\int_\gamma \omega = \int_\eta \omega$. If two curves are homotopic, then they are homologous.

Recall that Poincaré's lemma asserts that closed forms defined on some domain in $\mathbb{C}$ are locally exact (in fact, on any simply-connected domain). For closed 1-forms ω this is easy: obtain the function f such that $\omega = df$ by integration along a curve starting from some fixed point. The choice of curve is not important by the invariance of the integral under homotopies which fix endpoints (either in a small disk, or in the simply-connected case, globally). Thus, we can write $\omega = d\,f_0$ locally around p, say in a parametric disk. If c lies entirely in this disk, then

$$\int_c \omega = \int_c df_0 = f_0(q) - f_0(p)$$

by the fundamental theorem of calculus (or Proposition 1.17), whence (6.1). Otherwise, we can cover c by parametric disks $\{D_j\}$ in a way that gives rise to a chain of analytic continuations f_j as in Chapter 5. On each of these disks we then have

$$\int_{c_j} \omega = \int_{c_j} df_j = f_j(q_j) - f_j(p_j),$$

where $c_j \subset D_j$ arises from the natural partition of c induced by the chain of disks, and q_j, p_j are the respective endpoints of the segment c_j. Summing these relations then yields (6.1): the right-hand side telescopes due to $f_{j+1}(p_{j+1}) = f_j(q_j)$. $\qquad\square$

For meromorphic differentials, we have a version of the residue theorem and of the argument principle.

Proposition 6.5. *Suppose $\omega \in \mathcal{M}\Omega^1(M)$ with poles $\{p_j\}_{j=1}^{J}$. Then at each of these poles their orders $\mathrm{ord}(\omega, p_j) \in \mathbb{Z}^-$ and residues $\mathrm{res}(\omega; p_j) \in \mathbb{C}$ are well-defined. In fact,*

$$\mathrm{res}(\omega; p_j) = \frac{1}{2\pi i} \oint_c \omega,$$

where c is any small loop around p_j. Given any Stokes region $N \subset M$ so that ∂N does not contain any pole of ω, we have

(6.2)
$$\frac{1}{2\pi i} \oint_{\partial N} \omega = \sum_{p \in N} \mathrm{res}(\omega; p).$$

Finally, if M is compact, then

$$\sum_{p \in M} \mathrm{res}(\omega; p) = 0$$

for all $\omega \in \mathcal{M}\Omega^1(M)$.

Proof. Let $\omega = u\,dz$ with

$$u(p) = \sum_{n=-n_0}^{\infty} a_n\, z^n$$

in local coordinates (U, z) around p_j with $z(p_j) = 0$ and $a_{-n_0} \neq 0$. Note that n_0 does not depend on the choice of the chart but the coefficients do in general. However, since

$$a_{-1} = \frac{1}{2\pi i} \oint \omega,$$

this coefficient does not depend on the chart and it is the residue. The "residue theorem" (6.2) follows from Proposition 6.4 applied to

$$N' := N \setminus \bigcup_j D_j$$

where D_j are small parametric disks centered at $p_j \in N$. Finally, if M is compact, then we triangulate M in such a way that no edge of the triangulation passes through a pole (there are only finitely many of them). $\qquad\square$

The argument principle takes the following form:

Proposition 6.6. *With $N \subset M$ a Stokes region and $f \in \mathcal{M}(M)$,*

$$\frac{1}{2\pi i} \oint_{\partial N} \frac{df}{f} = \#\{p \in N \mid f(p) = 0\} - \#\{p \in N \mid p \text{ is a pole of } f\},$$

assuming that no zero or pole lies on ∂N. As usual, the right-hand side is counted with multiplicities (degree of zeros and order of poles).

Proof. This follows by setting $\omega = \frac{df}{f}$ in (6.2). $\qquad\square$

In the final section of this chapter we shall prove the following result for compact surfaces: *To any given finite sequence $\{p_j\}$ of points and complex numbers $\{c_j\}$ adding up to zero, there exists a meromorphic differential that has simple poles at* exactly *these points with residues equal to the c_j.*

This will be based on the Hodge theorem to which we now turn.

6.3. The Hodge-$*$ operator and harmonic differentials

The entry point for 20th century mathematics into this story is provided by the introduction of the space of square integrable 1-forms. This will allow us to invoke Hilbert space theory, which is crucial in order to establish basic existence results such as those for meromorphic differentials appearing later in this chapter.

Definition 6.7. To every $\omega \in \Omega^1(M; \mathbb{C})$ we associate a 1-form $*\omega$ defined as follows: if $\omega = u\, dz + v\, d\bar{z} = f\, dx + g\, dy$ in local coordinates, then

$$*\omega := -iu\, dz + iv\, d\bar{z} = -g\, dx + f\, dy.$$

Moreover, if $\omega, \eta \in \Omega^1_{\mathrm{comp}}(M; \mathbb{C})$ (the forms with compact support), we set

$$(6.3) \qquad\qquad \langle \omega, \eta \rangle := \int_M \omega \wedge \overline{*\eta}.$$

This defines an inner product on $\Omega^1_{\mathrm{comp}}(M; \mathbb{C})$. The completion of this space relative to the associated Euclidean norm is denoted by $\Omega^1_2(M; \mathbb{C})$.

Some comments are in order: first, $*\omega$ is well-defined, i.e., it does not depend on the choice of coordinates. Indeed, changing coordinates $z = z(w)$ yields

$$\omega = u\,dz + v\,d\bar{z} = uz'\,dw + v\,\overline{z'}\,d\bar{z},$$

and $*\omega$ transforms the same way.

Second, by definition (6.3) does not depend on coordinates and, moreover, if ω, η are supported in U where (U, z) is a chart, then with

$$\omega = u\,dz + v\,d\bar{z}, \quad \eta = r\,dz + s\,d\bar{z}$$

we obtain

$$\omega \wedge \overline{*\eta} = i(u\bar{r} + v\bar{s})\,dz \wedge d\bar{z} = 2(u\bar{r} + v\bar{s})\,dx \wedge dy.$$

In particular,

$$\langle \omega, \eta \rangle = 2 \iint_U (u\bar{r} + v\bar{s})\,dx \wedge dy,$$

which is a positive definite scalar product locally on U. By a partition of unity, this shows that indeed (6.3) is a scalar product on $\Omega^1_{\mathrm{comp}}(M)$ and, moreover, that the abstract completion $\Omega^1_2(M)$ consists of all 1-forms ω which in charts have measurable L^2_{loc} coefficients and which satisfy the global property

$$\|\omega\|_2^2 := \langle \omega, \omega \rangle < \infty.$$

Let us state some easy properties of the Hodge-$*$ operator.

Lemma 6.8. *For any* $\omega, \eta \in \Omega^1_2(M)$ *we have*

$$*\overline{\omega} = \overline{*\omega}, \quad **\omega = -\omega, \quad \langle *\omega, *\eta \rangle = \langle \omega, \eta \rangle.$$

Proof. The first two identities follow immediately from the representation in local coordinates, whereas the third is a consequence of the first two. □

We now come to the topic of **harmonic functions and forms**. Recall that the class of harmonic functions is invariant under conformal changes of coordinates; see Corollary 1.39. This allows us to define this class also on Riemann surfaces.

Definition 6.9. We say that $f \in \Omega^0(M; \mathbb{C})$ is *harmonic* if f is harmonic in every chart. We say that $\omega \in \Omega^1(M; \mathbb{C})$ is *harmonic* if $d\omega = d*\omega = 0$, i.e., if ω is both **closed** and **co-closed**. We denote the harmonic forms on M by $\mathfrak{h}(M; \mathbb{R})$ if they are real-valued and by $\mathfrak{h}(M; \mathbb{C})$ if they are complex-valued.

We begin by establishing basic properties of harmonic functions, with emphasis on the *maximum principle.*

Lemma 6.10. *Suppose $f \in \Omega^0(M; \mathbb{C})$ is harmonic with respect to some atlas. Then it is harmonic with respect the any equivalent atlas and therefore, also with respect to the conformal structure. Moreover, the* maximum principle *holds: if such an f is real-valued and the open connected set $U \subset M$ has compact closure in M, then*

$$\min_{\partial U} f \leq f(p) \leq \max_{\partial U} f \qquad \forall\, p \in U,$$

with equality being attained at some $p \in U$ if and only if f equals a constant. In particular, if M is compact, then f is constant.

Proof. Under the conformal change of coordinates $w = w(z)$ we have

$$\frac{\partial^2 f}{\partial z \partial \bar{z}} = |w'(z)|^2 \frac{\partial^2 f}{\partial w \partial \bar{w}}.$$

Thus, harmonicity is preserved under conformal changes of coordinates as claimed. For the maximum principle, we note that if $f : U \to \mathbb{R}$ is harmonic in a chart and attains a local maximum in that chart, then it is constant on the chart by the maximum principle for harmonic functions on open sets of $\mathbb{C}$. But then f would have to be constant on all of U by connectedness and by the fact that harmonic functions in the plane that are constant on some open subset of a planar domain have to be constant on the entire domain. Hence we have shown that f cannot attain a local maximum on U. Finally, if M is compact, then by taking $U = M$ we are done. $\qquad \square$

Harmonic forms are so-called because of the close relationship they enjoy with harmonic functions.

Lemma 6.11. *Let $\omega \in \mathfrak{h}(M; \mathbb{R})$ (or $\mathfrak{h}(M; \mathbb{C})$). Then locally around every point of M, $\omega = df$ where f is real-valued (or complex-valued) and harmonic. If M is simply-connected, then $\omega = df$ where f is a harmonic function on all of M. Conversely, if f is a harmonic function on M, then df is a harmonic 1-form. If u is a harmonic (and either real- or complex-valued) function, then the complex linear part of du is a holomorphic differential. In other words, in local coordinates, $\omega = \partial_z u\, dz \in \mathcal{H}\Omega^1(M)$.*

Proof. Since ω is locally exact, we have $\omega = df$ locally with f being either real- or complex-valued depending on whether ω is real- or complex-valued. Then ω is co-closed if and only if $d{*}df = 0$. In local coordinates, this is the same as

$$d(-f_y\, dx + f_x\, dy) = (f_{xx} + f_{yy})\, dx \wedge dy = 0,$$

which is the same as f being harmonic. This also proves the converse. If M is simply-connected, then f is a global primitive of ω. For the final statement, note that

$$\partial_{\bar{z}}\partial_z u = 0,$$

since u is harmonic. $\qquad\square$

Here is a useful characterization of harmonic differentials. We will omit the field $\mathbb{R}$ or $\mathbb{C}$ from our notation if this choice makes no difference.

Lemma 6.12. *Let $\omega \in \Omega^1(M)$ and suppose that $\omega = a\,dx + b\,dy$ in some chart (U, z). Then ω is harmonic if and only if $f := a - ib$ is holomorphic on $z(U)$.*

Proof. Since

$$d\omega = (-a_y + b_x)\,dx \wedge dy, \quad d{*}\omega = (b_y + a_x)\,dx \wedge dy,$$

we see that ω is harmonic if and only if $a, -b$ satisfy the Cauchy-Riemann system on $z(U)$ which is equivalent to $a - ib$ being holomorphic on $z(U)$. $\quad\square$

Next, we make the following observation linking holomorphic and harmonic differentials.

Lemma 6.13. *Let $\omega \in \Omega^1(M; \mathbb{C})$. Then the following are equivalent:*

(1) *ω is harmonic,*

(2) *$\omega = \alpha + \overline{\beta}$ where $\alpha, \beta \in \mathcal{H}\Omega^1(M)$,*

and the following are also equivalent:

(a) *$\omega \in \mathcal{H}\Omega^1(M)$,*

(b) *$d\omega = 0$ and $*\omega = -i\omega$,*

(c) *$\omega = \alpha + i*\alpha$ where $\alpha \in \mathfrak{h}(M; \mathbb{R})$.*

In particular, every holomorphic differential is harmonic and the only real-valued holomorphic differential is zero.

Proof. Write $\omega = u\,dz + v\,d\bar{z}$ in local coordinates. For (1), (2), observe that

$$d\omega = (-\partial_{\bar{z}}u + \partial_z v)\,dz \wedge d\bar{z},$$
$$d{*}\omega = i(\partial_{\bar{z}}u + \partial_z v)\,dz \wedge d\bar{z},$$

both vanish identically if and only if $\partial_{\bar{z}}u = 0$ and $\partial_z v = 0$. In other words, if and only if $\alpha = u\,dz$ and $\beta = \bar{v}\,dz$ are both holomorphic differentials.

For (a), (b), (c) we note that ω is holomorphic if and only if $v = 0$ and $\partial_{\bar{z}}u = 0$, which is further equivalent to $d\omega = 0$ and $*\omega = -i\omega$. If $\omega = \alpha + i*\alpha$ with α harmonic, then $d\omega = 0$ and

$$*\omega = *\alpha - i\alpha = -i\omega.$$

For the converse, set $\alpha = \frac{1}{2}(\omega + \bar{\omega})$. Then

$$*\alpha = \frac{i}{2}(-\omega + \bar{\omega}), \quad \alpha + i*\alpha = \omega,$$

and $\alpha \in \mathfrak{h}(M;\mathbb{R})$ as desired.

Finally, it is clear from (1), (2) that every holomorphic differential is also harmonic. On the other hand, if $\omega \in \mathcal{H}\Omega^1(M)$ and real-valued, then we can write

$$\omega = \alpha + i*\alpha = \bar{\omega} = \alpha - i*\alpha,$$

or $*\alpha = 0$ which is the same as $\alpha = 0$. $\square$

In the simply-connected compact case it turns out that there are no nonzero harmonic or holomorphic differentials.

Corollary 6.14. *If M is compact and simply-connected, then*

$$\mathfrak{h}(M;\mathbb{R}) = \mathfrak{h}(M;\mathbb{C}) = \mathcal{H}\Omega^1(M) = \{0\}.$$

Proof. Any harmonic 1-form ω can be written globally on M as $\omega = df$ with f harmonic (see Lemma 5.5). But then f equals a constant by the maximum principle and so $\omega = 0$. Consequently, the only holomorphic 1-form is also zero. $\square$

The obvious example for this corollary is of course $M = \mathbb{C}P^1$. Let us now consider some examples for which we do have many nontrivial forms.

1) In the case of $M \subset \mathbb{C}$ simply-connected we have in view of Lemmas 6.11–6.13,

$$\mathcal{H}\Omega^1(M) = \{df \mid f \in \mathcal{H}(M)\},$$
$$\mathfrak{h}(M;\mathbb{C}) = \{df + \overline{dg} \mid f, g \in \mathcal{H}(M)\},$$
$$(6.4) \quad \mathfrak{h}(M;\mathbb{R}) = \{a\,dx + b\,dy \mid a = \mathrm{Re}(f), \, b = -\mathrm{Im}(f), \, f \in \mathcal{H}(M)\}$$
$$= \{df + \overline{df} \mid f \in \mathcal{H}(M)\}$$
$$= \{du \mid u \text{ harmonic real-valued on } M\}.$$

In these examples harmonic (or holomorphic) 1-forms are globally differentials of harmonic (or holomorphic) functions.

2) For a non-simply-connected example, consider the annulus

$$M = \{r_1 < |z| < r_2\}$$

with $0 \le r_1 < r_2 \le \infty$. In these cases, a closed form ω is exact if and only if

$$\oint_{\gamma_r} \omega = 0, \qquad \gamma_r(t) = re^{2\pi it}$$

for one (and thus every) $\gamma_r \subset M$ (or any closed curve in M that winds around 0). This implies that every closed ω can be written uniquely as

$$\omega = k\,d\theta + df, \quad k = \frac{1}{2\pi}\oint_{\gamma_r}\omega, \quad f \in C^\infty(M)$$

and, with θ being any branch of the polar angle,

$$d\theta := -\frac{y}{r^2}\,dx + \frac{x}{r^2}\,dy, \quad r^2 = x^2 + y^2.$$

We remark that $d\theta \in \mathfrak{h}(M;\mathbb{R})$ since (any branch of) the polar angle is harmonic. Any reader familiar with de Rham cohomology will recognize the fact that $H^1(\mathbb{R}^2 \setminus \{0\}) \simeq \mathbb{R}$ (the space on the left is closed forms modulo exact forms). The conclusion is that

$$\mathfrak{h}(M;\mathbb{R}) = \{df + k\,d\theta \mid f \text{ harmonic and } \mathbb{R}\text{-valued on } M,\ k \in \mathbb{R}\},$$
$$\mathfrak{h}(M;\mathbb{C}) = \{df + k\,d\theta \mid f \text{ harmonic and } \mathbb{C}\text{-valued on } M,\ k \in \mathbb{C}\},$$

$$(6.5)\qquad \mathcal{H}\Omega^1(M) = \{f_z\,dz + ik\frac{dz}{z} \mid f \text{ harmonic, } \mathbb{R}\text{-valued on } M,\ k \in \mathbb{R}\}$$

$$(6.6)\qquad\qquad = \{dg + \kappa\frac{dz}{z} \mid g \in \mathcal{H}(M),\ \kappa \in \mathbb{C}\}.$$

The representation (6.5) follows from Lemma 6.13, whereas for (6.6) we note that $\omega \in \mathcal{H}\Omega^1(M)$ is exact if and only if

$$\oint_{\gamma_r}\omega = 0.$$

Hence (6.6) follows by setting

$$\kappa = \frac{1}{2\pi i}\oint_{\gamma_r}\omega,$$

which then allows us to define

$$g(z) := \int_1^z \left(\omega - \kappa\frac{dz}{z}\right)$$

along an arbitrary curve. To reconcile (6.6) with (6.5), we first observe that

$$\oint_{\gamma_r} f_z\,dz = -\oint_{\gamma_r} f_{\bar{z}}\,d\bar{z} = -\overline{\oint_{\gamma_r} f_z\,dz} \in i\mathbb{R}$$

since f is real-valued. Conversely, if $a \in \mathbb{R}$, then there exists f real-valued and harmonic on M such that

$$\oint_{\gamma_r} f_z\,dz = 2\pi i a.$$

Indeed, set $f(z) = a\log|z|$ for which

$$f_z(z)\,dz = a\frac{\bar{z}}{r^2}\,dz.$$

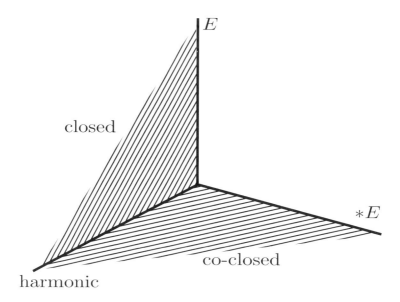

Figure 6.2. A schematic view of the Hodge decomposition

This explains why it suffices to add $ik\frac{dz}{z}$ with $k \in \mathbb{R}$ in (6.5).

3) As a final example, let $M = \mathbb{C}/\langle 1, \tau \rangle$ where $\langle 1, \tau \rangle \subset \mathrm{Aut}(\mathbb{C})$ is the group generated by $z \mapsto z + 1$, $z \mapsto z + \tau$ and $\mathrm{Im}\,\tau > 0$. Then any

$$\omega \in \mathfrak{h}(M; \mathbb{R})$$

lifts to the universal cover of M which is $\mathbb{C}$. Thus, we can write $\omega = a\,dx + b\,dy$ where $a - ib$ is an analytic function on M and thus constant. Hence

$$\dim_{\mathbb{R}} \mathfrak{h}(M; \mathbb{R}) = \dim_{\mathbb{C}} \mathfrak{h}(M; \mathbb{C}) = 2 = 2 \dim_{\mathbb{C}} \mathcal{H}\Omega^1(M).$$

Any reader familiar with the usual Hodge theorem on smooth compact manifolds will recognize the statement here that $H^1(M) \simeq \mathbb{R}^{2g}$ where M is a compact surface of genus g. As before, $H^1(M)$ is the space of closed 1-forms modulo exact forms.

6.4. Statement and examples of the Hodge decomposition

In Section 6.5 we shall prove the following version of Hodge's theorem:

(6.7) $$\Omega_2^1(M; \mathbb{R}) = E \oplus *E \oplus \mathfrak{h}_2(M; \mathbb{R}).$$

Here $\Omega_2^1(M; \mathbb{R})$ are the square integrable, real-valued, 1-forms from Definition 6.7,

$$\mathfrak{h}_2(M; \mathbb{R}) := \mathfrak{h} \cap \Omega_2^1(M; \mathbb{R}),$$

and

$$E := \overline{\{df \mid f \in \Omega^0_{\text{comp}}(M;\mathbb{R})\}}, \quad *E := \overline{\{*df \mid f \in \Omega^0_{\text{comp}}(M;\mathbb{R})\}}$$

where the closure is in the sense of the L^2-norm in $\Omega^1_2(M)$. Figure 6.2 describes the subspaces appearing in Hodge's theorem (the reason for the (co)closed planes will become clear later; see Lemma 6.17). Let us first clarify that $E \perp *E$: thus, let

$$f, g \in \Omega^0_{\text{comp}}(M;\mathbb{R})$$

and compute

$$\int_M df \wedge \overline{**dg} = -\int_M df \wedge dg = -\int_M d(f\,dg) = 0$$

by Stokes. Hence

$$\Omega^1_2(M;\mathbb{R}) = E \oplus *E \oplus (E^\perp \cap (*E)^\perp),$$

and the main issue then becomes equating the intersection at the end with $\mathfrak{h}_2(M;\mathbb{R})$. This is nontrivial, since we will need to prove that all forms in $E^\perp \cap (*E)^\perp$ are *smooth* while at first sight they only have L^2 coefficients. It will turn out that it is easy to see from the definition that all forms in $E^\perp \cap (*E)^\perp$ are *weakly harmonic*[1] so that the issue then is to prove that weakly harmonic forms are strongly harmonic. This of course is the content of Weyl's lemma which is a basic result in elliptic regularity theory.

The purpose of this section is to establish the Hodge decomposition (6.7) on four manifolds: $\mathbb{C}$, S^2, $\mathbb{C}/\mathbb{Z}^2$, and $\mathbb{D}$. In each case we shall determine the space of harmonic differentials and exhibit the role they play in (6.7). Heuristically speaking, the space $\mathfrak{h}_2$ is nonzero due to either nontrivial cohomology or a "large boundary" of M. The former is present in the torus $\mathbb{C}/\mathbb{Z}^2$, whereas the latter arises in the case of $\mathbb{D}$. More technically speaking, in each of the four examples we will prove the Hodge decomposition by solving the Poisson equation and the harmonic forms arise either because of an integrability condition or due to a boundary condition. We shall not make use of anything in the section that appears beyond this point. Nevertheless, seeing the general Hodge theorem in these special cases should give a better intuitive understanding of the phenomena that might arise.

Example 1: $M = \mathbb{C}$.

Pick any $\omega \in \mathfrak{h}_2(\mathbb{C})$. In view of (6.4), $\omega = a\,dx + b\,dy$ with a, b being harmonic and L^2 bounded:

$$\iint_{\mathbb{R}^2} (|a|^2 + |b|^2)\,dx\,dy < \infty.$$

---

[1] This will be made precise in Section 6.5.

We claim that necessarily $a = b = 0$. From the mean-value theorem (with $\zeta = \xi + i\eta$)

$$|a(z)|^2 = \left| \frac{1}{|D(z,r)|} \iint_{D(z,r)} a(\zeta)\, d\xi d\eta \right|^2$$

$$\leq \frac{1}{|D(z,r)|} \iint_{D(z,r)} |a(\zeta)|^2\, d\xi d\eta \leq \frac{\|a\|_2^2}{|D(z,r)|} \to 0,$$

as $r \to \infty$. So $\mathfrak{h}_2(M) = \{0\}$ in this case. Note that while $\mathfrak{h}(\mathbb{C};\mathbb{R})$ is a large space (since there are many entire functions by the Weierstrass theorem), the L^2 condition only leaves the zero form. This can be thought of as the boundary of $\mathbb{C}$ is small; in fact, it consists only of the point at infinity in S^2. Heuristically the previous argument can be viewed as follows: any form in $\mathfrak{h}_2$ can be continued to a harmonic form on S^2 which then needs to vanish.

Hence by (6.7) every L^2 form ω is the sum of an exact and a co-exact form (more precisely, up to L^2 closure). Let us understand this first for smooth, compactly supported ω. Thus, let

$$\omega = a\, dx + b\, dy, \quad a, b \in C^\infty_{\text{comp}}(\mathbb{R}^2).$$

Then we seek $f, g \in C^\infty(\mathbb{R}^2)$ with

$$(6.8) \qquad\qquad \omega = df + *dg.$$

Since $\mathbb{C}$ is simply-connected, this is equivalent to writing $\omega = \alpha + \beta$ where $d\alpha = 0$ and $d*\beta = 0$. This in turn shows that (6.8) is equivalent to writing a smooth, compactly supported vector field as the sum of a divergence-free field and a curl-free field. To find f, g, we apply d and $d*$ to (6.8) which yields

$$(6.9) \qquad\qquad \Delta f = a_x + b_y, \quad \Delta g = -a_y + b_x.$$

We therefore need to solve the Poisson equation $\Delta f = h$ with $h \in C^\infty_{\text{comp}}(\mathbb{R}^2)$. A solution to this equation is not unique; indeed, we can add linear polynomials to f. On the other hand, solutions that decay at infinity are necessarily unique from the maximum principle. To obtain existence, we invoke the *fundamental solution* of the Laplacian on $\mathbb{R}^2$, which is

$$\Gamma(z) = \frac{1}{2\pi} \log |z|.$$

This means that $\Delta \Gamma = \delta_0$ in the sense of distributions and we therefore expect to find a solution via $f = \Gamma * h$. We now derive the solution to Poisson's equation in the smooth setting; much weaker conditions suffice but we do not wish to dwell on that for now.

Lemma 6.15. *Let $h \in C^\infty_{\text{comp}}(\mathbb{R}^2)$. Then the function*

$$(6.10) \quad f(z) := \frac{1}{2\pi} \iint_{\mathbb{R}^2} h(\zeta) \log |z - \zeta|\, d\xi d\eta = \frac{1}{2\pi} \iint_{\mathbb{R}^2} h(z - \zeta) \log |\zeta|\, d\xi d\eta$$

(with $\zeta = \xi + i\eta$) satisfies $f \in C^\infty$ and solves $\Delta f = h$. Moreover,

$$(6.11) \qquad f(z) = \frac{1}{2\pi} \langle h \rangle \log |z| + O(1/|z|) \quad \text{as } |z| \to \infty$$

where $\langle h \rangle := \int_{\mathbb{R}^2} h \, d\xi d\eta$ is the mean of h. In fact, f is the unique solution which is of the form

$$(6.12) \qquad f(z) = k \log |z| + o(1) \quad \text{as } |z| \to \infty$$

for some constant $k \in \mathbb{R}$.

Proof. Differentiating under the integral sign yields

$$\Delta f(z) = \frac{1}{2\pi} \iint_{\mathbb{R}^2} \Delta_z h(z - \zeta) \log |\zeta| \, d\xi d\eta$$

$$= \frac{1}{2\pi} \lim_{\varepsilon \to 0} \iint_{|\zeta| > \varepsilon} \Delta_\zeta h(z - \zeta) \log |\zeta| \, d\xi d\eta.$$

Now apply Green's identity (which follows from Stokes theorem on manifolds)

$$\int_\Omega (v\Delta u - u\Delta v) \, d\xi d\eta = \int_{\partial\Omega} (v \frac{\partial u}{\partial n} - u \frac{\partial v}{\partial n}) \, d\sigma$$

together with the property that $\log |\zeta|$ is harmonic away from zero, to conclude that

$$\iint_{|\zeta| > \varepsilon} \log |\zeta| \, \Delta_\zeta h(z - \zeta) \, d\xi d\eta$$

$$= \iint_{|\zeta| > \varepsilon} \Big[\log |\zeta| \Delta_\zeta h(z - \zeta) - h(z - \zeta) \Delta_\zeta \log |\zeta| \Big] \, d\xi d\eta$$

$$= \int_{|\zeta| = \varepsilon} \Big[\log |\zeta| \frac{\partial}{\partial n_\zeta} h(z - \zeta) - h(z - \zeta) \frac{\partial}{\partial n_\zeta} \log |\zeta| \Big] \, d\sigma$$

where n is the outward pointing norm vector relative to the region $|\zeta| > \varepsilon$. Next, one has

$$\frac{\partial}{\partial n_\zeta} \log |\zeta| = -\frac{1}{|\zeta|}.$$

In conclusion, letting $\varepsilon \to 0$ yields $\Delta f = h$ as desired. We remark that in dimensions $d \geq 3$ the fundamental solutions of Δ are $c_d |x - y|^{2-d}$ with a dimensional constant c_d by essentially the same proof. In $d = 1$ a natural choice is $x_+ := \max(x, 0)$ or anything obtained from this by adding a linear function. Inspection of our solution formula (6.10) now establishes (6.11); indeed, expand the logarithm

$$\log |z - \zeta| = \log |z| + \log |1 - \zeta/z|.$$

To establish the uniqueness, we claim that the only harmonic function of the form (6.12) vanishes identically. First, by the mean value property one concludes that $k = 0$. Second, by the maximum principle the only harmonic function vanishing at infinity is zero. In particular, the solution f of $\Delta f = h$ and h as above decays at infinity if and only if $\langle h \rangle = 0$.   □

Returning to our discussion of Hodge's decomposition, recall that h is given by the right-hand sides of (6.9). Since a, b are compactly supported it follows that the integrals of the derivatives of these functions over $\mathbb{R}^2$ vanish. Hence, $\langle h \rangle = 0$ so that (6.10) yields smooth functions f, g decaying at the rate $1/|z|$ at infinity and which solve (6.9). It remains to check that indeed

$$\omega = df + *dg = (f_x - g_y)dx + (f_y + g_x)dy.$$

To this end we observe that

$$(f_x - g_y)(z) = \frac{1}{2\pi} \iint_{\mathbb{R}^2} \Delta a(\zeta) \log|z - \zeta| \, d\xi d\eta = a(z),$$

$$(f_y + g_x)(z) = \frac{1}{2\pi} \iint_{\mathbb{R}^2} \Delta b(\zeta) \log|z - \zeta| \, d\xi d\eta = b(z).$$

To obtain the final two equality signs of each line no calculations are necessary; in fact, since a vanishes at infinity, the only decaying solution to $\Delta f = \Delta a$ is given by $f = a$ and the same holds for b. To summarize: we have shown that every compactly supported $\omega \in \Omega^1(\mathbb{C}; \mathbb{C})$ is the sum of an exact and a co-exact smooth 1-form and each of these summands typically decay only like $|z|^{-2}$ (as differentials of functions decaying like $|z|^{-1}$). Note that this rate of decay is square integrable at infinity relative to Lebesgue measure in the plane; if this were not so, then one could not derive the Hodge decomposition in the L^2 setting. In particular, we see here how essential it is that we are dealing with forms and not functions, as the harmonic functions themselves only decay at the rate $|z|^{-1}$ which is not square integrable in the plane.

Our proof extends to the L^2 setting; that is, given $a, b \in L^2$ there exist $f, g \in H^1(\mathbb{R}^2)$ (which is the Sobolev space of L^2 functions with an L^2 weak derivative) so that

$$a \, dx + b \, dy = df + *dg$$

as an equality between L^2 functions. As usual, this can be obtained from the smooth, compactly supported case which we just discussed since those functions are dense in $H^1(\mathbb{R}^2)$. The required uniform control required to pass to the limit is given by the L^2 boundedness of the double Riesz transforms R_{ij}. We leave the details of this to the reader; see Problem 6.2.

Example 2: $M = S^2$ or M is any compact, simply-connected Riemann surface.

Since we already observed that $\mathfrak{h}(M) = \{0\}$ in this case, we see that trivially $\mathfrak{h}_2(M) = \{0\}$ so that Hodge's decomposition (6.7) again reduces to

$$\Omega_2^1(M) = E \oplus *E.$$

Indeed, it is easy to prove that every $\omega \in \Omega^1(M)$ is of the form

$$\omega = df + *dg, \quad f, g \in C^\infty(M).$$

Applying d to this yields $d\omega = \Delta_M g \, \mathrm{vol}$ where vol is a suitably normalized volume form on M and Δ_M is the Laplace-Beltrami operator on M. Recall that the Laplace-Beltrami operator Δ_M on any compact orientable manifold M has discrete spectrum and $L^2(M)$ has an orthonormal basis consisting of (smooth) eigenfunctions Y_n of Δ_M with eigenvalues $\{\lambda_n\}_{n=0}^\infty$,

$$0 = \lambda_0 < \lambda_1 \leq \lambda_2 \leq \ldots.$$

The lowest eigenvalue λ_0 is simple, i.e., Y_0 is necessarily a constant as follows from the maximum principle. Finally, from Weyl's law the eigenvalues λ_n grow at some power rate in n (the reader can just take this for granted; for the sphere the eigenvalues and eigefunctions are explicitly given, the latter in the form of spherical harmonics). Hence continuing in this degree of generality, one concludes that $\Delta_M f = h$ with $f \in C^\infty(M)$, say, has a solution if and only if

$$\langle h \rangle = \int_M h \, dv = 0$$

(v is the volume form on M). In that case the solution is given by

$$f = \sum_{n \geq 1} \lambda_n^{-2} \langle h, Y_n \rangle Y_n$$

which converges rapidly since h is smooth. Returning to $d\omega = \Delta_M g \, \mathrm{vol}$, one sees from Stokes' theorem that $\int_M d\omega = 0$ so that the integrability condition holds. This yields a smooth solution g whence $\omega - *dg$ is a closed form on M. Since M is simply-connected, it is also exact and thus

$$\omega = df + *dg$$

for some smooth f. Note that the simple connectivity of M entered only at the final step. In the following example, we shall see how the harmonic functions precisely eliminate the obstruction to the exactness of closed forms in the genus one case.

     Example 3: $M = \mathbb{T}^2 = \mathbb{C}/\mathbb{Z}^2 = \mathbb{C}/\langle z \mapsto z + 1, z \mapsto z + i \rangle$.

In view of our previous discussion of the harmonic forms in this case, (6.7) reduces to the following property: any $\omega = a \, dx + b \, dy$ with smooth, $\mathbb{Z}^2$-periodic functions a, b can be written as

(6.13) $a \, dx + b \, dy = df + *dg + c_1 \, dx + c_2 \, dy,$

where f, g are smooth, $\mathbb{Z}^2$-periodic functions and suitable constants c_1, c_2. It will turn out that

$$c_1 = \int_0^1 \int_0^1 a(x, y) \, dx \, dy, \quad c_2 = \int_0^1 \int_0^1 b(x, y) \, dx \, dy.$$

As in the discussion of the whole plane, finding f, g reduces to a suitable Poisson equation. Hence let us first understand how to solve $\Delta f = h$ on $\mathbb{T}^2$ with smooth h. Integrating over $\mathbb{T}^2$ shows that the vanishing condition

(6.14)
$$\int_0^1 \int_0^1 h(x, y) \, dx \, dy = 0$$

is necessary. It is also sufficient for solvability; indeed, any such smooth h has a convergent Fourier expansion

$$h(x, y) = \sum_{n_1, n_2} \hat{h}(n_1, n_2) e(x n_1 + y n_2)$$

where $\hat{h}(0, 0) = 0$ (and with $e(x) := e^{2\pi i x}$). The solution to $\Delta f = h$ is therefore given by

$$f(x, y) = -\sum_{(n_1, n_2) \neq (0,0)} \frac{\hat{h}(n_1, n_2)}{4\pi^2 (n_1^2 + n_2^2)} e(x n_1 + y n_2)$$

which is again smooth. We write this schematically as $f = \Delta^{-1} h$. As in the case of $M = \mathbb{C}$, solving (6.13) reduces to solving (6.9) on $\mathbb{T}^2$. Notice that our vanishing condition (6.14) is satisfied by $\hat{h}(0, 0) = 0$ and we therefore obtain smooth solutions f, g. In order to conclude that

$$\omega = df + *dg$$

it remains to check that $a = \Delta^{-1} \Delta a$ and the same for b. This is true if and only if a and b have vanishing means and confirms our choice of c_1, c_2 above. Here we see an example where $\mathfrak{h}(M) = \mathfrak{h}_2(M)$ plays a *topological* role; indeed the torus has genus 1 and therefore nontrivial cohomology. This is typical of the *compact* case but not of the noncompact case.

Example 4: $M = \mathbb{D}$.

Our fourth example is the disk $\mathbb{D}$ (which is the same as the upper half-plane or any other simply-connected true subdomain of $\mathbb{C}$). This is an example of a noncompact surface with a large boundary $\partial \mathbb{D}$. In this case there is not only an abundance of harmonic and holomorphic 1-forms, but also of *square integrable* ones. First, we remark that

$$E = \{ df \mid f \in H_0^1(\mathbb{D}) \},$$

where $H_0^1(\mathbb{D})$ is the usual Sobolev space with vanishing trace on $\partial\mathbb{D}$. Second, let us reformulate (6.7) as an equivalent fact for vector fields

$$\vec{v} = (v_1, v_2) \in L^2(\mathbb{D})$$

rather than forms: there exist $f, g \in H_0^1(\mathbb{D})$, as well as $\vec{\omega} = (\omega_1, \omega_2)$ smooth and both divergence-free and curl-free, and with $\omega_1, \omega_2 \in L^2(\mathbb{D})$ so that

$$\vec{v} = \vec{\nabla} f + \vec{\nabla}^\perp g + \vec{\omega}$$

where $\vec{\nabla}^\perp g := (-g_y, g_x)$. Recall that $H^{-1}(\mathbb{D})$ is the dual space $H_0^1(\mathbb{D})^*$. It consist of all distributions on $\mathbb{D}$ of the form

$$\varphi = a_1 \partial_1 f_1 + a_2 \partial_2 f_2, \quad f_j \in L^2(\mathbb{D}), \; a_1, a_2 \in \mathbb{R}.$$

The duality pairing between $\varphi \in H^{-1}$ and $g \in H_0^1(\mathbb{D})$ is given by

$$\langle \varphi, g \rangle = -\sum_{j=1}^{2} a_j \int_{\mathbb{D}} f_j \partial_j g \; dx_1 dx_2.$$

To find f, we need to solve

$$\Delta f = \operatorname{div} \vec{v} \in H^{-1}(\mathbb{D}), \quad f \in H_0^1(\mathbb{D}),$$

whereas for g, we need to solve

$$\Delta g = \operatorname{div}^\perp \vec{v} \in H^{-1}(\mathbb{D}), \quad g \in H_0^1(\mathbb{D}),$$

where

$$\operatorname{div}^\perp \vec{v} = -\partial_y v_1 + \partial_x v_2.$$

This can be done uniquely with $f, g \in H_0^1(\mathbb{D})$ via the usual machinery of weak solutions for elliptic equations. For the uniqueness, suppose that $\Delta g = 0$ and $g \in H_0^1(\mathbb{D})$. Then

$$\Delta g \in H^{-1}(\mathbb{D}) = H_0^1(\mathbb{D})^*$$

and

$$0 = \langle -\Delta g, g \rangle = \int_{\mathbb{D}} |\nabla g|^2 \, dx \, dy,$$

which implies that g is constant and therefore zero. This shows that any $\omega \in E$ which is also harmonic is zero. Notice the importance of the "boundary condition" in this regard which was built into the space E (coming from the compact support condition). Of course there are many (nonzero) harmonic differentials which are also in $L^2(\mathbb{D})$, but they are limits of differentials df with $f \in C_{\text{comp}}^\infty(\mathbb{D})$ only if they vanish identically.

6.5. Weyl's lemma and the Hodge decomposition

In these final two sections we develop some of the basic potential theory which is essential for various existence theorems on Riemann surfaces. Not only are we going to obtain the Hodge decomposition in this way, but we shall also be able to prove that every Riemann surface carries a nonconstant meromorphic function. This important result is one of the ingredients in the proof of Theorem 5.20 which establishes the equivalence of the class of compact Riemann surfaces with that of smooth projective algebraic curves.

We shall now prove Hodge's representation (6.7). Recall that $\Omega_2^1(M;\mathbb{R})$ is the space of real-valued 1-forms ω with measurable coefficients and such that

$$\|\omega\|^2 = \int_M \omega \wedge \overline{*\omega} < \infty.$$

Furthermore,

$$E := \overline{\left\{ df \mid f \in \Omega_{\mathrm{comp}}^0(M;\mathbb{R}) \right\}}, \quad *E := \overline{\left\{ *df \mid f \in \Omega_{\mathrm{comp}}^0(M;\mathbb{R}) \right\}},$$

where the closure is in the sense of $\Omega_2^1(M;\mathbb{R})$.

Theorem 6.16. *Let* $\mathfrak{h}_2(M;\mathbb{R}) := \mathfrak{h}(M;\mathbb{R}) \cap \Omega_2^1(M;\mathbb{R})$. *Then*

$$\Omega_2^1(M;\mathbb{R}) = E \oplus *E \oplus \mathfrak{h}_2(M;\mathbb{R}).$$

We begin with the following observation, which explains the meaning of Figure 6.2.

Lemma 6.17. *Let* $\alpha \in \Omega_2^1(M;\mathbb{R})$ *be a smooth* 1*-form. Then* $\alpha \in E^\perp$ *if and only if* $d*\alpha = 0$ *and* $\alpha \in (*E)^\perp$ *if and only if* $d\alpha = 0$. *In particular,* $E \subset (*E)^\perp$ *and* $*E \subset E^\perp$.

Proof. First,

$$\alpha \in E^\perp \iff \alpha \in \left\{ df \mid f \in C_{\mathrm{comp}}^\infty(M) \right\}^\perp.$$

Moreover,

$$0 = \langle \alpha, df \rangle = \langle *\alpha, *df \rangle = \int_M df \wedge *\alpha$$

$$= \int_M d(f*\alpha) - f d*\alpha = - \int_M f d*\alpha$$

for all $f \in C_{\mathrm{comp}}^\infty(M)$ is the same as $d*\alpha = 0$. Thus, α is co-closed. The calculation for $(*E)^\perp$ is essentially the same and we skip it. $\qquad\square$

In other words: *a smooth form is perpendicular to* $*E$ *if and only if it is closed, and it is perpendicular to* E *if and only if it is co-closed.*

Lemma 6.17 implies that

(6.15) $\Omega^1_2(M;\mathbb{R}) = E \oplus *E \oplus (E^\perp \cap (*E)^\perp),$

and our remaining task is to identify the intersection on the right. While it is easy to write down (6.15), it requires a basic nontrivial existence result in Hilbert spaces: namely the **existence of the orthogonal complement**. The reader should not dismiss this lightly, since it hinges on the *completeness* of a Hilbert space, which in turn for the space L^2 depends crucially on the Lebesgue integral. So we are relying on a lot of foundational material before we can even begin to give meaning to (6.15); see the appendix.

It follows from Lemma 6.17 that

$$E^\perp \cap (*E)^\perp \supset \mathfrak{h}_2(M;\mathbb{R}).$$

It remains to show equality here. This is remarkable in so far as the intersection thus consists of *smooth* 1-forms. The required [2]elliptic regularity ingredient in this context is the so-called Weyl lemma; see Lemma 6.19. The following lemma concludes the proof of Theorem 6.16.

Lemma 6.18.
$$E^\perp \cap (*E)^\perp = \mathfrak{h}_2(M;\mathbb{R}).$$

Proof. Take $\omega \in E^\perp \cap (*E)^\perp$. Then by Lemma 6.17,

$$\langle \omega, df \rangle = \langle \omega, *df \rangle = 0, \quad \forall\, f \in C^\infty_{\text{comp}}(M)$$

and f complex-valued (say). With

$$\omega = u\, dz + v\, d\bar{z}$$

in local coordinates (U, z), $z = x + iy$ and with f supported in U, we conclude that

$$\langle \omega, df \rangle = 2 \int (u\, \overline{f_z} + v\, \overline{f_{\bar{z}}})\, dx\, dy,$$

$$\langle \omega, *df \rangle = -2i \int (u\, \overline{f_z} - v\, \overline{f_{\bar{z}}})\, dx\, dy.$$

This system is in turn equivalent to

$$\int \bar{u} f_z\, dx\, dy = 0, \qquad \int \bar{v} f_{\bar{z}}\, dx\, dy = 0$$

for all such f. Now setting $f = g_{\bar{z}}$ and $f = g_z$, respectively, where g is supported in U, yields

$$\int \bar{u} \Delta g\, dx\, dy = \int \bar{v} \Delta g\, dx\, dy = 0,$$

---

[2]Any reader unfamiliar with elliptic PDEs can safely ignore this reference to elliptic regularity.

which implies by Weyl's lemma below that u, v are harmonic and thus smooth in U. In view of Lemma 6.17, ω is both closed and co-closed and therefore harmonic.   □

We now establish the Weyl lemma, which is the main analytical ingredient. It is a purely *real-variable* fact, and does not rely on complex variables.

Lemma 6.19. *Let $V \subset \mathbb{C}$ be open and $u \in L^1_{\text{loc}}(V)$. Suppose u is weakly harmonic, i.e.,*

$$\int_V u \Delta \phi \, dx \, dy = 0 \quad \forall \, \phi \in C^\infty_{\text{comp}}(V).$$

Then u is harmonic, i.e., $u \in C^\infty(V)$ and $\Delta v = 0$.

Proof. As a first step, we prove this: suppose $\{u_n\}_{n=1}^\infty \subset C^\infty(V)$ is a sequence of harmonic functions that converges in the sense of L^1_{loc} to u_∞. Then $u_\infty \in C^\infty(V)$ and u_∞ is harmonic.

This follows easily from the mean-value property. Indeed, for each n, and each disk $D(z, r) \subset V$, and with $\zeta = \xi + i\eta$,

$$u_n(z) = \frac{1}{|D(z,r)|} \iint_{D(z,r)} u_n(\zeta) \, d\xi d\eta.$$

Hence by the assumption of L^1_{loc} convergence, $\{u_n\}_n$ is a Cauchy sequence in $C(V)$ and therefore converges uniformly on compact subsets of V to u_∞ which is thus continuous. Moreover, it inherits the mean-value property

$$u_\infty(z) = \frac{1}{2\pi r} \int_{|z-\zeta|=r} u_\infty(\zeta) \, d\sigma(\zeta),$$

and is thus harmonic. Indeed, compare u to that harmonic function $\tilde{u}$ which takes values u on the boundary of some disk D (we know that $\tilde{u}$ exists from Chapter 3 since we can solve the Dirichlet problem for the Laplacian on a disk). Now observe that $\tilde{u} - u$ both satisfy the mean-value property and therefore also the maximum principle. Since $\tilde{u} - u = 0$ on the boundary of some disk D, necessarily also $\tilde{u} - u = 0$ on D.

To conclude the proof, we let $u \in L^1_{\text{loc}}(V)$ be weakly harmonic. Define

$$V_n := \{z \in V \mid \text{dist}(z, \partial V) > 1/n\}$$

and set

$$u_n(z) := (u * \phi_n)(z) \qquad \forall \, z \in V_n,$$

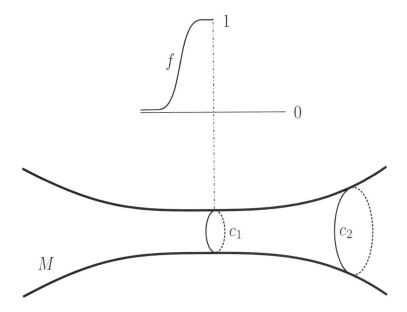

Figure 6.3. The function f giving rise to the loop-form η_c

where $\phi_n(\zeta) := n^2\phi(n\zeta)$ for all $n \geq 1$ with $\phi \geq 0$ a C^∞ function, $\mathrm{supp}(\phi) \subset \mathbb{D}$, and $\int \phi = 1$. Written out, we have $\forall\, z \in V_n$,

$$
(6.16)\qquad
\begin{aligned}
u_n(z) &= \int_{\mathbb{R}^2} u(z - \zeta)\phi_n(\zeta)\, m(d\zeta) \\
&= \int_{\mathbb{R}^2} u(\zeta)\phi_n(z - \zeta)\, m(d\zeta),
\end{aligned}
$$

with m being Lebesgue measure in the plane. Note that in the second line of (6.16) any derivatives hitting u_n fall onto ϕ_n.

Therefore, since u is weakly harmonic, $\Delta u_n = 0$ on V_n. Moreover, $u_n \to u$ in $L^1_{\mathrm{loc}}(V)$ by Lemma 3.3, which applies equally well to approximate identities such as $\{\phi_n\}_{n \geq 1}$ in $\mathbb{R}^2$. By the previous paragraph, u is smooth and harmonic. $\qquad\square$

Let us now explain why there is always a nonzero harmonic form on a compact surface with positive genus. This goes through the standard "loop-form" construction. Thus, let $c : [0, 1] \to M$ be a smooth, regular closed curve where M is an arbitrary Riemann surface. "Regular" here means that the tangent vector to c never vanishes. For simplicity, we shall also assume that $c([0, 1])$ is an imbedded one-dimensional manifold and we put the natural orientation on it, i.e., $c(t)$ is oriented according to increasing t (such a closed curve will be called a *loop*). Then let $\widetilde{N}_- \subset N_-$ be neighborhoods to the left of c obtained by taking the finite union of left halves (relative to

c) of parametric disks centered at points of c. Furthermore, the disks used in the construction of $\widetilde{N}_-$ are assumed to be compactly contained in those for N_-. Then let f be a smooth function on N_- with $f = 1$ on $\widetilde{N}_-$, $f = 0$ on $M \setminus N_-$; see Figure 6.3. While f is not smooth on M, the *loop-form of* c defined as

$$\eta_c := df \in \Omega^1(M; \mathbb{R})$$

is smooth and compactly supported. By construction, $d\eta_c = 0$ since $d^2 = 0$.

We claim that the *cohomology class of η_c is uniquely determined by the homology class* of c (cf. Figure 6.1).

First, if f and $\widetilde{f}$ are smooth functions constructed to the left of c as explained, then $f - \widetilde{f} \in C^\infty_{\text{comp}}(M)$, so that $df - d\widetilde{f}$ is exact. In other words, the cohomology class of c does not depend on the choice of function f in our construction.

Second, if $c_1 - c_2$ is the boundary of a compact submanifold $\bar{N}$ of M, then $\eta_{c_1} - \eta_{c_2} = dh$ for some smooth, compactly supported function on M. Indeed, choosing functions f_1, f_2 associated to loops c_1, c_2, respectively, we can set

$$h = f_1 + \chi_{\bar{N}} - f_2.$$

If we make sure that the neighborhoods N_- associated with the loops c_i are sufficiently small, then we indeed have $dh = \eta_{c_1} - \eta_{c_2}$.

Finally, if we had defined loop-forms $\widetilde{\eta}_c = dg$ with a function g that equals one on a neighborhood to the *right of c*, then $\eta_c - (-\widetilde{\eta}_c)$ is exact. In other words, reversing the orientation of c merely changes the sign of the cohomology class of η_c.

The importance of loop-forms can be seen from the following simple but crucial fact.

Lemma 6.20. *Let $\alpha \in \Omega^1$ be closed. Then*

$$\langle \alpha, *\eta_c \rangle = \int_c \alpha.$$

Proof. Compute

$$\langle \alpha, *\eta_c \rangle = \int \alpha \wedge **\eta_c = \int_{N_-} df \wedge \alpha$$

$$= \int_{N_-} d(f\alpha) = \int_{\partial N_-} f\alpha = \int_c \alpha,$$

as claimed. $\square$

This property of loop-forms immediately allows us to characterize all exact forms amongst the closed ones, which yields a general *topological criterion* guaranteeing that nonzero harmonic forms exist.

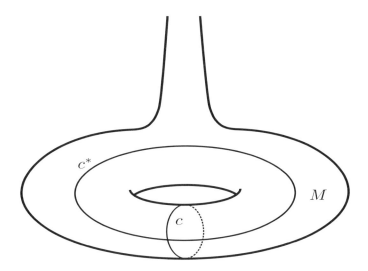

Figure 6.4. The curves c and c^*

Corollary 6.21. *The following criteria for exactness hold:*

1) *Let $\alpha \in \Omega^1(M;\mathbb{R})$. Then α is exact if and only if $\langle \alpha, \beta \rangle = 0$ for all co-closed $\beta \in \Omega^1(M;\mathbb{R})$ of compact support.*

2) *Let $\alpha \in E$ be smooth. Then α is exact, i.e., $\alpha = df$ for some real-valued $f \in C^\infty(M)$.*

3) *Supposed the closed loop c does not separate M, i.e., $M \setminus c([0,1])$ is connected. Then there exists a closed form $\alpha \in \Omega^1(M;\mathbb{R})$ which is not exact. In particular, $\mathfrak{h}_2(M;\mathbb{R}) \neq \{0\}$.*

Proof. If $\alpha = df$ is exact, then by Stokes theorem and using that M does not have a boundary,

$$\langle \alpha, \beta \rangle = \int_M df \wedge *\beta = -\int_M f\, d*\beta = 0$$

for any β as in 1). Conversely, $*\eta_c$ is co-closed and compactly supported for any loop. It follows that

$$0 = \langle \alpha, *\eta_c \rangle = \int_c \alpha$$

for any loop c. Thus, α is exact as claimed.

Property 2) follows from 1) via Lemma 6.17.

Finally, for 3), let c^* be a closed curve in M that crosses c transversally. See Figure 6.4. This exists since $M \setminus c$ is connected. Hence

$$\int_{c*} \eta_c = 1$$

and η_c is closed but not exact. From Theorem 6.16,

$$\eta_c = \alpha + \omega, \quad \alpha \in E, \quad \omega \in \mathfrak{h}_2(M; \mathbb{R}).$$

Since η_c is closed, it is perpendicular to $*E$, so there is no contribution from that subspace. Since ω and η_c are smooth, so is α. By 2), α is exact, so $\omega \neq 0$ as desired.   □

We know from the list of examples in the previous section that the criterion in part 3) above is not necessary: harmonic forms can also exist because of a large boundary, as in the case of the disk. However, it does highlight that positive genus on compact surfaces gives rise to harmonic forms. Note that the previous lemma does not require compactness and is thus more general.

6.6. Existence of nonconstant meromorphic functions

We shall now derive some consequences from Hodge's theorem. More precisely, we answer the fundamental question: *does a general Riemann surface carry a nonconstant meromorphic function?* It is essential that we ask for meromorphic functions rather than holomorphic ones: on compact surfaces the latter ones are trivial.

However, deeper questions will still elude us in this chapter such as: *Which Riemann surfaces carry a meromorphic function with exactly one simple pole?* The following chapter presents a version of the Riemann-Roch theorem which provides us with some machinery geared towards this type of a question.

The basis for the existence theory of this section will be Proposition 6.22. It shows that we can find harmonic functions on Riemann surfaces with prescribed singularities at a point.

To understand the issues, consider the following question: *Let $p \in M$. Can we find a function u harmonic on $M \setminus \{p\}$ so that in some parametric disk centered at p, u has a given singularity at p such as $\frac{1}{z}$ or $\log|z|$?*

Or, more generally: *let D be a parametric disk on a Riemann surface M centered at $p \in M$ and suppose h is a harmonic function on $D \setminus \{p\}$, differentiable on $\bar{D} \setminus \{p\}$. Can we find u harmonic on $M \setminus \{p\}$ with $u - h$ harmonic on all of D?*

These questions are part of potential theory and we shall address them by means of the Hodge theorem. As usual, M and N are arbitrary Riemann surfaces.

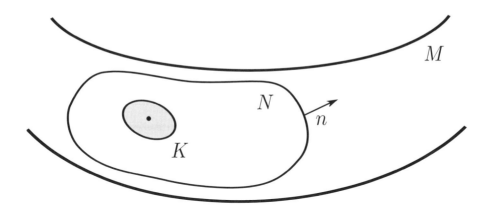

Figure 6.5. The sets in Proposition 6.22

Proposition 6.22. *Let $\bar{N} \subset M$, $\bar{N}$ compact with smooth boundary. Fix $p_0 \in N$ and h harmonic on $N \setminus \{p_0\}$ with $h \in C^1(\bar{N} \setminus \{p_0\})$ and $\frac{\partial h}{\partial n} = 0$ on ∂N where n is some nonvanishing normal vector field on ∂N that never vanishes.*

Then there exists u harmonic in $M \setminus \{p_0\}$, $u - h$ harmonic on N, and $u \in \Omega_2^1(M \setminus K)$ for any compact neighborhood K of p_0. Also, u is unique up to constants.

Proof. For the existence part, take θ a C^∞ function on N which agrees with h on $N \setminus K$ where K is an arbitrary but fixed (small) compact neighborhood of p_0. Then extend θ to M by setting it equal to zero outside of N and define $d\theta = 0$ on $M \setminus N$. Note that $d\theta \in \Omega_2^1(M; \mathbb{C})$. By the Hodge theorem,

$$d\theta = \alpha + \beta, \quad \alpha \in E, \ \beta \in E^\perp.$$

If $\phi \in C_{\text{comp}}^\infty(M)$, then

$$\langle d\theta, d\phi \rangle = \langle \alpha, d\phi \rangle, \qquad \langle \alpha, *d\phi \rangle = 0.$$

First, suppose that $\text{supp}(\phi) \subset M \setminus K$. Then from $\frac{\partial h}{\partial n} = 0$ and $d * dh = 0$ on N, we obtain that

$$\langle d\phi, d\theta \rangle = \int_N d\phi \wedge *d\bar{h} = \int_{\partial N} \phi \ \overline{i^*(*dh)} = 0$$

where $i : \partial N \hookrightarrow M$ is the inclusion map and i^* denotes the pullback. The main point to note here is that $i^*(*dh)$ is proportional to $\frac{\partial h}{\partial n} = 0$.

In summary, we have $\langle \alpha, d\phi \rangle = 0$ and $\langle \alpha, *d\phi \rangle = 0$ for all smooth ϕ with $\mathrm{supp}(\phi) \subset M \setminus K$. By the Hodge decomposition this implies that α is harmonic on $M \setminus K$.

Next, we look inside of N. If $\mathrm{supp}(\phi) \subset N$, then

$$(6.17) \qquad \langle d\theta - \alpha, d\phi \rangle = 0, \quad \langle d\theta - \alpha, *d\phi \rangle = 0,$$

so that $\alpha - d\theta$ is harmonic on N. The first equality in (6.17) follows since $d\theta - \alpha \in E^\perp$, and the second by "integration by parts", i.e., Stokes:

$$\langle d\theta - \alpha, *d\phi \rangle = \langle d\theta, *d\phi \rangle = \int_N d\theta \wedge **d\phi$$

$$= \int_N d\bar\phi \wedge d\theta = \int_N d(\bar\phi \, d\theta)$$

$$= \int_{\partial N} \bar\phi \, i^*(d\theta) = 0$$

since $\phi = 0$ on ∂N. Since α is harmonic, it is smooth on M and thus $\alpha = df$ with f smooth by part 2 of Corollary 6.21. Now set

$$u = f - \theta + h.$$

By construction, u has all the desired properties.

Finally, if v has the same properties as u, then $u - v$ is harmonic on M and $d(u - v) \in \Omega^1_2$. In conclusion,

$$d(u - v) \in E \cap \mathfrak{h}_2 = \{0\},$$

so $u - v$ equals a constant. $\qquad\square$

We remark that if h were harmonic on all of N, then h is necessarily a constant because of the Neumann condition $\frac{\partial h}{\partial n} = 0$ on ∂N. Indeed, this is merely the fact that

$$\|dh\|^2_{L^2(N)} = \int_N dh \wedge *d\bar h = \int_{\partial N} h \, i^*(*d\bar h) = 0$$

where $i : \partial N \to M$ is the inclusion and i^* the pullback as in the proof of the previous proposition.

Not surprisingly, the exact same proof allows for several exceptional points $p_0, \ldots, p_k \in N$. The statement is as follows.

Corollary 6.23. *Let $\bar N \subset M$, $\bar N$ be compact with smooth boundary. Fix finitely many points $\{p_j\}_{j=0}^k \in N$ and h harmonic on $N \setminus \{p_j\}_{j=0}^k$ with $h \in C^1(\bar N)$ and $\frac{\partial h}{\partial n} = 0$ on ∂N where n is some normal vector field on ∂N.*

Then there exists u harmonic in $M \setminus \{p_j\}_{j=0}^k$, $u - h$ harmonic on N, and $u \in \Omega^1_2(M \setminus K)$ for any compact neighborhood K of $\{p_j\}_{j=0}^k$. Also, u is unique up to constants.

Proof. The proof is essentially the same as that or Proposition 6.22, and we leave the details to the reader. □

The power of both Proposition 6.22 and Corollary 6.23 lies precisely with the fact that we can prescribe harmonic functions **locally in a chart**, in other words, with formulas in local coordinates and then extend them to the whole Riemann surface. Of course, we are required to fulfill the Neumann boundary condition. As we shall see shortly by means of the logarithmic singularity, this is not a mere technicality, but essential.

Our first result of this kind reads as follows.

Corollary 6.24. *Given $\ell \geq 1$ and a coordinate chart (U, z) around p_0 in M with $z(p_0) = 0$ there is u harmonic on $M \setminus \{p_0\}$ with $u - z^{-\ell}$ harmonic on U and $du \in \Omega_2^1(M \setminus K)$ for any compact neighborhood K of p_0.*

Proof. Assume, without loss of generality, $z(U) \supset \bar{\mathbb{D}}$ and define

$$h(z) = z^{-\ell} + \overline{z^\ell} \quad \forall \, |z| \leq 1.$$

Proposition 6.22 applies with $\bar{N} = z^{-1}(\bar{\mathbb{D}})$ since $\frac{\partial h}{\partial n} = 0$ on $|z| = 1$. □

Next, we would like to place a $\log |z|$ singularity on a Riemann surface. To apply Proposition 6.22, we need to enforce the Neumann condition $\frac{\partial h}{\partial n} = 0$ which amounts to solving the Neumann problem

$$\Delta u = 0 \ \text{ in } \ |z| < 1, \qquad \frac{\partial u}{\partial n} = -\frac{\partial}{\partial r} \log r = -1 \text{ on } |z| = 1.$$

But a solution does not exist, since the integral of -1 around $|z| = 1$ does not vanish—necessary by the divergence theorem. Now let us also note that with $M = \mathbb{C}$ the function $u(z) = \log |z|$ satisfies

$$du(z) = \frac{1}{2} \frac{dz}{z} + \frac{1}{2} \frac{d\bar{z}}{z}$$

which is not in L^2 around $|z| = \infty$ (it barely fails). Finally, this calculation also shows that if we could place a $\log |z|$ singularity on M then this would produce a meromorphic differential

$$\omega = du + i*du$$

with exactly one simple pole. If M is compact, then this violates the fact that the sum of the residues would have to vanish.

What all of this suggests is that we should try with *two* logarithmic singularities (in other words, instead of using a point charge, we use a dipole). This is indeed possible.

Corollary 6.25. *Let $p_0, p_1 \in M$ be distinct and suppose z and ζ are local coordinates around p_0 and p_1, respectively. Then there exists u harmonic on $M \setminus \{p_0, p_1\}$ with $u - \log|z|$ and $u + \log|\zeta|$ harmonic locally around p_0, p_1, respectively. Moreover, $du \in \Omega_2^1(M \setminus K)$ where K is any compact neighborhood of $\{p_0, p_1\}$.*

Proof. For this one, assume first that p_0, p_1 are close together. Then let (U, z) be a coordinate chart with $z(p_0) = z_0 \in \mathbb{D} \setminus \{0\}$, $z(p_1) = z_1 \in \mathbb{D} \setminus \{0\}$ and $z(U) \supset \bar{\mathbb{D}}$. Define

$$h(z) = \log\left|\frac{(z - z_0)(z - z_0^*)}{(z - z_1)(z - z_1^*)}\right|,$$

where z_0^*, z_1^* are the reflections of z_0, z_1 across $\partial\mathbb{D}$ (i.e., $z_j^* = \overline{z_j^{-1}}$). Then check that

$$|(z^* - z_j)(z^* - z_j^*)| = |z|^{-2}|(z - z_j)(z - z_j^*)|,$$

which gives $h(z^*) = h(z)$ (why?). This in turn implies the Neumann condition $\frac{\partial h}{\partial n} = 0$. Hence by Corollary 6.23, there exists u with all the desired properties. If p_0 and p_1 do not fall into one coordinate chart, then connect them by a chain of points that satisfy this for each adjacent pair. This yields finitely many functions u_0, u_1, u_2, etc. The desired function is the sum of all these. $\square$

To conclude our existence theory, we now state some simple but no less important corollaries on meromorphic differentials.

Corollary 6.26.   (a) *Given $n \geq 1$ and $p_0 \in M$ there exists a meromorphic differential ω with $\omega - \frac{dz}{z^{n+1}}$ holomorphic locally around p_0 (here z are local coordinates at p_0). Moreover, $\omega \in \Omega_2^1(M \setminus K)$ for every compact neighborhood K of p_0.*

   (b) *Let $p_0, p_1 \in M$. There exists ω meromorphic on M with $\omega - \frac{dz}{z}$ holomorphic around p_0 and $\omega + \frac{d\zeta}{\zeta}$ holomorphic around p_1, respectively (with z, ζ local coordinates). Moreover, $\omega \in \Omega_2^1(M \setminus K)$ for every compact neighborhood K of $\{p_0, p_1\}$.*

Proof. With u as in Corollary 6.24 and 6.25, respectively, we set $\alpha = du$. In the first case, $\omega = \frac{-1}{2n}(\alpha + i*\alpha)$, whereas in the second case, $\omega = \alpha + i*\alpha$. $\square$

As a reality check, take $M = \mathbb{C}$ and $p_0 = 0$, say. Then for (a) we would obtain

$$\omega = \frac{dz}{z^{n+1}}.$$

Note that the L^2 condition holds when $n \geq 1$ but not for $n = 0$. For (b), we would take

$$\omega = \frac{dz}{z - p_0} - \frac{dz}{z - p_1}.$$

This has all the desired properties, including the L^2 condition at $z = \infty$. In the classical literature, meromorphic differentials all of whose residues vanish (as in (a)) are called *differentials of the second kind*, whereas those with simple poles are called *differentials of the third kind* (the holomorphic differentials are called *abelian* or *of the first kind*).

From the existence of differentials of the second kind we can easily derive the following special case of the *uniformization theorem*.

Corollary 6.27. *Let M be compact and simply-connected. Then M carries a meromorphic function of degree one. In particular, $M \simeq S^2$. In other words, up to conformal isomorphisms, there is exactly one compact simply-connected Riemann surface, namely $\mathbb{C}P^1 \simeq S^2 \simeq \mathbb{C}_\infty$.*

Proof. Let $\omega \in \mathcal{H}\Omega^1(M \setminus \{p_0\})$ where $p_0 \in M$ is arbitrary and such that $\omega = \frac{dz}{z^2}$ in local coordinates around p_0. Then set

$$f(p) := \int_{p_1}^{p} \omega,$$

where the integration path connects an arbitrary but fixed $p_1 \in M \setminus \{p_0\}$ with p without passing through p_0. Since M is simply-connected and since $\mathrm{res}(\omega; p_0) = 0$, it follows that f is well-defined. Clearly, f has a simple pole at p_0 and is holomorphic elsewhere. Since $\deg(f) = 1$, this map induces an isomorphism $M \to \mathbb{C}_\infty$ as desired. $\qquad \square$

At this point it is natural to ask many questions, for example:

- What can one say about the non-simply-connected case? More precisely, on a compact surface of genus g, what is the minimal degree that a nonconstant meromorphic function can achieve?

- How many (in the sense of dimension) meromorphic functions are there on a compact Riemann surface which have poles at finitely many points $p_\nu \in M$ with orders at most s_ν (a positive integer)?

The Riemann-Roch theorem in the following chapter attempts to answer these questions. For now, let us mention that the proof of Corollary 6.27 gives the following, more precise, statement:

Let M be a compact, simply-connected Riemann surface. Define the linear space

(6.18) $V := \{f \in \mathcal{M}(M) : f \in \mathcal{H}(M \setminus \{p_0\}), \operatorname{ord}(f, p_0) \leq 1\}.$

Then $\dim(V) = 2$.

The reader will have no difficulty verifying this assertion from the previous proof; see also the problems below. Note that we need dimension 2 here since the constants are in V. The Riemann-Roch theorem will generalize these dimension counts to arbitrary "divisors" on compact surfaces; see the following chapter for the definition of a divisor. In Problem 6.9 we give an extension of our observation concerning $\dim(V)$, which is a special case of Riemann-Roch for genus zero.

Finally, we can now state and prove the following result which applies to *every* Riemann surface.

Theorem 6.28. *Let $\{p_j\}_{j=1}^J \subset M$, $J \geq 2$, and $c_j \in \mathbb{C}$ with*

$$\sum_{j=1}^J c_j = 0.$$

Then there exists a meromorphic differential ω, holomorphic on

$$M \setminus \{p_1, p_2, \ldots, p_J\}$$

so that ω has a simple pole at each p_j with residue c_j.

Proof. Pick any other point $p_0 \in M$ and let ω_j be meromorphic with simple poles at p_0, p_j and residues $-c_j, c_j$, respectively. The differential $\omega = \sum_{j=1}^J \omega_j$ has all the desired properties. $\square$

From here we immediately conclude the following remarkable result. It is the main missing ingredient in the proof of Theorem 5.20.

Corollary 6.29. *Every Riemann surface carries a nonconstant meromorphic function. In fact, given any distinct points $p_0, p_1, p_2 \in M$, there exists a meromorphic function f on M for which $f(p_1) = 1$, and so that f has a simple pole at p_0 and a simple zero at p_2. In particular, the function field $\mathcal{M}(M)$ separates points[3] on every Riemann surface M.*

Proof. Take three points $p_0, p_1, p_2 \in M$ and let ω_1 be a meromorphic 1-form with simple poles at p_0, p_1 and residues $1, -1$, respectively, and holomorphic everywhere else. Similarly, let ω_2 be a meromorphic 1-form with simple

---

[3]This means that for any two distinct points there exists a meromorphic function taking distinct values at these points. Note that we cannot separate points by means of holomorphic functions, in general, as they might all be constant (as on a compact surface).

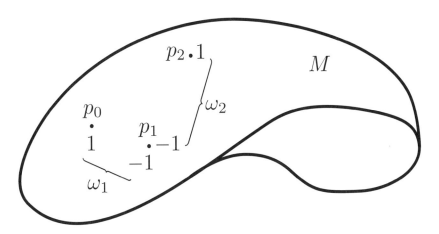

Figure 6.6. The construction of a meromorphic function with a pole at p_0 (and possibly other poles)

poles at p_1, p_2 and residues $-1, 1$, respectively and holomorphic everywhere else. See Figure 6.6. Now set $f = \frac{\omega_1}{\omega_2}$ where the division is well-defined in local coordinates and defines a meromorphic function. Clearly, $f(p_1) = 1$ and $f(p_2) = 0$, and the function f is not constant, and meromorphic with a pole at p_0. $\square$

Let us now state an existence theorem for meromorphic differentials with given singularities at finitely many points. It is implicit in the preceding, but for the sake of completeness we state it explicitly. Moreover, we shall confine ourselves to the compact case.

Corollary 6.30. *Let M be a compact Riemann surface. Given finitely many points $p_j \in M$, charts (U_j, z_j) near p_j, and finitely many numbers $c_{j,\ell} \in \mathbb{C}$ the following are equivalent:*

- *there exists a meromorphic differential ω which is holomorphic away from p_j and such that in the chart (U_j, z_j)*

$$\omega(z_j) - \sum_{\ell \geq 1} \frac{c_{j,\ell}}{z_j^\ell}$$

  is holomorphic.
- $\sum_j c_{j,1} = 0.$

The vanishing condition here is nothing other than the fact that we need

$$\sum_j \mathrm{res}(\omega; p_j) = 0.$$

In the following chapter we shall study the vector space of meromorphic functions and differentials with zeros and poles at prescribed points.

6.7. Examples of meromorphic functions and differentials

In the previous chapter we emphasized the algebraic nature of compact Riemann surfaces, although the proof of this fact will not be completed until the next chapter. Thus, any compact surface M is given by analytic continuation of a solution $w = w(z)$, holomorphic near $z = z_0$ of the equation $P(w(z), z) = 0$ where $P(w, z)$ is irreducible. How do we express meromorphic functions on M in terms of P? Can we find all of them?

If $P(w, z) = w - r(z)$ with a nonconstant rational function $r(z)$ then $M = S^2$ for which all meromorphic functions are those rational in z. If

$$P(w, z) = w^2 + r(z)w + s(z),$$

with rational r, s, then

$$P(w, z) = u^2 + s(z) - \frac{r^2(z)}{4}, \quad u = w + r(z)/2.$$

As we observed in Section 5.6, the surface is isomorphic to the one generated by the equation

(6.19)
$$w^2 - \prod_{j=1}^{2g+1} (z - z_j) = 0,$$

and **hyper-elliptic** (or elliptic if $g = 1$). Here $g \geq 0$ is the genus. We normalized so that the surface branches at $z = \infty$.

Now suppose f is meromorphic on the surface defined by (6.19) and nonconstant. Let

$$z \in \mathbb{C} \setminus \{z_1, \ldots, z_{2g+1}\}$$

and consider the two points $(z, w_1), (z, w_2)$ lying above z on the surface. Associated with them are the values f_1, f_2, respectively, which we can assume to be finite (in other words, f is "multi-valued" when viewed as a function of z). However, $\sigma_1 = f_1 + f_2$ and $\sigma_2 = f_1 f_2$ are single-valued functions of z. Moreover, they have at most poles at the finitely many points $\{z_1, \ldots, z_{2g+1}\} \cup \{\infty\}$. In other words, σ_1, σ_2 are rational functions of z. In conclusion, f satisfies a quadratic equation with rational coefficients,

(6.20)
$$f^2 - \sigma_1(z)f + \sigma_2(z) = 0.$$

Solving for f, we obtain

(6.21)
$$f(z) = \rho_1(z) \pm \rho_2(z) \sqrt{\prod_{\ell=1}^{m}(z - \zeta_\ell)}$$

with rational ρ_1, ρ_2. This formula cannot determine a meromorphic function on M unless the points ζ_ℓ are all included in the set $\{z_1, \ldots, z_{2g+1}\}$; otherwise a contradiction is obtain by analytic continuation along a small loop about ζ_ℓ. Now select any pair of distinct points z_j, z_k and perform analytic continuation along a loop surrounding this pair. Then we come back to the same value of w on M, and thus also need to return to the same value of f on M. But this can only be the case if *all zeros* z_j appear in the set $\{\zeta_\ell\}$.

In other words, with w determined by (6.19), one has the representation

$$(6.22) \qquad f(z) = \rho_1(z) + \rho_2(z)w$$

where ρ_j are rational. Conversely, any such function (6.22) is meromorphic on the surface (6.19). What we have just shown is equivalent to the following: *every meromorphic function on the hyper-elliptic surface* (6.19) *is rational in z and w*.

Indeed, if

$$f = \frac{p_1(w,z)}{p_2(w,z)}$$

is nonconstant then we can use (6.19) to reduce p_j to degree 1:

$$f = \frac{a(z)w + b(z)}{c(z)w + d(z)}$$

with rational a, b, c, d and $ad - bc$ not vanishing identically. If $c = 0$, then we arrive at (6.22). Otherwise we can assume that $c = 1$ whence

$$\begin{aligned}
f &= \frac{a(z)w + b(z)}{w + d(z)} = \frac{(a(z)w + b(z))(w - d(z))}{w^2 - d(z)^2} \\
&= \frac{a(z)w^2 + w(b(z) - a(z)d(z)) - b(z)d(z)}{w^2 - d(z)^2},
\end{aligned}$$

which is of the form (6.22) thanks to (6.19).

In the following chapter we shall prove that of every meromorphic function on **any compact Riemann surface** is represented in terms of z, f provided (5.6) is irreducible.

We can analyze the behavior of $f(z)$ near any point in $\mathbb{C}_\infty$. As usual, around $z = \infty$ we set $z = \frac{1}{\zeta}$ with ζ near 0. Then (6.22) transforms into another equation of the same type. Away from the branch points of w in $\mathbb{C}$ the function (6.22) is meromorphic in z in the usual sense and we can apply Laurent expansions. Clearly, f can be finite even if ρ_1, ρ_2 are infinite. At the branch points we set $z = z_j + t^2$ with small t to obtain a meromorphic representation in that variable.

Let us now switch to meromorphic differentials ω on hyper-elliptic surfaces. Since (z, w) parametrizes the surface, we can write

$$\omega = R_1(z,w)\,dz + R_2(z,w)\,dw$$

with $R_j(z, w)$ meromorphic. Using $w^2 = R(z)$ as in (6.19) yields

$$2w \, dw = R'(z) \, dz$$

and so

(6.23) $\omega = (\rho_1(z) + \rho_2(z)w) \, dz$

with rational $\rho_j(z)$ gives us all meromorphic differentials. Strictly speaking, (6.23) only applies away from the branch points, i.e., away from infinity and $w = 0$. But at a branch point we can use

$$2 \frac{dw}{R'(z)} = \frac{dz}{w}$$

since $R' \neq 0$ near these points. Alternatively, we substitute the uniformizing variables $z = z_j + t^2$ with t small to see that

(6.24) $\omega = (t \, \widetilde{\rho}_1(t^2) + \widetilde{\rho}_2(t^2)t^2) \, dt,$

which is clearly meromorphic ($\widetilde{\rho}_j$ are rational). Now let us identify the holomorphic differentials amongst (6.23). Away from branch points, ρ_j needs to be analytic. At the branch points we read off from (6.24) that $\widetilde{\rho}_1$ cannot be singular, since otherwise $t \, \widetilde{\rho}_1(t^2) + \widetilde{\rho}_2(t^2)t^2$ would exhibit odd negative powers in its Laurent expansion. Thus, $\rho_1(z)$ is a polynomial. In contrast, ρ_2 can have a pole at each branch point in $\mathbb{C}$, but from (6.24) we see that it cannot be more singular than a pole of first order. Hence the rational function

$$\rho_2(z) = \frac{s(z)}{R(z)} = \frac{s(z)}{w^2}$$

with s a polynomial. In summary, the holomorphic differentials take the form

(6.25) $\omega = \left(p_1(z) + \frac{p_2(z)}{w} \right) dz$

with polynomials $p_j(z)$. Let us now consider the behavior of this differential near $z = \infty$. Since $p_1(z) \, dz$ does not branch at that point, but $\frac{p_2(z)}{w} \, dz$ does, we can consider these two differentials separately. Setting $z = \frac{1}{\zeta}$ we conclude that p_1 must vanish. On the other hand, p_2 yields

$$p_2(\zeta^{-1})\zeta^{g-\frac{3}{2}} \, d\zeta.$$

If p_2 has degree m, substituting $\zeta = t^2$ transforms this into

$$t^{-2m+2g-2}(1 + O(t)) \, dt.$$

This is analytic near $t = 0$ only if $m \leq g - 1$.

In summary, the holomorphic differentials on the Riemann surface associated with (6.19) are precisely those spanned by

$$(6.26) \qquad \frac{dz}{w}, \ \frac{z \, dz}{w}, \ \frac{z^2 \, dz}{w}, \dots, \frac{z^{g-1} \, dz}{w},$$

provided that $g \geq 1$. As we already noted before, on the sphere there are no nontrivial differentials of the first kind.

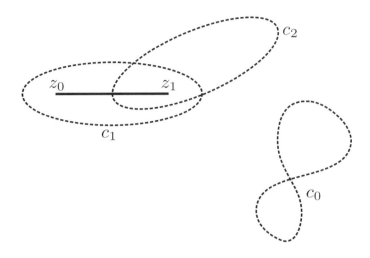

Figure 6.7.   The three types of curves for a genus zero surface

In the next chapter we will prove that on *every Riemann surface of genus g* the holomorphic 1-forms are a linear space of complex dimension g, including of course $g = 0$. Let us consider now consider an example of that latter genus, namely the surface defined by

$$(6.27) \qquad w^2 = (z - z_0)(z - z_1) \qquad z_0 \neq z_1.$$

Then the differential $\omega = \frac{dz}{w}$ is holomorphic everywhere in $\mathbb{C}$, but setting $z = \frac{1}{\zeta}$ yields

$$(6.28) \qquad \omega = - \frac{d\zeta}{\zeta \sqrt{(1 - \zeta z_0)(1 - \zeta z_1)}},$$

which has a simple pole near $\zeta = 0$. Thus, $\frac{dz}{w}$ is truly meromorphic and not holomorphic as expected (in $g = 1$ we observed that it is in fact *holomorphic*). Consider now the integrals

$$I_j := \int_{c_j} \omega, \quad j = 0, 1, 2$$

with the curves c_0, c_1, c_2 as shown in Figure 6.7, say with the clockwise orientation. First, these integrals need to be interpreted carefully. If we take a closed curve γ **on the surface defined by** (6.27), then $\int_\gamma \omega = 0$. Indeed, since this surface is just the sphere, we can freely deform the contour and in fact contract it to a point whence the claim. However, the issue here is that Figure 6.7 is not on the Riemann surface but instead in $\mathbb{C}$. This of course leads to a built-in ambiguity since z alone does not parametrize the surface—only (z, w) does. In other words, in the integral we will need to consider the choice of branch.

First, c_0 depicts a curve that neither surrounds nor intersects the segment $[z_0, z_1]$. Then $I_0 = 0$ since we can view c_0 as a curve on the surface and contract it to a point. In other words, the branch w remains fixed throughout.

As for c_1, we can deform the contour freely within $\mathbb{C} \setminus [z_0, z_1]$ again without ever changing the branch. In particular, we can either pull it tight so that it consists entirely of the cut $[z_0, z_1]$, but running above right-to-left and then below left-to-right. We leave the explicit calculation of the integral, which is easy by trigonometric substitution, to the reader. Alternatively, we can push the contour all the way to infinity to conclude from (6.28) that $I_1 = \pm 2\pi i$ where the sign depends on the choice of branch.

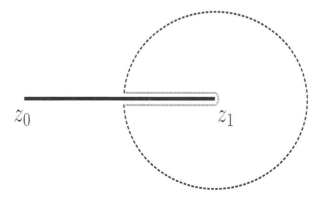

Figure 6.8.   Deforming c_2

The integral over c_2 can be deformed as shown in Figure 6.8. In other words, without moving the location of the intersection between c_2 and the cut $[z_0, z_1]$ we can push the curve entirely onto the cut. The resulting integration is explicit and left to the reader—the value depends on the location of the intersection point.

Contrast this to the calculation of the integral of $\frac{dz}{w}$ in degree $g = 1$ given by
$$w^2 = (z - z_0)(z - z_1)(z - z_2)(z - z_3)$$
over the curves a, b shown in Figure 6.9.

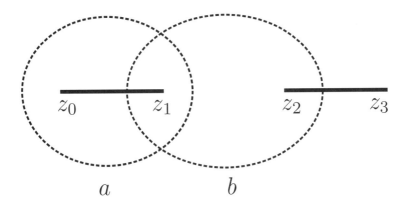

Figure 6.9. Curves a, b in genus $g = 1$

As before, we can push a onto the cut $[z_0, z_1]$ without changing the value. Hence

$$\int_a \omega =: I(z_0, z_1, z_2, z_3).$$

Figure 6.10 shows that we can place the cuts differently without changing anything. In other words, we can push b onto the cut $[z_1, z_2]$ and conclude that

$$\int_b \omega =: J(z_0, z_1, z_2, z_3).$$

In the following chapter we will study such integrals more systematically, and recognize I, J as the **periods of the differential** (of the first kind) $\frac{dz}{w}$ associated with the homology basis $\{a, b\}$. The left and right cuts in Figure 6.10 go to infinity. These considerations lead us back to elliptic functions as discussed in Chapter 4. Indeed, integrals of the form $\int_\gamma \omega$ where γ is a curve in $\mathbb{C} \setminus \{z_0, z_1, z_2, z_3\}$ are well-defined up to addition of expressions of the form

(6.29) $$nI + mJ, \qquad n, m \in \mathbb{Z}$$

since a, b form a homology basis of the Riemann surface defined by

$$w = \sqrt{(z - z_0)(z - z_1)(z - z_2)(z - z_3)}.$$

In Problem 6.11 the reader is asked to show that I, J are independent over the reals, amongst other things.

Let us now return to more general considerations by recalling from Chapter 4 that any orientable smooth two-dimensional surface M in $\mathbb{R}^3$ (or viewed as a manifold without an ambient space) is a Riemann surface. This was a

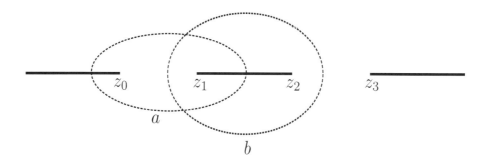

Figure 6.10. Curves a, b in genus $g = 1$ with different cuts

consequence of the existence of isothermal coordinates. On any such manifold M we can speak of (smooth) 1-forms ω. In coordinates

$$\omega = a(x, y)\, dx + b(x, y)\, dy$$

where a, b are real-valued and smooth. Let us assume that $\omega \neq 0$ on some open set. Then $a^2 + b^2 \neq 0$ and in each tangent space $T_p M$ the kernel of $\omega(p)$ defines a unique line. Thus, we obtain a smooth line-field in the tangent bundle (to every point a line is attached, and the lines vary smoothly with the point). We can visualize a differential form by means of such a line-field, although the form contains more information. We say that the field can be *integrated* if and only if there exists a function f, with $df \neq 0$, and such that the field is tangent to the level curves of f. This means that $\omega = \lambda\, df$ with some smooth function $\lambda \neq 0$. A particular instance of this arises when λ is constant on the level curves of f, which is the same as $\lambda = \varphi(f)$. If $\Phi' = \varphi$, then $\omega = dg$ with $g = \Phi(f)$, which precisely means that ω is **closed**. In local coordinates,

$$\omega = a(x, y)\, dx + b(x, y)\, dy$$

is closed if and only if $a_y = b_x$ which is the standard *integrability condition* deriving from the equality of mixed partials.

Amongst the closed forms we single out the harmonic ones as those for which g is harmonic. Strictly speaking, defining harmonic functions on a general n-dimensional manifold M requires a metric; the harmonic functions are characterized by $\Delta_M g = 0$ where Δ_M is the Laplace-Beltrami operator defined in terms of the metric. It is given by (4.7) as well as by $\Delta = \operatorname{div} \circ \nabla$, both of which have coordinate independent meaning. We can of course assume a metric exists, such as the one inherited by $\mathbb{R}^3$ if our surface sits there. But recall that on a two-dimensional surface the concept of a harmonic function is *conformally invariant* so that we can define this concept independently of the choice of a specific metric.

This being said, we can pick **any metric** on the surface, given by

$$ds^2 = E\,dx^2 + 2F\,dx\,dy + G\,dy^2$$

as in (4.2) in local coordinates. It is a standard fact that any smooth manifold carries a metric, which follows by gluing together such local representations by means of a partition of unity. The *conformal class* of a metric is the family $\{e^\varphi\,ds^2\}$ where φ is smooth. Considering isothermal coordinates we conclude that the conformal structure is well-defined by the conformal class (any two metrics in the class define the same conformal structure), *and conversely.*

The metric allows us to switch between forms and vector fields, the latter being natural due to the interpretation via flow lines. Closed forms then correspond to vector fields which are gradients, i.e., ∇f, also called conservative fields (or *irrotational*). The incompressible ones are then characterized by $\operatorname{div}\nabla f = 0$, in other words, they are given by *harmonic potential functions*.

Notes

In this chapter we carry out the work needed to obtain such basic results as the existence of a global nonconstant meromorphic function. Indispensable in this endeavor is the concept of a holomorphic and meromorphic differential form. These objects of course have a rich but still rigid integration theory which ultimately plays itself out in the Riemann-Roch, Abel and Jacobi theorems, to which we will come in the next chapter.

The concept of harmonic, closed, and co-closed forms carries over to any differentiable manifold, and for that matter, to forms of any degree. The study of differential forms in and of itself is not part of analytic function theory. See for example Rosenberg's book [**71**].

In the discussion of S^2 in Section 6.4 we referred to spherical harmonics. A nice presentation of these functions is given in Stein, Weiss [**78**]. For general compact manifolds we referred to the Weyl law for the growth of the eigenvalues of the Laplacian (or for that matter, general elliptic operators). This is a well-developed area, see for example Sogge's book [**75**].

In the final example of Section 6.4, i.e., the disk $\mathbb{D}$, we relied on standard results on Sobolev spaces on finite domains as well as the weak formulation of the Dirichlet problem. These can be found in many places. A standard reference is Evans' book [**22**]; see the chapters on Sobolev spaces and elliptic equations.

The results of the final two sections are our key to accessing some basic results for Riemann surfaces. With the existence of nontrivial meromorphic functions we were able to establish a pillar in the proof of Theorem 5.20. More remains to be done, however, in terms of classification of meromorphic functions and differentials. Some answers are provided in the following chapter.

The potential-theoretic proofs we gave in this chapter are by no means the only available ones. The more modern approach based on $\partial, \bar{\partial}$ and the Dolbeault cohomology is presented in numerous places, such as the beautiful recent book by Donaldson [**18**], as well as Forster [**29**]. For an elegant as well as concise exposition of complex line bundles, Dolbeault cohomology, Serre duality, and Chern classes, see Varolin's text [**84**] in this series. Perhaps it is advisable, however, to see the more elementary, albeit less comprehensive and powerful, path chosen here before venturing into these deeper waters.

6.8. Problems

Problem 6.1. Provide a detailed proof of Corollary 6.23.

Problem 6.2. Provide the details for the L^2 extension of our proof of the Hodge decomposition in the plane (see Example 1 in Section 6.4).

Problem 6.3. In this problem the reader is asked to apply Hodge's theorem to the Riemann surfaces

$$M = \{r_1 < |z| < r_2\}$$

where $0 \le r_1 < r_2 \le \infty$. Identify $\Omega_2^1(M), \mathfrak{h}_2(M)$ as well as E for each of these cases and show directly that

$$\Omega_2^1(M) = E \oplus *E \oplus \mathfrak{h}_2(M).$$

Problem 6.4. Let M be a simply-connected Riemann surface and let u be a harmonic function on M. Show that u has a global harmonic conjugate on M.

Problem 6.5. Show that every compact Riemann surface admits a triangulation.

Problem 6.6. Show that the meromorphic functions on a simply-connected Riemann surface separate points in the following strong sense: given distinct points $\{p_j : 1 \le j \le n\}$ on some Riemann surface M, and n distinct values $c_j \in \mathbb{C}_\infty$, there exists a meromorphic function on M which takes the value c_j at p_j (of course $f(p_j) = \infty$ means that f has a pole at p_j). In the next chapter we will establish the same for arbitrary genus.

Problem 6.7. Let M be a compact, simply-connected Riemann surface. Prove that the space in (6.18) has dimension 2.

Problem 6.8. Let M be a Riemann surface. Here you are asked to give an alternative proof for the existence of a meromorphic differential ω which has poles of order 2 at prescribed points $p_1, \ldots, p_n \in M$ with vanishing residues and is holomorphic everywhere else by means of the following strategy: by linearity, $n = 1$. Pick a parametric disk (U, z) around p_1 with $z(p_1) = 0$. Then let $\omega := \chi(z)\frac{dz}{z^2}$ where χ is a smooth cut-off function which is supported in the unit disk and so that $\chi = 1$ near zero. Then ω is a smooth 1-form on $M \setminus \{p_1\}$ with the property that $\eta := \omega - i * \omega$ is smooth on M, and in fact, $\eta = 0$ near p_1. Apply the Hodge decomposition theorem to write, with a harmonic form ρ,

$$\eta = df + *dg + \rho,$$

where f, g are smooth (since η is smooth—prove it). Now use this to define a meromorphic differential with the desired properties.

Problem 6.9. Let[4] M be a simply-connected compact Riemann surface. Select finitely many points $\{p_\nu\}_{\nu=1}^n \subset M$ as well as a positive integer s_ν for each $1 \le \nu \le n$. Define

$$V := \{f \in \mathcal{M}(M) \mid f \in \mathcal{H}(M \setminus \{p_\nu\}_{\nu=1}^n),$$

$$\text{the pole of } f \text{ at } p_\nu \text{ has order at most } s_\nu\}$$

Prove that $\dim(V) = 1 + \sum_{\nu=1}^n s_\nu$.

Problem 6.10. Let M_g be a hyper-elliptic surface of genus $g \ge 1$ (including the elliptic case $g = 1$). Show that the dimension of the linear space of holomorphic differentials vanishing at any given point of M_g is $g - 1$. In the following chapter we will establish this for all compact manifolds; see Corollary 7.17.

Problem 6.11. Let

$$I(z_0, z_1, z_2, z_3), \quad J(z_0, z_1, z_2, z_3)$$

be as in (6.29). Determine how these quantities transform if the points $\{z_0, z_1, z_2, z_3\}$, which are assumed to be distinct, are mapped onto four other points by means of a Möbius transformation. In particular, by moving one point off to infinity, reduce the general case to the integral

$$(6.30) \qquad \int_a \frac{dz}{\sqrt{(1 - z^2)(\zeta - z)}}$$

where $\zeta \in \mathbb{C} \setminus [-1, 1]$ and a is a simple closed contour around $[-1, 1]$ which does not encircle or hit ζ. Show that (6.30) is of the form $\sqrt{\zeta}\Phi(\zeta)$ where Φ is analytic in $\mathbb{C}_\infty \setminus [-1, 1]$. Find the series expansions of Φ around $\zeta = \infty$. Show that I, J do not vanish and that $I/J \notin \mathbb{R}$.

---

[4]This problem is exactly the genus zero case of the Riemann-Roch theorem for integral divisors.

Chapter 7

The Theorems of Riemann-Roch, Abel, and Jacobi

7.1. Homology bases and holomorphic differentials

After having studied the question of existence of a nonconstant meromorphic function, we will now turn to the following much deeper question: *What kind of nonconstant meromorphic functions does a given Riemann surface admit?* More precisely, *if M is compact and of genus g, what can we say about the minimal degree of a meromorphic function on M?* Answering this question will lead us to the Riemann-Roch theorem.

To appreciate this circle of ideas, note the following: Suppose M is compact and admits a meromorphic function f of degree one. Then M defines an isomorphism between M and $\mathbb{C}P^1$. This implies that no such function exists if M has genus one or higher! On the other hand, we will show (from Riemann-Roch) that for the simply-connected compact case there is such a function.

In this chapter, we will use some basic notions from the topology of compact surfaces: homology, the canonical homology basis, the fundamental polygon of a compact surface of genus g. These topics are briefly discussed in the appendix (see the section on topology). In addition, we depend heavily on the loop-forms from the previous chapter.

Let M be a compact Riemann surface of genus g. The intersection numbers between two closed curves γ_1, γ_2 are defined as

$$(7.1) \qquad \gamma_1 \cdot \gamma_2 = \int_M \eta_{\gamma_1} \wedge \eta_{\gamma_2} = -\langle \eta_{\gamma_1}, *\eta_{\gamma_2} \rangle = \int_{\gamma_1} \eta_{\gamma_2};$$

see Corollary 6.21. We remark that the integral on the right-hand is always an integer. In fact, if γ_1 and γ_2 do not intersect, then the integral vanishes. Indeed, in that case we can replace η_{γ_2} by $d\widetilde{f}$ where $\widetilde{f}$ is a globally smooth and compactly supported extension of the "neck function"; see Figure 6.3. If they do intersect, then each crossing contributes ± 1 depending on the orientation. To see this, we should first define a *crossing* between γ_1 and γ_2, which really means a *transverse crossing*: $\gamma_1(t_1) = \gamma_2(t_2)$ and $\gamma_1(t)$ lies on opposite sides of γ_2 depending on whether $t > t_1$ or $t < t_1$, respectively. This occurs, in particular, if the tangent vectors $\gamma_1'(t_1)$ and $\gamma_2'(t_2)$ are not parallel (we assumed in the definition of loop form that the curves had nonvanishing tangent vectors). If the crossing is not transverse, in other words, if $\gamma_1(t)$ stays on the same side of γ_2 near $t = t_1$, then we can again replace η_{γ_2} by $d\widetilde{f}$ as above. This then shows that such an intersection contributes 0 to the integral.

The homology class of γ determines the cohomology class of η_γ. Hence the intersection number is well-defined as a product between homology classes in $H_1(M;\mathbb{Z})$. Note that

$$b \cdot a = -a \cdot b, \quad (a+b) \cdot c = a \cdot c + b \cdot c$$

for any classes a, b, c. This follows directly from the definition and the linearity of the scalar product.

Pick a canonical homology basis for the 1-cycles, and denote it by $\{A_j\}_{j=1}^{2g}$. Here $A_j = a_j$ if $1 \le j \le g$ and $A_j = b_{j-g}$ if $g+1 \le j \le 2g$ where

$$a_j \cdot b_k = \delta_{jk}, \quad a_j \cdot a_k = 0, \quad b_j \cdot b_k = 0$$

for each $1 \le j, k \le g$. Next, we define a dual basis $\{\beta_k\}_{k=1}^{2g}$ for the cohomology. It is simply

$$\beta_k = \eta_{b_k}, \quad 1 \le k \le g,$$
$$\beta_k = -\eta_{a_{k-g}}, \quad g+1 \le k \le 2g,$$

and satisfies the duality relation

$$(7.2) \qquad\qquad \int_{A_j} \beta_k = \delta_{jk}.$$

We also record the fact

$$(7.3) \qquad\qquad \left\{ \int_M \beta_j \wedge \beta_k \right\}_{j,k=1}^{2g} = \begin{bmatrix} 0 & I \\ -I & 0 \end{bmatrix} =: J.$$

This is due to the fact that the entries of this matrix are all possible intersection numbers of the curves a_j, b_k.

Let us collect some properties of these forms (a form α is called real if $\alpha = \bar{\alpha}$).

Lemma 7.1. *Let M be a compact Riemann surface. The real one-forms $\{\beta_j\}_{j=1}^{2g}$ are a basis of $H^1(M; \mathbb{R})$ (the linear space of all closed 1-forms). Let α_j denote the orthogonal projection of β_j onto the harmonic forms (from the Hodge theorem). Then α_j is a real one-form, and $\{\alpha_j\}_{j=1}^{2g}$ is a basis of both $\mathfrak{h}(M; \mathbb{R})$ and $\mathfrak{h}(M; \mathbb{C})$, the real and complex-valued harmonic forms, respectively. In particular,*

$$\dim_{\mathbb{R}} \mathfrak{h}(M; \mathbb{R}) = \dim_{\mathbb{C}} \mathfrak{h}(M; \mathbb{C}) = 2g.$$

The relation (7.3) holds also for $\int_M \alpha_j \wedge \alpha_k$.

Proof. Since $\{A_j\}$ is a basis of $H_1(M; \mathbb{Z})$, a closed form α is exact if and only if

$$\int_{A_j} \alpha = 0 \qquad \forall\, 1 \leq j \leq 2g.$$

Hence the linear map $H^1(M; \mathbb{R}) \to \mathbb{R}^{2g}$,

$$\alpha \mapsto \left\{ \int_{A_j} \alpha \right\}_{j=1}^{2g}$$

is injective. Because of (7.2) this map is also onto and is thus an isomorphism. It is called the *period map*. The exact same argument also works over $\mathbb{C}$. Since every cohomology class has a unique harmonic representative, we obtain the statements about $\mathfrak{h}$.

Next, apply the Hodge decomposition to β_j. Since for any smooth, compactly supported g,

$$\langle \beta_j, *dg \rangle = -\int \beta_j \wedge d\bar{g} = -\int_c d\bar{g} = 0$$

where c defines β_j, we see that $\beta_j \in (*E)^\perp$. Consequently, $\beta_j = df_j + \alpha_j$ with f_j smooth. To check that α_j is real, write

$$\beta_j = df_j + \alpha_j,$$
$$\overline{\beta_j} = \beta_j = \overline{df_j} + \overline{\alpha_j},$$

so that

$$-\alpha_j + \overline{\alpha_j} = d(f_j - \overline{f_j})$$

is both harmonic and exact, and thus zero. $\qquad\square$

Next, we find a basis for the holomorphic 1-forms $\mathcal{H}\Omega^1$. In the classical literature, these are called *differentials of the first kind* (also known as *Abelian differentials*).

Lemma 7.2. *With α_j as above, define the holomorphic differential $\omega_j = \alpha_j + i*\alpha_j$ (where $i^2 = -1$). Then $\{\omega_j\}_{j=1}^{g}$ is a basis in $\mathcal{H}\Omega^1$. In particular, $\dim_{\mathbb{C}} \mathcal{H}\Omega^1 = g$.*

Proof. The dimension statement is immediate from

$$\mathfrak{h}(M;\mathbb{C}) = \mathcal{H}\Omega^1 \oplus \overline{\mathcal{H}\Omega^1};$$

see Lemma 6.13. To obtain the assertion about the basis, we express $*$ as a matrix relative to the basis $\{\alpha_j\}_{j=1}^{2g}$. This is possible, since $*$ preserves the harmonic forms. Also, note that it preserves real forms. Hence with $\lambda_{jk} \in \mathbb{R}$, and $\mathcal{G} = \{\lambda_{jk}\}_{j,k=1}^{2g}$,

$$*\alpha_j = \sum_{k=1}^{2g} \lambda_{jk}\,\alpha_k, \quad *\mathcal{A} = \mathcal{G}\mathcal{A}, \quad \mathcal{G} = \left[\begin{array}{cc} \Lambda_1 & \Lambda_2 \\ \Lambda_3 & \Lambda_4 \end{array}\right] \in GL(2g,\mathbb{R})$$

where $\mathcal{A}$ is the column vector with entries $\alpha_1,\ldots,\alpha_{2g}$. From $** = -\mathrm{Id}$ we deduce $\mathcal{G}^2 = -I_{2g}$. We expect Λ_2, Λ_3 to be invertible since heuristically $*$ should correspond to a switch between the a_j and the b_k curves. Indeed, we have

$$\langle \alpha_j, \alpha_\ell \rangle = \langle *\alpha_j, *\alpha_\ell \rangle = \sum_{k=1}^{2g} \lambda_{jk}\langle \alpha_k, *\alpha_\ell \rangle = \sum_{k=1}^{2g} \lambda_{jk} \int_M \alpha_\ell \wedge \alpha_k$$

or, in matrix notation,

$$\Gamma = \mathcal{G}J^t = \left[\begin{array}{cc} \Lambda_2 & -\Lambda_1 \\ \Lambda_4 & -\Lambda_3 \end{array}\right]$$

where $\Gamma = \{\langle \alpha_j, \alpha_\ell \rangle\}_{j,\ell=1}^{2g}$ is a positive definite matrix (since it is the matrix of a positive definite scalar product) and J is as above (see (7.3)). Hence $\Lambda_2 > 0$ and $-\Lambda_3 > 0$; in particular, these matrices are invertible.

Suppose there were a linear relation

$$c_1\omega_1 + \ldots + c_g\omega_g = (v^t + iw^t) \cdot (\mathcal{A}_1 + i*\mathcal{A}_1) = 0$$

where $v, w \in \mathbb{R}^g$ are column vectors, and $\mathcal{A} = \binom{\mathcal{A}_1}{\mathcal{A}_2}$. By the preceding paragraph, $*\mathcal{A}_1 = \Lambda_1\mathcal{A}_1 + \Lambda_2\mathcal{A}_2$ so that

$$[v^t \cdot \mathcal{A}_1 - w^t \cdot (\Lambda_1\mathcal{A}_1 + \Lambda_2\mathcal{A}_2)] + i[w^t \cdot \mathcal{A}_1 + v^t \cdot (\Lambda_1\mathcal{A}_1 + \Lambda_2\mathcal{A}_2)] = 0.$$

Since the terms in brackets are real 1-forms, it follows that they both vanish. Therefore, we obtain the following relation between the linearly independent vectors $\mathcal{A}_1, \mathcal{A}_2$ of 1-forms:

$$(v - \Lambda_1^t w)^t \cdot \mathcal{A}_1 = (\Lambda_2 w)^t \cdot \mathcal{A}_2, \quad (\Lambda_1^t v + w)^t \cdot \mathcal{A}_1 = -(\Lambda_2 v)^t \cdot \mathcal{A}_2$$

which finally yields $\Lambda_2 w = \Lambda_2 v = 0$, and thus $v = w = 0$ as desired. $\square$

7.2. Periods and bilinear relations

To proceed, we need the following remarkable identity.

Lemma 7.3. *Let* $\theta, \widetilde{\theta}$ *be closed 1-forms. Then*

$$(7.4) \qquad \int_M \theta \wedge \widetilde{\theta} = \sum_{j=1}^{g} \left(\int_{a_j} \theta \int_{b_j} \widetilde{\theta} - \int_{b_j} \theta \int_{a_j} \widetilde{\theta} \right).$$

In particular,

$$\|\theta\|_2^2 = \sum_{j=1}^{g} \left(\int_{a_j} \theta \int_{b_j} \ast\bar{\theta} - \int_{b_j} \theta \int_{a_j} \ast\bar{\theta} \right).$$

Proof. The integral on the left-hand side of (7.4) only depends on the cohomology classes of θ and $\widetilde{\theta}$, respectively. Thus, we can write

$$\theta = \sum_{j=1}^{2g} \mu_j \alpha_j + df, \quad \widetilde{\theta} = \sum_{j=1}^{2g} \widetilde{\mu}_j \alpha_j + d\widetilde{f}$$

where $\mu_j = \int_{A_j} \theta$, $\widetilde{\mu}_j = \int_{A_j} \widetilde{\theta}$. It follows that

$$\int_M \theta \wedge \widetilde{\theta} = \sum_{j,k=1}^{2g} \mu_j \widetilde{\mu}_k \int_M \alpha_j \wedge \alpha_k = \sum_{j=1}^{g} \left(\mu_j \widetilde{\mu}_{j+g} - \mu_{j+g} \widetilde{\mu}_j \right)$$

by (7.3). $\qquad\square$

The integrals on the right-hand side of (7.4) are called *periods*. We now state two corollaries.

Corollary 7.4. *Suppose* $\theta \in \mathcal{H}\Omega^1$. *Assume that either*

- *all a-periods vanish, i.e.,* $\int_{a_j} \theta = 0$ *for all* $1 \leq j \leq g$,
- *all b-periods vanish,*
- *or all periods of* θ *are real.*

Then $\theta = 0$.

Proof. From the previous lemma, since $\ast\theta = -i\theta$,

$$\|\theta\|^2 = \int_M \theta \wedge \overline{\ast\theta} = i \int_M \theta \wedge \bar{\theta}$$

$$= i \sum_{j=1}^{g} \left(\int_{a_j} \theta \int_{b_j} \bar{\theta} - \int_{b_j} \theta \int_{a_j} \bar{\theta} \right)$$

which vanishes under any of our assumptions. $\qquad\square$

Corollary 7.5. *The map*

$$\begin{cases} \omega & \mapsto \left(\int_{a_1} \omega, \ldots, \int_{a_g} \omega \right), \\ \mathcal{H}\Omega^1 & \to \mathbb{C}^g, \end{cases}$$

is a linear isomorphism. In particular, there exists a unique basis $\{\zeta_j\}_{j=1}^g$ of $\mathcal{H}\Omega^1$ for which $\int_{a_j} \zeta_k = \delta_{jk}$.

Proof. This is an immediate consequence of the previous corollary and the fact that $\dim_{\mathbb{C}} \mathcal{H} = g$. $\qquad\square$

This result raises the question as to what the other periods $\Pi_{jk} := \int_{b_j} \zeta_k$ might look like. Before proceeding, consider the most basic example with $g = 1$, i.e., $M = \mathbb{C}/\langle 1, \tau \rangle$ where $\langle 1, \tau \rangle$ is the group generated by the translations $z \mapsto z + 1$, $z \mapsto z + \tau$ with $\operatorname{Im} \tau > 0$. It is clear that in this case the basis of the previous corollary reduces to $\zeta = dz$ with a-period 1, and b-period τ. Here we chose the a-loop to be the edge given by $z \mapsto z + 1$, and the b-loop as the edge $z \mapsto z + \tau$.

Returning to the general case, given a basis $\{\theta_j\}_{j=1}^g$ of $\mathcal{H}\Omega^1$, we call the $g \times 2g$ matrix whose j^{th} row consists of the periods of θ_j, the *period matrix* of the basis.

Lemma 7.6. *Riemann's bilinear relations: the period matrix of the basis $\{\zeta_j\}_{j=1}^g$ from above has the form*

$$(I, \Pi), \quad I = \operatorname{Id}_{g \times g}, \quad \Pi^t = \Pi, \quad \operatorname{Im} \Pi > 0.$$

Here $\operatorname{Im} \Pi$ is the matrix of imaginary parts.

Proof. If $\theta, \widetilde{\theta}$ are holomorphic, then $\theta \wedge \widetilde{\theta} = 0$. Indeed, in local coordinates $\theta \wedge \widetilde{\theta} = u\, dz \wedge v\, dz = 0$. Hence

$$0 = \sum_{j=1}^g \left(\int_{a_j} \theta \int_{b_j} \widetilde{\theta} - \int_{b_j} \theta \int_{a_j} \widetilde{\theta} \right).$$

In particular, setting $\theta = \zeta_k$, $\widetilde{\theta} = \zeta_\ell$,

$$0 = \sum_{j=1}^g \left(\int_{a_j} \zeta_k \int_{b_j} \zeta_\ell - \int_{a_j} \zeta_\ell \int_{b_j} \zeta_k \right) = \Pi_{k\ell} - \Pi_{\ell k}.$$

Next, we have

$$\langle \zeta_k, \zeta_j \rangle = \int_M \zeta_k \wedge \overline{*\zeta_j} = i \int_M \zeta_k \wedge \overline{\zeta_j}$$

$$= i \sum_{\ell=1}^g \left(\int_{a_\ell} \zeta_k \int_{b_\ell} \overline{\zeta_j} - \int_{b_\ell} \zeta_k \int_{a_\ell} \overline{\zeta_j} \right) = 2 \operatorname{Im} \Pi_{kj}$$

which implies that $\operatorname{Im} \Pi > 0$. $\qquad\square$

In the case of the torus from the previous example, $\Pi = \tau$ and $\operatorname{Im}\Pi = \operatorname{Im}\tau > 0$ by construction. In other words, the periods $1, \tau$ define a lattice in $\mathbb{C} = \mathbb{C}^g$ (since $g = 1$ here). This turns out to have a generalization to higher genera, leading to the *Jacobian variety*. Thus, let $\{\omega_k\}_{k=1}^g$ be *any* basis of the holomorphic differentials $\mathcal{H}\Omega^1(M)$. It follows from Riemann's bilinear relations that the columns of the period matrix of this basis are linearly independent over the reals.

Lemma 7.7. *Let $\{\omega_k\}_{k=1}^g$ be any basis of the holomorphic differentials $\mathcal{H}\Omega^1(M)$ and let $\{A_j\}_{j=1}^{2g}$ be the canonical homology basis as above. Then the $2g$ vectors in $\mathbb{C}^g$ (the columns of the period matrix)*

$$p_j := \left(\int_{A_j} \omega_1, \dots, \int_{A_j} \omega_g \right)^t$$

for $1 \le j \le 2g$ are linearly independent over $\mathbb{R}$. In particular,

$$L(M) := \left\{ \sum_{j=1}^{2g} n_j p_j \mid n_j \in \mathbb{Z} \right\}$$

is a lattice in $\mathbb{C}^g$. The quotient $J(M) := \mathbb{C}^g / L(M)$ is called the Jacobian variety *and it is a compact, commutative complex Lie group of dimension g.*

Proof. Suppose the columns $\{p_j\}_{j=1}^{2g}$ are linearly dependent over $\mathbb{R}$. Then there exist $\lambda_j \in \mathbb{R}$, $1 \le j \le 2g$ for which

$$\sum_{j=1}^{2g} \lambda_j \int_{A_j} \omega_\ell = 0 \qquad \forall\, 1 \le \ell \le g.$$

In other words,

$$\left\langle \omega_\ell, \sum_{j=1}^{2g} \lambda_j *\eta_{A_j} \right\rangle = 0 \qquad \forall\, 1 \le \ell \le g.$$

Thus, for any $\omega \in \mathcal{H}\Omega^1(M)$,

$$\left\langle \omega, \sum_{j=1}^{2g} \lambda_j \eta_{A_j} \right\rangle = 0$$

and by the reality of the 1-form in the second slot here,

$$\left\langle \alpha, \sum_{j=1}^{2g} \lambda_j \eta_{A_j} \right\rangle = 0$$

for any *harmonic* differential α. But this implies that $\sum_{j=1}^{2g} \lambda_j \eta_{A_j} = 0$ and so $\lambda_j = 0$ for all $1 \le j \le 2g$. That $L(M)$ is a lattice means that $L(M)$

is a discrete subgroup of $\mathbb{C}^g$ which is clear, as are the stated properties of $J(M)$. $\qquad\square$

In the case of torus $M = \mathbb{C}/\langle 1, \tau \rangle$ we see that $J(M) = M$. Later in this chapter it will become clear that for all genus 1 surfaces one has $M \simeq J(M)$. For higher genera, there is always a (canonical) holomorphic map that takes a compact Riemann surface into its Jacobian variety. See Section 7.7 for all this.

We begin our analysis of $J(M)$ by introducing the canonical Jacobi map (7.5). In the following lemma we state that this map has maximal rank. This follows from the fact that in genus $g \geq 1$ not all holomorphic 1-forms can vanish at any given point. We shall not supply the proof of this latter property immediately, since it requires the Riemann-Roch theorem. We will come to that later.

Lemma 7.8. *The map* $\phi : M \to J(M)$ *defined as*

$$(7.5) \qquad p \mapsto \left(\int_{p_0}^{p} \omega_1, \ldots, \int_{p_0}^{p} \omega_g \right)^t$$

where $p_0 \in M$ *is an arbitrary point and the integration curves* $p_0 \to p$ *are arbitrary but* the same *for each* ω_j, *is a well-defined holomorphic mapping with maximal rank 1 (over* $\mathbb{C}$*).*

Proof. Let γ and $\widetilde{\gamma}$ be two paths connecting p_0 to p. Since $\gamma - \widetilde{\gamma}$ is a closed loop, it follows that for all $1 \leq k \leq g$,

$$(7.6) \qquad \int_{\gamma} \omega_k = \int_{\widetilde{\gamma}} \omega_k + \sum_{j=1}^{2g} n_j \int_{A_j} \omega_k$$

with $n_j \in \mathbb{Z}$. The choice of these integers is such that

$$(\gamma - \widetilde{\gamma}) - n_j \cdot A_j$$

is a boundary whence by Stokes (7.6) holds true.

It follows that the two realizations of $\phi(p)$ only differ by an element of $L(M)$, as claimed. It is clear that $d\phi(p) = 0$ if and only if all ω_j vanish at p. But this is impossible by Corollary 7.17 below. Hence $d\phi$ has rank 1 as claimed. $\qquad\square$

Naturally, we would like to know more about the map ϕ. Since $J(M)$ is a much easier object than M, we should try to obtain information about M from $J(M)$. This is especially appealing if ϕ is an isomorphism. However, just from the dimensions alone we conclude that this is possible only for $g = 1$, whereas for $g > 1$ the map ϕ can at most be an embedding. Thus, it is natural to ask:

- For $g = 1$ is ϕ an isomorphism?
- For $g > 1$ is ϕ an embedding?

Since the properties hold locally by Lemma 7.8, we conclude that they amount to nothing other than injectivity. In Section 7.7 on the theorems by Abel and Jacobi we shall demonstrate this injectivity and thus give affirmative answers to both of these questions.

For now we return to the investigation of *bilinear relations*. The name "bilinear relation" in Riemann surface theory refers to any relation that originates by applying Lemma 7.3 to a specific choice of $\theta, \widetilde{\theta}$. Next, we wish to obtain bilinear relations for meromorphic differentials, and not just holomorphic ones. In order to do so, we first reprove this lemma in a somewhat more intuitive fashion via Stokes' theorem.

Second proof of Lemma 7.3. We use the fundamental polygon of the Riemann surface M, which is the polygon $\mathcal{F}$ bounded by the curves

$$a_1, b_1, a_1^{-1}, b_1^{-1}, a_2, \ldots$$

and with appropriate identifications on the boundary. Since $\mathcal{F}$ is simply-connected, $\theta = df$ on $\mathcal{F}$. With some $z_0 \in \mathcal{F}$,

$$f(z) = \int_{z_0}^{z} \theta.$$

Note that f does not necessarily agree at identified points. By Stokes,

$$
\begin{aligned}
\int_M \theta \wedge \widetilde{\theta} &= \int_{\mathcal{F}} df \wedge \widetilde{\theta} = \int_{\mathcal{F}} d(f\widetilde{\theta}) = \int_{\partial \mathcal{F}} f\widetilde{\theta} \\
&= \sum_{j=1}^{g} \left(\int_{a_j} f\widetilde{\theta} + \int_{b_j} f\widetilde{\theta} + \int_{a_j^{-1}} f\widetilde{\theta} + \int_{b_j^{-1}} f\widetilde{\theta} \right).
\end{aligned}
$$

(7.7)

To proceed, let $z, z' \in \partial \mathcal{F}$ be identified points on a_j, a_j^{-1}, respectively. Then

$$
\begin{aligned}
\int_{a_j} f\widetilde{\theta} + \int_{a_j^{-1}} f\widetilde{\theta} &= \int_{a_j} \left(\int_{z_0}^{z} \theta - \int_{z_0}^{z'} \theta \right) \widetilde{\theta} \\
&= -\int_{a_j} \left(\int_{b_j} \theta \right) \widetilde{\theta} = -\int_{a_j} \widetilde{\theta} \int_{b_j} \theta.
\end{aligned}
$$

In Figure 7.1 the curve c depicts the curve joining z to z'. A similar formula holds for the b_j, b_j^{-1} integrals. Plugging this into (7.7) yields (7.4). $\qquad\square$

The importance of this method of proof lies with the fact that it applies to the case when $\widetilde{\theta}$ is a *meromorphic* differential as well. In that case we also pick up residues when applying Stokes' theorem. We now present an example of where this happens, which uses the L^2 existence theory. In what

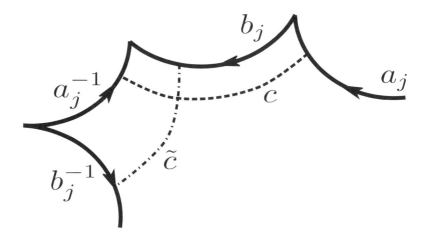

Figure 7.1. Bilinear relations via a fundamental polygon

follows, it will be understood automatically that the a, b-loops representing a homology basis do not pass through any pole of a meromorphic form. In particular, we regard them as *fixed* loops now rather than as homology classes.

Lemma 7.9. *Fix some* $p \in M$ *and a parametric disk* (U, z) *at* p *with* $z(p) = 0$, *and let* $n \geq 2$. *Denote by* $\tau_p^{(n)}$ *the unique meromorphic differential, holomorphic on* $M \setminus \{p\}$, *with singularity[1]* $\frac{dz}{z^n}$ *locally at* p, *and with vanishing* a-*periods. Then*

$$(7.8) \qquad \int_{b_\ell} \tau_p^{(n)} = \frac{2\pi i}{n-1} \, \alpha_{\ell, n-2} \quad \forall \, 1 \leq \ell \leq g$$

where $\alpha_{\ell, k}$ *denotes the Taylor coefficients of* ζ_ℓ *locally at* p, *i.e.,*

$$(7.9) \qquad \zeta_\ell(z) = \left(\sum_{k=0}^{\infty} \alpha_{\ell, k} \, z^k \right) dz$$

in the same *local coordinates* z *in which* $\tau_p^{(n)}$ *has singularity* $\frac{dz}{z^n}$.

Proof. To start, note that $\tau_p^{(n)} = \omega + \theta$ where ω is as in Corollary 6.26 and θ is holomorphic and chosen in such a way that the a-periods of $\tau_p^{(n)}$ vanish. To prove (7.8), pick a small positively oriented loop γ around p and let $\mathcal{F}'$ denote the fundamental polygon $\mathcal{F}$ with the disk bounded by γ deleted. Let $\zeta_\ell = df_\ell$ on $\mathcal{F}$ and thus also on $\mathcal{F}'$. Then by the second proof of Lemma 7.3

---

[1] This means that $\tau_p^{(n)} - \frac{dz}{z^n}$ is holomorphic around p.

presented above,

$$(7.10) \quad 0 = \int_{\mathcal{F}'} \zeta_\ell \wedge \tau_p^{(n)} = \sum_{j=1}^{g} \left(\int_{a_j} \zeta_\ell \int_{b_j} \tau_p^{(n)} - \int_{b_j} \zeta_\ell \int_{a_j} \tau_p^{(n)} \right) - \int_\gamma f_\ell \, \tau_p^{(n)}.$$

The vanishing of the left-hand side is the fact that $\theta \wedge \widetilde{\theta} = 0$ for holomorphic one-forms. In local coordinates,

$$\int_\gamma f_\ell \, \tau_p^{(n)} = \int_{|z|=\varepsilon} \left(\sum_{k=0}^{\infty} \frac{\alpha_{\ell,k}}{k+1} z^{k+1} \right) \frac{dz}{z^n} = \frac{2\pi i}{n-1} \alpha_{\ell,n-2}$$

whereas

$$\sum_{j=1}^{g} \left(\int_{a_j} \zeta_\ell \int_{b_j} \tau_p^{(n)} - \int_{b_j} \zeta_\ell \int_{a_j} \tau_p^{(n)} \right) = \int_{b_\ell} \tau_p^{(n)}.$$

In view of (7.10) we are done. $\qquad\square$

This lemma is needed in the proof of the Riemann-Roch theorem. For the Abel and Jacobi theorems we shall also require another type of bilinear relation dealing with differentials of the *third kind*. Recall from the previous chapter that this refers to meromorphic differentials which only have simple poles. Those of the *second kind* have vanishing residues at all poles, whereas those of the *first kind* are holomorphic.

Lemma 7.10. *Let ω be a differential of the third kind on M with poles at $\{p_j\}_{j=1}^{n}$. Fix a homology basis $\{A_j\}_{j=1}^{2g}$ as above so that the curves do not pass through any of these points. Assume that ω has vanishing a-periods. Then*

$$(7.11) \qquad\qquad \frac{1}{2\pi i} \int_{b_j} \omega = \sum_{\ell=1}^{n} \mathrm{res}(\omega, p_\ell) \int_{p_0}^{p_\ell} \zeta_j$$

where $p_0 \in M$ is arbitrary, and the integration paths from p_0 to p_ℓ are chosen suitably. The ζ_j are the basis in the holomorphic differentials uniquely associated to the homology basis.

Suppose that we shift the point p_0 to some other location $\widetilde{p}_0$. Pick any curve connecting $\widetilde{p}_0$ to p_0 and adjoin that segment to each of the curves $p_0 \to p_\ell$. Due to the fact that $\sum_{\ell=1}^{n} \mathrm{res}(\omega, p_\ell) = 0$ we conclude that this does not change the right-hand side of (7.11). Generally speaking, we can change the curves $p_0 \to p_\ell$ as long as the change is the same to each integral and thus makes no contribution due to $\sum_{\ell=1}^{n} \mathrm{res}(\omega, p_\ell) = 0$.

Problem 7.5 asks the reader to carry out the proof of Lemma 7.10, which is quite similar to the proof of Lemma 7.9.

7.3. Divisors

We now introduce a useful and standard book-keeping device for meromorphic functions and divisors. Given $f \in \mathcal{M}(M)$ where M is compact, we associate with it the "word" (formal expression),

$$(7.12) \qquad (f) := (\{\nu_1, p_1\}, \ldots, \{\nu_r, p_r\}, \{-\mu_1, q_1\}, \ldots, \{-\mu_s, q_s\}),$$

where the ν_j are the order of the zeros p_j, and μ_i the order of the poles q_i of f. Both ν_j and μ_i are positive integers. By the argument principle (see Proposition 6.6), we conclude that

$$(7.13) \qquad \sum_{j=1}^{r} \nu_j - \sum_{i=1}^{s} \mu_i = 0.$$

In the same way, we associate a word (ω) to a meromorphic differential. These "words" are well-defined, i.e., they do not depend on the choice of coordinates. There is no need to distinguish between zeros and poles, since they are distinguished in a word by the signs of their integer weights. Thus, we can write

$$(7.14) \qquad (f) = (\{s_k, p_k\})_{k=1}^{m}$$

where p_k are either zeros or poles, and $s_k \in \mathbb{Z}$ are their respective orders. Note that we are allowing $s_k = 0$ here for convenience, with the understanding that m is always finite.

Given two meromorphic functions $f, g \in \mathcal{M}(M)$, we see a clear relation between the words (fg), (f), and (g), respectively. Indeed, if p_k appears in both f and g, then we add their respective weights. Otherwise, we include the distinct points and their weights in the word of fg. Note that a zero or pole of f, and its order, can only change if it is also the location of a zero or pole of g. Moreover, if such locations coincide, then the orders are indeed added. So we obtain exactly the rule for computing the words of products that we just stated.

This additive feature suggests that we introduce an additive notation from the start, namely that of a formal sum

$$(7.15) \qquad (f) = \sum_k s_k \, p_k$$

in place of (7.14). Then we see that $(fg) = (f) + (g)$ where the addition of words is precisely that of a free abelian group. The presence of this group as an ambient object suggests further that we introduce *all sums* as in (7.15) without any reference to a meromorphic function.

Definition 7.11. A *divisor* D on a compact Riemann surface M is a finite formal sum $D = \sum_\nu s_\nu p_\nu$ where $p_\nu \in M$ are distinct and $s_\nu \in \mathbb{Z}$. $\mathrm{Div}(M)$

denotes the additive free group of divisors on M. The *degree* of D is the integer

$$\deg(D) = \sum_\nu s_\nu.$$

If f is a nonconstant meromorphic function on M, then we define the divisor of f as

$$(f) = \sum_\nu \pm\text{ord}(f; p_\nu)\, p_\nu$$

where the sum runs over the zeros and poles of f with the sign $\pm$ being chosen depending on whether p_ν is a zero or pole, respectively. If f is a constant (but neither 0 nor ∞), then $(f) = 0$. In the same way, we define the divisor of a nonzero meromorphic differential:

$$(\omega) = \sum_\nu \pm\text{ord}(\omega; p_\nu)\, p_\nu$$

where the sign is chosen again via the zero/pole dichotomy. This does not depend on the choice of coordinates.

So we have the free group of divisors, $\text{Div}(M)$, as an ambient object, and within it, the divisors associated with all meromorphic functions, excluding the constants 0 and ∞. It is natural to study the quotient of $\text{Div}(M)$ by this subgroup. As we shall see shortly, the resulting quotient is relevant to the divisors associates with meromorphic differentials. But first we state our observations formally by means of standard algebraic terminology.

Lemma 7.12. *Let M be a compact Riemann surface. Then*

- $\deg : \text{Div}(M) \to \mathbb{Z}$ *is a group homomorphism.*
- *The map $f \mapsto (f)$ is a homomorphism from the multiplicative group $\mathcal{M}(M)^*$ of the field $\mathcal{M}(M)$ (which excludes $f \equiv \infty$) of meromorphic functions to $\text{Div}(M)$. The image under this map is called the subgroup of* principal *divisors and the quotient $\text{Div}(M)/\mathcal{M}(M)^*$ is called* divisor class group *and the conjugacy classes are called* divisor classes. *The homomorphism* deg *factors through to the divisor class group.*

There is nothing really new here, as we have essentially already covered all this above. In the final sentence, "factors through to the divisor class group" means that deg is well-defined on the equivalence classes of divisors in the quotient; in other words, we can compute the degree of a class by picking an arbitrary element of it. This is immediate from (7.13). As a particular instance of Lemma 7.12 we note that $-(f) = (1/f)$ for meromorphic functions f which are not the excluded ones, the constants 0 and ∞.

Next, we turn our attention to the divisors of meromorphic differentials. Their relation to meromorphic functions is as follows: given any two nonzero $\omega_1, \omega_2 \in \mathcal{M}\Omega^1(M)$, we express them in a chart as $\omega_j = u_j \, dz$. Then abusing notation somewhat, $\frac{\omega_1}{\omega_2} = \frac{u_1}{u_2}$ is meromorphic in the chart and, moreover, well-defined: if we change coordinates $z = z(\zeta)$, then $\frac{\omega_1}{\omega_2} = \frac{u_1 \zeta'}{u_2 \zeta'} = \frac{u_1}{u_2}$. Thus, we can form the global meromorphic function $\frac{\omega_1}{\omega_2} \in \mathcal{M}(M)$ which is neither constant equal to zero nor constant ∞, leading to the following conclusion.

Corollary 7.13. *The divisors of nonzero meromorphic differentials always belong to the same divisor class (called the* canonical class K*).*

We can rephrase this as an answer to the following existence question: *given any divisor D, does there exist $\omega \in \mathcal{M}\Omega^1(M)$ with the property that $(\omega) = D$?*

The answer is: *if and only if $D \in K$*. The necessity is clear from the corollary. For the sufficiency take any $\omega_0 \in \mathcal{M}\Omega^1(M)$ which is not zero. Then by definition $D - (\omega_0) = (f)$ for some $f \in \mathcal{M}(M)$ which is neither 0 nor ∞. But then the meromorphic 1-form $\omega_1 = f\omega_0$ has the property that $(\omega_1) = D$ as desired.

So what does K look like for our standard examples, starting with the Riemann sphere $\mathbb{C}P^1$? As we have known since the first two chapters of this textbook, the meromorphic functions on this surface are precisely the rational ones $f(z) = \frac{P(z)}{Q(z)}$ with polynomials P, Q where $Q \neq 0$. The coordinate is $z = \frac{\xi}{\eta}$ where $[\xi : \eta] \in \mathbb{C}P^1$, $\eta \neq 0$. The extension to the point at infinity, $[1 : 0]$ is given by taking limits $z \to \infty$. In particular, the divisor (f) associated with such a rational function is of degree 0 which must be the case on any compact surface. Conversely, *any divisor D of degree zero is of the form (f) with f rational*: if none of the points in D lie at ∞, then those with positive weights determine the zeros of P, and those with negative ones, the zeros of Q. The extension to the case where ∞ is in the divisor is immediate.

So we conclude that for $\mathbb{C}P^1$ the principal divisors are those of vanishing degree, and the divisor class group is isomorphic to $\mathbb{Z}$ via the degree.

To determine the canonical class, just take $\omega = dz$ in the same coordinates as above. Setting $z = \frac{1}{\zeta}$ yields $\omega = -\zeta^{-2} \, d\zeta$ for $\zeta \neq 0$. The divisor is $(\omega) = -2[1 : 0]$, corresponding to the pole of order 2 at infinity. We conclude that the canonical class in this case are all divisors D with $\deg(D) = -2$.

Working more directly, any meromorphic differential is of the form $\omega = f(z) \, dz$ with $f \in \mathcal{M}(\mathbb{C})$ in the coordinates from before. If f is analytic at $z = \infty$, then ω has a pole of order 2 at infinity. Since $\deg(f) = 0$, we have

$\deg(\omega) = -2$. See Problem 7.1 for a detailed analysis of all meromorphic forms with a given divisor.

Next, we turn to the tori $\mathbb{C}/\Lambda$ with $\tau \notin \mathbb{R}$ and $\Lambda = \langle 1, \tau \rangle$ the lattice generated by $1, \tau$. Theorem 4.17 gives a complete description of all meromorphic functions in that case, in fact of their divisors D. They are precisely those with $\deg(D) = 0$ and $\sigma(D) \in \Lambda$ where

$$\sigma(D) := \sum_j n_j z_j \in \Lambda.$$

This sum is over the complex field $\mathbb{C}$, whereas the divisor is the same sum, but in the formal sense. The map $\sigma : \mathrm{Div}(M) \to \mathbb{C}$ is a homomorphism. Hence the principal divisors are

(7.16) $\qquad \{D \in \mathrm{Div}(M) \mid \deg(D) = 0,\ \sigma(D) \equiv 0 \mod \Lambda\}$

and the divisor class group is isomorphic to $\mathbb{Z} \times \Lambda$, the direct product of the integers with the torus itself. To find the canonical class we again just pick one form, say $\omega = dz$ in the universal cover of M, which is $\mathbb{C}$. But this shows that for the tori $\mathbb{C}/\Lambda$ the principal and canonical classes coincide.

In Section 7.5 we shall see that the degree of K is always $2g - 2$. A most natural question presents itself now: *How do we characterize the principal divisors amongst those of vanishing degree?* An answer will be given in Section 7.7 in terms of the Jacobian variety $J(M)$ from above. In fact, the *divisor class group, restricted to vanishing degree, is isomorphic to $J(M)$.*

In the previous chapter the existence theorems of meromorphic functions and differentials played a prominent role. Problem 6.9 introduces the linear space of meromorphic functions whose poles lie within a given finite set $\{p_j\}_{j=1}^J$, and with orders not exceeding some prescribed positive integers $\{s_j\}_{j=1}^J$. Under the condition that the compact surface M is **simply-connected**, one can give an explicit description of this space as integrals of linear combinations of meromorphic differentials with poles of order $2 \leq k \leq s_j + 1$ at p_j, but holomorphic away from that point. The latter exist by Corollary 6.26. Note carefully that since we assume M is compact, the L^2 condition which is intrinsic to the existence theory of the previous chapter, holds automatically.

So, in particular, we see that the dimension of this linear space is $1 + \sum_j s_j$. The 1 here coming from the constant functions which are the only holomorphic ones.

What if M is not simply-connected? One of the main objectives of this chapter is to develop the tools to answer this question, as well as many other related ones. For this purpose, it will be convenient to rephrase it in terms of divisors as we now do.

Definition 7.14. Let $D = \sum_\nu s_\nu p_\nu$ be a divisor as above. If $s_\nu \geq 0$ for all ν, then D is called *integral*. We write $D \geq D'$ for two divisors if $D - D' = \sum_\nu s_\nu p_\nu$ is integral. Given a divisor D, we define the $\mathbb{C}$-linear space

$$L(D) = \{f \in \mathcal{M}(M) \mid (f) \geq D \text{ or } f = 0\}$$

where $\mathcal{M}(M)$ are the meromorphic functions. Analogously, we define the space

$$\Omega(D) = \{\omega \in \mathcal{M}\Omega^1(M) \mid (\omega) \geq D \text{ or } \omega = 0\}$$

where $\mathcal{M}\Omega^1(M)$ are the meromorphic differentials.

We note that the degree is monotone under this ordering: if $D \geq D'$, then $\deg(D) \geq \deg(D')$. If M is a compact Riemann surface of genus g, then $\Omega(0) = \mathcal{H}\Omega^1 \simeq \mathbb{C}^g$.

The linear space of meromorphic functions in Problem 6.9 therefore equals $L(-D)$ where $D = \sum_\nu s_\nu p_\nu$. The space of differentials that we encountered in the description of $L(-D)$ is $\Omega(-D')$ where $D' := \sum_\nu (s_\nu + 1) p_\nu$. The latter space is easier to understand than $L(-D)$. Indeed, while for the meromorphic functions on a general surface there is no partial fraction decomposition as in the plane (Mittag-Leffler), we have essentially such a representation for meromorphic differentials thanks to Corollary 6.26. See also Problem 7.3 below.

Further elementary observations about the spaces in Definition 7.14 (all dimensions here are over $\mathbb{C}$) are as follows.

Lemma 7.15. *For any compact surface M the following properties hold:*

(1) *If $D \geq D'$, then $L(D) \subset L(D')$ and $\Omega(D) \subset \Omega(D')$.*

(2) *$L(0) = \mathbb{C}$ and $L(D) = \{0\}$ if $D > 0$.*

(3) *If $\deg(D) > 0$, then $L(D) = \{0\}$.*

(4) *$\dim L(D)$ and $\dim \Omega(D)$ only depend on the divisor class of D and they are finite. Moreover, $\dim \Omega(D) = \dim L(D - K)$ where K is the canonical class.*

Proof. (1) is clear. For (2), note that $f \in L(D)$ with $D \geq 0$ implies that f is holomorphic and thus constant. For (3), observe that $(f) \geq D$ implies that $0 = \deg((f)) \geq \deg(D)$. For (4), suppose that $D = D' + (h)$ where h is nonconstant meromorphic (the constant case being trivial). Then $f \mapsto fh$ takes $L(D')$ $\mathbb{C}$-linearly and isomorphically onto $L(D)$. In particular, $\dim L(D) = \dim L(D')$. The map $\eta \mapsto \frac{\eta}{\omega}$ takes $\Omega(D)$ isomorphically onto

$L(D - K)$ where $K = (\omega)$ is the canonical class, whence the dimension statement. Finally,

$$\dim \Omega(D) = \dim L(D - K) = \dim L(D' - K) = \dim \Omega(D')$$

as claimed. The finiteness of the dimension is a consequence of compactness.

It is not immediately clear how to construct bases in $L(D)$, but we can consider the map $d : L(D)/\mathbb{C} \to \Omega(\widetilde{D})$ where

$$D = \sum_\nu s_\nu \, p_\nu, \qquad \widetilde{D} = \sum_{s_\nu < 0} (s_\nu - 1) \, p_\nu.$$

We discard here all $s_\nu = 0$ and $L(D)/\mathbb{C}$ just equates functions that differ by a constant. This map is injective since $df = 0$ implies that f is a constant. We can exhibit an explicit basis in $\Omega(\widetilde{D})$: this space is spanned by all meromorphic differentials with poles precisely at p_ν (and holomorphic away from that point) and of order s where $2 \le s \le 1 - s_\nu$. We know from the previous chapter that such differentials exist; see Corollary 6.26.   □

We now turn to the main result which allows us to compute the dimensions of these spaces.

7.4. The Riemann-Roch theorem

We state the theorem first for integral divisors. In the following section we shall derive the general case. For applications we refer the reader to the following section.

Theorem 7.16 (Riemann-Roch). *Let D be an integral divisor. Then*

(7.17)
$$\dim L(-D) = \deg(D) - g + 1 + \dim \Omega(D)$$
$$= \deg(D) - g + 1 + \dim L(D - K).$$

Before delving into the proof let us consider some examples. First, we already know the $g = 0$ case. Indeed, since $\Omega(D) \subset \Omega(0) = \{0\}$ it follows that (7.17) becomes

$$\dim L(-D) = 1 + \deg(D).$$

But this is precisely the content of Problem 6.9. Recall that $D = p$ gave us the existence of a meromorphic function with a single simple pole at p, whence also the isomorphism $M \simeq \mathbb{C}P^1$.

Now suppose $g = 1$. Then we are asked to prove that

$$\dim L(-D) = \deg(D) + \dim \Omega(D) = \deg(D) + \dim L(D - K).$$

For example, take $M = \mathbb{C}/\Lambda$ where $\Lambda = \langle 1, \tau \rangle$, $\tau \notin \mathbb{R}$. Since we determined the canonical class to be equal to the principal one, the Riemann-Roch count relates dimensions of different spaces of meromorphic functions on the torus:

$$(7.18) \qquad \dim L(-D) = \deg(D) + \dim L(D) = \deg(D)$$

since $L(D) = \{0\}$ for $\deg(D) > 0$. Take $D = 1 \cdot p$, a single point with weight 1. Since there can be no function with a single simple pole on the torus, it follows that $L(-D)$ contains only holomorphic functions, in other words, the constants. So indeed, $\dim L(-p) = 1 = \deg(D)$ in that case. Now take $D = 2 \cdot p$. Then $L(-D) = \text{span}_{\mathbb{C}}(1, \wp)$, where $\wp$ is the Weierstrass function from Proposition 4.14. If $D = m \cdot p$ with $m \geq 3$, then $L(-D)$ is spanned by 1, $\wp$, and all the series in (4.16) with $3 \leq n \leq m$. So these examples agree with (7.18).

Now suppose we take $D = 1 \cdot p_1 + 1 \cdot p_2$ with distinct p_1, p_2. By Theorem 4.17 there exists a meromorphic function in $L(-D)$ since we can assign zeros so as to satisfy the conditions of that theorem. Note that this choice is not relevant, as the meromorphic function with simple poles at $\{p_1, p_2\}$ is unique up to the addition of a constant. Moreover, the sum of the residues needs to be zero so we cannot have only one of these poles. This again agrees with (7.18).

For $D = 1 \cdot p_1 + 2 \cdot p_2$ we use the function from the previous paragraph together with the $\wp$ function at p_2 and as usual the constant 1. So we have dimension 3 as needed. In Problem 7.4 we ask the reader to cover all integral divisors in this fashion.

Unfortunately, these examples do not suggest any kind of proof strategy for the general case. What we do is to pass from $f \in L(-D)$ to df. This form then has vanishing periods and residues. Conversely, each $f \in L(-D)$ is obtained by integrating such a form. We use the differentials $\tau_p^{(\nu)}$ which have vanishing residues from above to span the space of these forms. But we need to enforce the vanishing condition on the periods, which introduces a linear dependency condition involving the basis forms $\{\zeta_\ell\}$ via Lemma 7.9 (see in particular (7.9)). This finally leads us to the space of holomorphic differentials vanishing at the points of D. In other words, to the space $\Omega(D)$. We might recognize in this argument, and in the appearance of both $L(-D)$ and $\Omega(D)$, some form of duality. See the notes for more comments on this important issue.

Proof of Riemann-Roch for integral divisors. Since $\Omega(0)$ is the space of holomorphic differentials, and thus of dimension g, (7.17) holds for $D = 0$. Hence we can assume that $\deg(D) > 0$. Thus, assume that $D = \sum_{\nu=1}^{n} s_\nu p_\nu$ with $s_\nu > 0$. To expose the ideas with a minimum of technicalities, we let $s_\nu = 1$ with p_ν distinct for all $1 \leq \nu \leq n$. We can also assume that $g \geq 1$.

If $(f) \geq -D$, then $df \in \mathcal{M}\Omega^1$ is holomorphic on $M \setminus \bigcup_\nu \{p_\nu\}$ with $\operatorname{ord}(df, p_\nu) \geq -2$; clearly, df exhibits vanishing periods and residues. Conversely, if $\eta \in \mathcal{M}\Omega^1$ has all these properties, then

$$f(q) = \int_p^q \eta$$

is well-defined where $p \in M$ is fixed and the integration is along an arbitrary curve avoiding the p_ν. It satisfies $df = \eta$ and $(f) \geq -D$. Hence

$$\dim L(-D) = \dim V + 1$$

$$V := \Big\{ \omega \in \mathcal{M}\Omega^1 \mid \omega \text{ has vanishing periods and residues,}$$

$$\omega \text{ is holomorphic on } M \setminus \bigcup_\nu \{p_\nu\}, \text{ and } \operatorname{ord}(\omega, p_\nu) \geq -2 \Big\}.$$

To compute $\dim V$, we define for any $\underline{t} := (t_1, \ldots, t_n)$

$$\beta_{\underline{t}} := \sum_{n=1}^n t_\nu \tau_{p_\nu}^{(2)}$$

where $\tau_p^{(2)}$ is as in Lemma 7.9. By construction, $\beta_{\underline{t}}$ has vanishing a-periods and vanishing residues. Second, we define the map Φ as

$$\Phi : \beta_{\underline{t}} \mapsto \Big\{ \int_{b_\ell} \beta_{\underline{t}} \Big\}_{\ell=1}^g.$$

Every $\omega \in V$ satisfies $\omega = \beta_{\underline{t}}$ for some unique $\underline{t}$ but not every $\beta_{\underline{t}} \in V$; in fact, $V = \ker \Phi$ under this identification since the a-periods of $\tau_p^{(2)}$ vanish by construction. With $\{\zeta_\ell\}_{\ell=1}^g$ the basis from above,

$$\int_{b_\ell} \beta_{\underline{t}} = 2\pi i \sum_{\nu=1}^n t_\nu \, \alpha_{\ell,0}(p_\nu)$$

(see (7.8)), where

$$\zeta_\ell(z) = \Big[\sum_{j=0}^\infty \alpha_{\ell,j}(p_\nu) \, z^j \Big] dz$$

locally around p_ν. Thus, Φ is defined by the matrix

$$(7.19) \qquad 2\pi i \begin{bmatrix} \alpha_{1,0}(p_1) & \cdots & \alpha_{1,0}(p_n) \\ & \cdots & \\ \alpha_{g,0}(p_1) & \cdots & \alpha_{g,0}(p_n) \end{bmatrix}.$$

The number of linear relations between the rows of this matrix equals

$$\dim\{\omega \in \mathcal{H}\Omega^1 \mid \omega(p_\nu) = 0 \ \forall \, 1 \leq \nu \leq n\} = \dim \Omega(D) = \dim L(D - K).$$

In summary,

$$\dim L(-D) = \dim V + 1 = \dim \ker \Phi + 1$$
$$= n - \operatorname{rank} \Phi + 1 = n - (g - \dim L(D - K)) + 1$$
$$= \deg(D) - g + 1 + \dim L(D - K)$$

as claimed. We remark that for $g = 0$ periods have no relevance and for integral D with $\deg(D) > 0$ one has $\dim V = n = \deg(D)$ and $\dim L(D - K) = 0$ whence $\dim L(-D) = n + 1 = \deg(D) + 1$.

For the case of integral D, which is not the sum of distinct points, the proof is only notationally more complicated. We again consider the case $g \geq 1$. Then with $D = \sum_{\nu} s_{\nu} p_{\nu}$ and $n = \deg(D)$, consider

$$\beta_{\underline{t}} := \sum_{\nu} \sum_{k=2}^{s_{\nu}+1} t_{\nu,k} \tau_{p_{\nu}}^{(k)}, \qquad \underline{t} = \{t_{\nu,k}\}_{2 \leq k \leq s_{\nu}+1}$$

Every ω in the linear space

$$V := \Big\{ \omega \in \mathcal{M}\Omega^1 \,\big|\, \omega \text{ has vanishing periods and residues},$$
$$\omega \text{ is holomorphic on } M \setminus \bigcup_{\nu} \{p_{\nu}\}, \text{ and } \operatorname{ord}(\omega, p_{\nu}) \geq -s_{\nu} - 1 \Big\}$$

satisfies $\omega = \beta_{\underline{t}}$ for some $\underline{t} \in \mathbb{C}^n$. As before, we have $\dim L(-D) = \dim V + 1$. With Φ as above, $\beta_{\underline{t}} \in V$ if and only if $\Phi(\beta_{\underline{t}}) = 0$ so that $\dim V = \dim \ker \Phi$. From Lemma 7.9 we compute the b-periods as

$$\int_{b_{\ell}} \beta_{\underline{t}} = 2\pi i \sum_{\nu} \sum_{2 \leq k \leq s_{\nu}+1} t_{\nu,k} \frac{\alpha_{\ell,k-2}(p_{\nu})}{k-1}.$$

For the purposes of computing dimensions, we can evidently replace $t_{\nu,k}$ with $\frac{t_{\nu,k}}{k-1}$. By the same argument as in the case $s_{\nu} = 1$ one now concludes that

$$\dim \ker \Phi = n - (g - \dim L(D - K))$$

and (7.17) follows.   □

The examples preceding the proof exhibited genus $g = 0$ and $g = 1$. In those cases the space $\Omega(D)$ did not contribute to the dimension count. This is also apparent from the proof: in those cases either the map Φ does not occur ($g = 0$) or there is only one row in the matrix (7.19) and therefore no linear relations ($g = 1$).

7.5. Applications and general divisors

The easiest example is given by the divisor $D = p$, in other words, a single point with weight 1. Then (7.17) gives us

$$(7.20) \qquad \dim L(-p) = 2 - g + \dim \Omega.$$

If $g = 0$, then the only holomorphic differential is 0 whence $\dim \Omega(p) = 0$ and $\dim L(-p) = 2$. This means that the space $L(-p)$ is spanned by two functions, namely the constant 1 and some meromorphic function f_0 with a simple pole at one point.

If $g \geq 1$, then we know that there can be no such function f_0 since it would map M isomorphically onto $\mathbb{C}P^1$. We can also obtain a contradiction directly from Riemann-Roch. Indeed, suppose there were such a function f_0, with a unique simple pole at p_0. Then for any integer $n \geq 1$ we have

$$\dim L(-n \cdot p_0) \geq n + 1$$

since the powers f_0^ℓ, $0 \leq \ell \leq n$ are linearly independent in this space. Thus,

$$n + 1 \leq \dim L(-n \cdot p_0) = n + 1 - g + \dim \Omega(n \cdot p_0)$$

whence $g = \dim \Omega(0) \geq \dim \Omega(n \cdot p_0) \geq g \geq 1$. In other words, all holomorphic differentials vanish to arbitrary order at p_0 which is impossible.

In conclusion, if $g \geq 1$, then $L(-p)$ contains only constants and thus has dimension 1. Hence (7.20) implies $\dim \Omega(p) = g - 1$, and we have obtained the following result.

Corollary 7.17. *Let M be compact with $g \geq 1$. Then there is no point in M at which all $\omega \in \mathcal{H}\Omega^1$ vanish. In fact, the holomorphic differentials vanishing at a given point form a hyperplane in the space of all holomorphic differentials.*

Corollary 7.17 can be viewed as a statement about projective embeddings. Indeed, let $\{\omega_j\}_{j=1}^g$ be a basis of $\mathcal{H}\Omega^1(M)$ and define

$$\imath_M : M \to \mathbb{C}P^g, \; p \mapsto [f_1(p) : \ldots : f_g(p)]$$

where $\omega_j = f_j \, dz$ in local coordinates. This is clearly well-defined as changes of coordinates only multiply the entries by a nonzero factor; moreover, at least one f_j does not vanish. Thus, χ is well-defined and, in fact, analytic.

The analogue of $M \simeq \mathbb{C}P^1$ for $g = 0$ is the following assertion about **branched covers of the sphere in higher genera**.

Corollary 7.18. *Let M be compact with genus $g \geq 1$. Then M can be represented as a branched cover of $\mathbb{C}P^1$ with at most $g + 1$ sheets. In other words, there exists a nonconstant meromorphic function on M of degree at most $g + 1$.*

Proof. Take $D = (g + 1)p_0$. Then $\dim L(-D) \geq 2$ by Riemann-Roch. Hence there exists $f : M \to \mathbb{C}P^1$ meromorphic, f holomorphic everywhere on $M \setminus \{p_0\}$ with $\mathrm{ord}(f, p_0) \geq -g - 1$. Evidently, such an f defines the branched covering. $\square$

This shows, in particular, that every compact Riemann surface of genus 1 admits a two-sheeted branched cover. This is the missing piece in the proof of Corollary 5.21 which states that *every compact Riemann surface of genus 1 is an elliptic curve.*

In Chapters 4 and 5 we encountered a class of polynomials $P(w, z)$ called hyper-elliptic curves. These furnish examples of compact surfaces of *arbitrarily large genus* which can still be written as *two-sheeted branched covers of the sphere.*

Definition 7.19. A compact Riemann surface M is called **hyper-elliptic** if it is a 2-sheeted branched cover of S^2. In other words, if it carries a meromorphic function of degree 2. Equivalently, if M carries a meromorphic function with precisely two poles (counted with multiplicity).

If f is such a function, then each branch point of f has branching number 1. Thus, by Riemann-Hurwitz, the genus of M satisfies $B = 2(g + 1)$ where B is the number of branch points. Notice that we did not require that the genus satisfies $g \geq 2$ as we did in Chapter 5 (there we followed common practice by calling curves with $g = 1$ *elliptic*). In order to explore this notion, we need to determine the degree of the canonical class. This is an interesting result in its own right.

Lemma 7.20. *The degree of the canonical class is given by*
$$\deg(K) = 2g - 2 = -\chi(M).$$
In particular, if $\deg(D) > 2g - 2$, *then* $\Omega(D) = \{0\}$.

Proof. If $g = 0$, then take $M = \mathbb{C}_\infty$ and $\omega = dz$ in the chart $z \in \mathbb{C}$. Under the change of variables $z \mapsto \frac{1}{z}$, this transforms into $\omega = -\frac{dz}{z^2}$. Hence $\deg(K) = -2$. If $g \geq 1$, pick any nonzero $\omega \in \mathcal{H}\Omega^1(M)$ (which can be done since this space has dimension g). Then $(\omega) = K$ is integral and by Theorem 7.16,
$$\dim L(-K) = \deg(K) - g + 1 + \dim L(0) = \deg(K) - g + 2,$$
whereas $L(-K) = \mathcal{H}\Omega^1(M)$. Hence $\dim L(-K) = \dim \mathcal{H}\Omega^1(M) = g$, and $\deg(K) = 2g - 2$ as claimed.

An alternative proof based on the Riemann-Hurwitz formula is as follows: by Theorem 7.16 there exists a meromorphic function f with n simple poles for some integer $n \geq 2$ and holomorphic elsewhere. In particular,

$\deg(f) = n$. Take $\omega = df$. Suppose that $p \in M$ is a branch point of f. Then p is not a pole of f and

$$\operatorname{ord}(\omega; p) = b_f(p)$$

where $b_f(p)$ is the branch number of f at p. If p is a pole of f, then $\operatorname{ord}(\omega; p) = -2$ so that

$$\deg((\omega)) = -2n + \sum_{p \in M} b_f.$$

By the Riemann-Hurwitz formula (see (4.11)),

$$2(g - 1) = -2n + \sum_{p \in M} b_f(p)$$

and we are done.

Now suppose that $(\omega) \geq D$ with some nonzero ω. Then

$$2g - 2 \geq \deg((\omega)) \geq \deg(D)$$

which implies the final assertion. □

We can also obtain the previous result by looking at the differential $\frac{df}{f}$ (see Problem 7.2 below). For example, take a torus $\mathbb{C}/\Lambda$. Then the canonical class has degree 0 and all holomorphic differentials are of the form $a\,dz$ with a constant. Such a form can only vanish at a point if it is identically zero, which is in agreement with the final assertion of the lemma.

Next we establish the Riemann-Roch theorem for arbitrary divisors, and not just integral ones. This relies on Lemma 7.20 and Theorem 7.16.

Theorem 7.21. *Equation (7.17) holds for all divisors D.*

Proof. We already covered the case where D is equivalent to an integral divisor. Suppose D is such that $K - D$ is equivalent to an integral divisor. Then from Theorem 7.16,

$$\begin{aligned} \dim L(D - K) &= \deg(K - D) - g + 1 + \dim L(-D) \\ &= -\deg(D) + g - 1 + \dim L(-D), \end{aligned}$$

which is the desired statement. Suppose therefore that neither D nor $K - D$ are equivalent to an integral divisor. Then

$$\dim L(-D) = \dim L(D - K) = 0.$$

It remains to be shown that $\deg(D) = g - 1$. For this we write $D = D_1 - D_2$ where D_1 and D_2 are integral and have no point in common. Clearly, $\deg(D) = \deg(D_1) - \deg(D_2)$ with both degrees on the right-hand side positive. By Theorem 7.16,

$$\dim L(-D_1) \geq \deg(D_1) - g + 1 = \deg(D) + \deg(D_2) - g + 1.$$

If $\deg(D) > g$, then $\dim L(-D_1) \geq \deg(D_2) + 1$ and there exists a function $f \in L(-D_1)$ which vanishes at all points of D_2 to the order prescribed by D_2. Indeed, this vanishing condition imposes $\deg(D_2)$ linear constraints which leaves us with one dimension in $L(-D_1)$ (for example, if $\deg(D_2) = 1$ then we use the constant function to make any nonconstant meromorphic f with $(f) \geq -D_1$ vanish at the point given by D_2). For this f,

$$(f) + D \geq -D_1 + D_2 + D = 0$$

so that $f \in L(-D)$ contrary to our assumption. This shows that $\deg(D) \leq g - 1$. Similarly,

$$\deg(K - D) = 2g - 2 - \deg(D) \leq g - 1 \Longrightarrow \deg(D) \geq g - 1$$

and we are done. $\qquad\square$

7.6. Applications to algebraic curves

We shall now return to our investigation of the relation between compact Riemann surfaces and equations of the form $P(w, z) = 0$ where P is a polynomial. First, Lemma 7.20 leads to the following observation relating the genus to the notion of hyper-elliptic surface.

Proposition 7.22. *If M is of genus $g \leq 2$, then it is hyper-elliptic.*

Proof. We already covered the cases $g = 0$ and $g = 1$. If $g = 2$, then we first note that the canonical class has degree 2. Take any nonzero holomorphic differential ω. Then $D = (\omega)$ is an integral divisor with $\deg(\omega) = 2$, whence $D = p + q$ where $p, q \in M$ are not necessarily distinct. By Riemann-Roch,

$$\dim L(-p - q) = 1 + \dim \Omega(p + q) \geq 2.$$

Thus, there exists a meromorphic function with poles precisely at p, q. If these points are distinct, then the poles are simple. If they coincide the pole is of order 2. $\qquad\square$

There is still one loose end that needs to be tied up in the proof of Theorem 5.20, namely to choose f in such a way that (5.6) is irreducible. This can now be settled easily by means of Riemann-Roch, which completes the proof of Theorem 5.20.

Proposition 7.23. *Given z of degree n as in Proposition 5.16, there exists a meromorphic function f on M which renders the polynomial in (5.6) irreducible.*

Proof. We can assume that the degree satisfies $n > 1$, since otherwise there is nothing to prove. Pick $z_0 \in \mathbb{C}$ in such a way that $z^{-1}(z_0)$ consists of n distinct points, say $\{p_j\}_{j=1}^n$. Then for each $1 \leq j \leq n$ we can find a meromorphic function g_j with the property that g_j has a simple pole at p_j and simple zeros at each p_k for $k \neq j$. Such a meromorphic function exists by Riemann-Roch: take $D = p_j - \sum_{k \neq j} p_k + (n - 1 + g) \cdot q$ as divisor where $q \in M$ is some point distinct from $\{p_j\}_{j=1}^n$. Then $\deg(D) = g + 1$ and so $\dim L(-D) \geq 2$. So there exists a function g as described, which in addition can have a pole at q, as well as a number of zeros.

Select any distinct complex numbers $\{w_\ell\}_{\ell=1}^n$ and set

$$f := \frac{\sum_\ell w_\ell \, g_\ell}{\sum_\ell g_\ell}.$$

This is clearly meromorphic on M and $f(p_j) = w_j$ for each $1 \leq j \leq n$. In other words, f separates the points $p_1, p_2, \ldots, p_n$. Note that this step generalizes Problem 6.6 to arbitrary genus (there we did not have Riemann-Roch at our disposal so we assumed $g = 0$).

By Proposition 5.16 there exists $P \in \mathbb{C}[w, z]$ so that $P(f, z) = 0$ on all of M. If $P(w, z) = P_1(w, z)P_2(w, z)$ where P_1, P_2 both have positive degrees, then it follows that either $P_1(f, z) = 0$ or $P_2(f, z) = 0$ on M by the uniqueness principle. But evaluating these identities at the points $p_1, p_2, \ldots, p_n$ yields a contradiction since one would need to satisfy

$$P_i(w_\ell, z_0) = 0 \quad \forall \, 1 \leq \ell \leq n$$

where either $i = 1, 2$. But this is impossible since the degree of P_i is strictly less than n. $\qquad \square$

The reader might find it instructive to review the examples given by (5.8) in the context of this proposition. The previous proof accomplishes the irreducibility of the defining polynomial (5.6) in the most natural way, namely by forcing f to be as independent of z as possible.

For the sake of completeness, we now restate the equivalence between compact Riemann surfaces and smooth projective algebraic curves, but also include a description of all meromorphic functions on a compact surface. Note that this latter assertion is a vast generalization of Proposition 4.16.

Theorem 7.24. *Let M be any compact Riemann surface. Choose any meromorphic function z on M of positive degree, and let f be given by Proposition 7.23 with associated irreducible polynomial $P(w, z)$. Then the map $M \ni p \mapsto (f(p), z(p))$ is a conformal isomorphism between M and the Riemann surface associate with the algebraic equation $P(w, z) = 0$ over $\mathbb{C}P^1$, as defined in Chapter 5.*

Moreover, any meromorphic function on M is a polynomial in f with coefficients which are rational functions of z.

Proof. For the proof of the first part see Theorem 5.20.

For the second part we remove the critical points $\mathcal{C} := \{z_j\}_{j=0}^J$ from $\mathbb{C}_\infty$ as in the proof of Proposition 5.16. Thus, for any $\zeta \in \mathbb{C} \setminus \mathcal{C}$ one has that $z^{-1}(\zeta) = \{p_j\}_{j=1}^n$ consists of distinct points in M (in other words, we are not at a branch point of z). Then for any $g \in \mathcal{M}(M)$ we consider the function

$$(7.21) \qquad \sum_{j=1}^n \frac{g(p_j)}{w - f(p_j)} = \frac{G(w, \zeta)}{F(w, \zeta)}$$

locally around a fixed but arbitrary $\zeta_0 \in \mathbb{C} \setminus \mathcal{C}$. We claim that (as in the Lagrange interpolation formula) G, F may be chosen to be polynomials in w with coefficients in the field of rational functions of ζ. First, F is the same as (5.6):

$$F(w, \zeta) = \prod_{j=1}^n (w - f(p_j)) = \sum_{\ell=0}^n w^\ell \sigma_{n-\ell}(\zeta).$$

On the other hand,

$$G(w, \zeta) = \sum_{j=1}^n g(p_j) \prod_{k \neq j} (w - f(p_j)) = \sum_{\ell=0}^n w^\ell \tau_{n-\ell}(\zeta)$$

where $\tau_{n-\ell}(\zeta)$ are symmetric under permutations of the points p_j. It is clear that the functions $\tau_{n-\ell}(\zeta)$ are analytic near ζ_0. Moreover, we can analytically continue them to any other point within $\mathbb{C} \setminus \mathcal{C}$. Finally, if we analytically continue $\tau_{n-\ell}(\zeta)$ around a small loop centered at any point in $\mathcal{C}$, then we return to the same value due to the aforementioned symmetry under permutations and the fact that the values of z^{-1} remain distinct as we move around the loop. Thus, $\tau_{n-\ell}$ is analytic in $\mathbb{C} \setminus \mathcal{C}$ and the isolated singularities at $\mathcal{C}$ are either removable or poles—the latter being a consequence of the fact that f, g are meromorphic. Consequently, the $\tau_k \in \mathcal{M}(\mathbb{C}P^1)$ are rational and we see that G has the desired form.

Finally, from (7.21),

$$g(p_j) = \frac{G(w, \zeta)}{\partial_w F(w, \zeta)}\bigg|_{w = f(p_j)}.$$

Recall that $F(w, \zeta)$ is irreducible. So we can apply the Euclidean algorithm in the ring of polynomials $K[w]$ where K is the field of meromorphic functions in ζ to conclude the following:

$$A(w, \zeta)\partial_\zeta F(w, \zeta) + B(w, \zeta)F(w, \zeta) = 1$$

where A, B lie in this polynomial ring. Setting $w = f(p_j)$ in this identity implies that

$$(7.22) \quad g(p_j) = G(f(p_j), \zeta)\, A(f(p_j), \zeta) = G(f(p_j), z(p_j))\, A(f(p_j), z(p_j))$$

for all p_j which are not branch points of z. Since the latter are isolated and both sides of (7.22) are meromorphic we conclude that

$$g = G(f, z) A(f, z)$$

as an identity on M and we are done. □

See Problem 7.6 for a different approach to the representation of an arbitrary meromorphic function via f, z. It is common to call the meromorphic functions (f, z) as in Proposition 7.23 a *primitive pair*. The simply-connected case, i.e, $g = 0$, is characterized by the fact that there is a linear relation between f and z. In other words, every rational function on a simply-connected surface M is a rational function of a meromorphic function z on M of degree 1. In other words, we recover the fact (which we have been using extensively) that the meromorphic functions on the Riemann sphere are the rational ones.

Corollary 7.25. *Let M be a compact Riemann surface. For any primitive pair (f, z) with associated polynomial $P(w, z)$ the field of meromorphic functions satisfies*

$$\mathcal{M}(M) \simeq \mathbb{C}(z)[w] / \langle P(w, z) \rangle$$

in the sense of field isomorphisms. Here $\langle P(w, z) \rangle$ is the ideal generated by P in the ring $\mathbb{C}(z)[w]$.

Proof. To any $F(w, z) = \sum_{k=0}^{N} b_k(z) \, w^k \in \mathbb{C}(z)[w]$ we associate

$$g(z) = F(f(z), z) \in \mathcal{M}(M).$$

By choice of $P(w, z)$, this map factors through to the field $\mathbb{C}(z)[w] / \langle P(w, z) \rangle$. By Theorem 7.24 the map is onto, and since it is a nontrivial homomorphism of fields it is also injective. □

7.7. The theorems of Abel and Jacobi

We shall now study the Jacobian variety $J(M) = \mathbb{C}^g / L(M)$ in more detail, which was introduced in Lemmas 7.7 and 7.8.

Let us first recall Theorem 4.17 for the tori $M = \mathbb{C} / \langle \omega_1, \omega_2 \rangle$ which we proved in Chapter 4 in the context of elliptic functions. That theorem asserts the existence of a meromorphic function on M with zeros z_j and poles ζ_k if and only if conditions (4.23) and (4.24) hold.

Using the language of divisors, this is in agreement with the following more general result, known as *Abel's theorem*. It completely characterizes **all principal divisors**.

As above, M is a compact Riemann surface and we let $\{\omega_j\}_{j=1}^{g}$ be an arbitrary basis of $\mathcal{H}\Omega^1(M)$, g the genus of M.

Theorem 7.26. *Let D be a divisor on the compact Riemann surface M. There exists a meromorphic function f on M with $(f) = D$ if and only if the following two conditions hold:*

- $\deg(D) = 0$,
- *with[2] $D = \sum_{\nu=1}^{n}(p_\nu - q_\nu)$ one has[3]*

$$(7.23) \qquad \Phi(D) := \sum_{\nu=1}^{n}\left(\int_{p_\nu}^{q_\nu}\omega_1,\ldots,\int_{p_\nu}^{q_\nu}\omega_g\right)^t \equiv 0 \mod L(M)$$

where $L(M)$ is the lattice associate with the homology basis and the basis $\{\omega_j\}_{j=1}^{g}$ as in Lemma 7.7.

Proof. If $g = 0$, then only $\deg(D) = 0$ is relevant. Thus, we are reduced to the fact that a meromorphic function exists on S^2 with poles and zeros at prescribed locations and with prescribed orders as long as the combined order of the zeros is the same as the combined order of the poles.

Let us therefore assume that $g \geq 1$. Clearly, $\deg(D) = 0$ is necessary. We will give two different arguments for the second assertion.

Let $z \in \mathcal{M}(M)$ be of degree $n \geq 1$ and satisfy $D = (z)$. Suppose ω is any holomorphic 1-form on M and define its **trace relative to** z as follows. With $\mathcal{C}$ the critical points of z as in the proof of Proposition 5.16, fix some $\zeta_0 \in \mathbb{C} \setminus \mathcal{C}$ and set

$$(7.24) \qquad \mathrm{Tr}_z(\omega) := \sum_{j=1}^{n}(z_j)_*\omega$$

locally around any point in $\mathbb{C} \setminus \mathcal{C}$ where (U_j, φ_j) are local coordinates on M around the distinct points $\{p_j\}_{j=1}^{n} = z^{-1}(\zeta_0)$ and z_j is the map z_j restricted to U_j, and $(z_j)_*$ is the associated push-forward of 1-forms. Then (7.24) is a holomorphic 1-form in $\mathbb{C}$ locally near ζ_0, which does not depend on the choice of the coordinates. We can analytically continue (7.24) along any path in $\mathbb{C} \setminus \mathcal{C}$ and due to the permutation invariance of the trace we obtain the same 1-form if we move along a closed loop. Each point in $\mathcal{C}$ is a removable singularity of $\mathrm{Tr}_z(\omega)$ and therefore $\mathrm{Tr}_z(\omega)$ is a holomorphic 1-form on $\mathbb{C}P^1$. But this means that $\mathrm{Tr}_z(\omega) \equiv 0$.

Next, assume for simplicity that z branches over neither 0 nor ∞. Pick a smooth curve γ connecting these two points in $\mathbb{C}P^1$ which does not pass through any critical point. Then $z^{-1}(\gamma)$ consists of n smooth curves $\{\eta_j\}_{j=1}^{n}$

---

[2]The p_ν do not need to be pairwise distinct, and the same holds for the q_ν. However, $p_\nu \neq q_\mu$ for any $1 \leq \nu, \mu \leq n$. Notice that the ordering is arbitrary and does not matter, since we only introduce an ambiguity on the level of the lattice $L(M)$.

[3]This definition extends the map ϕ defined for points in (7.5) to divisors. The integration curves are arbitrary, but the same in each slot. In this way we only generate ambiguity which factors out through $L(M)$.

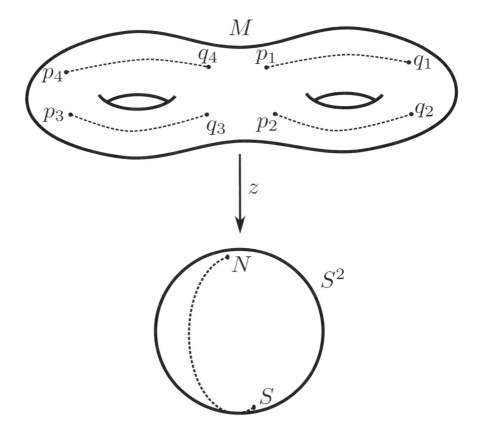

Figure 7.2. The curves η_j on M and γ on S^2

on M. The endpoints of these curves are precisely the *zero/pole* pairs (p_ν, q_ν)
which make up the divisor $D = (z)$ relative to some ordering. Finally, for
any holomorphic 1-form ω on M,

$$(7.25) \qquad \sum_j \int_{\eta_j} \omega = \int_\gamma \mathrm{Tr}_z \,\omega = 0.$$

If z does branch over either 0 or ∞, then we can shift γ slightly so that it
connects noncritical points. Applying the previous case and taking limits
(which is legitimate since M is compact) we then obtain the general case.
Alternatively, we can also apply the exact same construction of the $\{\eta_j\}$
starting from γ as before even if z branches over 0 or ∞. In that case some
of the η_j will begin or end at the same point which is no issue either.

Now suppose we were to order the zero/pole pairs as in (7.23) and we
select some paths σ_ν connecting p_ν to q_ν, respectively. Then there exist

$n_k \in \mathbb{Z}$ such that

$$\sum_j \eta_j - \sum_\nu \sigma_\nu \equiv \sum_{k=1}^{2g} n_k \cdot A_k \quad \text{modulo boundaries}$$

(in the sense of homology, with the collection of all A_k forming the homology basis) whence for every holomorphic 1-form ω,

$$0 = \sum_j \int_{\eta_j} \omega = \sum_\nu \int_{\sigma_\nu} \omega + \sum_{k=1}^{2g} n_k \int_{A_k} \omega.$$

If we specialize to one of the basis forms ω_j, then we see that

$$\sum_\nu \left(\int_{\sigma_\nu} \omega_1, \ldots, \int_{\sigma_\nu} \omega_g \right)^t = -\sum_{k=1}^{2g} n_k \left(\int_{A_k} \omega_1, \ldots, \int_{A_k} \omega_g \right)^t$$

$$= -\sum_{k=1}^{2g} n_k p_k \in L(M)$$

which is precisely (7.23).

An alternative elegant argument is based on the idea of deformation. To be specific, consider the map

(7.26) $\Psi : [\xi_1 : \xi_2] \mapsto \Phi((\xi_1 f + \xi_2))$

from $\mathbb{C}P^1 \to J(M)$. Problem 7.8 asks the reader to verify that Ψ is continuous and lifts to a continuous map $\widetilde{\Psi} : \mathbb{C}P^1 \to \mathbb{C}^g$ which is, moreover, holomorphic (i.e., each component is). Taking this for granted, we conclude that each component is constant whence

$$0 = \Psi([0:1]) = \Psi([1:0]) = \Phi(D)$$

as claimed.

Neither of the previous two arguments suggests a proof of the converse, i.e., of the sufficiency. Let us now present a third approach which does. The idea is that for any nonconstant meromorphic function f the differential $\frac{df}{f}$ is of the third kind with divisor

$$D = \sum_\nu \mathrm{ord}(f, p_\nu) \cdot p_\nu - \sum_\mu \mathrm{ord}(f, q_\mu) \cdot q_\mu$$

with zeros p_ν and poles q_μ, and $\mathrm{ord}(\omega, p)$ denotes their respective orders. Now let ω be a differential of the third kind with poles at exactly these points such that

(7.27) $\mathrm{res}(\omega, p_\nu) = \mathrm{ord}(f, p_\nu), \qquad \mathrm{res}(\omega, q_\mu) = -\mathrm{ord}(f, q_\mu).$

We denote the set of all poles of ω by $\mathcal{P}$. By Corollary 6.30 such a differential exists since the sum of these orders vanishes. Moreover, we normalize such that all a-periods of ω vanish (shifting the base curves if needed such that they do not intersect with the poles). Since $\frac{df}{f} - \omega$ is holomorphic, one has

$$(7.28) \qquad \frac{df}{f} = \omega + \sum_{j=1}^{g} c_j \, \zeta_j$$

where the ζ_j are from Corollary 7.5 and

$$(7.29) \qquad \int_{a_k} \frac{df}{f} = \sum_{j=1}^{g} c_j \int_{a_k} \zeta_j = c_k.$$

Locally, away from the poles $\mathcal{P}$, one has $\frac{df}{f} = d\log f$. This implies that

$$\int_{\gamma} \frac{df}{f} \in 2\pi i \mathbb{Z}$$

for any closed curve which avoids the points in $\mathcal{P}$. In particular, $c_k = 2\pi i n_k$ for some $n_k \in \mathbb{Z}$. Using Lemmas 7.10 and 7.6, one obtains

$$(7.30)
\begin{aligned}
2\pi i m_k &= \int_{b_k} \frac{df}{f} = \int_{b_k} \omega + \sum_{j=1}^{g} c_j \int_{b_k} \zeta_j \\
&= 2\pi i \sum_{p \in \mathcal{P}} \operatorname{res}(\omega, p) \int_{p_0}^{p} \zeta_k + 2\pi i \sum_{j=1}^{g} \Pi_{kj} n_j.
\end{aligned}$$

By the symmetry of the matrix Π the order of the indices does not matter. If we interpret this last line correctly, then it precisely means that

$$\sum_{m=1}^{n} \left(\int_{p_m}^{q_m} \zeta_1, \ldots, \int_{p_m}^{q_m} \zeta_g \right)^t = (\mathrm{I}, \Pi) \vec{v} \in L(M)$$

where $\vec{v} \in \mathbb{Z}^{2g}$; see Lemma 7.6 for the notation. This is precisely (7.23) for the canonical basis $\omega_j = \zeta_j$. The general case follows by linear algebra (changing the basis).

This argument gives us a strategy for the converse, i.e., the sufficiency of (7.23). Indeed, given a divisor D as in the theorem, we need to **construct a form** Ω of the third kind in such a way that the differential equation $\frac{df}{f} = d\log f = \Omega$ defines a meromorphic function with the desired properties. Solving for f we conclude that

$$(7.31) \qquad f(p) = \exp\left(\int_{p_0}^{p} \Omega \right).$$

This freedom of choice of p_0 amounts to an integration constant. The essential issue now is to ensure that the ambiguity resulting from the choice of integration path $p_0 \to p$ has no other effect than an integer multiple of $2\pi i$. Once this is ensured by means of (7.23), it is indeed clear that (7.31) defines a function which is holomorphic away from the points in D and has zeros and poles as prescribed by D. This can be read off from $\frac{df}{f} = \Omega$.

To construct Ω we just go back to (7.27). We start with

$$\omega := \sum_\nu (\omega_{p_0 p_\nu} - \omega_{p_0 q_\nu})$$

where ω_{pq} is the unique differential of the third kind, with poles at $p \neq q$ and residues, $-1, +1$, respectively, and with vanishing a-periods. Then set

$$(7.32) \qquad \Omega = \omega + \sum_{j=1}^{g} c_j \, \zeta_j$$

as in (7.28).The c_j are determined as follows. By (7.31) we have a representation (relative to the ζ_j-basis)

$$(7.33) \qquad \sum_{\nu=1}^{n} \left(\int_{p_\nu}^{q_\nu} \zeta_1, \ldots, \int_{p_\nu}^{q_\nu} \zeta_g \right)^t = (\mathrm{I}, \Pi)\vec{v} \in L(M)$$

where $\vec{v} \in \mathbb{Z}^{2g}$. Now set $c_j := 2\pi i v_{g+j}$ for $1 \leq j \leq g$. On the one hand, (7.32) implies that

$$\int_{a_j} \Omega = c_j \in 2\pi i \mathbb{Z}.$$

On the other hand, by (7.33),

$$\int_{b_j} \Omega = 2\pi i v_j \in 2\pi i \mathbb{Z} \quad \forall \, 1 \leq j \leq g;$$

cf. (7.30). Thus, we have exactly what we need so that (7.31) defines a meromorphic function on M and Abel's theorem is proved. $\square$

We can now establish that the Jacobi map of Lemma 7.8 is one-to-one.

Corollary 7.27. *Let M be compact of genus $g \geq 1$. The map ϕ defined in (7.5) is injective. In particular, for $g = 1$ there is a conformal isomorphism $M \simeq J(M)$ and for $g \geq 2$ the map ϕ is an embedding.*

Proof. Suppose not. Then $\phi(p) \equiv \phi(q) \mod L(M)$ where $p \neq q$. This means precisely that

$$\Phi(p - q) \equiv 0 \mod L(M)$$

where Φ is the map in (7.23). It follows from Theorem 7.26 that for some meromorphic f one has $(f) = (p - q)$. But this means that f has a unique simple pole whence $g = 0$, contrary to what we have assumed.

Thus, $\phi : M \to J(M)$ is injective of maximal rank and thus an embedding. If $g = 1$, it follows that $J(M)$ is another compact Riemann surface with $\phi(M)$ an open, compact subset of $J(M)$. Hence $\phi(M) = J(M)$ and so ϕ is also onto, and therefore an isomorphism. For $g > 1$ it is an embedding onto a two-dimensional manifold inside of the $2g$-dimensional manifold $J(M)$. $\quad\square$

Let us note that we have completely classified all compact Riemann surfaces of genus $g = 0$ (they are the sphere) and $g = 1$ (they are a torus $\mathbb{C}/\Lambda$ where $\Lambda = \langle 1, \tau \rangle$, $\operatorname{Im} \tau > 0$). In (7.16) we observed that the divisor class group for $g = 1$ is isomorphic to $J(M)$. The Jacobi theorem says that this is always the case. To formulate this result, we extend the map ϕ defined in (7.5) linearly from points to divisors. I.e., for $D = \sum_\nu s_\nu \cdot p_\nu$ we set

$$(7.34) \qquad \phi(D) := \sum_\nu s_\nu \phi(p_\nu).$$

Note that this definition involves the choice of some arbitrary base point p_0.

Theorem 7.28. *Let M be compact of genus $g \geq 1$. Then relative to any basis $\{\omega_j\}_{j=1}^g$ in the space of holomorphic differentials the map ϕ in (7.34) has the following property: for every $\lambda \in J(M)$ there exists an integral divisor D of degree g such that $\phi(D) = \lambda$ (this is called* Jacobi inversion*).*

In particular, the map Φ defined in (7.23) constitutes an isomorphism between the class group restricted to degree zero and the Jacobi variety $J(M)$.

Proof. Consider the map $\Psi : M^g \to J(M)$ defined in terms of (7.34) as

$$(p_1, \ldots, p_g) \mapsto \phi\Big(\sum_j p_j\Big) = \sum_j \phi(p_j).$$

We claim that we can choose points $p_j \in M$ such that the map Ψ has maximal rank g at $P := (p_1, \ldots, p_g)$. Start by selecting any point $p_1 \in M$. By Corollary 7.17 we can assume that $\omega_1(p_1) \neq 0$. Subtracting multiples of ω_1 from ω_j for $j \geq 2$ one can further achieve that $\omega_j(p_1) = 0$ for $j \geq 2$. Next choose any $p_2 \in M$ such that $\omega_2(p_2) \neq 0$. Subtracting multiples of ω_2 we can then assume that $\omega_k(p_2) = 0$ for $k \geq 3$.

Proceeding in this fashion shows that the differential of Ψ at P is represented in local coordinates by an upper triangular matrix with nonzero entries on the diagonal. Thus, Ψ is a local diffeomorphism near P in M^g onto some open set $U \subset J(M)$.

Now fix an arbitrary $\lambda \in J(M)$. There exists an integer $N \geq 1$ so that $\Psi(P) + N^{-1}\lambda \in U$. Hence

$$\Psi(P) + N^{-1}\lambda = \Psi(Q)$$

for some $Q = (q_1, \ldots, q_g) \in M^g$ near P. In other words, if we set

$$D := N \sum_j q_j - N \sum_j p_j + g p_0,$$

then

$$\underline{\lambda} = N \sum_j (\phi(p_j) - \phi(q_j)) = \Phi(D - g p_0).$$

By Riemann-Roch,

$$\dim L(-D) = \deg(D) - g + 1 + \dim \Omega(D) \geq 1.$$

Thus, there exists f meromorphic on M with $(f) \geq -D$. Setting $\widetilde{D} = (f) + D \geq 0$ we see that $\deg(\widetilde{D}) = g$ and therefore $\widetilde{D} = \sum_{\nu=1}^g \widetilde{p}_\nu$. Furthermore, we conclude from Abel's theorem that modulo the lattice $L(M)$,

$$\underline{\lambda} = \Phi(D - g p_0) = \Phi(\widetilde{D} - g p_0) = \sum_{\nu=1}^g \phi(\widetilde{p}_\nu).$$

Thus, we have solved the Jacobi inversion problem.

For the final isomorphism statement, we have just seen that for given $\underline{\lambda}$ there exists a divisor D with $\deg(D) = 0$ and such that $\Phi(D) = \underline{\lambda}$. Thus, denoting the divisors of degree 0 by Div_0, we see that $\Phi : \mathrm{Div}_0 \to J(M)$ is a surjective group homomorphism. By Abel's theorem, the kernel consists precisely of the principal divisors, and thus we have our isomorphism. $\qquad \square$

Notes

This chapter presents some of the core results for compact Riemann surfaces. See Griffiths' text [**35**] for a beautiful exposition of some of the more algebraic points of view, and for an explanation of the role the Riemann-Roch theorem plays. In modern terminology, this theorem is expressed in terms of the Euler characteristic of a complex line bundle. The duality aspect of the classical proof presented in this chapter is made much more explicit through the concept of Serre duality. See, for example, Varolin's book [**84**] for an exposition of these ideas. The Riemann-Roch theorem has been generalized, especially through the work of Hirzebruch and Grothendieck. Perhaps the most far-reaching generalization is the Atiyah-Singer Index theorem; see, for example, Rosenberg's book [**71**].

Our presentation is clearly in the analytical style, drawing upon the Hodge theory results on differential forms in Chapter 6. Much of the theory developed here is only interesting in genus $g = 1$ and higher genera $g \geq 2$. Typical examples are the hyper-elliptic surfaces which have been studied in previous chapters. This class provides for appealing and computationally accessible examples, since the case of two sheets is the first nontrivial class of examples beyond the Riemann sphere. The calculations in Section 6.7 in particular provide concrete examples of bases of holomorphic differentials in all genera, as well as show how to generate meromorphic functions on such algebraic curves. Much more in terms of concrete calculations on can be found in the appendices of the books by Gesztesy, Holden; see [**33**].

The material of this chapter connects naturally with the fundamental theta functions; see Mumford [**64**] as well as Gunning's books [**37, 38**]. In particular, the Jacobi inversion problem was already attacked by Riemann by means of these functions.

7.8. Problems

Problem 7.1. Given any divisor D with $\deg(D) = -2$, describe all meromorphic forms $\omega = f(z) \, dz$ in $\mathbb{C}P^1$ which satisfy $(\omega) = D$. Use the partial fraction representation of the meromorphic function f, and pay careful attention to the point at infinity.

Problem 7.2. Let M be a compact Riemann surface and f a nonconstant meromorphic function on it. Verify the formula for the degree of the canonical class by determining the divisor of $\frac{df}{f}$. Use the Riemann-Hurwitz formula to find the degree of this divisor.

Problem 7.3. For an integral divisor D and any compact surface M, describe a basis of the space $\Omega(-D)$. In particular, determine the dimensions of this space. Check that the full Riemann-Roch theorem holds for the divisor $-D$.

Problem 7.4. Prove (7.18) for **all** integral divisors on the torus using the methods of Section 4.6.

Problem 7.5. Show that for a differential ω of the third kind the periods are not uniquely determined by the homology class of the base curves. Determine the exact nature of the ambiguity. So we need to fix representatives $\{A_j\}_{j=1}^{2g}$ for the integration of ω to be meaningful. Prove Lemma 7.10.

Problem 7.6. Give a different proof of the final assertion of Theorem 7.24 by following this approach: in the notation of the proof of that theorem write $g(p_j) = \sum_{k=0}^{n-1} a_j(\zeta) \, f(p_j)^k$ for each $1 \le j \le n$. Solve this system by Carmer's rule and verify (Vandermonde determinant) that the coefficients are rational. This requires $\{f(p_j)\}_{j=1}^n$ to be distinct which holds for generic ζ (see Lemma 5.15) by irreducibility of $P(w, z)$ defined by f, z.

Problem 7.7. Let M be compact of genus $g \ge 1$ and let $\{\omega_j\}_{j=1}^g$ be a basis of $\mathcal{H}\Omega^1(M)$. Prove that

$$ds^2(p) := \sum_{j=1}^{g} |\omega_j(p)|^2 \quad \text{on} \ \ T_p M$$

with $p \in M$ arbitrary defines a positive definite metric on M. Show that it has nonpositive curvature. Discuss the possible vanishing of the curvature.

Problem 7.8. Provide the details for the properties of the map (7.26) that were required in the second proof of the necessity part of Theorem 7.26.

Problem 7.9. Analyze the Riemann surface determined by the equations

$$(7.35) \qquad\qquad w^3 = \prod_{j=1}^{n}(z - z_j)^{\nu_j}$$

where $\nu_j = 1$ or $\nu_j = 2$ and $n \geq 1$. Determine the genus. Are any of these surfaces hyper-elliptic?

Problem 7.10. Let M be the compact Riemann surface associated with the algebraic equation $w^4 - z^4 + 1 = 0$. Show that M has genus 3 and that $\frac{dz}{f^3}, \frac{z\,dz}{f^3}, \frac{f\,dz}{f^3}$ are a basis of the holomorphic differentials. By comparing the ratios of these differentials with those of a basis of the hyper-elliptic surface of genus 3 conclude that M is not hyper-elliptic.

Chapter 8

Uniformization

In this chapter we present the basic classification of Riemann surfaces (called *uniformization*): in the simply-connected case they are conformally equivalent to either $\mathbb{C}P^1$, $\mathbb{C}$, or $\mathbb{D}$. We have already treated the compact case by means of Hodge theory (see Corollary 6.27). The same result follows also from the more sophisticated Riemann-Roch theorem. This leaves us with the surfaces $\mathbb{C}$ and $\mathbb{D}$, the latter being isomorphic to $\mathbb{H}$ as well as *any simply-connected true subdomain* of the plane by the Riemann mapping theorem. One natural—as well as viable—approach to the uniformization theorem is to try to extend the Riemann mapping theorem to surfaces. But which surfaces? Clearly, we cannot hope to do this for $\mathbb{C}$. Moreover, the proof of the mapping theorem which we presented in Chapter 2 is not robust in the sense that it really requires the setting of the plane.

Here, we will resolve both questions—the question of which surfaces admit an extension of the mapping theorem, and by which method—by means of subharmonic functions. We already encountered this class of functions, which are more flexible and versatile than harmonic functions, in Chapter 3. In that case the essential feature was of a more algebraic nature, namely that analytic functions F lead to subharmonic ones when passing to $|F|^\alpha$, say, with $\alpha > 0$.

Here, we will exploit another feature of this class, namely its closure under the operation of passing to the upper envelope. In more technical terms, the maximum of two subharmonic functions is again subharmonic. First, note that there is no issue in defining subharmonic functions on Riemann surfaces, just as there is no issue in defining harmonic functions on surfaces: they are those functions which are subharmonic in charts. The reason that we wish to use the upper envelope comes from desire to solve the *Dirichlet problem* on surfaces, for which we shall follow Perron's maximization method.

But before we launch into a systematic investigation of these topics, we begin by laying some of the groundwork required for the uniformization theorem itself. This means that we need to rethink the Riemann mapping theorem from scratch. The key concept in doing this will be that of a *Green function*.

8.1. Green functions and Riemann mapping

On several occasions in this text we already encountered the problem of solving the so-called Poisson equation in the plane

$$(8.1) \qquad\qquad\qquad \Delta u = f$$

when $f \in C^2_{\mathrm{comp}}(\mathbb{R}^2)$. Such a u is not unique (add any linear function). However, we singled out the solution

$$(8.2) \qquad\qquad u(z) = \frac{1}{2\pi} \int_{\mathbb{R}^2} \log|z - \zeta|\, f(\zeta)\, d\xi d\eta$$

where $\zeta = \xi + i\eta$. The reader will easily verify that it is the *unique* solution of (8.1) with the property that $u(z) = k \log|z| + o(1)$ as $|z| \to \infty$ for some constant k. In fact, necessarily $k = \int_{\mathbb{R}^2} f$.

The function $\Gamma(z, \zeta) = \frac{1}{2\pi} \log|z - \zeta|$ is of great importance. It is called the *fundamental solution* of Δ which means that $\Delta\Gamma(\cdot, \zeta) = \delta_\zeta$ in the sense of distributions. Next, we wish to solve (8.1) on a bounded domain $\Omega \subset \mathbb{C}$ (for example on $\Omega = \mathbb{D}$). To obtain uniqueness, an immediate consequence of the maximum principle, we impose a Dirichlet boundary condition $u = 0$ on $\partial\Omega$. By a *solution* of

$$(8.3) \qquad\qquad \Delta u = f \ \text{ in } \ \Omega, \qquad u = 0 \ \text{ on } \ \partial\Omega$$

with $f \in C(\Omega)$ we mean a function $u \in C^2(\Omega) \cap C(\overline{\Omega})$ which satisfies (8.3) in the pointwise sense. To solve (8.3), we try to emulate (8.2) by means of the following construction.

Definition 8.1. We say that $\Omega \subset \mathbb{C}$ *admits a Green function* if there exists G with the following properties:

- $G(\cdot, \cdot) \in C(\overline{\Omega} \times \Omega \setminus \{z = \zeta\})$.
- The function $h(z, \zeta) := G(z, \zeta) - \Gamma(z, \zeta)$ is harmonic on Ω in the first variable for all $\zeta \in \Omega$, and jointly continuous on $\Omega \times \Omega$.
- $G(z, \zeta) = 0$ for all $(z, \zeta) \in \partial\Omega \times \Omega$.

It is useful to note that this definition applies to unbounded $\Omega \subset \mathbb{C}$, but in that case we view $\Omega \subset \mathbb{C}_\infty$ so that $\infty \in \partial\Omega$. In particular, we require vanishing at infinity in that case. It is clear that if G exists, then it is unique. Also, $z \mapsto G(z, \zeta)$ is subharmonic in Ω for every $\zeta \in \Omega$. By the maximum principle for subharmonic functions, $G(z, \zeta) < 0$ for all $(z, \zeta) \in \Omega \times \Omega$.

The notion of a Green function is intimately tied to electrostatics: suppose we place a point charge into a bounded domain in $\mathbb{C}$ with a smooth boundary which we consider to be a grounded conductor. Then the potential has a logarithmic singularity at the point charge, and is constant equal to zero on the boundary. So the potential is the Green function. There is ample evidence that this connection with physics (in a much wider sense) played an instrumental role in the development of Riemann surface theory, see the notes at the end of this chapter.

Lemma 8.2. *If Ω admits a Green function, then* (8.3) *has a unique solution for every*[1] $f \in C^2_{\mathrm{comp}}(\Omega)$ *given by*

$$u(z) = \int_\Omega G(z, \zeta) f(\zeta)\, d\zeta \qquad \forall\, z \in \Omega.$$

Proof. Uniqueness follows from the maximum principle. By the continuity assumptions on G, u is continuous on $\overline{\Omega}$ and satisfies $u = 0$ on $\partial\Omega$. Moreover, with $\zeta = \xi + i\eta$, we can write

$$u(z) = \int_\Omega [G(z, \zeta) - \Gamma(z, \zeta)] f(\zeta)\, d\xi d\eta + \int_\Omega \Gamma(z, \zeta) f(\zeta)\, d\xi d\eta$$
$$=: u_1(z) + u_2(z).$$

The second integral on the right-hand side, which we denoted by u_2, satisfies $\Delta u_2 = f$. Indeed, setting $f = 0$ outside of Ω leads to $f \in C^2_{\mathrm{comp}}(\mathbb{R}^2)$ and we can apply the discussion above concerning (8.2). As for u_1, we have

$$u_1(\cdot) = \int_\Omega h(\cdot, \zeta) f(\zeta)\, d\xi d\eta \in C(\Omega)$$

by continuity of h. Moreover, the mean value property holds:

$$\int_0^1 u_1(z_0 + re^{2\pi i\theta})\, d\theta = u_1(z_0)$$

for all $z_0 \in \Omega$ and small $r > 0$. This follows from Fubini's theorem since $h(\cdot, \zeta)$ is jointly continuous and satisfies the mean value property in the first variable. Thus, u_1 is harmonic and $\Delta u = f$ as desired. $\square$

Green functions can be defined much more generally than for the Laplacian in the plane. For example, Figure 8.1 shows the Green function for the

---

[1]The assumptions on f in the previous lemma can be relaxed, but this does not concern us here.

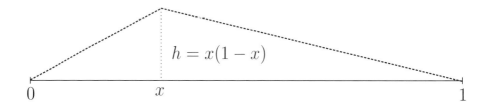

Figure 8.1. The Green function for $-\frac{d^2}{dx^2}$ on $[0,1]$

positive Laplacian on the interval $[0,1]$ which allows for an explicit expression.

Which regions $\Omega \subset \mathbb{C}$ admit a Green function? For example, take $\Omega = \mathbb{D}$. Then $G(z,0) = \frac{1}{2\pi} \log |z|$ satisfies all the desired properties for $\zeta = 0$. Next, we map ζ to 0 by the Möbius transformation $T(z) = \frac{z-\zeta}{1-z\bar\zeta}$. This yields

$$G_{\mathbb{D}}(z,\zeta) = \frac{1}{2\pi} \log \left| \frac{z-\zeta}{1-z\bar\zeta} \right|$$

as the Green function for $\mathbb{D}$. It clearly satisfies Definition 8.1. Moreover, by inspection,

$$G_{\mathbb{D}}(z,\zeta) = G_{\mathbb{D}}(\zeta,z) \quad \forall\, z,\zeta \in \mathbb{D}.$$

Now let Ω be the disk with $n \geq 1$ points removed, i.e.,

$$\Omega = \mathbb{D} \setminus \{z_1,\ldots,z_n\}.$$

If G were a Green function on Ω, then for all $\zeta \in \Omega$, $z \mapsto G(z,\zeta)$ would need to be continuous in a neighborhood of z_j for all $1 \leq j \leq n$ and harmonic away from z_j. Then each z_j would constitute a removable singularity and $G(z,\zeta)$ (see Problem 3.2) therefore be harmonic in a disk around each z_j. In other words, G would be the Green function of $\mathbb{D}$ and therefore negative at each z_j violating the vanishing condition. In conclusion, Ω does not admit a Green function in the sense of Definition 8.1.

Any simply-connected $\Omega \subset \mathbb{C}$ for which the Riemann mapping $f : \Omega \to \mathbb{D}$ extends continuously to $\overline{\Omega}$ admits a Green function (for this it suffices to assume that $\partial\Omega$ consists of finitely many C^1 arcs). Indeed, observe that

$$G_{\Omega}(z,\zeta) := G_{\mathbb{D}}(f(z),f(\zeta))$$

satisfies Definition 8.1. This procedure also applies to unbounded Ω, for example $\Omega = \mathbb{H}$. It automatically enforces the vanishing condition at infinity required by the fact that we view $\Omega \subset \mathbb{C}_\infty$.

We now turn this around and ask the following question: *is it possible to construct the Riemann mapping $\Omega \to \mathbb{D}$ from the Green function on Ω, assuming it exists?* We shall now demonstrate that this is indeed the case.

Theorem 8.3. *Suppose $\Omega \subset \mathbb{C}_\infty$ is simply-connected and admits a Green function. Then G gives rise to a biholomorphic mapping $f : \Omega \to \mathbb{D}$.*

Proof. The idea is to write, with $\zeta \in \Omega$ fixed,

$$2\pi G(z, \zeta) = \log |z - \zeta| + \operatorname{Re} F(z)$$

where $F \in \mathcal{H}(\Omega)$. We are using here that on a simply-connected domain such as Ω, we can find a global harmonic conjugate to a given harmonic function (see Proposition 1.38). Then we set

$$f_\zeta(z) := (z - \zeta) \exp(F(z)) \in \mathcal{H}(\Omega).$$

Note that f_ζ is unique up to a unimodular number. By construction,

$$|f_\zeta(z)| = \exp(\log |z - \zeta| + \operatorname{Re} F(z)) = \exp(2\pi G(z, \zeta)) < 1$$

for all $z \in \Omega$ so that $f_\zeta : \Omega \to \mathbb{D}$; furthermore, $|f_\zeta(z)| = 1$ for all $z \in \partial\Omega$ and $|f_\zeta|$ extends as a continuous mapping to all of $\overline{\Omega}$.

We claim that $f(\Omega) = \mathbb{D}$. By analyticity and since f is not constant, $f(\Omega)$ is open. To show that this set is closed, suppose that $f(z_n) \to w \in \mathbb{D}$. Then $z_n \to z_\infty \in \overline{\Omega}$ (if needed, pass to a subsequence of z_n, which we call z_n again; recall that we are viewing $\Omega \subset \mathbb{C}_\infty$ which is compact). If $z_\infty \in \partial\Omega$, necessarily $|w| = 1$ which is a contradiction. So $z_\infty \in \Omega$ and $f(z_n) \to f(z_\infty) = w$ which shows that $f(\Omega)$ is closed.

It remains to show that f is one-to-one. Locally around ζ this is clear (why?), but not globally on Ω. We also remark that $f_\zeta(z) = 0$ if and only if $z = \zeta$. In view of this property, we note the following: suppose f_ζ is one-to-one for any $\zeta \in \Omega$. Then $T := f_\eta \circ f_\zeta^{-1} \in \operatorname{Aut}(\mathbb{D})$ is a Möbius transformation which takes $f_\zeta(\eta)$ to 0. This suggests we establish a kind of converse for arbitrary $\eta \in \Omega \setminus \{\zeta\}$. More specifically, we make a

Claim: Let $f_\zeta(\eta) = w$ and $T(w) = 0$, $T \in \operatorname{Aut}(\mathbb{D})$. Then $|T \circ f_\zeta| = |f_\eta|$.

If the claim holds, then we are done: assume that $f_\zeta(\eta) = f_\zeta(\widetilde{\eta}) = w \in \mathbb{D}$ and let $T(w) = 0$ with $T \in \operatorname{Aut}(\mathbb{D})$. Then

$$|T \circ f_\zeta| = |f_\eta| = |f_{\widetilde{\eta}}|,$$

so that $f_{\widetilde{\eta}}(\eta) = 0$ implies $\eta = \widetilde{\eta}$ as desired.

To prove the claim, note that for any $0 < \varepsilon < 1$, and some integer $k \geq 1$,

$$\log |T \circ f_\zeta(z)| = k \log |z - \eta| + O(1) \leq \log |z - \eta| + O(1)$$
$$\leq 2\pi(1 - \varepsilon)G(z, \eta)$$

as $z \to \zeta$. Moreover,

$$\limsup_{z \to \zeta} \log |T \circ f_\zeta(z)| \leq 0, \quad G(z, \eta) \to 0 \ \text{ as } z \to \partial\Omega.$$

Hence on $\Omega \setminus D(\zeta, \delta)$ for all $\delta > 0$ small, we see that the harmonic function $2\pi G(\cdot, \eta)$ dominates the subharmonic function $\log|T \circ f_\zeta(\cdot)|$ on $\Omega \setminus \{\eta\}$. In conclusion,

$$\log|T \circ f_\zeta(\cdot)| \le 2\pi G(\cdot, \eta).$$

In particular, since $T(z) = \frac{z-w}{1-z\bar{w}}$ and thus $T(0) = -w$,

(8.4)
$$\begin{aligned} 2\pi G(\eta, \zeta) = \log|f_\zeta(\eta)| &= \log|w| = \log|T(0)| \\ &= \log|T \circ f_\zeta(\zeta)| \le 2\pi G(\zeta, \eta), \end{aligned}$$

whence $G(\eta, \zeta) \le G(\zeta, \eta)$, which implies

(8.5)
$$G(\zeta, \eta) = G(\eta, \zeta).$$

This is the well-known symmetry property of the Green function. It follows that we have equality in (8.4)

$$\log|T \circ f_\zeta(\zeta)| = 2\pi G(\zeta, \eta),$$

from which we conclude via the strong maximum principle on $\Omega \setminus \{\eta\}$ that

$$\log|T \circ f_\zeta(\cdot)| = 2\pi G(\cdot, \eta) = \log|f_\eta(\cdot)|$$

as claimed. This finishes the proof. □

The importance of this argument lies with the fact that it extends from domains $\Omega \subset \mathbb{C}$ to simply-connected Riemann surfaces M, at least to those that *admit a Green function*. What this exactly means will be explained in Section 8.4. We caution the reader that a Green function G on a Riemann surface will not necessarily conform to Definition 8.1 above in case $M \subset \mathbb{C}$.

8.2. Perron families

Let us now address the problem of finding the Green function on bounded domains $\Omega \subset \mathbb{C}$. Fix $\zeta \in \Omega$ and solve—if possible—the Dirichlet problem

(8.6) $\Delta u(z) = 0$ in Ω, $u(z) = -\log|z - \zeta|$ on $\partial\Omega$.

Then $G(z, \zeta) := u(z) + \log|z - \zeta|$ is the Green function. This was Riemann's original approach, but he assumed that (8.6) always has a solution via the so-called "Dirichlet principle". In modern terms this refers to the fact that the variational problem, with $f \in C^1(\overline{\Omega})$ and $\partial\Omega$ being C^2 regular,

$$\inf_{u \in \mathcal{A}} \int_\Omega |\nabla u|^2 \, dx \, dy$$
$$\mathcal{A} := \{u \in H^1(\Omega) \mid u - f \in H_0^1(\Omega)\}$$

has a unique minimizer $u_0 \in \mathcal{A}$ (minimizer means that u_0 attains the infimum). By

$$H^1(\Omega) = \{u \in L^2(\Omega) \mid \nabla u \in L^2(\Omega)\},$$

we mean the Sobolev space where ∇u is the distributional derivative, and $H_0^1(\Omega) \subset H^1(\Omega)$ is the subspace of vanishing trace. It is a standard fact that Dirichlet's principle holds and that the minimizer u_0 is a harmonic function so that $u_0 - f \in C(\overline{\Omega})$ vanishes on $\partial\Omega$. Riemann and his contemporaries, however, did not have the needed Hilbert space machinery at their disposal and thus could not justify the existence of a minimizer.

Instead of the variational approach, we shall use an elegant method due to Perron based on subharmonic functions. It requires less on the boundary than the variational methods. We first need to lift the concept of subharmonic functions to a general Riemann surface M. We refer the reader to Section 3.5 for the concept of a subharmonic function in a region of $\mathbb{C}$ (see Definition 3.20).

Definition 8.4. A function $u : M \to [-\infty, \infty)$ is subharmonic if it is continuous and subharmonic in every chart. We denote the class of subharmonic functions on the Riemann surface M by $\mathfrak{sh}(M)$.

Since subharmonicity is preserved under conformal transformations, this definition is meaningful. From our definition it is clear that subharmonicity is a *local* property. Hence properties that can be checked in charts immediately lift from the planar case to Riemann surfaces. Here are two examples:

- If $u \in C^2(M)$, then u is subharmonic if and only if $\Delta u \geq 0$ in every chart on M.
- If $u_1, \ldots, u_k \in \mathfrak{sh}(M)$, then $\max(u_1, \ldots, u_k) \in \mathfrak{sh}(M)$ and one has $\sum_{j=1}^k a_j u_j \in \mathfrak{sh}(M)$ for any $a_j \geq 0$.

The following lemma collects several global properties of this class which mirror those in the planar case. We begin with the maximum principle.

Lemma 8.5. *The following properties hold for subharmonic functions:*

(1) *If $u \in \mathfrak{sh}(M)$ attains its supremum on M, then $u = $ const.*

(2) *Let h be harmonic on M and $u \in \mathfrak{sh}(M)$. If $u \leq h$ on M, then either $u < h$ or $u = h$ everywhere on M.*

(3) *Let $\Omega \subset M$ be a domain with compact closure in M. Suppose h is harmonic on Ω and continuous on $\overline{\Omega}$. If*

(8.7)
$$\limsup_{\substack{p \to q \\ p \in \Omega}} u(p) \leq h(q) \quad \forall\, q \in \partial\Omega,$$

then $u \leq h$ in Ω. Equality here can only be attained in Ω if $u = h$ throughout Ω.

Proof. For (1), assume that $u \leq u(p_0)$ with $p_0 \in M$. Then
$$E = \{p \in M \mid u(p) = u(p_0)\}$$

is both open (since that is a local property and follows by considering charts) and closed. Hence $E = M$, as desired.

For (2), apply (1) to $u - h \in \mathfrak{sh}(M)$.

For (3), it suffices to consider the case $h = 0$ (otherwise consider $u - h$). If $u(p) > 0$ for any $p \in \Omega$, then u attains its supremum on Ω and is therefore constant. But this would contradict (8.7). Hence $u \leq 0$ on Ω with equality being attained at one point forcing constancy by (2). $\square$

We remark that property (2) above characterizes $\mathfrak{sh}(M)$ and gives a nice way of defining subharmonic functions intrinsically on Riemann surfaces. For future purposes we denote property (8.7) by $u \ll h$ on $\partial\Omega$. We are now going to describe Perron's method for solving the following Dirichlet problem on a Riemann surface M:

Let $\Omega \subset M$ be a domain with $\overline{\Omega}$ compact and suppose $\phi : \partial\Omega \to \mathbb{R}$ is continuous. Find $u \in C(\overline{\Omega})$ so that u is harmonic on Ω and $u = \phi$ on $\partial\Omega$.

The first step towards the solution is furnished by showing that the upper envelope of all subharmonic functions v on Ω with $v \ll \phi$ is harmonic. The second step then addresses how to ensure that the boundary data are attained continuously. For the first step we need the following easy result.

Lemma 8.6. *Let D be a parametric disk and suppose $f \in \mathfrak{sh}(M)$ is real-valued. Let h be the harmonic function on D which has f as boundary values on ∂D. The function*

$$f_D := \begin{cases} f & on \ M \setminus D, \\ h & on \ D, \end{cases}$$

satisfies $f_D \in \mathfrak{sh}(M)$ and $f_D \geq f$.

Proof. It is clear that f_D is continuous. By the maximum principle, one has $f_D \geq f$. It is clear that f_D is subharmonic on $M \setminus \partial D$. However, if $p \in \partial D$, then we see from $f_D \geq f$ that the submean value property holds at p for sufficiently small circles (relative to some chart at p). Therefore, $f_D \in \mathfrak{sh}(M)$ as claimed. $\square$

Now for the first step in Perron's method.

Proposition 8.7. *Let $\Omega \subset M$ be a domain with compact closure. Let ϕ be any bounded function on $\partial\Omega$. Then*

$$(8.8) \qquad\qquad u = \sup\{v \mid v \in \mathfrak{sh}(\Omega), \ v \ll \phi \ \ on \ \partial\Omega\}$$

is harmonic on Ω.

Proof. Denote the set on the right-hand side of (8.8) by $\mathcal{S}_\phi$. First note that any $v \in \mathcal{S}_\phi$ satisfies

$$\sup_\Omega v \le \sup_{\partial\Omega} \phi < \infty.$$

Moreover, replacing any $v \in \mathcal{S}_\phi$ by $\max(v, \inf_{\partial\Omega} \phi)$, we can assume that all $v \in \mathcal{S}_\phi$ are bounded below. Take any $p \in \Omega$ and a sequence of $\{v_n\}_{n=1}^\infty \subset \mathcal{S}_\phi$ so that $v_n(p) \to u(p)$. Replacing the sequence by

$$v_1, \; \max(v_1, v_2), \; \max(v_1, v_2, v_3), \ldots$$

we can assume that $\{v_n\}_{n=1}^\infty$ is nondecreasing. In addition, by Lemma 8.6 each v_n can be assumed to be harmonic on some parametric disk D centered at p. By Harnack's inequality (see Problem 3.10) on D, $v_n \to v_\infty$ uniformly on compact subsets of D with v_∞ harmonic on D.

It remains to check that $u = v_\infty$ on D. Take any $q \in D$ and let $\{w_n\}_{n=1}^\infty \subset \mathcal{S}_\phi$ with $w_n(q) \to u(q)$. As before, we can assume that w_n is harmonic and increasing on D. In fact, we can also assume that $w_n \ge v_n$ for each n. We conclude that $w_n \to w_\infty$ uniformly on compact sets with w_∞ harmonic on D and $w_\infty(p) = v_\infty(p)$. Since $w_\infty \ge v_\infty$ in D, it follows that $w_\infty = v_\infty$ on D. In particular, $u(q) = v_\infty(q)$ and we are done. $\qquad\square$

It is worth noting that this proof has little to do with ϕ. In fact, it applies to any *Perron family* which we now define.

Definition 8.8. A family $\mathcal{F}$ of real-valued subharmonic functions on a Riemann surface M is called a *Perron family* if

- for any $f, g \in \mathcal{F}$ there is $h \in \mathcal{F}$ with $h \ge \max\{f, g\}$,
- for any parametric disk $D \subset M$ and any $v \in \mathcal{F}$ there exists $w \in \mathcal{F}$ with w harmonic on D and $w \ge v$.

We have the following immediate corollary of the proof of Proposition 8.7 concerning suprema of Perron families.

Lemma 8.9. *For any Perron family $\mathcal{F}$ on a Riemann surface M the function*

$$u := \sup_{v \in \mathcal{F}} v$$

is either $\equiv \infty$ or harmonic on M.

Figure 8.2 shows a Perron family on the line where subharmonic means convex, and harmonic linear. To be specific, if we connect two points, say $(0, a)$ and $(1, b)$ by a line, consider the family of all convex functions that lie below that line. The pointwise supremum of all these functions coincides with that line. This is the one-dimensional content of Lemma 8.9.

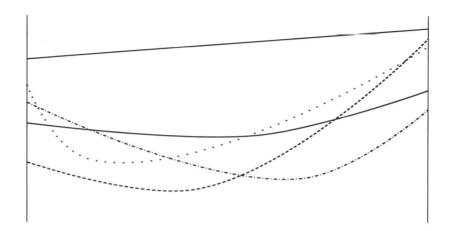

Figure 8.2. Example of functions in a Perron family for $-\frac{d^2}{dx^2}$

8.3. Solution of Dirichlet's problem

Next, we turn to the boundary behavior. For a standard example of what can go wrong on the boundary consider $\Omega = \mathbb{D} \setminus \{0\}$. Setting $\phi(0) = 0$ and $\phi(z) = 1$ for $|z| = 1$ we see that Perron's method yields $u = \text{const} = 1$; indeed, for any $\varepsilon > 0$ the function $v(z) = 1 + \varepsilon \log|z| \in \mathcal{S}_\phi$.

Definition 8.10. A *barrier* at a point $p \in \partial\Omega$ is defined to be a function β with the following properties:

- $-\beta \in \mathfrak{sh}(\Omega)$,
- $\beta \in C(\overline{\Omega})$ and $\beta \geq 0$ on $\overline{\Omega}$ with $\beta > 0$ on $\overline{\Omega} \setminus \{p\}$, and $\beta(p) = 0$.

Any point $q \in \partial\Omega$ which admits a barrier is called *regular* and $\partial\Omega$ is called regular if and only if all of its points are regular.

It turns out that regularity of a boundary point is a mild condition.

Lemma 8.11. *Suppose $p \in \partial\Omega$ satisfies an* exterior disk condition*, i.e., there exists a disk $D(z_0, \varepsilon)$ in local coordinates (U, z) around p so that*

$$\overline{z(U \cap \Omega)} \cap \overline{D(z_0, \varepsilon)} = \{p\}.$$

Then p is regular. In particular, any C^2 boundary is regular. Moreover, suppose that $p \in \partial\Omega$ is accessible*, i.e.,*

$$z(U \cap \Omega) \subset \mathbb{D} \setminus (-1, 0]$$

in some chart (U, z) with $z(p) = 0$. Then p is regular.

Proof. For the exterior disk condition, we define for all $q \in \Omega$,

$$\beta(q) = \begin{cases} \log(|z(q) - z_0|/\varepsilon) & \text{if } |z(q) - z_0| \leq \delta, \\ \log(\delta/\varepsilon) & \text{if } |z(q) - z_0| > \delta, \end{cases}$$

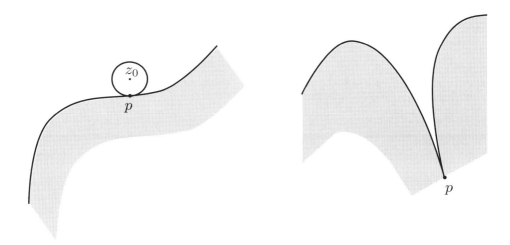

Figure 8.3. Exterior disk condition and accessibility

where $\delta > \varepsilon > 0$ are sufficiently small. If $p \in \partial\Omega$ is accessible, then we map $\mathbb{D} \setminus (-1, 0]$ conformally onto a sector of angle $\leq \pi$ which guarantees the exterior disk condition at p. $\qquad\square$

An obvious example of a nonaccessible boundary point is $p = 0$ for $\Omega = \mathbb{D} \setminus \{0\}$. The importance of barriers lies with the following result.

Proposition 8.12. *Let $\Omega \subset M$ be a domain with compact closure. Suppose $p \in \partial\Omega$ is regular and ϕ a bounded function on $\partial\Omega$ which is continuous at p. Then the function u from Proposition 8.7 satisfies*

$$\lim_{\substack{q \to p \\ q \in \Omega}} u(q) = \phi(p).$$

In particular, if $\partial\Omega$ is regular and $\phi : \partial\Omega \to \mathbb{R}$ is continuous, then u is a solution of Dirichlet's problem on Ω with boundary data ϕ.

Proof. Let $\mathcal{S}_\phi$ be as in Proposition 8.7. Recall that

$$(8.9) \qquad\qquad \inf_{\partial\Omega} \phi \leq v \leq \sup_{\partial\Omega} \phi$$

for any $v \in \mathcal{S}_\phi$. We now claim the following: given $\varepsilon > 0$ there exists $C = C(\varepsilon)$ such that

$$(8.10) \qquad\qquad v(q) - C\beta(q) \leq \phi(p) + \varepsilon \quad \forall\, q \in \Omega$$

for any $v \in \mathcal{S}_\phi$. To prove this, we let D be a small parametric disk centered at p. It can be chosen so that

$$\sup_{\partial(\Omega \cap D)} v - C\beta \leq \phi(p) + \varepsilon,$$

due to the continuity of ϕ, the positivity

$$\min_{\overline{\Omega}\setminus D} \beta > 0,$$

and provided C is large enough. The maximum principle now shows that (8.10) holds on $\Omega \cap D$. On $\overline{\Omega} \setminus D$, we let C be so large that (8.10) holds due to (8.9).

In conclusion,

$$\limsup_{q\to p} u(q) \le \phi(p) + \varepsilon.$$

For the lower bound, we observe by the same arguments that

$$-C\beta + \phi(p) - \varepsilon \in \mathcal{S}_\phi.$$

Hence

$$u \ge -C\beta + \phi(p) - \varepsilon,$$

so that

$$\liminf_{q\to p} u(q) \ge \phi(p) - \varepsilon$$

as desired. $\square$

We remark that the regularity of $\partial\Omega$ is also necessary for the solvability of the Dirichlet problem for general continuous boundary data; indeed, the boundary data $f(p) = |p - p_0|$ yields a barrier.

Let us make another remark concerning the solvability of the Dirichlet problem *outside* some compact set $K \subset M$. As the example $K = \mathbb{D} \subset 2\mathbb{D}$ shows, we cannot expect *unique* solvability of the Dirichlet problem with data on ∂K. However, the Perron method always yields *existence of bounded harmonic functions* with given continuous boundary data. More precisely, we have the following variant of Proposition 8.12.

Corollary 8.13. *Let $K \subset M$ be compact and ∂K regular. Then for any $\phi : \partial K \to \mathbb{R}$ continuous and any constant $A \ge \max_{\partial K} \phi$ there exists a harmonic function u on $\Omega := M \setminus K$ with $u \in C(\overline{\Omega})$, $u = \phi$ on $\partial\Omega$ and*

$$\min_{\partial\Omega} \phi \le u \le A$$

on Ω.

Proof. Define

(8.11) $u := \sup\{v \mid v \in \mathfrak{sh}(\Omega),\ v \ll \phi \text{ on } \partial\Omega,\ v \le A\}.$

The set on the right-hand side is a nonempty Perron family and u is harmonic on Ω and satisfies (8.11). Let β_0 be a barrier at $p \in \partial\Omega$. Let D, D' be parametric disks centered at p and D' compactly contained in D (which means that $\overline{D'} \subset D$ is compact) and $\bar{D}$ compact. Then for $\varepsilon > 0$ sufficiently small, the function

$$\beta := \min\{\beta_0, \varepsilon\} \text{ on } D \cap \Omega$$

is superharmonic on D with the property that $\beta = \varepsilon$ on $\Omega \cap D \setminus D'$. This shows that we can extend β to all of Ω by setting

$$\beta = \varepsilon \text{ on } \Omega \setminus D.$$

The point is that we have constructed a barrier β at p which is uniformly bounded away from zero on $\Omega \setminus D$ (this is another expression of the fact that being regular is a local property around a point). Since u is bounded from above and below, the reader will have no difficulty verifying that the exact same proof as in Proposition 8.12 applies in this case; see the problems to this chapter. $\square$

In the next section it will become clear that the solution constructed in Corollary 8.13 is unique if and only if M does not admit a negative nonconstant subharmonic function (or in the terminology of Section 8.4, if M is not hyperbolic). An example would be $M = \mathbb{C}$. See Section 8.5.2 for a proof of uniqueness in Corollary 8.13 for that case. Note that this uniqueness is clear, as is the existence from Proposition 8.12, if M is compact. From the classification that we develop below it will become clear that uniqueness in Corollary 8.13 with M not compact holds if and only if M is conformally equivalent to $\mathbb{C}$ while it does not hold if and only if M is conformally equivalent to $\mathbb{D}$.

To summarize, we have solved the Dirichlet problem for all domains $\Omega \subset M$ with compact closure and regular boundary. In particular, if $M = \mathbb{C}_\infty$, any such domain admits a Green function. Moreover, if $\Omega \subset \mathbb{C}$ is simply-connected, then G gives rise to a biholomorphic map $f : \Omega \to \mathbb{D}$. This latter fact (the Riemann mapping theorem) we proved earlier in a completely different way which did not require any information on the boundary.

8.4. Green's functions on Riemann surfaces

We would like to generalize the proof of the Riemann mapping theorem from Section 8.1 to any Riemann surface M which admits a Green function. But what is the correct definition of a Green function G on M? Since there is no boundary, at least in the topological sense, we need to find a substitute for the crucial vanishing condition at the boundary. One option would be to require "vanishing at infinity", i.e.,

$$\inf_{K \text{ compact}} \sup_{p \in M \setminus K} |G(p, q)| = 0,$$

where q is some arbitrary point. However, this turns out to be too restrictive. As an example, consider $M = \mathbb{D}\setminus\{0\}$. "Infinity" here is the set $\{0\}\cup\{|z| = 1\}$ but we cannot enforce vanishing at $\{0\}$; cf. Problem 3.2. However, the Green function on $\mathbb{D}$ is, in a precise sense, also the Green function of $\mathbb{D}\setminus\{0\}$. In fact, uniquely so, as we shall see. The issue here is that a single point is negligible (more generally, sets of *zero logarithmic capacity* are negligible). While it is of course true that this M is not simply-connected, it would be unwise to introduce simple connectivity into the concept of the Green function.

As often in analysis, the correct definition of a Green function on M imposes a *minimality* condition on G. Following a time-honored tradition, we will consider *positive* Green functions rather than negative ones. Of course, this just amounts to switching the sign. In addition, we drop the factor of 2π.

Definition 8.14. By a *Green function* with singularity at $q \in M$ we mean a real-valued function $G(p, q)$ defined on $M \setminus \{q\}$ such that

- $G(p, q) + \log|z|$ is harmonic locally around $p = q$ where z are local coordinates near q with $z(q) = 0$,
- $p \mapsto G(p, q)$ is harmonic and positive on $M \setminus \{q\}$,
- if $g(p, q)$ is any other function satisfying the previous two conditions, then $g(\cdot, q) \geq G(\cdot, q)$ on $M \setminus \{q\}$.

It is evident that G is unique if it exists. Also, if $f : N \to M$ is a conformal isomorphism, then it is clear that $G(f(p), f(q))$ is the Green function on N with singularity at $f(q)$. By the maximum principle, if G is a Green function as in the previous chapter, then $-G$ satisfies Definition 8.14. We remark that no compact surface M admits such a Green function (since $-G(\cdot, q)$ would then be a negative subharmonic function on M and therefore constant by the maximum principle). Note that $M = \mathbb{C}$ does not admit a Green function either:

Lemma 8.15. *Suppose $u < \mu$ is a subharmonic function on $\mathbb{C}$ with some constant $\mu < \infty$. Then $u = $ const.*

Proof. Let us first observe the following: suppose v is subharmonic and negative on $0 < |z| < 2$ and set $v_\varepsilon(z) := v(z) + \varepsilon \log|z|$ where $0 < \varepsilon < 1$. Then v_ε is subharmonic on $0 < |z| < 1$. Moreover, $v_\varepsilon(z) = v(z)$ for all $|z| = 1$ and $v_\varepsilon(z) \to -\infty$ as $z \to 0$. It follows from the maximum principle that $v_\varepsilon(z) \leq \max_{|z|=1} v(z) < 0$ for all $0 < |z| < 1$. Now send $\varepsilon \to 0$ to conclude that $v(z) \leq \max_{|z|=1} v(z) < 0$ for all $0 < |z| \leq 1$.

To prove the lemma, we can assume that $u < 0$ everywhere and $\sup_\mathbb{C} u = 0$. Consider $u(1/z)$ on $0 < |z| < 2$. It is subharmonic and negative and therefore by the preceding paragraph

$$\sup_{|z|\geq 1} u(z) < 0.$$

It follows that $\sup_{|z|\leq 1} u(z) = 0$ which is impossible by the maximum principle. $\qquad\square$

So which M *do* admit Green functions? As we saw, the disk $\mathbb{D}$ and hence any domain in $\mathbb{C}$ conformally equivalent to it. Note that these surfaces obviously admit negative nonconstant subharmonic functions. This suggests a classification:

Definition 8.16. A Riemann surface M is called *hyperbolic* if it carries a nonconstant negative subharmonic function. If M is not hyperbolic and noncompact, then it is called *parabolic*.

The logic here is as follows: using the exact same proof idea as in Theorem 8.3 we will show that the hyperbolic, simply-connected surfaces are conformally equivalent to $\mathbb{D}$ whereas parabolic ones are equivalent to $\mathbb{C}$.

We now turn to the construction of a Green function as in Definition 8.14. We will do this via a Perron-type argument by setting

$$(8.12) \qquad\qquad G(p,q) := \sup_{v\in\mathcal{G}_q} v(p),$$

the supremum being taken over the family $\mathcal{G}_q$ that we now define.

Definition 8.17. Given any $q \in M$ we define a family $\mathcal{G}_q$ of functions as follows:

- any v in $\mathcal{G}_q$ is subharmonic on $M \setminus \{q\}$,
- $v + \log|z|$ is bounded above on U where (U, z) is some chart around q,
- $v = 0$ on $M \setminus K$ for some compact $K \subset M$.

Since $0 \in \mathcal{G}_q$ we have $\mathcal{G}_q \neq \emptyset$. Note that if $G(p,q)$ is a Green function on some domain $\Omega \subset \mathbb{C}$ in the sense of the previous section, then

$$(-G(p,q) - \varepsilon)_+ \in \mathcal{G}_q$$

for any $\varepsilon > 0$. As another example, let $M = \mathbb{C}$ and $q = 0$. Then $-\log_-(|z|/R) \in \mathcal{G}_0$ for any $R > 0$. This shows that $G(p,0)$ as defined in (8.12) satisfies $G(p,0) = \infty$ for all $p \in \mathbb{C}$. As we shall see shortly, this agrees with the fact that $\mathbb{C}$ does not admit a negative nonconstant subharmonic function. In general, one has the following result.

Theorem 8.18. *Let $q \in M$ be fixed and let $G(p, q)$ be defined as in* (8.12). *Then either $G(p, q) = \infty$ for all $p \in M$ or $G(p, q)$ is the Green function of M with singularity at q. Moreover,*

$$\inf_{p \in M} G(p, q) = 0.$$

Proof. Observe that $\mathcal{G}_q$ is a Perron family. Hence by the methods of the previous section, either $G(\cdot, q) = \infty$ identically or it is harmonic in $M \setminus \{q\}$. Next, we need to check that $p \mapsto G(p, q) + \log |z(p)|$ is harmonic locally near $p = q$. In fact, it suffices to check that

$$(8.13) \qquad G(p, q) = -\log |z(p)| + O(1) \quad \text{as } p \to q$$

where $z = z(p)$ since $G(p, q) + \log |z(p)|$ then has a removable singularity at $p = q$ as a harmonic function. If $v \in \mathcal{G}_q$, then locally around q and for any $\varepsilon > 0$,

$$v(p) + (1 + \varepsilon) \log |z(p)|$$

is subharmonic and tends to $-\infty$ as $p \to q$. Therefore, by the maximum principle, for any $p \in z^{-1}(\mathbb{D} \setminus \{0\})$,

$$v(p) + (1 + \varepsilon) \log |z(p)| \leq \sup_{z^{-1}(\partial \mathbb{D})} v \leq \sup_{z^{-1}(\partial \mathbb{D})} G(\cdot, q) =: k(q).$$

Hence locally around q,

$$G(p, q) \leq -\log |z(p)| + k(q).$$

For the reverse direction, note that

$$v(p) = \log_+(1/|z(p)|) \in \mathcal{G}_q.$$

Let $\mu = \inf_{p \in M} G(p, q) \geq 0$. If $v \in \mathcal{G}_q$, then outside some compact set K, and with $\varepsilon > 0$ arbitrary

$$v = 0 \leq G(p, q) - \mu,$$

whereas

$$(1 - \varepsilon) v(p) \leq G(p, q) - \mu \quad \text{as } p \to q.$$

By the maximum principle,

$$(1 - \varepsilon) v \leq G(\cdot, q) - \mu \quad \text{on } M \setminus \{q\}.$$

Letting $\varepsilon \to 0$ and by the definition of G, $G(\cdot, q) \leq G(\cdot, q) - \mu$ which implies that $\mu \leq 0$ and thus $\mu = 0$ as claimed.

Finally, suppose that $g(\cdot, q)$ satisfies the first two properties in Definition 8.14. Then for any $v \in \mathcal{G}_q$, and any $0 < \varepsilon < 1$,

$$(1 - \varepsilon) v \leq g(\cdot, q)$$

by the maximum principle. It follows that $G \leq g$ as desired. $\qquad \square$

Next, we establish the connection between M being hyperbolic and M admitting a Green function.

This is subtle and introduces the notion of a *harmonic measure*.

Theorem 8.19. *For any Riemann surface M the following are equivalent:*

- *M is hyperbolic,*

- *the Green function $G(\cdot, q)$ with singularity at q exists for some $q \in M$,*

- *the Green function $G(\cdot, q)$ with singularity at q exists for each $q \in M$.*

Proof. If $G(\cdot, q)$ is a Green function on M, then $-G(\cdot, q)$ is a negative nonconstant subharmonic function.

We need to prove that a hyperbolic surface admits a Green function with an arbitrary singularity. The ideas are as follows: we need to show that $G(p, q) < \infty$ if $p \neq q$ which amounts to finding a "lid" for our family $\mathcal{G}_q$. In other words, we need to find a function, say $w_q(p)$, harmonic or superharmonic on $M \setminus \{q\}$ and positive there, and so that $w_q(p) = -\log|z(p)| + O(1)$ as $p \to q$. Indeed, in that case we observe that $v \leq w$ for every $v \in \mathcal{G}_q$. Of course, G itself is such a choice if it exists—so realistically we can only hope to make w_q superharmonic. Thus, we need to find a subharmonic function v_1 (which would be $-w_q$) which is bounded from above and has a $\log|z(p)| + O(1)$ type singularity as $p \to q$. By assumption, there exists a negative subharmonic function v_0 on M. It does not fit the description of v_1 since it does not necessarily exhibit the desired logarithmic singularity. So we shall need to "glue" $\log|z(p)|$ in a chart around q to a subharmonic function like v_0 which is bounded from above. However, it is hard to glue subharmonic functions. Instead, we will produce a harmonic function u that vanishes on the boundary of some parametric disk D and which is positive[2] on $M \setminus D$ (by solving the Dirichlet problem outside of D). The crucial property of u is its positivity on $M \setminus D$ and this is exactly where we invoke the nonconstancy of v_0.

The details are as follows. Pick any $q \in M$ and a chart (U, z) with $z(q) = 0$. We can assume that $D_2 := z^{-1}(2\mathbb{D})$ and its closure are contained in U. Set $D_1 := z^{-1}(\mathbb{D})$. Consider the Perron family $\mathcal{F}$ of all $v \in \mathfrak{sh}(M \setminus \bar{D}_1)$ with $v \ll 0$ on ∂D_1 and such that $0 \leq v \leq 1$ on $M \setminus D_1$. By Corollary 8.13, $u := \sup_{v \in \mathcal{F}} v$ is continuous on $M \setminus D_1$ with $u = 0$ on ∂D_1 and $0 \leq u \leq 1$. We claim that $u \not\equiv 0$. To this end, let $v_0 < 0$ be a nonconstant subharmonic

---

[2]$1 - u$ is called the **harmonic measure** of ∂D relative to $M \setminus D$ (see Definition 8.20 below for a general definition).

function on M and set $\mu = \max_{\bar{D}_1} v_0$. Then $\mu < 0$ and

$$1 - \frac{v_0}{\mu} = 1 + \frac{v_0}{|\mu|} \in \mathcal{F}.$$

Hence $|\mu| + v_0 \leq |\mu| u$. By the nonconstancy of v_0,

$$\max_{\bar{D}_2} v_0 > \mu,$$

so that $u > 0$ somewhere and therefore $u > 0$ everywhere on $M \backslash \bar{D}_1$. We shall now build a subharmonic function v_1, globally defined on M and bounded above, and such that v_1 behaves like $\log |z|$ around q. In fact, define

$$v_1(z) := \begin{cases} \log |z| & \forall\, |z| \leq 1, \\ \max\{\log |z|, ku(z)\} & \forall\, 1 \leq |z| \leq 2, \\ ku(z) & \forall\, z \in M \setminus D_2. \end{cases}$$

Here the constant $k > 0$ is chosen such that

$$ku(z) > \log 2 \quad \forall\, |z| = 2.$$

Due to this property, and the fact that $u = \log |z| = 0$ on $|z| = 1$, $v_1 \in C(M)$. Moreover, checking in charts reveals that v_1 is a subharmonic function off the circle $|z| = 1$. Since the submean value property holds locally at every $|z| = 1$ we finally conclude that v_1 is subharmonic everywhere on M.

We are done: indeed, any $v \in \mathcal{G}_q$ (see Definition 8.17) satisfies

$$v \leq \nu - v_1.$$

Hence $G(p, q) \leq \nu - v_1(p) < \infty$ for any $p \in M \setminus \{q\}$. $\qquad\square$

We now formally introduce *harmonic measures*, which appeared as an element in the previous proof.

Definition 8.20. Let K be a compact subset of the Riemann surface M, with $M' := M \setminus K$ connected. Let V_K be the Perron family consisting of the following functions v:

    a) v is defined and subharmonic on M',

    b) v satisfies $v \leq 1$ on M',

    c) Given any $\varepsilon > 0$ there exists K_ε compact such that $v \leq \varepsilon$ on $M \backslash K_\varepsilon$.

Let $u_K := \sup_{v \in V_K} v$. If $0 < u_K < 1$, then u_K is called the *harmonic measure* of K.

Since $0 \in V_K$, it follows that $0 \leq u_K \leq 1$. It can happen that u_K vanishes identically, as it does if $K = \{0\}$ and $M = \mathbb{D}$. In Problem 8.2 the reader is asked to show that $u_K > 0$ if K has an interior point. If so, then by the maximum principle the only remaining possibilities are $0 < u_K < 1$ (where u_K is the harmonic measure), or u_K constant equal to 1.

Item c) of Definition 8.20 can also be phrased in terms of the *ideal boundary of M*. This refers to the complement of all compact subsets of M. The proof of Theorem 8.19 shows that if some compact parametric disk admits a harmonic measure, then M is hyperbolic. Problem 8.3 makes this, as well as another equivalence with the maximum principle, explicit.

Let us now elucidate the symmetry property of the Green function. We already encountered it in the previous chapter as part of the Riemann mapping theorem. However, it has nothing to do with simple connectivity as we will now see.

We begin with the following observation.

Lemma 8.21. *Let M be hyperbolic with Green function G, and suppose $N \subset M$ is a sub-Riemann surface with piecewise C^2 boundary[3] and such that $\bar{N}$ is compact. Then N is hyperbolic, $G_N \leq G$, and $G_N(p,q) = G_N(q,p)$ for all $p, q \in N$.*

Proof. Fix any $q \in N$ and let u_q be harmonic on N, continuous on $\bar{N}$ and with boundary data $-G(\cdot, q)$. This can be done by the solution of the Dirichlet problem in the previous section. Then

$$G_N(p, q) := G(p, q) + u_q(p)$$

is the Green function on N. It follows from the maximum principle that $G_N \leq G$. To prove the symmetry property, fix $p \neq q \in N$ and let

$$N' = N \setminus D_1 \cup D_2 \quad \text{where} \quad D_1, D_2 \subset N$$

are parametric disks around p, q, respectively. Define

$$u = G_N(\cdot, p), \qquad v = G_N(\cdot, q).$$

Then by Green's formula on N,

$$(8.14) \qquad 0 = \int_{\partial N'} u * dv - v * du = -\int_{\partial D_1 \cup \partial D_2} u * dv - v * du.$$

The $*$-operator is the Hodge-$*$ from Chapter 6, and Green's formula is nothing other than the Stokes theorem. In fact, we can rewrite (8.14) in the following form using Stokes:

$$\int_{N'} d(u * dv - v * du) = \int_{\partial N'} u * dv - v * du$$

$$= -\int_{\partial D_1 \cup \partial D_2} u * dv - v * du.$$

---

[3]This means that we can write the boundary as a finite union of C^2 curves $\gamma : [0,1] \to M$.

The sign here comes from the orientation, and ∂N does not contribute because $u = v = 0$ there. Invoking harmonicity, i.e., $d*du = 0$, $d*dv = 0$ the left-hand side reduces further:

$$\int_{N'} d(u *dv - v *du) = \int_{N'} du \wedge *dv - dv \wedge *du$$

$$= \int_{N'} du \wedge *dv + **du \wedge *dv = \int_{N'} du \wedge *dv - du \wedge *dv = 0;$$

see Lemma 6.8. In summary, one has (8.14). Again by Green's formula, but this time on D_1 with local coordinates z, centered at p $(z(p) = 0)$,

$$\text{(8.15)} \quad \int_{\partial D_1} u *dv - v *du = \int_{\partial D_1} (u + \log|z|) *dv - v *d(u + \log|z|)$$

$$- \int_{\partial D_1} \log|z| *dv - v *d\log|z| = G_N(p, q).$$

The final equality follows by first invoking that both $u + \log|z|$ and v are smooth on D_1, so sending the radius of D_1 to 0 makes the first integral vanish. As for the second one, in this limit

$$\int_{\partial D_1} \log|z| *dv \to 0,$$

whereas

$$\int_{\partial D_1} v *d\log|z| \to v(p) = G_N(p, q).$$

Similarly,

$$\int_{\partial D_2} u *dv - v *du = -G_N(q, p),$$

which in conjunction with (8.14) and (8.15) gives the desired symmetry. $\quad\square$

To obtain the symmetry of G itself we take the supremum over all N as in the lemma. We will refer to those N as *admissible*.

Proposition 8.22. *Let M be hyperbolic. Then the Green function is symmetric: $G(p, q) = G(q, p)$ for all $q \neq p \in M$.*

Proof. Fix $q \in M$ and consider the family

$$\mathcal{F}_q = \{G_N(\cdot, q) \mid q \in N, \ N \text{ is admissible}\},$$

where we extend each G_N to be zero outside of N. This extension is subharmonic on $M \setminus \{q\}$ and $\mathcal{F}_q$ is a Perron family on $M \setminus \{q\}$:

$$\max\{G_{N_1}(\cdot, q), G_{N_2}(\cdot, q)\} \leq G_{N_1 \cup N_2}(\cdot, q),$$

and $G_{N \cup D}(\cdot, q) \geq G_N(\cdot, q)$ for any parametric disk $D \subset M \setminus \{q\}$ with $G_{N \cup D}(\cdot, q)$ harmonic on D. Note that both $N_1 \cup N_2$ and $N \cup D$ are admissible. Let

$$g(\cdot, q) := \sup_{v \in \mathcal{F}_q} v \leq G(\cdot, q).$$

Moreover, it is clear that

$$g(\cdot, q) \geq \sup_{v \in \mathcal{G}_q} v = G(\cdot, q).$$

Indeed, use that every compact $K \subset M$ is contained in an admissible N (take N to be the union of a finite open cover by parametric disks). In conclusion, $g(p, q) = G(p, q)$ which implies that

$$G_N(q, p) = G_N(p, q) \leq G(p, q)$$

for all admissible N. Hence taking suprema, $G(q, p) \leq G(p, q)$ and we are done. $\qquad \square$

Any bounded open region in $\mathbb{C}$ is hyperbolic as a Riemann surface. In fact, a disk is, and since surfaces contained inside a hyperbolic surface are themselves hyperbolic, the claim follows. There are many explicit examples of negative subharmonic functions on bounded domains: $\log(|z|/R)$ where R is large enough, or $-M + u(z)$ where u is harmonic, nonconstant and M is large enough (take, for example, $u(z) = \operatorname{Re} z$).

By conformal equivalence, any open region contained in a half-plane is a hyperbolic surface. An explicit example of a negative subharmonic function in this case is $-M + \operatorname{Re}(z\bar{\zeta})$ where ζ is perpendicular to the boundary line of the half-space and M is large.

The exterior of a compact disk is hyperbolic: either use the logarithmic potential $\log(R/|z - z_0|)$ as a negative subharmonic function, or use the inversion about a point in the disk. By Problem 1.10 the map $z \mapsto \frac{1}{2}(z + z^{-1})$ is an isomorphism between $\mathbb{D} \setminus \{0\}$ and $\mathbb{C} \setminus [-1, 1]$. Since the former is hyperbolic, so is the latter. Thus, if we remove a finite collection of bounded or unbounded closed line segments from $\mathbb{C}$, the result is a hyperbolic Riemann surface.

If we remove a compact circular arc from S^2, then we obtain a hyperbolic surface. First, by a Möbius transformation we can assume the circular arc lies on a great circle (circles on S^2 get mapped to circles in $\mathbb{C}_\infty$ under stereographic projection; map the circle onto a line). Second, if we select any point on the arc and apply a stereographic projection from that point, then we obtain an isomorphic image in $\mathbb{C}$ which consists of $\mathbb{C}$ with two closed rays removed. By the previous paragraph, this is a hyperbolic surface. In fact, much more can be said.

The sphere S^2 is compact and therefore not hyperbolic. If we remove one point from S^2, then we obtain the plane which is not hyperbolic. If we remove two points, then we obtain the punctured plane $\mathbb{C}^* := \mathbb{C} \setminus \{0\}$ which has the plane $\mathbb{C}$ as its universal covering space; the exponential being the covering map. If there were a negative nonconstant subharmonic function on $\mathbb{C}^*$, then we could lift it to $\mathbb{C}$, which is impossible.

However, if we remove three (or more) points from S^2, then the resulting surface *is hyperbolic*. This follows immediately from Chapter 4 where we showed that the twice punctured plane is covered by the disk. To be more specific, our construction showed that $\mathbb{C} \setminus \{0, 1\}$ is isomorphic to the union of any open triangle in Figure 4.5 with one of its reflections across a side. Since this union is a subdomain of $\mathbb{D}$ it is hyperbolic, and so $\mathbb{C} \setminus \{0, 1\}$ is, too.

What these examples suggest is that *hyperbolic surfaces are "common"*. We shall see much more evidence of this when we address uniformization for non-simply-connected surfaces. It is "rare" for a surface to be covered by the plane or the sphere. The latter in fact only covers itself since every automorphism of S^2 has a fixed point, whereas the plane only covers the punctured plane (topologically the same as a cylinder), and tori of genus 1; cf. Problem 4.1. Thus, any compact surface of genus $g \geq 2$ has the disk as its universal cover. It is essential here that we view the covering spaces as Riemann surfaces, rather than in the purely topological sense. Indeed, the disk and plane are homeomorphic, but they are not conformally isomorphic.

8.5. Uniformization for simply-connected surfaces

We now state and prove the uniformization theorem.

Theorem 8.23. *Every simply-connected surface M is conformally equivalent to either $\mathbb{C}P^1 \simeq S^2$, $\mathbb{C}$, or $\mathbb{D}$. These correspond exactly to the compact, parabolic, and hyperbolic cases, respectively.*

Riemann-Roch shows that the compact simply-connected surfaces are conformally equivalent to $\mathbb{C}P^1$. This leaves the noncompact cases, and we begin with the hyperbolic one for which we employ the Green function technique that led to a proof of the Riemann mapping theorem in the beginning of this chapter.

If M is not simply-connected, then we pass to the universal cover of M, which is again a Riemann surface $\widetilde{M}$, and therefore classified by the theorem. One then proves that M is obtained from $\widetilde{M}$ (in other words, one of $\mathbb{C}P^1$, $\mathbb{C}$, $\mathbb{D}$) by factoring by the deck group. This then constitutes the full *uniformization theorem* which takes up this as well as the next section.

8.5.1. Hyperbolic surfaces.

Proof of Theorem 8.23 in the hyperbolic case. Let $q \in M$ and $G(p,q)$ be the Green function with singularity at q. Then there exists f_q holomorphic on M with

$$|f_q(p)| = \exp(-G(p,q)) \quad \forall \, q \in M,$$

with the understanding that $f_q(q) = 0$. This follows from the gluing technique of Lemma 5.5 since such a representation holds locally everywhere on M (alternatively, apply the monodromy theorem). Now $f_q : M \to \mathbb{D}$ with $f_q(p) = 0$ if and only if $p = q$. It remains to be shown that f_q is one-to-one since then $f_q(M)$ is a simply-connected subset of $\mathbb{D}$ and therefore, by the Riemann mapping theorem, conformally equivalent to $\mathbb{D}$. We proceed as in the planar case (see Theorem 8.3). Thus, let $p \in M$ with $q \neq p$ and T a Möbius transform with $T(f_q(p)) = 0$. We claim that $|T \circ f_q| = |f_p|$. This will then show that f_q is one-to-one. Indeed, suppose $f_q(p) = f_q(p')$; then by the claim, $|f_p| = |f_{p'}|$ and thus $f_p(p') = 0$ and $p = p'$).

To prove the claim, we observe that

$$w_q := -\log|T \circ f_q| \geq G(\cdot, q) \quad \text{on } M \setminus \{q\}.$$

In fact, locally around $p = q$ we have, for some integer $k \geq 1$,

$$\log|T \circ f_q(p)| \leq k \log|z(p) - z(q)| + O(1) \quad \text{as } p \to q,$$

where z is any local coordinate around q. In addition, $w_q > 0$ everywhere on M. From these properties we conclude via the maximum principle that

$$w_q \geq v \quad \forall \, v \in \mathcal{G}_q \implies w_q \geq G(\cdot, q),$$

as desired (here $\mathcal{G}_q$ is the family from Definition 8.17). Since

$$-G(p,q) = \log|f_q(p)| = \log|T(0)| = \log|(T \circ f_q)(q)| \leq -G(q,p) = -G(p,q),$$

we obtain from the maximum principle that $w_q = G(\cdot, p)$ whence the claim.

$\square$

8.5.2. Parabolic surfaces.
It remains for us to understand the parabolic case, for which we need to resolve more technical issues. The logic is as follows, provided M is simply-connected: in the compact case we established the existence of a meromorphic function with a simple pole. This followed from the Riemann-Roch theorem, or for that matter on the existence of meromorphic differentials with a prescribed $\frac{dz}{z^2}$ singularity at a given point.

In the hyperbolic case, we were able to place a positive harmonic function on M with a $-\log|z|$ singularity at a given point—in fact, the hyperbolic surfaces M are precisely those that allow for this. Amongst all such harmonic functions we selected the minimal one (the Green function) and constructed a conformal equivalence from it.

For parabolic surfaces we would like to mimic the proof for the compact ones by constructing a meromorphic function of degree 1. In view of the fact that we are trying to show that M is equivalent to $\mathbb{C}$, and therefore compactifiable by the addition of one point, this is reasonable.

Assuming therefore that $f : M \to \mathbb{C}P^1$ is meromorphic and one-to-one, note that f cannot be onto as otherwise M would then need to be compact. Without loss of generality, we can thus assume that $f : M \to \mathbb{C}$. If f were not onto $\mathbb{C}$, then by the Riemann mapping theorem we could make $f(M)$ and thus M equivalent to $\mathbb{D}$. But this would mean that M is hyperbolic.

So it remains to find a suitable meromorphic function on M for which we need several more technical ingredients. The first is the maximum principle outside a compact set which establishes uniqueness in Corollary 8.13.

Proposition 8.24. *Let M be a parabolic Riemann surface and $K \subset M$ compact. Suppose u is harmonic and bounded above on $M \setminus K$, and $u \ll 0$ on ∂K. Then $u \leq 0$ on $M \setminus K$.*

Proof. We have already encountered this idea in the proof of Theorem 8.19. There K was a parametric disk and we proved that a hyperbolic surface does admit what is called a harmonic measure of K—here we are trying to prove the nonexistence of a harmonic measure. Since the latter was shown there to imply the existence of a Green function, we are basically done. The only issue here is that K does not need to be a parametric disk so we have to be careful when applying the Perron method because of ∂K not necessarily being regular. However, this is easily circumvented.

Suppose the proposition fails and let $u > 0$ somewhere on $M \setminus K$. Extend u to M by setting $u = 0$ on K. Then $K \subset \{u < \varepsilon\}$ is an open neighborhood of K for every $\varepsilon > 0$. This implies that for some $\varepsilon > 0$ we have

$$u_0 := (u - \varepsilon)_+ \in \mathfrak{sh}(M)$$

and $u_0 > 0$ somewhere. Moreover, $\{u_0 = 0\} \supset \bar{D}$ for some parametric disk D. Now define

$$\mathcal{F} =: \{v \in \mathfrak{sh}(M \setminus \bar{D}) \,|\, v \ll 0 \text{ on } \partial D, \, 0 \leq v \leq 1\}.$$

It is a Perron family, and we infer that

$$w := \sup_{v \in \mathcal{F}} v$$

is harmonic on $M \setminus \bar{D}$ with $w = 0$ on ∂D and $0 \leq w \leq 1$ on $M \setminus D$. Since $u_0 \in \mathcal{F}$ we further conclude that $w > 0$ somewhere and thus everywhere on $M \setminus D$. As in the proof of Theorem 8.19 we are now able to construct a Green function with singularity in D, contrary to our assumption of M being parabolic. $\qquad\square$

Definition 8.25. We refer to the property stated in Proposition 8.24 as the *maximum principle* for K, which is compact and nonempty.

The proof of the proposition shows that the maximum principle is a property of the surface and not of the compact set K. In fact, we also see that it holds if and only if the surface is not hyperbolic; see Problem 8.3 for more on this matter. The intuition is as follows: if M has a *large ideal boundary* (see Definition 8.20), then we cannot hope to force the behavior of the function on that boundary by means of global boundedness and the condition on ∂K. This is exactly the case for the disk, and the maximum principle fails for it. On the other hand, compact surfaces have no ideal boundary, and $\mathbb{C}$ has a small ideal boundary, namely the point at ∞.

Corollary 8.26. *A positive harmonic function on a parabolic Riemann surface is constant.*

Proof. Let u be such a function. Apply the maximum principle to $-u$ and compact sets $K = \{p\}$ and $K = \{q\}$, respectively, where $p, q \in M$ are distinct, to conclude that

$$-u(q) \leq -u(p) \leq -u(q),$$

whence the constancy. □

It is instructive to give an independent proof of the maximum principle for the case of $\mathbb{C}$: we can assume that $0 \in K$. Then $v(z) := u(1/z)$ is harmonic on $\Omega := \{1/z \mid z \in \mathbb{C} \setminus K\}$ and $v \ll 0$ on $\partial\Omega \setminus \{0\}$. Moreover, v is bounded above on Ω. Given $\delta > 0$ there exists R large so that for all $\varepsilon > 0$,

$$v(z) \leq \delta - \varepsilon \log(|z|/R) \quad \forall\, z \in \Omega.$$

Sending $\varepsilon \to 0$ and then $\delta \to 0$ shows that $v \leq 0$ on Ω as claimed.

Now let us make another observation concerning any u harmonic and bounded on $\mathbb{C} \setminus K$ with K compact: for any $R > 0$ with $K \subset \{|z| < R\}$ we have

$$(8.16) \qquad \int_{|z|=R} \frac{\partial u}{\partial n}\, d\sigma = 0.$$

Indeed, $v(z) = u(1/z)$ is bounded and harmonic on $0 < |z| < \frac{1}{R} + \varepsilon$ for some $\varepsilon > 0$. By Problem 3.2, v is necessarily harmonic on a neighborhood of zero. Hence

$$0 = \iint_{|z| \leq \frac{1}{R}} \Delta v\, dx\, dy = \oint_{|z|=\frac{1}{R}} \frac{\partial v}{\partial n}\, d\sigma,$$

and (8.16) follows.

An analogous result holds on any parabolic Riemann surface, but the previous proof in $\mathbb{C}$ does not generalize to that setting. Let us therefore present one for the planar case that does generalize. Without loss of generality, $K \subset \mathbb{D}$. For any $R > 1$ denote by ω the harmonic function so that $\omega = 1$ on $\{|z| = 1\}$ and $\omega = 0$ on $\{|z| = R\}$ (harmonic measure). This exists by Perron but there is an explicit formula:

$$\omega(z) = \frac{\log(R/|z|)}{\log R}, \quad 1 \leq |z| \leq R.$$

Then by Stokes' theorem,

$$0 = \oint_{|z|=1} \frac{\partial u}{\partial r} \, d\sigma + \oint_{|z|=R} u \frac{\partial \omega}{\partial r} \, d\sigma - \oint_{|z|=1} u \frac{\partial \omega}{\partial r} \, d\sigma.$$

Since $\frac{\partial \omega}{\partial r} = \frac{-1}{r \log R}$, it follows upon sending $R \to \infty$ that

$$0 = \oint_{|z|=1} \frac{\partial u}{\partial r} \, d\sigma$$

as desired. This proof can be made to work on a general parabolic Riemann surface and we obtain the following result.

Lemma 8.27. *Let D be a parametric disk on a parabolic surface M and suppose u is harmonic and bounded on $M \setminus D$. If $u \in C^1\big(\overline{M \setminus D}\big)$, then*

$$\int_{\partial D} *du = 0.$$

Proof. We say that $N \subset M$ is *admissible* if $\bar{N}$ is compact, $\bar{D} \subset N$, and ∂N is piecewise C^2. Then by ω_N we mean the harmonic function on $N \setminus \bar{D}$ so that $\omega = 1$ on ∂D and $\omega = 0$ on ∂N. We claim that

$$\mathcal{F} := \{\omega_N \mid N \text{ admissible}\}$$

is a Perron family on $M \setminus \bar{D}$ where we set each $\omega_N = 0$ on $M \setminus N$. In this way, each ω_N becomes subharmonic on $M \setminus \bar{D}$. To verify that $\mathcal{F}$ is a Perron family, observe that from the maximum principle,

$$\max\{\omega_{N_1}, \omega_{N_2}\} \leq \omega_{N_1 \cup N_2},$$
$$(\omega_N)_K \leq \omega_{N \cup K},$$

where $K \subset M \setminus \bar{D}$ is any parametric disk in the second line. Since $N_1 \cup N_2$ and $N \cup K$ are again admissible, $\mathcal{F}$ is indeed such a family and

$$\omega_\infty := \sup_{v \in \mathcal{F}} v$$

is harmonic on $M \setminus D$ with $0 \leq \omega_\infty \leq 1$ and $\omega_\infty = 1$ on ∂D. Applying the maximum principle for parabolic surfaces as given by Proposition 8.24 to $1 - \omega_\infty$ yields $\omega_\infty = 1$ everywhere on $M \setminus D$.

Returning to any admissible N as above, we infer from Stokes' theorem that

$$0 = \int_{\partial(N \setminus D)} \omega_N * du - u * d\omega_N$$

or, with suitable orientations,

$$(8.17) \qquad \int_{\partial D} * du = - \int_{\partial N} u * d\omega_N + \int_{\partial D} u * d\omega_N.$$

It is clear that $*d\omega_N$ is of definite sign on both ∂D and ∂N. Indeed, on these boundaries this differential form, evaluated at a tangent vector $\vec{e}$ to the boundary, is the directional derivative of ω_N along $\vec{e}^\perp$ (with a fixed sense of orientation along the boundary). Furthermore, again by Stokes,

$$\int_{\partial D} * d\omega_N = \int_{\partial N} * d\omega_N.$$

In view of (8.17) and the boundedness of u it therefore suffices to show that

$$\inf_{N \text{ admissible}} \left| \int_{\partial D} * d\omega_N \right| = 0.$$

However, this follows immediately from the fact that $\omega_\infty = 1$ everywhere on $M \setminus D$. $\qquad \square$

Before continuing with the technical development, let us get to the point of parabolic uniformization. The following result establishes the existence of certain harmonic functions on parabolic surfaces. The reader might want to try and construct such functions by means of a carefully chosen Perron family. The issue with such an approach hinges on the difficulty in asserting that such a Perron family is nonempty.

Proposition 8.28. *Let M be a parabolic surface. Then for every $p_0 \in M$ there exists a harmonic function u on $M \setminus \{p_0\}$ such that u is bounded outside every parametric disk centered at p_0 and so that for a specific choice of local coordinates z near p_0 we have*

$$(8.18) \qquad \lim_{p \to p_0} \left[u(p) - \mathrm{Re}(1/z(p)) \right] = 0.$$

The function u is unique with these properties (for a specific choice of z).

The uniqueness is clear by the maximum principle. Before discussing the existence of u, let us show that armed with these harmonic functions we can complete the proof of the uniformization theorem.

Proof of Theorem 8.23 in the parabolic case. Fix $p_0 \in M$ and let u be as in Proposition 8.28. Locally, near any point, u has a harmonic conjugate. In other words, locally near every point there exists a meromorphic function f such that $u = \mathrm{Re}(f)$ in that neighborhood. We now wish to extend f to all of M. This is indeed possible. By simple connectivity and Lemma 5.5, there exists a meromorphic function f on M such that in local coordinates z around p_0,

$$(8.19) \qquad f(p) = \frac{1}{z(p)} + \sum_{n=1}^{\infty} a_n z(p)^n,$$

where we have removed the constant term. Repeating this process with the local coordinate $-iz$ yields another meromorphic function

$$(8.20) \qquad \widetilde{f}(p) = \frac{i}{z(p)} + \sum_{n=1}^{\infty} b_n z(p)^n.$$

We claim that $\widetilde{f} = if$. By the proposition, $|\mathrm{Re}\, f| \leq M$ and $|\mathrm{Re}\, \widetilde{f}| \leq M$ outside a fixed parametric disk D_0 centered at p_0. Let p_1 be given by $z(p_1) = r(1 + i)$ in local coordinates. For $r > 0$ sufficiently small,

$$\mathrm{Re}\, f(p_1) > M, \qquad \mathrm{Re}\, \widetilde{f}(p_1) > M.$$

Then $f(p) \neq f(p_1)$ for all $p \in M \setminus D_0$, and in fact $\mathrm{Re}(f(p) - f(p_1)) < 0$ on ∂D_0. It follows from the argument principle (see Proposition 2.13), that $f(p) - f(p_1)$ has a unique (and thus simple) zero in D_0, namely $p = p_1$. We used here that $f(p) - f(p_1)$ has a simple pole in D_0. The same holds for $\widetilde{f}$, which implies that

$$
(8.21) \qquad
\begin{aligned}
F(p) &= \frac{f(p)}{f(p) - f(p_1)} = \frac{A}{z - z_1} + \sum_{n=0}^{\infty} A_n (z - z_1)^n, \\
\widetilde{F}(p) &= \frac{\widetilde{f}(p)}{\widetilde{f}(p) - \widetilde{f}(p_1)} = \frac{\widetilde{A}}{z - z_1} + \sum_{n=0}^{\infty} \widetilde{A}_n (z - z_1)^n.
\end{aligned}
$$

By the preceding, for all $p \in M \setminus D_0$,

$$|F(p)| \leq 1 + \frac{|f(p_1)|}{\mathrm{Re}\, f(p_1) - M}, \qquad |\widetilde{F}(p)| \leq 1 + \frac{|\widetilde{f}(p_1)|}{\mathrm{Re}\, \widetilde{f}(p_1) - M}.$$

In view of this and (8.21) it follows that $g := \widetilde{A} f - A \widetilde{f}$ is bounded and holomorphic on M. By Corollary 8.26 it follows that g is a constant. So $\widetilde{f} = T(f)$ where T is a Möbius transform. Comparing (8.19) and (8.20) implies that $\widetilde{f} = if$ as claimed.

In conclusion, $f = f(\cdot, p_0)$ is bounded outside of D_0, and not just its real part. For $p_1 \in D_0$ we similarly obtain functions $f(\cdot, p_1)$ using the same local coordinate z. Comparing (8.21) with the Laurent expansion of $f(\cdot, p_1)$ near

p_1, and using Corollary 8.26 again implies that $F = af(\cdot, p_1) + b$ globally. In other words, $f(\cdot, p_1) = Sf(\cdot, p_0)$ with a Möbius transform S. By chaining, this relation persists even if p_0 and p_1 are not close.

It is now easy to obtain injectivity. Indeed, suppose $f(p, p_0) = f(p_1, p_0)$. Then

$$f(p, p_1) = Sf(p, p_0) = Sf(p_1, p_0) = f(p_1, p_1) = \infty.$$

Since p_1 is the only pole of f it follows that $p = p_1$ as desired.

We have constructed $f : M \to \mathbb{C}P^1$ meromorphic and one-to-one. First, f cannot be onto as otherwise M would then need to be compact. By means of a Möbius transform, we can assume that f misses ∞ so that $f : M \to \mathbb{C}$. If f were not onto $\mathbb{C}$, then by the Riemann mapping theorem we could make $f(M)$ and thus M equivalent to $\mathbb{D}$. But this would mean that M is hyperbolic. $\qquad\square$

The previous proofs rests on a strong and perhaps surprising rigidity property of the harmonic functions promised by Proposition 8.28. Indeed, note that *arbitrary* coordinates enter into the defining equation (8.18). But the assumption of global boundedness implies that *all information* of the specific form of z is lost, other than the **residue** in (8.19) (the constant term being arbitrary anyway). The other terms are then uniquely determined from that residue, essentially from the global geometry of M. This property is what allows us to establish the extremely strong fractional linear relation between the functions $f(\cdot, p_0)$ and $f(\cdot, p_1)$.

This being said, it is now also clear that the proof of Proposition 8.28 will not be possible in some fixed local coordinate neighborhood. In fact, we will construct u by "zooming into" p_0. This effectively removes all "fine structures" of the choice of coordinates.

Before carrying out this limiting procedure, we need one more estimate on the oscillation of harmonic functions.

Lemma 8.29. *Suppose $u(z)$ is harmonic in the annulus $\mathcal{A}_\rho := \{\rho \le |z| \le 1\}$ and constant on $|z| = \rho$. Let $S_r(u) = \max_{|z|=r} u(z) - \min_{|z|=r} u(z)$ (the oscillation of u on $|z| = r$). Then*

$$(8.22) \qquad\qquad S_r(u) \le S_1(u)\frac{4}{\pi}\arctan r$$

for all $\rho \le r \le 1$.

Proof. Rotating the real axis about the origin if necessary, we can assume that the maximum and minimum of u on $\{|z| = r\}$ are attained at z_0 and $\bar{z}_0$, respectively. Consider the function $v(z) := u(z) - u(\bar{z})$. It is harmonic in $\mathcal{A}_\rho$, and vanishes on $|z| = \rho$ as well as on the real axis. Thus, by the

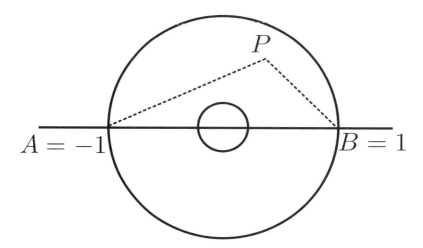

Figure 8.4. The geometry in Lemma 8.29

maximum principle $v(z) \leq w(z)$ on the region $\Omega := \mathcal{A}_\rho \cap \{\operatorname{Im} z \geq 0\}$ where w is the harmonic function in $\{|z| < 1, \operatorname{Im} z > 0\}$ with boundary values $w(z) = 0$ on $\operatorname{Im} z = 0$ and $w(z) = S_1(u)$ on $\{|z| = 1, \operatorname{Im} z > 0\}$. Now

$$w(z) = \frac{2}{\pi}(\pi - \sphericalangle(APB)),$$

where P stands for the point z (see Figure 8.4). The smallest value of the angle $\sphericalangle(APB)$ is reached at $z = ir$. This implies $w(z) \leq \frac{4}{\pi} \arctan r$ and establishes the inequality (8.22). $\qquad\square$

Armed with this estimate, we can now carry out the required limiting procedure needed for the proof of Proposition 8.28.

Proof of Proposition 8.28. Let D_ρ denote the parametric disk of radius ρ in the local coordinate z. By Corollary 8.13 for every small $\rho > 0$ we obtain a function u_ρ harmonic and bounded in $M \setminus D_\rho$ and with boundary values $\operatorname{Re}(1/z)$ on ∂D_ρ. By the maximum principle it is unique, and Lemma 8.27 applies to u_ρ.

We now claim that $u = \lim_{\rho \to 0} u_\rho$ exists and has the desired properties. First, we can assume that the range of z extends to all of $\{|z| \leq 1\}$. Set $v_\rho := u_\rho - \operatorname{Re}(1/z)$ and denote $q(r) = \frac{4}{\pi} \arctan r$. From Lemma 8.29,

$$(8.23) \qquad\qquad S_r(v_\rho) \leq q(r)S_1(v_\rho),$$

which implies

$$(8.24) \qquad\qquad S_r(u_\rho) - \frac{2}{r} \leq q(r)(S_1(u_\rho) + 2).$$

By the maximum principle on $M \setminus D_\rho$ we have $S_1(u_\rho) \le S_r(u_\rho)$ for every $\rho \le r \le 1$. From (8.24), therefore,

$$S_1(u_\rho) \le \frac{2q(r) + 2/r}{1 - q(r)} \quad \forall\, \rho \le r \le 1.$$

This implies that $S_1(u_\rho) \le C$ for all $\rho \le 1$ whence (8.23) yields

$$(8.25) \qquad\qquad S_r(v_\rho) \le q(r)(C + 2).$$

By Lemma 8.27 and the fact that $\mathrm{Re}(1/z)$ has zero average over parametric circles it follows that v_ρ has zero average over parametric circles. Hence (8.25) implies that

$$(8.26) \qquad
\begin{aligned}
\max_{|z|=r} \big|v_\rho(z)\big| &\le q(r)(C + 2), \\
\max_{|z|=r} \big|u_\rho(z) - u_{\rho'}(z)\big| &\le q(r)(C + 2) \quad \forall\, \rho, \rho' \le r \le 1.
\end{aligned}$$

By the maximum principle, $u_\rho(z) - u_{\rho'}(z)$ satisfies the same bound outside of D_r. Thus, $u = \lim_{\rho \to 0} u_\rho$ does indeed exist uniformly outside of any neighborhood of p_0. Passing to the limit in (8.26) yields

$$(8.27) \qquad
\begin{aligned}
\max_{|z|=r} \big|u(z) - \mathrm{Re}(1/z)\big| &\le q(r)(C + 2), \\
\max_{|z|=r} \big|u_\rho(z) - u(z)\big| &\le q(r)(C + 2) \quad \forall\, \rho, \rho' \le r \le 1.
\end{aligned}$$

The first inequality verifies the limit (8.18), and the second shows that u is bounded outside of any neighborhood of p_0. $\qquad\square$

8.6. Uniformization of non-simply-connected surfaces

We have already dispensed with all surfaces that are covered by the plane $\mathbb{C}$ (which comprises a complete list of parabolic non-simply-connected Riemann surfaces): they are given by the quotients $\mathbb{C}/\Lambda$ where $\Lambda < \mathrm{Aut}(\mathbb{C})$ is generated by one or two translations. The former is isomorphic to the punctured plane, and the latter is a torus. In Section 7.7 we established that every compact surface of genus $g = 1$ is isomorphic to its Jacobian variety, which is a standard torus $\mathbb{C}/\langle 1, \tau \rangle$ with $\mathrm{Im}\,\tau > 0$.

For general Riemann surfaces M, we pass to the universal cover $\widetilde{M}$. It is understood that this universal cover inherits the conformal structure from M. The result is as follows.

Theorem 8.30. *Let M be a non-simply-connected Riemann surface. Then the following is a complete list of isomorphism classes:*

(A) M is conformally isomorphic to the punctured plane, or compact and of genus 1, and isomorphic to $\mathbb{C}/\Lambda$ where $\Lambda = \langle 1, \tau \rangle$, with $\mathrm{Im}\,\tau > 0$.

(B) $M \simeq \mathbb{D}/G$ where $G < \mathrm{Aut}(\mathbb{D})$ acts properly discontinuously on $\mathbb{D}$ and apart from the identity, no Möbius transform in G has a fixed point in $\mathbb{D}$. $G \simeq \pi_1(M)$ as groups, and for any two points $p, q \in \widetilde{M}$ which lie above the same point in M, there exists a deck transformation which moves p onto q.

Proof. Passing to the universal cover $\widetilde{M}$ of M, we obtain from the preceding section that $\widetilde{M}$ is either S^2, $\mathbb{C}$ or $\mathbb{D}$. Moreover, by standard topology, $M \simeq \widetilde{M}/G$ where G is a group of homeomorphisms of $\widetilde{M}$ which leave the natural projection $\pi : \widetilde{M} \to M$ invariant: $f \in G$ if and only if f is a homeomorphism of $\widetilde{M}$ such that $\pi \circ f = \pi$. If f is not the identity, then f has no fixed point; indeed, otherwise the set of fixed points, which is open and closed by the nature of a covering space, would equal $\widetilde{M}$ and thus f would be the identity. This G is called the *deck group*. By writing $f \in G$ in local coordinates we see that it is in fact a conformal isomorphism of $\widetilde{M}$; in other words, $G < \mathrm{Aut}(\widetilde{M})$.

Moreover, we claim that each G acts properly discontinuously (cf. Theorem 4.12). Thus, let $p_0 \in \widetilde{M}$. Then we can find a neighborhood U of p_0 in $\widetilde{M}$ so that π is a homeomorphism on U. If $f \in G$ has the property that $U \cap f(U) \neq \emptyset$, then it would mean that $p = f(q)$ for $p, q \in U$ whence $\pi(p) = \pi(f(q)) = \pi(q)$. By choice of U therefore $p = q$ which further means that $p = f(p)$. But f cannot have a fixed point unless it is the identity and we arrive at a contradiction. In conclusion, $U \cap f(U) = \emptyset$ for every $f \in G$ which is not the identity. So we have obtained all properties required by Theorem 4.12.

If $\widetilde{M} = S^2$, then we are done since every Möbius transform has a fixed point in S^2. Thus, $M = S^2$ in that case which is a contradiction to M being not simply-connected. If $\widetilde{M} = \mathbb{C}$, then the deck group is described by Problem 4.1. In conclusion, $M \simeq \widetilde{M}/G$ is either the punctured plane or a torus of genus $g = 1$. If $\widetilde{M} = \mathbb{D}$, then we have many possibilities which are of the general form stated in the theorem.

The final claims of the theorem come from general topology. $\qquad\square$

The reader will have noticed that the proof of Theorem 8.30 is relatively soft and does not offer much concrete information. The strength of this theorem lies with its generality, but often individual examples are hard to analyze. For example, remove two points from $\mathbb{D}$. This is a hyperbolic surface and thus of the form $\mathbb{D}/G$ for some discrete subgroup of $\mathrm{Aut}(\mathbb{D})$, and hence a *Fuchsian group* (see Problems 4.7, 4.6). But determining the exact nature of this group and its geometric action on the disk is another matter.

To offer some more basic examples: the punctured disk $\mathbb{D}^* = \mathbb{D} \setminus \{0\}$ is covered by the upper half-plane with the exponential $z \mapsto e^{2\pi i z}$ as associated projection. The deck group are the translations $z \mapsto z + n$, $n \in \mathbb{Z}$. This is in agreement with the fact that $\pi_1(M) \simeq \mathbb{Z}$, the latter isomorphism being given by the winding number. Even though the punctured plane $\mathbb{C}^*$ is homeomorphic to the punctured disk, it is not conformally equivalent, for otherwise the universal covers would need to carry the same conformal structure as well. However, for the former this surface is $\mathbb{C}$, whereas for the latter it is $\mathbb{D}$.

The latter distinction highlights an important feature of our analysis: while the sphere S^2 admits only a *single conformal structure*, as proved in the uniformization theorem for compact surfaces, the disk admits **exactly two**, namely the conformal structure of the plane or that of the disk itself.

Now suppose we factor the punctured plane by the subgroup G generated by the scaling $z \mapsto \lambda z$, $\lambda > 1$. Then $\mathbb{C}^*/G$ is a torus, i.e., the annulus $\{1 < |z| < \lambda\}$ with its two boundary circle identified. We know that the latter is given by $\mathbb{C}/\langle 1, \tau \rangle$ and to pass from this presentation to the previous multiplicative one we apply the exponential map.

We already noted towards the end of Section 8.4 that every subregion (open connected subset) of $\mathbb{C}$ is hyperbolic in the sense of Riemann surfaces. Its universal covering surface can therefore only be the disk (indeed, we can lift a Green function onto the cover). But understanding the covering map or the deck group inside of $\mathrm{Aut}(\mathbb{D})$ is another matter altogether. Even for the twice punctured plane this was not obvious, but the reader is invited to picture $\mathbb{C}$ with a Cantor set removed.

What we can say in general is that the deck group is Fuchsian (see Problem 4.7) and therefore is associated with a fundamental region which can be taken to be bounded by geodesic arcs. Many natural questions pose themselves, such as: (i) which fundamental regions can occur in the process (ii) suppose we start from some polygonal region in the disk (with finitely many geodesics as sides) with prescribed identifications of its boundary segments. Can we reverse the process, i.e., find a surface $\mathbb{D}/G$ associated with this polygon as a fundamental region?

A theorem by Poincaré precisely addresses question (ii); see the following section. In general, though, the complexity of groups G that might be associated with surfaces $\mathbb{D}/G$ (especially those bounded by fundamental regions with infinitely many geodesic sides) is daunting.

In Section 4.2 it was shown that oriented smooth surfaces in $\mathbb{R}^3$, endowed with the Euclidean metric of the ambient space, carry a conformal structure. Assume further that these surfaces are compact and denote any of them by $\mathcal{S}$. If $\mathcal{S}$ is isometric to a sphere, then a well-known result of surface theory states that it is in fact a sphere. The uniformization theorem, on the other hand, shows that we can continuously deform a sphere in any way we want and the result will always be conformally equivalent to S^2. This is a rather remarkable fact, but it can be encountered in nature: anybody who has squashed a ballon and seen the different shades the rubber exhibits as a result of the stretching, has observed the conformal equivalence: if we were to quantify the different hues in the rubber by means of a smooth function of position, it would tell us the scaling the metric undergoes (without, however, making the scaling depend on the direction).

It is well-known that if we were to fill in the spheres and ask about conformal equivalence of the squashed ball with a standard one in the sense of $\mathbb{R}^3$, then the result fails; there are few conformal maps in three or higher dimensions (see the notes). This is a result of the increased number of degrees of freedom which renders conformality too strong of a condition. On the other hand, *quasi-conformality* in higher dimensions is a difficult and exciting research area with many unsolved problems.

Suppose we are given some squashed sphere $\mathcal{S}$ and wish to find the conformal identification $f : \mathcal{S} \to S^2$. Clearly, this map f will be quite special; if g is another such map, then $f \circ g^{-1}$ is an isomorphism of S^2 and therefore Möbius. As often in mathematics, we can hope to find f via a minimization procedure, or in other words, by means of some variational principle based on minimizing a suitable "energy" in the class of smooth homeomorphism between the surfaces. This is indeed possible, and leads to the theory of harmonic maps between manifolds which we do not pursue in this text (see the notes for references).

The uniformization theorem appears even more remarkable for compact orientable surfaces $\mathcal{S}$ in $\mathbb{R}^3$ of higher genus, such as a sphere with five handles attached. It is perhaps somewhat mysterious how geometric intuition might lead one to guess that such concrete objects are conformally equivalent to quotients of the disk.

8.7. Fuchsian groups

We shall now study Fuchsian groups and their associated fundamental regions in more detail. Recall from Definition 4.23 that a *Fuchsian group* acts properly discontinuously on a disk and leaves the boundary circle invariant. In Problem 4.6 the reader was asked to establish various equivalent formulations of the properly discontinuous action, namely discreteness of the group (in the sense of topological groups), or locally finite orbits. Problem 4.7 explored some of the more geometric notions associated with a Fuchsian group, such as the fundamental region and fixed points, and their classification as elliptic, hyperbolic, or parabolic. We now set out to investigate these geometric entities in more detail with the goal of obtaining a better understanding of the quotients $\mathbb{D}/G$ that might arise in Theorem 8.30. Throughout, we take the invariant circle to be $\mathbb{R} \cup \{\infty\}$, with G acting on $\mathbb{H}$. We will use the *hyperbolic metric* on $\mathbb{H}$ which we encountered in Section 1.5 (see also Problem 1.13). In particular, we will make use of the geodesics in this metric $d = d_{\mathbb{H}}$ as described in that section, as well as the fact that $\mathrm{PSL}(2, \mathbb{R})$ is the group of orientation-preserving isometries on $\mathbb{H}$. Finally, the Gauss-Bonnet formula (see Theorem 1.15) will play an essential role in our analysis. We begin with the observation that fixed points are isolated.

Lemma 8.31. *Let $z_0 \in \mathbb{H}$ be a fixed point of some $g \in G$ other than the identity. Then there exists a neighborhood of z_0 free of any other fixed points of maps in G.*

Proof. Suppose not. Then there exit $z_n \to z$ and $g_n \in G$ with $g_n z_n = z_n$. We can find $\varepsilon > 0$ so that $d(z_0, z_n) < \varepsilon$ and $d(g_n z_0, z_0) > 2\varepsilon$ for $n > n_0$, the latter being a result of the properly discontinuous action. But

$$2\varepsilon < d(g_n z_0, z_0) \leq d(g_n z_0, g_n z_n) + d(g_n z_n, z_0) = 2d(z_n, z_0) < 2\varepsilon,$$

which is impossible. $\qquad\square$

Next, we recall the notion of a fundamental region.

Definition 8.32. We say that a closed connected set $F \subset \mathbb{H}$ is a *fundamental region* for the Fuchsian group G provided:

- $\mathbb{H} = \bigcup_{g \in G} gF$,
- $\dot{F} \cap g(\dot{F}) = \emptyset$ for all $g \in G$ which are not the identity. Here $\dot{F}$ denotes the interior of F.

One refers to the union in the first item as a *tessellation*.

For examples of fundamental regions of Fuchsian groups see Figures 4.5 and 4.7, the latter being a region for the modular group. Fundamental regions are far from unique. Indeed, we can slightly deform boundary segments which do not contain fixed points of any nonidentity element of G provided congruent boundary segments are changed accordingly. For the remainder of this section, we call two points *congruent* if they belong to the same orbit, i.e., if one point is moved onto another by a group element.

On the other hand, the hyperbolic area of a fundamental region is uniquely determined by the group. Henceforth, μ denotes the hyperbolic area.

Lemma 8.33. *Let F_1, F_2 be fundamental regions for the Fuchsian group G. Assume that the boundaries $\partial F_1, \partial F_2$ have zero hyperbolic area. Then $\mu(F_1) = \mu(F_2)$ (which includes possibly infinite area).*

Proof. Assume one of the regions has finite area, say $\mu(F_1) < \infty$. Then

$$\mu(F_1) \geq \mu\big(F_1 \cap \bigcup_{g \in G} g\dot{F}_2\big) = \sum_{g \in G} \mu(gF_1 \cap \dot{F}_2)$$

(8.28)

$$\geq \mu\big(\bigcup_{g \in G} gF_1 \cap \dot{F}_2\big) = \mu(\dot{F}_2) = \mu(F_2).$$

In the first equality sign we used the invariance of the measure under transformations in $\mathrm{PSL}(2, \mathbb{R})$. So we can reverse the roles of F_1 and F_2. □

We now come to the Dirichlet region, which is a special fundamental region. In Problem 4.5 we already encountered the notion of a lattice. By Lemma 8.31, we can pick $p \in \mathbb{H}$ which is not fixed by any nonidentity element of G.

Definition 8.34. Let p be as above. Define the *Dirichlet region* for G centered at p to be

(8.29) $$D_p(G) := \bigcap_{g \in G} H_g(p), \quad H_g(p) := \{\zeta \in \mathbb{H} \mid d(z, p) \leq d(z, gp)\}.$$

The sets $H_g(p)$ are half-planes in $\mathbb{H}$ bounded by the perpendicular bisector of the geodesic arc joining p to gp. They are closed sets, and so is $D_p(G)$ which is, moreover, convex (relative to geodesic line segments), and thus connected. Figure 4.7 shows an example of a Dirichlet region (see Problem 8.6). The boundary ∂D_p consists of finitely or infinitely many circular arcs, namely geodesic ones given by perpendicular bisectors of points $p \neq gp$. In particular, the boundary arcs belong to circles which are orthogonal to the real axis. Any such perpendicular bisector does not intersect the interior of D_p, and a perpendicular bisector of an arc $\overline{p, gp}$ is mapped onto another such bisector.

Lemma 8.35. *If $p \in \mathbb{H}$ is not fixed by any element in G other than the identity, then $D_p(G)$ is a fundamental region for G. Two distinct points in $D_p(G)$ can only be congruent if they both lie on the boundary. The tessellation associated with a Dirichlet region is locally finite. This means that any compact subset of $\mathbb{H}$ intersects only finitely many of the domains congruent to D_p.*

Proof. Take any $z \in \mathbb{H}$. Any compact neighborhood of p contains only finitely many points of the orbit $Gz = \{gz \mid g \in G\}$. So there exists one which is closest to p, i.e., $z_1 := g_1 z$ satisfies

$$d(z_1, p) \le d(g z_1, p) = d(z_1, g^{-1} p) \quad \forall g \in G.$$

So $z_1 \in D_p(G)$. In other words, D_p contains a point of every G-orbit whence $\mathbb{H} = \bigcup_{g \in G} g D_p$.

Now assume that z is in the interior of D_p. Then $d(z, p) < d(z, gp)$ for all $g \in G$ other than the identity. Let $G \ni h \ne \mathrm{id}$. Then

$$d(hz, p) = d(z, h^{-1} p) > d(z, p) = d(hz, hp),$$

whence $hz \notin D_p$.

For the final statement, it suffices to fix a closed hyperbolic ball $K = \overline{B}(p, r)$ for some $r > 0$. Suppose that $K \cap g_n(D_p) \ne \emptyset$ for distinct $g_n \in G$. Thus, $w_n := g_n z_n \in K$ with $z_n \in D_p$ and

$$d(p, g_n p) \le d(p, w_n) + d(w_n, g_n p) = d(p, w_n) + d(z_n, p) \le 2 d(p, w_n) \le 2r,$$

where we used that $d(z_n, p) \le d(w_n, p)$ by definition of D_p. By local finiteness of orbits it follows that there can be only finitely many g_n and we are done. $\qquad \square$

We now turn to a discussion of possible fixed points of matrices in $\mathrm{PSL}(2, \mathbb{R})$; cf. Problem 4.3. Thus, consider $Tz = \frac{az+b}{cz+d}$ where $ad - bc = 1$ and $a, b, c, d \in \mathbb{R}$. If $|a + d| = 2$, then T has a unique fixed point on the extended real line $\mathbb{R} \cup \{\infty\}$. If $|a + d| < 2$, then it has a pair of fixed points on the extended real line (the *hyperbolic* case). If $|a + d| > 2$, then it has a pair of complex conjugate fixed points in $\mathbb{C}$ off the extended real line (the *elliptic* case). To understand the action of T in the case of a distinct pair of fixed points, draw all circles passing through such a pair. This family of circular arcs is invariant under T (but not necessarily the individual circles). Associated with these so-called *axes* is another family of circles, orthogonal to the axes. The configuration on the left of Figure 8.5 shows the action of T at hyperbolic fixed points, whereas the right-hand fixed-point pair is elliptic. Models of these maps are given by $z \mapsto \lambda z$ with $\lambda > 0$ (hyperbolic fixed point-point pair 0 and ∞), whereas the elliptic case is represented by $z \mapsto e^{i\theta} z$ (with the same fixed points). The parabolic maps are all conjugate to the translation $z \mapsto z + 1$. Problem 4.3 gives an alternative characterization of the different types of fixed points through the "normal form" (4.43) involving the parameter K.

Proposition 8.36. *Two nonidentity elements of a Fuchsian group G commute if and only if they have identical fixed points. In that case, these fixed points are of the same type.*

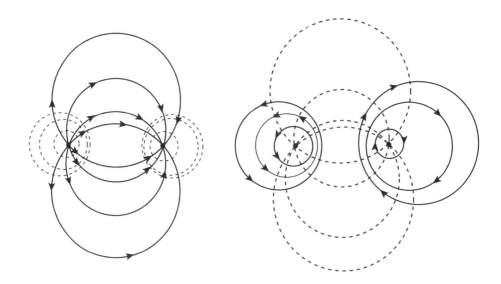

Figure 8.5.   The action near fixed points

Proof. Suppose $g, h \in G$ commute and $gp = p$. Then $g(hp) = h(gp) = hp$. Thus, h keeps the fixed-point set of g invariant. In the proof we shall reduce g to various specials forms (depending on the context) by conjugation fgf^{-1}.

For the parabolic case we take $G = \mathrm{PSL}(2, \mathbb{R})$ with the fixed point at ∞. Then $gz = z + 1$. If $gh = hg$, then $h\infty = \infty$ and so $hz = az + b$. But

$$hgz = h(z + 1) = az + b + a = az + b + 1 = ghz$$

requires $a = 1$ and so $hz = z + b$ with $b \in \mathbb{R}$.

In the hyperbolic case, we take $gz = \lambda z$ with $\lambda > 0$. Then h preserves the set $\{0, \infty\}$ and so it is either $hz = \mu z$, $\mu > 0$ or $hz = -\mu z^{-1}$. In the latter case (inversion) one checks that $gh = hg$ entails $\lambda = 1$, which is excluded.

In the elliptic case, we take $G = \mathrm{Aut}(\mathbb{D})$ and $gz = e^{i\theta}z$ a rotation. By Problem 4.2,

$$hz = \frac{az + \bar{b}}{bz + \bar{a}}, \quad |a|^2 - |b|^2 = 1.$$

By assumption

$$e^{i\theta}\frac{az + \bar{b}}{bz + \bar{a}} = \frac{ae^{i\theta}z + \bar{b}}{be^{i\theta}z + \bar{a}}.$$

If $b \neq 0$, then $e^{i\theta} = 1$, which is excluded. So $b = 0$ and $hz = e^{i\varphi}z$ as desired.

The final statement follows from the characterization of the types from the locations of the fixed points alone. $\square$

We can also read off from Figure 8.5 that the location of the fixed points determine their types: a pair of points on the real axis can only be hyperbolic since otherwise the individual circles in the family of axes would not be invariant, contradicting that the real axis is preserved. Likewise, a pair of conjugate fixed points can only be elliptic since otherwise the family of circles orthogonal to the axes would be moved within itself. This also shows that a Fuchsian group cannot exhibit any loxodromic fixed points (see Problem 4.3).

Corollary 8.37. *A Fuchsian group all of whose elements have the same fixed-point set is cyclic. In the hyperbolic and parabolic cases, the group is infinite cyclic, whereas in the elliptic case it is finite cyclic. In particular, abelian Fuchsian groups are cyclic and no Fuchsian group is therefore isomorphic to $\mathbb{Z} \times \mathbb{Z}$.*

Proof. By conjugation, we can assume in the hyperbolic case that G is a subgroup of the multiplicative group $\mathbb{R}^+$ via $z \mapsto \lambda z$; or after taking the logarithm, G is isomorphic to a discrete subgroup of the additive group $\mathbb{R}$. The only discrete subgroups of $\mathbb{R}$ are the cyclic ones, which are infinite. Likewise, in the parabolic case we are reduced to translations $z \mapsto z + b$, $b \in \mathbb{R}$ and the same argument applies.

In the elliptic case, we work with the disk and rotations about 0. So G is a discrete subgroup of S^1, and is thus finite and cyclic.

The final statement follows by combining these observations with Proposition 8.36.   □

The final statement in the corollary is relevant to Theorem 8.30. Indeed, we see again that no torus of genus 1 is of the form $\mathbb{D}/G$.

Suppose $z \in \mathbb{H}$ is a fixed point of some $g \in G$ which is not the identity. Then it is necessarily elliptic and by Corollary 8.37 g is of finite order. In fact, g lies in the stabilizer subgroup $\mathrm{Stab}_z(G) < G$ of z which is finite cyclic of degree $k \geq 2$. Any element hz in the orbit Gz is fixed by the map hgh^{-1}, which is again elliptic. The entire orbit lies on boundaries of fundamental regions in the tessellation induced by D_p. In particular, the intersection of Gz with D_p is called an *elliptic cycle* and the number of such cycles equals the number of noncongruent elliptic points in D_p.

The elements of $\mathrm{Stab}_z(G) < G$ map D_p onto other fundamental regions with z on the boundary. Thus, the angle that the boundary ∂D_p makes at the vertex z is $2\pi/k$. This includes π, as is the case for $k = 2$. This means that z is in the middle of a side and g exchanges to two boundary arcs to the left and right of z.

Lemma 8.38. *Let $\{v_j\}_{j-1}^{\ell}$ be an elliptic cycle on ∂D_p, with internal angles θ_j at these points. Let m be the order of the stabilizer subgroup of G associated with any of these points. Then*

$$(8.30) \qquad\qquad \sum_{j=1}^{\ell} \theta_j = \frac{2\pi}{m}.$$

Proof. First note that the stabilizer subgroups at two congruent points are conjugates of each other, and therefore have the same order.

We have $v_j = g_j v_1$ for $2 \leq j \leq \ell$. The elements of $\mathrm{Stab}_{v_1}(G)$ map D_p onto m congruent and pairwise disjoint regions (up to the boundaries) which meet at v_1 and each make an angle θ_1 at that vertex. Similarly, $\mathrm{Stab}_{v_j} = g_j \circ \mathrm{Stab}_{v_1} \circ g_j^{-1}$ generates m congruent copies of D_p making an angle θ_j at v_j. Next, we map this configuration via g_j^{-1} to v_1. By the tessellation property, we see that this process must cover a disk near v_1 (i.e., we cannot miss a sector) and (8.30) holds. $\qquad\square$

We deduce from the uniformization theorem that the quotient $\mathbb{D}/G$ can be both compact and noncompact. This justifies some more terminology.

Definition 8.39. We say that a Fuchsian group G is *co-compact* if $\mathbb{D}/G$ is compact.

We would naturally expect in the co-compact case that D_p has only finitely many vertices. This is indeed the case.

Lemma 8.40. *The vertices of a Dirichlet region associated with a Fuchsian group are isolated. In particular, a compact Dirichlet region has only finitely many vertices.*

Proof. Let $D_p(G)$ be such a region. The boundary consists of perpendicular bisectors of the geodesic segments joining p with gp, $g \in G$ not the identity. Any hyperbolic ball $K_r := \overline{B}(p, r)$ contains only finitely many of these points by the local finiteness of orbits. This implies that only finitely many such bisectors can intersect K_r since they must arise from points $gp \in K_{2r}$. This shows that any compact neighborhood of p contains only finitely many boundary segments of D_p as claimed. $\qquad\square$

If G is co-compact and operating on $\mathbb{D}$, denote the genus of $M := \mathbb{D}/G$ by γ. The genus is meaningful, since M always carries the structure of a topological manifold of dimension 2, and the Euler relation can be applied: $\chi(M) = 2 - 2\gamma$. If some nonidentity elements of G possess fixed points, then $\mathbb{D}/G$ is in general not a Riemann surface but an object called an *orbifold*; cf. Theorem 4.12 and Problem 5.8.

We shall now find a relation between the area of a fundamental region, well-defined by Lemma 8.33, the genus γ, and the *periods* of the elliptic cycles on any Dirichlet region $\partial D_p(G)$. The latter are defined as the order of the stabilizer group associated with a given (elliptic) cycle. They are well-defined by the group G and do not depend on the choice of $D_p(G)$. Indeed, the cycles are in one-to-one correspondence with conjugacy classes of maximal, nontrivial, cyclic subgroups of G.

Theorem 8.41. *Let $G < \mathrm{PSL}(2, \mathbb{R})$ be a co-compact Fuchsian group, and set $M := \mathbb{H}/G$. Define the co-area of G to be $\mu(M)$ which means the hyperbolic area of any Dirichlet region. Let γ be the genus of M and let $m_j \geq 2$, $1 \leq j \leq r$ denote the periods of G. Then*

$$(8.31) \qquad \mu(M) = 2\pi\Big(2\gamma - 2 + \sum_{j=1}^{r}(1 - 1/m_j)\Big).$$

Proof. Let F be any compact Dirichlet region for G. Let $V := \{v_n\}_{n=1}^{N}$ be the vertices of F. We decompose $V = V_0 \cup \bigcup_{j=1}^{r} V_j$ with V_0 being the vertices not fixed by any element of G other than the identity, whereas V_j, $1 \leq j \leq r$ is an enumeration of the cycles. We further organize the vertex set $V_0 = \bigcup_{k=1}^{s} W_k$ into cycles of congruent vertices. From the Gauss-Bonnet formula (see Theorem 1.15), and triangulation we obtain

$$\mu(F) = \pi(N - 2) - \sum_{n=1}^{N} \theta_n$$

with θ_n being the interior angle of F at the vertex v_n. From (8.30),

$$\sum_{n=1}^{N} \theta_n = 2\pi\Big(s + \sum_{j=1}^{r}\frac{1}{m_j}\Big).$$

M is homeomorphic to F with the boundary identifications on ∂F given by the congruence relation. Thus, with n denoting the number of edges *after identifying edges under congruence*,

$$2 - 2\gamma = \chi(M) = r + s - n + 1.$$

The edges of F are identified in pairs, whence $N = 2n$. This follows from the tessellation: for each edge on ∂F, there is exactly one congruent region gF which abuts to F along that edge. Recall at this point that we also count vertices with angle π, which is essential for this count. In summary,

$$\mu(F) = \pi(N-2) - 2\pi\Big(s + r + \sum_{j=1}^{r}\Big(\frac{1}{m_j} - 1\Big)\Big)$$

$$= 2\pi(n-1) - 2\pi\Big(1 - 2\gamma + n + \sum_{j=1}^{r}\Big(\frac{1}{m_j} - 1\Big)\Big)$$

$$= 2\pi\Big(2\gamma - 2 + \sum_{j=1}^{r}\Big(1 - \frac{1}{m_j}\Big)\Big),$$

as claimed.   □

One refers to $(\gamma, m_1, \ldots, m_r)$ as the *signature* of the co-compact Fuchsian group G. Poincaré's theorem states that (8.31) is the only obstruction. Thus, given a vector

$$(\gamma, m_1, \ldots, m_r)$$

with integer entries such that $\gamma \geq 0$, and $m_j \geq 2$ and such that the right-hand side of (8.31) is positive, there exists a co-compact group Fuchsian group of that signature. This is really only relevant to Theorem 8.30 provided G is fixed-point free, in other words, provided $r = 0$. In that case, the aforementioned positivity condition becomes $\gamma > 1$. So Poincaré's theorem implies the existence of a compact Riemann surface of any genus $\gamma > 1$, but by a *direct construction* of a quotient $\mathbb{D}/G$. On the other hand, we of course know that such a G exists from the uniformization theorem: starting from a compact orientable surface in $\mathbb{R}^3$ with genus $\gamma > 1$ (S^2 with γ handles attached), apply Theorem 8.30 to arrive at the same conclusion.

Many natural questions pose themselves at this point:

(Q_1) How does one characterize (or recognize) co-compact groups?

(Q_2) What role do parabolic vertices (necessarily on the extended real line) play?

(Q_3) How do we construct a Riemann surface starting from a geodesic polygon in $\mathbb{D}$ with identifications of the boundaries by elements of $\mathrm{Aut}(\mathbb{D})$? In other words, which conditions do we need to impose on such a polygon and the identifications via automorphisms to be sure that it gives rise to a fixed-point free properly discontinuous group action?

(Q_4) Given a noncompact surface such as $\mathbb{H}$ with two or more points removed, how do we find the Fuchsian group G so that this surface is isomorphic to $\mathbb{H}/G$? What do the Dirichlet regions associated to G look like?

(Q_5) Suppose M is a compact Riemann surface of genus $g > 1$. As we proved in preceding chapters, M is given by an irreducible algebraic equation $P(w, z) = 0$, and is isomorphic to a quotient $\mathbb{D}/G$. What is the relation between $P(w, z)$ and G?

We now state some results without detailed proofs. We leave it to the reader to explore these matters as well as similar questions further; see the notes for references.

For the first question Q_1 we have the following criterion: a Fuchsian group G is co-compact if and only if any Dirichlet region is compact. It is also necessary that G does not possess any parabolic elements. In fact, $G < \mathrm{Aut}(\mathbb{H})$ *is co-compact if and only if* $\mu(\mathbb{H}/G) < \infty$ *and* G *contains no parabolic elements.* The geometric meaning of parabolic transformations is revealed by their action on *horocycles*. These are circles in $\mathbb{H}$ tangent to the real line, including horizontal lines (tangent to ∞). The translations $z \mapsto z + 1$ leave these lines invariant. By conjugation, any parabolic transformation with fixed point $x \in \mathbb{R}$ leaves the horocycles tangent to $\mathbb{R}$ at x invariant.

Any vertex at infinity of a Dirichlet region is parabolic. To be more precise, we have the following theorem

Theorem 8.42. *Let* $G < \mathrm{PSL}(2, \mathbb{R})$ *have a noncompact Dirichlet region* D_p *of finite hyperbolic area. Then:*

- *each vertex of* D_p *at infinity is parabolic,*
- *if* x *is a fixed point of some parabolic element in* G, *then there exists* $g \in G$ *with* $gx \in \partial D_p$.

As for Question Q_3, Poincaré established the following converse to Theorem 8.42.

Theorem 8.43. *Let* $D \subset \bar{\mathbb{D}}$ *be closed (in the Euclidean topology), and bounded by finitely many geodesic arcs, as well as arcs on the unit circle, denoted by* $s_1, \ldots, s_n$ *and* $s'_1, \ldots, s'_n$. *Suppose there exist* $g_j \in \mathrm{Aut}(\mathbb{D})$ *with* $s'_j = g_j(s_j)$ *for* $1 \leq j \leq n$ *and such that each* g_j *is not elliptic. Further, suppose that* $g_j(D) \cap D = s'_j$, *and let* G *be the group generated by* $g_1, \ldots, g_n$. *If* D *has a vertex on* $\partial \mathbb{D}$ *which is not the endpoint of an arc on* $\partial \mathbb{D}$, *then assume that it is parabolic for* G. *Finally, assume that the sum of the interior angles at* G-*congruent vertices of* D *equals* 2π. *Then* G *is Fuchsian and* $\mathbb{D}/G$ *is a Riemann surface homeomorphic to* D *with the stated boundary identifications.*

Finally, for questions Q_4, Q_5 there is no general easy way of passing from one representation of a Riemann surface to another. Let us nevertheless offer some general comments. In order to represent $\mathbb{D}/G$ as an algebraic curve, as we have seen in previous chapters, it is necessary to construct sufficiently many meromorphic functions on this surface. To do this on an arbitrary compact Riemann surface, one has to solve linear PDEs, but in the case of $\mathbb{D}/G$ there is an easier way; namely, one can find many holomorphic modular forms on $\mathbb{D}/G$ using Poincaré series. Then one can construct meromorphic functions on this surface as ratios of holomorphic modular forms.

Notes

We have followed the classical potential theory approach to uniformization as in Ahlfors [2]; see also Beardon's text [6]. Irrespective of the technical approach chosen, uniformization hinges on the introduction of special meromorphic or harmonic functions on surfaces. This is to be expected, as the point of uniformization is of course to introduce global coordinates on a surface which then furnish examples of such functions (strictly speaking, in the compact case we cannot speak of a global coordinate unless we make ∞ an admissible value). Or to say this differently, we have to explain how to introduce complex numbers z on a general Riemann surface which of course means introducing an injective map into $\mathbb{C}_\infty$. For the modern approach based on $\bar{\partial}$-complex and Dolbeault cohomology, see Donaldson's course [18], or Varolin's book [84] in this series. Either of these texts would make for a natural and most beneficial second reading after this book. For ample historical evidence concerning the importance of "electrical fluids" to Riemann's early work, which we had alluded to in the beginning of this chapter, see Klein's text [51].

The reader is urged to consult Ahlfors' timeless monograph [2]. It has little overlap with this text other than through this uniformization chapter, and much important material of an inherently geometric nature is studied there. For example, Löwner's evolution, which was developed for the purpose of proving Bieberbach's conjecture and is presented in Chapter 6 of [2], lead to the resolution of long-standing open problems in statistical physics through SLE (Schramm-Löwner evolution); see Lawler's presentation of this exciting area [57]. The reader will also find an introduction to Teichmüller theory in [2], and the problem of moduli for Riemann surfaces.

For the geometrical results on isometric images of S^2 and conformal maps in $\mathbb{R}^3$ quoted in the final section, see do Carmo's books [15, 16]. The variational approach to Riemann surfaces based on harmonic mappings between surfaces is presented in Jost's book on compact Riemann surfaces [48].

The final section does not even scratch the surface of the vast landscape exhibited by discontinuous group actions on the disk. The literature on the topic is correspondingly vast, see for example [28, 7, 50, 59]. The study of functions on those Riemann surfaces becomes the study of automorphic functions, i.e., those analytic functions on the disk (or upper half-plane) which are invariant under the deck group. A fascinating account of the history of the subject is Hadamard's survey [39]. Theorem 8.42 is a standard result, see for example Theorem 4.2.5 in [50]. Poincaré's classical Theorem 8.43 is Theorem 9.3.1 in [6]. Poincaré's theorem on the sufficiency of (8.31) is Theorem 4.3.2 in Katok's book.

Quasi-conformal maps, which were mentioned briefly in the final section, constitute another large area that we did not develop at all here; see for example the recent book by Fletcher and Markovic [**26**].

8.8. Problems

Problem 8.1. Complete the proof of Corollary 8.13.

Problem 8.2. Suppose K has nonempty interior. Show that u_K as given by Definition 8.20 satisfies $u_K > 0$.

Problem 8.3. By combining various arguments of this chapter prove that the following are equivalent on any Riemann surface:

- the Green function $G(p, q)$ exists for one or every point q,
- the harmonic measure u_K exists as in Definition 8.20 for one or every compact K of nonempty interior,
- the maximum principle is not valid for one or every compact K.

Problem 8.4. Adapt the proof of the uniformization theorem from the parabolic case to compact surfaces. I.e., give an alternative, potential-theoretic proof of the fact that simply-connected compact Riemann surfaces are conformal to S^2, *without using* Riemann-Roch or the Hodge theorem as we did in earlier chapters.

Problem 8.5. This problem generalizes Problem 4.8 from tori to general Riemann surfaces. Let M be one of the standard simply-connected surfaces, and suppose $G_j < \mathrm{Aut}(M)$, $j = 1, 2$ are two subgroups acting properly discontinuously on M. Show that M/G_1 and M/G_2 are isomorphic if and only if G_1 and G_2 are conjugate subgroups of $\mathrm{Aut}(M)$. Clearly, only the case of $M = \mathbb{D}$ is really new here, the case of $M = \mathbb{C}$ being Problem 4.8, and $M = S^2$ trivial.

Problem 8.6. Show that the shaded region in Figure 4.7 is the Dirichlet region associated with the point $p = ik$, $k > 1$ arbitrary.

Problem 8.7. Show that no two distinct $\Delta_r = \{r < |z| < 1\}$ are conformally equivalent for $0 < r < 1$. Use the covering map $\pi_r : \mathbb{H} \to \Delta_r$ given by $\pi_r(z) = \exp\left(2\pi i b \log z\right)$ where $b \log r = -1$, and reduce this to the previous problem.

Problem 8.8. Let M be a hyperbolic surface described in Theorem 8.30. Assume that G is such that

$$\sum_{g \in G} (1 - |g(0)|) < \infty.$$

Show that

$$F(z) := -\sum_{g \in G} \log |g(z)|$$

converges and satisfies $F(gz) = F(z)$ for all $g \in G$. If $\pi : \mathbb{D} \to \mathbb{D}/G$ is the natural projection, prove that $F(\pi^{-1}z)$ is a Green function for $\mathbb{D}/G$.

Problem 8.9. The complex domains $\mathbb{C} \setminus \{0, 1\}$ and $\mathbb{D} \setminus \{0, 1/2\}$ are homeomorphic hyperbolic Riemann surfaces. Determine whether they are conformally isomorphic. Generalize to more than two removed points.

Suppose we remove n points from $\mathbb{C}$ where $n \geq 2$. Determine a necessary and sufficient condition for two such surfaces to be conformally isomorphic. Repeat for the case of the disk.

Problem 8.10. Show that all doubly-connected plane regions (i.e., $\Omega \subset \mathbb{C}$ open and connected with $\pi_1(\Omega) \simeq \mathbb{Z}$) are conformally equivalent to one of the following three:

- the punctured plane $\mathbb{C}^*$,
- the punctured disk $\mathbb{D}^*$,
- an annulus $\{r_0 < |z| < r_1\}$ with $0 < r_0 < r_1 < \infty$.

Problem 8.11. By means of the Jacobian variety we concluded in the previous chapter that all compact surfaces of genus $g = 1$ are standard tori. Deduce the same result by means of Theorem 8.30 by noting that the fundamental group of a torus is abelian and then analyzing which groups of Möbius transformations are of this type. You should find that only those generated by two translations give rise to such a surface.

Problem 8.12. For any meromorphic function f on some domain define the Schwarzian derivative to be

$$S_f(z) := \left(\frac{f''(z)}{f'(z)}\right)' - \frac{1}{2}\left(\frac{f''(z)}{f'(z)}\right)^2.$$

- Show that

$$S_{f \circ g}(z) = S_f(g(z))(g'(z))^2 + S_g(z)$$

  where $f \circ g$ is the composition of the maps.
- Check that $S_f = 0$ if $f(z) = az + b$ or $f(z) = 1/z$. Conclude that $S_{T \circ f} = S_f$ for any Möbius transform T. In particular, $S_T = 0$.
- Show that $S_f = 0$ implies that f is Möbius.

Problem 8.13. Let $\Omega \subset \mathbb{C}_\infty$ be simply-connected. Show that if $\text{Aut}(\Omega)$ contains only Möbius transformations then Ω is $\mathbb{C}, \mathbb{C}_\infty$ or a disk.

Problem 8.14. Give several examples of Fuchsian groups which act on the disk with fixed points, and so that the action is proper in the sense of Problem 5.8. Conclude that the quotient of the disk by the group action is a Riemann surface.

Review of some basic background material

A.1. Geometry and topology

A.1.1. Covering spaces and fundamental group.

Given two topological spaces X, Y and a map $p : X \to Y$, suppose that every point $y \in Y$ has a neighborhood U so that $p^{-1}(U) = \bigcup_\alpha V_\alpha$ as a disjoint union of open sets and $p : V_\alpha \to U$ is a homeomorphism, see Figure A.1. In that case, X covers Y with covering map p. The homeomorphism $\varphi : X \to X$ such that $p \circ \varphi = p$ form a group known as *deck transformations*.

As an example, the line $\mathbb{R}$ covers the circle S^1 by the map $p : x \mapsto e^{2\pi i x}$. The shift $T(x) = x + 1$ on the line satisfies $p \circ T = p$.

Covering spaces enjoy the following crucial lifting property. Suppose $c : [0,1] \to Y$ is any continuous curve and let $x \in X$ be such that $p(x) = c(0)$. Then there exists a unique lift of c to X starting at x. In other words, there exists $\widetilde{c} : [0,1] \to X$ a continuous curve with $\widetilde{c}(0) = x$ and $p \circ \widetilde{c} = c$. More generally, suppose $f : Z \to Y$ is a continuous map from a path connected and locally path connected space Z. If Z is, moreover, simply-connected, then we may lift f to a continuous map $\widetilde{f} : Z \to X$.

Covering spaces are closely related to the fundamental group $\pi_1(Y)$ which is defined as follows. Consider a point $y_0 \in Y$ and all continuous curves $c : [0,1] \to Y$ with $c(0) = c(1) = y_0$. In other words, we look at all loops that start and end at y_0. A group operation is defined on these loops by concatenation, which refers to the following new loop over the interval $[0,1]$: given two loops c_1, c_2, we define their product $c_2 * c_1$ as the continuous curve that traces out c_1 for $0 \le t \le \frac{1}{2}$, and then proceeds with

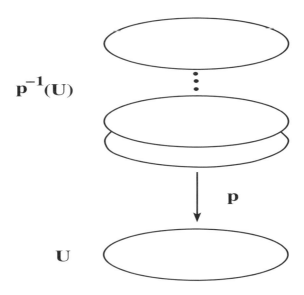

Figure A.1. A covering space

c_2 for $\frac{1}{2} \leq t \leq 1$. Finally, we identify any two loops which can be deformed continuously into each other, which means that one is obtained from the other via a homotopy. This process leads to a group, called the *fundamental group* at the point y_0 and denoted by $\pi_1(Y, y_0)$. If Y is path-connected then all these groups are the same up to a group isomorphism and one speaks of the fundamental group $\pi_1(Y)$ in that case.

If $p : X_0 \to Y$ defines a covering space, and if X_0 is simply-connected, then we say that X_0 is the *universal cover*. Such a topological space X_0 is unique up to a homeomorphism: if $\widetilde{p} : \widetilde{X}_0 \to X$ is another covering map with $\widetilde{X}_0$ simply-connected, then $X_0 \simeq \widetilde{X}_0$ in the sense of homeomorphisms. So there is only one universal cover. The group of deck transformations in that case equals (up to isomorphism) $\pi_1(Y)$. If $p : X \to Y$ defines any other covering space, then the deck transformations associated with this space form a subgroup of $\pi_1(Y)$. And to any subgroup of $\pi_1(Y)$ we may find a cover whose deck group equals that subgroup.

If Y is a Riemann surface, then by the local homeomorphism property of covering maps we may lift the complex structure to X. Every Riemann surface M has a universal cover in the topological sense from above, which inherits a conformal structure from M.

A.1.2. Homology and cohomology of surfaces. A *topological manifold* M is a second countable, connected, Hausdorff space, which is locally homeomorphic to open subsets of the plane. Note that we restrict ourselves to dimension 2. A curve in M is a continuous map $c : [0, 1] \to M$ and a

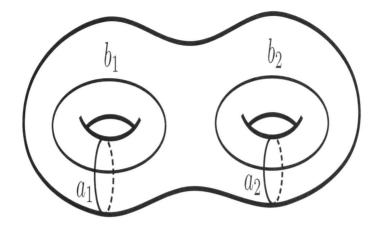

Figure A.2. A homology basis

closed curve satisfies $c(0) = c(1)$. On those curves, we define a *boundary operator* $\partial c := c(1) - c(0)$ which characterizes the closed curves c as all curves satisfying $\partial c = 0$. The difference of points here is a formal construction.

We further define a *0-cycle* to be an arbitrary finite sum $\sum_j m_j p_j$ where $m_j \in \mathbb{Z}$ and $p_j \in M$. A *1-cycle* is a formal finite sum of closed curves with integer coefficients $c := \sum_j n_j c_j$ where all c_j are closed curves. The boundary operator ∂ extends via linearity, i.e., $\partial c = \sum_j n_j \partial c_j$. We say that c is *closed* if $\partial c = 0$ and *exact* if $c = \partial \sigma$ where σ is a 2-cycle. The latter refers to a continuous map $f : [0,1]^2 \to M$. Naturally, the boundary of a 2-cycle is the closed curve c given as the restriction of f to the boundary $\partial[0,1]^2$ traversed counterclockwise.

Simplicial n-chains ξ_n are formal sums of n-simplicies, with $n = 0, 1, 2$. They form a group, which is also a module over the integers. The boundary operator ∂ extends to such chains by linearity. We say that an n-chain ξ_n is closed if $\partial \xi_n = 0$, and we say it is a boundary if $\xi_n = \partial \eta_{n+1}$ for an $n+1$-chain η_{n+1}. This only makes sense for $n = 0, 1$. The closed n-chains form a group denoted by Z_n, and the boundaries do, too, which we denote by B_n. By construction, $B_n < Z_n$. The *homology* groups of M, denoted by $H_k(M; \mathbb{Z})$ are defined as the quotients Z_n / B_n. These groups are defined for $n = 0, 1, 2$ where by definition, $B_2 := \{0\}$.

Returning to the homology groups, it is easy to see that $H_k(M; \mathbb{Z}) \simeq \mathbb{Z}$ for $k = 0, 2$, but somewhat deeper lies the fact that $H_1(M; \mathbb{Z}) \simeq \mathbb{Z}^{2g}$.

The dual concept to homology is cohomology, which is formulated in terms of differential forms. The concept of closed and exact chains which we encountered above is mirrored in the notions of closed and exact differential forms. Once again, we will consider quotients of closed by exact which in this case is a vector space over the reals. Remarkably, the *dimension count* is preserved and equals exactly the dimensions of the homology spaces $\mathbb{Z}^\ell$ which we just encountered. This is the content of de Rahm's cohomology to which we now turn.

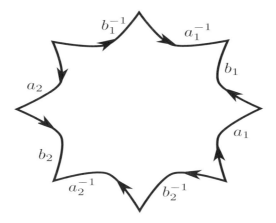

Figure A.3. The fundamental polygon of a compact surface of genus g

A.1.3. Differential forms. For the material here, see, for example, do Carmo [**17**], and Madsen, Tornehave [**61**]. Every differentiable manifold M carries vector fields, which are formally defined as smooth sections of the tangent bundle, and differential 1-forms, defined as smooth sections of the cotangent bundle. In local coordinates $(x^1, x^2, \ldots, x^n)$ with $n = \dim(M)$, a 1-form is given by

$$\omega = \sum_{j=1}^{n} a_j \, dx^j.$$

The coefficients a_j are smooth on some open set. If we change coordinates from x to y, then

$$\omega = \sum_{j,k=1}^{n} a_j \frac{\partial x^j}{\partial y^k} \, dy^k.$$

This is referred to as a covariant transformation rule of the coefficients. In contrast, vector fields transform contravariantly

$$v = \sum_{j=1}^{n} v^j \frac{\partial}{\partial x^j} \quad \longrightarrow \quad v = \sum_{j,k=1}^{n} v^j \frac{\partial y^k}{\partial x^j} \frac{\partial}{\partial y^k}.$$

More generally, the k-forms $\Omega^k(M)$ are smooth sections of the bundle $\Lambda^k(M)$ of alternating k-forms on M. In this book, $\dim(M) = 2$ and only $k = 0, 1, 2$ are relevant. However, $\Omega^0(M) = C^\infty(M)$ and $\Omega^2(M)$ is the space of the so-called volume forms.

This refers to the fact that

$$\int_M f\omega$$

is well-defined for every $f \in C^\infty(M)$ with compact support and $\omega \in \Omega^2(M)$. If M is orientable, as any Riemann surface is, then there exists a volume form ω_0 so that at every point $p \in M$ there are local coordinates (x, y) with $(x, y)(p) = (0, 0)$ and

$$\omega_0 = f(x, y)\, dx \wedge dy$$

with $f(0, 0) \neq 0$. This then implies that $\Omega^2(M) \simeq C^\infty(M)$ since every 2-form is a multiple of ω_0.

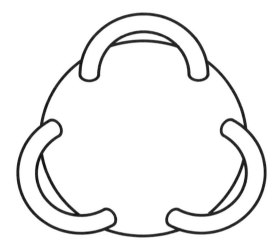

Figure A.4. A sphere with k handles has genus k

There are two operations on forms that we shall need: the *exterior product* denoted by $\wedge$, and the *exterior differentiation*, denoted by d. If $\omega_1 \in \Omega^{\ell_1}(M)$ and $\omega_2 \in \Omega^{\ell_2}(M)$, then

$$\omega_1 \wedge \omega_2 \in \Omega^{\ell_1 + \ell_2}(M), \qquad \omega_1 \wedge \omega_2 = (-1)^{\ell_1 \ell_2} \omega_2 \wedge \omega_1,$$

as well as

$$d(\omega_1 \wedge \omega_2) = (d\omega_1) \wedge \omega_2 + (-1)^{\ell_1} \omega_1 \wedge (d\omega_2), \quad d(f\omega) = df \wedge \omega + f\, d\omega$$

for any $f \in \Omega^0(M)$. In local coordinates,

$$df = \sum_{j=1}^{n} \frac{\partial f}{\partial x^j}\, dx^j,$$

$$d(a_j\, dx^j) = \sum_{j,k=1}^{n} \frac{\partial a_j}{\partial x^k}\, dx^k \wedge dx^j.$$

From the chain rule one verifies that exterior product and differentiation commute with pullbacks. I.e., if $f : M \to N$ is a smooth map between differentiable manifolds, then the pullback f^* satisfies

$$f^*(\omega \wedge \eta) = f^*\omega \wedge f^*\eta, \qquad d(f^*\omega) = f^*(d\omega)$$

for any differential forms ω, η on N. If S is a k-simplex, and ω a $k-1$-form, then *Stokes' theorem* is the relation

$$\int_S d\omega = \int_{\partial S} \omega$$

which can be viewed as a form of the fundamental theorem of calculus.

By equality of mixed partials $d^2 f = 0$, and $d^2\omega = 0$ for any $\omega \in \Omega^1$ because $d\Omega^2 = \{0\}$ (in fact, $d^2 = 0$ always). We say that $\omega \in \Omega^1(M)$ is *closed* if and only if $d\omega = 0$ and ω is *exact* if $\omega = df$ for some $f \in \Omega^0(M)$. By the preceding, *exact forms are closed*, but the converse is not true, the quintessential example being the angle form $d\theta$ in $\mathbb{R}^2 \setminus \{(0,0)\}$ where θ is the polar angle.

The Poincaré lemma says that *locally* all closed forms are exact. For 1-forms ω this is particularly easy: we may define $f(q) = \int_{p \to q} \omega$ where p is fixed and q is near p. Then by Stokes' theorem the integral does not depend on the path chosen to connect p to q. Indeed, we note that

$$\int_{\partial N} \omega = \int_N d\omega = 0,$$

where N is bounded by a finite number of smooth curves, for example.

Furthermore, from Poincaré's lemma and Stokes' theorem one obtains that for any closed 1-form ω,

$$\int_{c_1} \omega = \int_{c_2} \omega$$

if c_1, c_2 have the same endpoints and are homotopic. Similarly,

$$\oint_{c_1} \omega = \oint_{c_2} \omega$$

if c_1, c_2 are closed homotopic curves.

A.1.4. de Rham cohomology. Of great topological importance are the de Rham spaces, which are defined as closed forms modulo exact forms, i.e., for each $k \geq 1$,

$$H^k(M) := \{f \in \Omega^k(M) \, : \, df = 0\}/\{dg \, : \, g \in \Omega^{k-1}(M)\}.$$

If M is compact, then these spaces have finite dimension. The dimensions are the Betti numbers $\beta_k(M)$ and the de Rham theorem establishes that they agree with the dimensions (over $\mathbb{Z}$) of the homology groups. For us the only really relevant case is $k = 1$, whereas for $k = 2$ one has $H^2(M) \simeq \mathbb{R}$ due to the orientability of M. Finally, we note that the pullback via smooth maps is well-defined on the cohomology since it commutes with the exterior differentiation. Moreover, the pullback map on the cohomology is the same for any two smooth functions which are homotopic.

A.1.5. The degree. Next, we recall the notion of degree from topology and check that it coincides with the degree defined in Chapter 4 for Riemann surfaces. For the sake of this paragraph alone, let M, N be n-dimensional smooth orientable, connected compact manifolds. Then integration defines a linear isomorphism

$$H^n(M) \to \mathbb{R}, \quad [\omega] \mapsto \int_M \omega,$$

where $H^n(M)$ is the de Rham space of n-forms modulo exact n-forms. Let $f : M \to N$ be a smooth map and $f^* : H^n(N) \to H^n(M)$ the induced map defined via the pullback. There exists a real number denoted by $\deg(f)$ such that

$$\int_M f^*(\omega) = \deg(f) \int_N \omega \qquad \forall \omega \in H^n(N).$$

Since the pullback map on the cohomology spaces H^n only depends on the homotopy class, so does $\deg(f)$. It is also easy to see that it is multiplicative with regard to composition. Changing variables in charts, it is easy to verify that for any *regular* value $q \in N$, which means that $Df(p) : T_p M \to T_q N$ is invertible for every p with $f(p) = q$,

$$\deg(f) = \sum_{p \in M: \, f(p)=q} \mathrm{Ind}(f; p)$$

where $\mathrm{Ind}(f; p) = \pm 1$ depending on whether $Df(p)$ preserves or reverses the orientation. In particular, $\deg(f) \in \mathbb{Z}$ and $\deg(f) \neq 0$ implies that f is onto. By Sard's theorem, the regular values are always dense in N (an excellent reference for all of this is [**61**]). Returning to Riemann surfaces, we see that this notion of degree coincides exactly with the one from Chapter 4 since every analytic $f : M \to N$ necessarily preserves the orientation.

A.1.6. Euler characteristic. Every topological two-dimensional compact manifold M has an associated integer $\chi(M)$, called the Euler characteristic. It is defined as

$$V - E + F = \chi(M), \quad V = \text{vertices}, \ E = \text{edges}, \ F = \text{faces}$$

relative to an arbitrary triangulation of M (this is the *homological* characterization of $\chi(M)$); this is well-defined, in other words, $V - E + F$ does not depend on the particular choice of triangulation. Another important theorem relates the Euler characteristic with the genus g of M: if we realize M as S^2 with g handles attached, then we have the Euler-Poincaré formula

$$(A.1) \qquad\qquad \chi(M) = 2 - 2g.$$

Finally, let us recall the cohomological characterization of $\chi(M)$: let M be a compact, smooth two-dimensional manifold and let $H^k(M)$ denote the de Rham spaces of closed k forms modulo exact forms, $0 \le k \le 2$. Then, with $\beta_k := \dim H^k(M)$,

$$\chi(M) = \beta_0 - \beta_1 + \beta_2.$$

If M is orientable (as in the case of a Riemann surface), then it is easy to see that $\beta_0 = \beta_2 = 1$. Thus, $\beta_1 = 2g$ where g is the genus.

A compact surface M (recall that we are assuming $\dim M = 2$) is characterized by its genus g, and is in fact homeomorphic to a sphere with g handles attached; see Figure A.4. Equivalently, if $g \ge 1$ then the surface is homeomorphic to g doughnuts glued together. It is convenient to represent such a manifold via its *fundamental polygon*; see Figure A.3. This object is obtained by introducing the *homology basis* $a_1, a_2, \ldots, a_g, b_1, b_2, \ldots, b_g$ on the manifold; cf. Figure A.2. We then cut the surface along these curves observing the natural identifications. Conversely, we may reglue a fundamental polygon along its boundary to obtain the compact manifold back.

A.1.7. Curvature. In the first chapter of the book we discussed the hyperbolic plane, and we made a passing reference to its curvature, and to the Gauss Bonnet theorem. We therefore include in this appendix a brief discussion of these topics. We begin with a surface in $\mathbb{R}^3$.

Consider a smooth map $\vec{x} = \vec{x}(u,v) : U \to \mathbb{R}^3$ of maximal rank where $U \subset \mathbb{R}^2$ is open and connected. This means that $d\vec{x}$ has rank 2 and so $\vec{x}_u$ and $\vec{x}_v$ are linearly independent. We then call $\vec{x}$ (or $\vec{x}(U)$) a *smooth surface* in $\mathbb{R}^3$, and denote it by $\mathcal{S}$, say. The map $\vec{x}$ is then called a parameterization of $\mathcal{S}$. A *change of parameterization* refers to a (local) diffeomorphism Φ of (an open subset of) U onto some other open set $V = \Phi(U)$ with an induced new map $\vec{x} \circ \Phi$. In geometry, we are only interested in concepts which *do not depend on the choice of parameterization*. In other words, they need to be invariant under changes of coordinates.

If $\vec{x}$ is a homeomorphism onto its image, then we say that this surface is embedded. There is a natural normal vector the the surface given by the cross product

$$\vec{N} = \frac{\vec{x}_u \times \vec{x}_v}{\|\vec{x}_u \times \vec{x}_v\|},$$

where the length in the denominator is the Euclidean one. There is an ambiguity in the choice of sign, and assigning an orientation means choosing

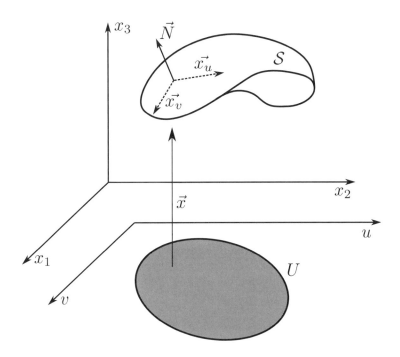

Figure A.5. A parametrized surface

one of these signs. The *first fundamental form* on $\mathcal{S}$ refers to the induced Euclidean metric on the surface. In coordinates

$$ds^2 = E\,du^2 + 2F\,du dv + G\,dv^2, \quad E = \|\vec{x}_u\|^2,\ F = \langle \vec{x}_u, \vec{x}_v \rangle,\ G = \|\vec{x}_v\|^2.$$

This metric determines the way in which lengths of curves $\gamma : [0,1] \to \mathcal{S}$ are measured on $\mathcal{S}$:

$$L(\gamma) = \int_0^1 \|\dot{\gamma}(t)\|\,dt,$$

where $\|\dot{\gamma}(t)\|$ is the Euclidean length in the ambient space $\mathbb{R}^3$. In coordinates, we may write $\gamma(t) = \vec{x}(u(t), v(t))$ which gives

$$L(\gamma)$$
$$= \int_0^1 \sqrt{E(u(t), v(t))\,\dot{u}^2(t) + 2F(u(t), v(t))\,\dot{u}(t)\dot{v}(t) + G(u(t), v(t))\,\dot{v}(t)^2}\,dt.$$

Since these two formulas agree, and the first does not depend on coordinates, it follows immediately that length is coordinate invariant. Areas are naturally computed as follows:

$$\mathrm{Area}(\mathcal{S}) = \int_U \sqrt{EG - F^2}\,dudv.$$

It follows from the algebra of determinants and the substitution formula for integrals that this is also invariant under a change of coordinates.

Notions such as length and area which only depend on the first fundamental form (i.e., the metric on S) are called *intrinsic* since they make no
reference to the ambient space. In other words, it is not important how
the surface sits in $\mathbb{R}^3$. For example, we may cut a cylinder along a line and
unroll it into the plane. The way in which we measure lengths is not affected
by this process, but clearly the planar surface has less "curvature" than the
first one—at least in a naive sense.

To make all of this more precise, we define the *second fundamental form*
as follows. Given any point $p \in S$, set

$$S_p(\vec{\xi}, \vec{\eta}) := -\langle d\vec{N}(p)\vec{\xi}, \vec{\eta}\rangle,$$

where $\vec{\xi}, \vec{\eta} \in \mathbb{R}^3$ are tangent to S at p. The differential $d\vec{N}(p)$ is not well-
defined per se on the surface. But note that $d\vec{N}(p)\vec{\xi}$ is well-defined since it
equals

$$d\vec{N}(p)\vec{\xi} = \frac{d}{dt}\bigg|_{t=0} \vec{N}(c(t)), \quad c(0) = p, \ \dot{c}(0) = \vec{\xi}.$$

So S_p is a quadratic form defined in the tangent space $T_p(M)$, and by construction it does not depend on the choice of coordinates. It turns out to
be a *symmetric quadratic form* and thus associated to a symmetric 2×2
matrix. To prove this, it suffices to observe that for a surface given locally
as a graph of some function f the second fundamental at a point p where
$df = 0$ coincides with the Hessian Hf of f at p.

The eigenvalues of this matrix are called *principal curvatures* at p, and
denoted $\kappa_1(p), \kappa_2(p)$. They are clearly *not intrinsic*, since the cylinder and
plane have different principal curvatures; for the latter they both vanish,
whereas for the former one of them is not zero, in fact it equals $1/r$ where
$r > 0$ is the radius of the cylinder.

To find the principal curvatures, we typically need to compute in coordinates. The second fundamental form is then associated with the matrix

$$B := \begin{pmatrix} L & M \\ M & N \end{pmatrix}, \ L = -\vec{N}_u \cdot \vec{x}_u, \ M = -\vec{N}_u \cdot \vec{x}_v, \ N = -\vec{N}_v \cdot \vec{x}_v.$$

This means that

$$S_p(a_1\vec{x}_u + b_1\vec{x}_v, a_2\vec{x}_u + b_2\vec{x}_v) = La_1a_2 + M(a_1b_2 + a_2b_1) + Na_2b_2.$$

Then finding the principal curvatures is the same as solving the quadratic
polynomial

$$\det(B - \lambda A) = 0, \quad A := \begin{pmatrix} E & F \\ F & G \end{pmatrix}.$$

The Gaussian curvature is defined as $K := \kappa_1 \kappa_2$. In terms of the first and second fundamental forms it equals

$$K = \frac{\det B}{\det A} = \frac{LN - M^2}{EG - F^2}.$$

Gauss' *Theorema Egregium* asserts that the product $K(p)$ *is intrinsic.* This shows for example that no planar map of the earth can correctly represent true geographic lengths and areas. Assuming as we may that the first fundamental form is diagonal, i.e., $F = 0$, then this fact follows from an explicit computation of the Gaussian curvature which establishes

$$(A.2) \qquad K = -\frac{1}{2\sqrt{EG}} \left(\frac{\partial}{\partial u} \frac{G_u}{\sqrt{EG}} + \frac{\partial}{\partial v} \frac{E_v}{\sqrt{EG}} \right).$$

The Theorema Egregium is the starting point of modern geometry. Indeed, it shows that we may introduce curvature on an abstract two-dimensional manifold endowed with a metric

$$ds^2 = \sum_{i,j=1}^{2} g_{ij} \, dx^i dx^j$$

without any reference to an ambient space. For example, for the metric of the hyperbolic plane, i.e.,

$$ds^2 = \frac{dx^2 + dy^2}{y^2}$$

formula (A.2) produces the value $K = -1$. Integrating K over a compact surface $\mathcal{S}$ gives

$$(A.3) \qquad \int_{\mathcal{S}} K \, d\,\mathrm{vol} = 2\pi \chi(\mathcal{S})$$

where $\chi(\mathcal{S})$ is the Euler characteristic. If T is a triangle in $\mathcal{S}$ all of whose edges are geodesics, then

$$(A.4) \qquad \int_{T} K \, d\,\mathrm{vol} = 2\pi + \sum_{j=1}^{3} (\alpha_j - \pi)$$

where α_j are the interior angles at the vertices. This is the Gauss-Bonnet theorem. By a triangulation of $\mathcal{S}$ and summing, (A.4) implies (A.3).

A.2. Algebra

A.2.1. Resultants and discriminants. For the material here, see, for example, [**56**]. Given two relatively prime polynomials $P, Q \in \mathbb{C}[w, z]$, there exist $A, B \in \mathbb{C}[w, z]$ such that

$$A(w,z)P(w,z) + B(w,z)Q(w,z) = R(z) \in \mathbb{C}[z],$$

is a *nonzero* polynomial in z alone; it is called the *resultant* of P and Q. If P and Q are not relatively prime, then we set $R = 0$. The proof of this fact is Euclid's algorithm carried out in the polynomials in $K(z)[w]$ where $K(z)$ is the quotient field of $\mathbb{C}[z]$, i.e., the field of rational functions of z. The resultant has many interesting properties, for example, if both P and Q have leading coefficient 1, then

$$R(z) = \prod_{\zeta_j, \eta_k} (\zeta_j(z) - \eta_k(z)),$$

where ζ_j runs over all zeros of $P(w, z)$ and η_k runs over all zeros of $Q(w, z)$ in w, respectively. Thus, $R(z_0) = 0$ if and only if $P(w, z_0)$ and $Q(w, z_0)$ have a common zero in w. Moreover, with

$$P(w, z) = \sum_{j=0}^{n} a_j(z) w^j, \qquad Q(w, z) = \sum_{k=0}^{m} b_k(z) w^k,$$

it follows that $R(z)$ equals the following determinant in the coefficients a_j, b_k:

(A.5)
$$\begin{vmatrix}
\overbrace{a_k \quad 0}^{m} \quad \cdots & \overbrace{b_m \quad 0 \quad \cdots \quad 0}^{n} \\
a_{k-1} \quad a_k \quad \cdots & b_{m-1} \quad b_m \quad \cdots \quad \cdots \\
a_{k-2} \quad a_{k-1} \quad \cdots & b_{m-2} \quad b_{m-1} \quad \cdots \quad \cdots \\
\cdots \quad \cdots \quad \cdots & \cdots \quad \cdots \quad \cdots \quad \cdots \\
a_0 \quad a_1 \quad \cdots & \cdots \quad \cdots \quad \cdots \quad \cdots \\
0 \quad a_0 \quad \cdots & \cdots \quad \cdots \quad \cdots \quad \cdots \\
0 \quad 0 \quad \cdots & \cdots \quad \cdots \quad \cdots \quad \cdots \\
\cdots \quad \cdots \quad \cdots & \cdots \quad \cdots \quad \cdots \quad \cdots
\end{vmatrix}.$$

The resultant makes sense for polynomials $P(z)$ of a single variable as well, just by adding w as a dummy variable. The *discriminant* of a polynomial $P(z)$ is the resultant of $P(z)$ and its derivative $P'(z)$. It vanishes if and only if P has a double zero.

A.2.2. Cyclotomic polynomials. Section 5.5 made use of cyclotomic polynomials. They are defined as follows: given an integer $N \geq 1$ consider the Nth roots of unity, i.e., all solutions of $\zeta^N = 1$. They form a cyclic group. A *primitive root* is a generator of this group. These are given precisely by the exponentials $\zeta_k := \exp\left(2\pi i k/N\right)$ where $1 \leq k \leq N$ and k, N are relatively prime; in other words, with $\gcd(k, N) = 1$. The cyclotomic polynomial χ_N is defined as

$$\chi_N(z) = \prod_{\substack{1 \leq k \leq N \\ \gcd(k, N) = 1}} (z - \zeta_k).$$

In other words, we only retain the factors $z - \zeta$ where ζ is a primitive N^{th} root of unity. There are exactly $\phi(N)$ of these roots where ϕ is the Euler totient function counting the number of integers $1 \leq n \leq N$ which are relatively prime to N. If p is a prime, then $\phi(p) = p - 1$. For prime powers we have $\phi(p^k) = p^k - p^{k-1}$. From the Chinese remainder theorem it follows that ϕ is multiplicative:

$$\phi(mn) = \phi(m)\phi(n), \quad \gcd(n, m) = 1.$$

In summary,

$$\phi(N) = N \prod_{p|N} \left(1 - p^{-1}\right),$$

where the product runs over all prime divisors of N.

It was already shown by Gauss that the cyclotomic polynomials are irreducible. The factorization

$$z^N - 1 = \prod_{d|N} \chi_d(z)$$

is therefore the decomposition into prime factors. As far as the degrees are concerned, we note that we have agreement because of the elementary relation

$$N = \sum_{d|N} \phi(d), \quad \phi(1) := 1.$$

A.3. Analysis

A.3.1. Hilbert space. A *Hilbert space* is a vector space V (over the real or the complex fields) with an inner product $\langle \cdot, \cdot \rangle$ such that in the induced topology the resulting metric space is *complete*, i.e., Cauchy sequences converge. If $E \subset V$ is a closed subspace, then there exists a linear map $P : V \to V$ which is continuous (in other words, a *bounded operator*) and represents the *orthogonal projection* onto E. This means that the range of P is exactly E, that P acts as the identity on E, and that the kernel of P which we denote by $E^\perp$ is the subspace of all vectors perpendicular to E. The existence of P rests on the assumed completeness of the Hilbert space. For any vector $v \in V$ it is realized as the minimizing vector $v_E \in E$ which makes the distance $\text{dist}(v, v_E)$ as small as possible. In other words, it realizes

$$\inf\{\text{dist}(v, w) \mid w \in E\}.$$

The important fact here is that this infimum is indeed attained. It is a nice exercise in Euclidean geometry to prove that any minimizing sequence is Cauchy and therefore converges to the sought after minimum.

Orthogonal projections may also be characterized directly on the level of bounded operators. Indeed, suppose P is such a bounded linear operator which satisfies $P^2 = P$ and $P^* = P$. The latter condition refers to the *adjoint* of P which is defined by the relation

$$\langle Pv, w \rangle = \langle v, P^*w \rangle \quad \forall\, v, w \in V.$$

Then P^* is another bounded linear operator, in fact, its norm defined by

$$\|P^*\| = \sup_{\|v\|=1} \|P^*v\|$$

is the same as $\|P\|$.

Under the two conditions $P^2 = P$ and $P^* = P$ it turns out that P is an orthogonal projection onto E given by the range of P. This is easy to see, since we may write

$$v = Pv + (1 - P)v$$

for any $v \in V$. But

$$P(1 - P)v = (P - P^2)v = 0$$

whence $(1 - P)v \in \ker P$. Moreover, $P(Pv) = Pv \in E$,

$$\langle Pv, (1 - P)v \rangle = \langle v, P^*(1 - P)v \rangle = \langle v, P(1 - P)v \rangle = 0,$$

so that we have an orthogonal decomposition into an element of E and $E^\perp$, respectively.

A fundamental result in Hilbert spaces is the *Riesz representation theorem* which asserts that any continuous linear functional ϕ (in other words, an element of the dual space of V) is given by a scalar product: there exists $w \in V$ with

$$\phi(v) = \langle v, w \rangle, \quad \forall\, v \in V,$$

and we have identification of norms: $\|\phi\| = \|w\|$. This, in particular, says that the dual space of a Hilbert space is isometric to the Hilbert space itself.

On the level of topology, next to the Euclidean one, the *weak topology* plays a fundamental role. It is defined as the coarsest topology (the one with the fewest open sets) which renders each linear functional $v \mapsto \langle v, w \rangle$ continuous. In other words, a basis for the open sets is given by the half-spaces

$$\{ v \in V \mid \langle v, w \rangle < \lambda \}, \qquad \lambda \in \mathbb{R},\ w \in V.$$

This is for the case of the real field with obvious modifications for the complex one. Of critical importance in Chapter 3 is the *compactness of the closed unit ball* in the weak topology. The unit ball is not compact in the strong topology in infinite dimensions (for example, take an infinite orthonormal sequence), but it is a remarkable fact that in the thinner weak topology compactness property of the ball survives when we move from finite dimensions to infinite dimensions.

A fundamental class of theorems in Hilbert space theory deals with the generalization of the spectral theorem for Hermitian matrices to infinite dimensions. This refers to the fact that Hermitian matrices are diagonalized by an orthonormal basis of eigenvectors. However, we make no use of this type of result in this book.

A.3.2. Banach spaces. Given a measure space (X, μ) where we assume that μ is a positive, σ-finite Borel measure, we define the L^p spaces as all measurable complex-valued functions $f : X \to \mathbb{C}$ with the property that

$$\|f\|_p^p := \int_X |f(x)|^p \, \mu(dx) < \infty$$

where $1 \leq p < \infty$. For $p = \infty$ we require the *essential supremum* to be finite. By Hölder's (or Minkowski's) inequalities, $\| \cdot \|_p$ satisfies the triangle inequality and thus defines a norm. Thus, the L^p spaces are normed linear spaces which are complete in the metric sense. In other words, the L^p spaces are *Banach spaces*.

The dual spaces, meaning the linear spaces of all *bounded linear functionals* on $L^p(X, \mu)$, are canonically isomorphic to $L^{p'}(X, \mu)$ where

$$\frac{1}{p} + \frac{1}{p'} = 1$$

is the dual exponent. For this we need to assume that $1 \leq p < \infty$. The functional given by $g \in L^{p'}(X, \mu)$ is simply integration

$$f \mapsto \int_X f(x) \bar{g}(x) \, \mu(dx)$$

By Hölder's inequality the absolute value of the right-hand side is $\leq \|f\|_p \|g\|_{p'}$ and this bound is achieved. Thus each such integral does define a bounded linear functional. In fact, *all* functionals arise in this fashion.

Three basic theorems in Banach spaces X are the *Hahn-Banach, open mapping, and uniform boundedness* theorems. The final two do not appear in this text, but the Hahn-Banach theorem is used in the proof of Runge's theorem in Chapter 2. The Hahn-Banach theorem can be formulated in a number of ways. The best one, at least to the author, is the geometric formulation:

Any closed convex set $K \subset X$ can be separated from a point $x_0 \in X$ outside of itself by means of a closed subspace.

Naively speaking, this seems obvious. But the issue here is that we are working in infinitely many dimensions and asserting the existence of a closed subspace is equivalent to asserting the existence of a *bounded linear functional* which is positive at x_0 but negative on K. This is why the Hahn-Banach theorem is often formulated in a more technically sounding way, namely that bounded linear functionals defined on subspaces of X can be extended to all of X without increasing the norm of the functional. This is the formulation which was used in the proof of Runge's theorem.

A Banach space (and thus in particular the L^p spaces from above) carries a weak topology which is defined exactly as in the case of Hilbert spaces; while we have no inner product in general, we may still define the weak topology as the coarsest one which makes all linear functionals continuous. In general, the unit ball is *not weakly compact* as the example of an approximate identity in $L^1(\mathbb{T})$ shows. However, suppose that a Banach space is the dual of another, say Y. In symbols, $X = Y^*$. Examples are precisely the L^p spaces from above with $1 < p < \infty$. Another very important example are the complex measures on $\mathbb{R}^n$ (or more general, on any locally compact Hausdorff space) of finite total variation: they form a Banach space with the total variation norm, which is the dual of all continuous functions vanishing at infinity. In those cases, the *Alaoglu theorem* asserts that the unit ball of X is compact in the weak-$*$ topology. The latter is defined as the coarsest topology which makes all *evaluation functionals* on X given by $x \mapsto x(y)$ for $y \in Y$ arbitrary but fixed, continuous.

A.3.3. Interpolation of operators. In Chapter 3 we also make use of the following two fundamental interpolation theorems. We only state the results, and refer the reader to standard references, such as Stein, Weiss [**78**]. The first one is due to Riesz-Thorin.

Theorem A.1. *Let (X, μ) be a measure space. Suppose $1 \leq p_1, p_2 \leq \infty$ and assume that $Y \subset L^{p_1}(X, \mu) \cap L^{p_2}(X, \mu)$ is a subspace which is dense in both $L^{p_1}(X, \mu)$ and $L^{p_2}(X, \mu)$. Let T be a linear operator defined on Y that takes its values in the measurable functions on some other space $(\widetilde{X}, \widetilde{\mu})$ in such a way that $\forall f \in Y$ one has*

$$\|Tf\|_{L^{q_j}(\widetilde{X}, \widetilde{\mu})} \leq A_j \|f\|_{L^{p_j}(X, \mu)} \quad j = 1, 2$$

where $1 \leq q_1, q_2 \leq \infty$. Then

$$\|Tf\|_{L^q(\widetilde{X}, \widetilde{\mu})} \leq A_1^\theta A_2^{1-\theta} \|f\|_{L^p(X, \mu)} \quad \forall f \in Y,$$

where

(A.6)
$$\frac{1}{p} = \frac{\theta}{p_1} + \frac{1-\theta}{p_2}, \quad \frac{1}{q} = \frac{\theta}{q_1} + \frac{1-\theta}{q_2}$$

for all $0 \leq \theta \leq 1$.

As with Hölder's inequality, this interpolation result is based on convexity, precisely *log-convexity*. The standard proof relies on the three-lines theorem from complex analysis, which states that the maximum of the absolute value along vertical lines of a function holomorphic in a vertical strip is log-convex. See Problem 3.8.

Next to operators which are bounded on Lebesgue spaces, we also need the following weak-type property. Let T be a map from $L^p(X, \mu)$ to the measurable functions on $(\widetilde{X}, \widetilde{\mu})$. For $1 \leq q < \infty$ we say that T is weak-type (p, q) if and only if

$$\widetilde{\mu}(\{x \in \widetilde{X} \mid |(Tf)(x)| > \lambda\}) \leq A\lambda^{-q}\|f\|^q_{L^p(X,\mu)} \qquad \forall \lambda > 0$$

for all $f \in L^p(X, \mu)$. We further define weak-type (p, ∞) to be the same as strong-type (p, ∞), which simply means bounded in the usual Lebesgue sense. In the following *Marcinkiewicz interpolation theorem* we allow operators T to be quasi-linear which means that for some constant $\kappa > 0$ one has

$$|T(f_1 + f_2)| \leq \kappa(|f_1| + |f_2|)$$

for all step functions f_1, f_2.

Theorem A.2. *Suppose* $1 \leq p_1 < p_2 < \infty$ *and* $q_j \geq p_j$ *with* $q_1 \neq q_2$. *Let* (p, q) *be as in* (A.6) *with* $0 < \theta < 1$. *If* T *is a quasilinear operator which is weak-type* (p_j, q_j) *for* $j = 1, 2$, *then* T *is strong-type* (p, q).

This is proved by breaking functions up according to the sizes of level sets. It applies in the wider context of Lorentz spaces. To be more specific, one can weaken the hypotheses of Theorem A.2 further by requiring only weak-type bounds when T is applied to indicator functions of sets. This is referred to as *restricted weak-type* (p, q) and the resulting interpolation theorem can be very helpful in applications.

Bibliography

[1] Ahlfors, L., *Complex analysis. An introduction to the theory of analytic functions of one complex variable.* Third edition. International Series in Pure and Applied Mathematics. McGraw-Hill Book Co., New York, 1978

[2] Ahlfors, L., *Conformal invariants. Topics in geometric function theory.* Reprint of the 1973 original. With a foreword by Peter Duren, F. W. Gehring and Brad Osgood. AMS Chelsea Publishing, Providence, RI, 2010.

[3] Ahlfors, L., Sario, L. *Riemann surfaces*, Princeton University Press, 1960.

[4] Alekseev, V. B., *Abel's theorem in problems and solutions. Based on the lectures of Professor V. I. Arnold.* With a preface and an appendix by Arnold and an appendix by A. Khovanskii. Kluwer Academic Publishers, Dordrecht, 2004.

[5] Ash, R., Novinger, W. *Complex variables: Second Edition*, Dover, Mineola, N.Y., 2004.

[6] Beardon, A., *A primer on Riemann surfaces*, London Mathematical Society Lecture Notes Series 78. Cambridge University Press, Cambridge, 1984.

[7] Beardon, A., *The geometry of discrete groups.* Corrected reprint of the 1983 original. Graduate Texts in Mathematics, 91. Springer-Verlag, New York, 1995.

[8] Beardon, A., *Algebra and geometry.* Cambridge University Press, Cambridge, 2005.

[9] Beukers, F., Heckman, G., *Monodromy for the hypergeometric function $_nF_{n-1}$.* Invent. Math. 95 (1989), no. 2, 325–354.

[10] Chandrasekharan, K. *Elliptic functions.* Grundlehren der Mathematischen Wissenschaften, 281. Springer-Verlag, Berlin, 1985.

[11] Chern, S. S., *Proceedings of the American Mathematical Society*, Vol. 6, No. 5 (1955), 771–782.

[12] Conway, J. *Functions of one complex variable*, Springer, Second Edition, 1978.

[13] Costin, O., Costin, R. D. *On the formation of singularities of solutions of nonlinear differential systems in antistokes directions.* Invent. Math. 145 (2001), no. 3, 425–485.

[14] Dixon, J., *A brief proof of Cauchy's integral theorem.* Proc. Amer. Math. Soc. 29 (1971), 625–626.

[15] do Carmo, M., *Diffferential geometry of curves and surfaces*, Prentice Hall, 1976.

[16] do Carmo, M., *Riemannian geometry*, Birkhäuser, Boston 1992.

[17] do Carmo, M., *Differential forms and applications*. Universitext. Springer-Verlag, Berlin, 1994.

[18] Donaldson, S., *Riemann surfaces*. Oxford Graduate Texts in Mathematics, 22. Oxford University Press, Oxford, 2011.

[19] Dubrovin, B. A., *Theta-functions and nonlinear equations*. With an appendix by I. M. Krichever. Uspekhi Mat. Nauk 36 (1981), no. 2(218), 11–80.

[20] Dubrovin, B. A., Krichever, I. M., Novikov, S. P. *Topological and algebraic geometry methods in contemporary mathematical physics*. Classic Reviews in Mathematics and Mathematical Physics, 2. Cambridge Scientific Publishers, Cambridge, 2004

[21] Ekedahl, T., *One semester of elliptic curves*. EMS Series of Lectures in Mathematics, European Mathematical Society (EMS), Zürich, 2006.

[22] Evans, L., *Partial differential equations*, AMS, Graduate Studies in Mathematics, vol. 19, 1998.

[23] Farkas, H., Kra, I., *Riemann surfaces*. Second edition. Graduate Texts in Mathematics, 71. Springer-Verlag, New York, 1992.

[24] Fay, J. *Theta functions on Riemann surfaces*. Lecture Notes in Mathematics, Vol. 352. Springer-Verlag, Berlin-New York, 1973.

[25] Feldman, J., Knörrer, H., Trubowitz, E. *Riemann surfaces of infinite genus*. CRM Monograph Series, 20. American Mathematical Society, Providence, RI, 2003.

[26] Fletcher, A., Markovic, V., *Quasiconformal maps and Teichmueller theory*, Oxford Graduate Texts in Mathematics, 11, Oxford University Press, Oxford, 2007.

[27] Folland, G. B., *Introduction to partial differential equations*. Second edition. Princeton University Press, Princeton, NJ, 1995.

[28] Ford, L., *Automorphic functions*, McGraw-Hill, 1929.

[29] Forster, O., *Lectures on Riemann surfaces*. Reprint of the 1981 English translation. Graduate Texts in Mathematics, 81. Springer-Verlag, New York, 1991.

[30] Fuchs, E., Meiri, C., Sarnak, P., *Hyperbolic monodromy groups for the hypergeometric equation and Cartan involutions*, arXiv:1305.0729 [math.GR], 2013.

[31] Garnett, J., *Bounded analytic functions*. Revised first edition. Graduate Texts in Mathematics, 236. Springer, New York, 2007.

[32] Garnett, J., Marshall, D., *Harmonic measure*. New Mathematical Monographs, 2. Cambridge University Press, Cambridge, 2005.

[33] Gesztesy, F., Holden, H., *Soliton equations and their algebro-geometric solutions*. Vol. I. (1+1)-dimensional continuous models. Cambridge Studies in Advanced Mathematics, 79. Cambridge University Press, Cambridge, 2003.

[34] Godement, R. *Analyse mathématique. III.* Fonctions analytiques, différentielles et variétés, surfaces de Riemann. Springer-Verlag, Berlin, 2002.

[35] Griffiths, P., *Introduction to algebraic curves.* Translations of Mathematical Monographs, 76. American Mathematical Society, Providence, RI, 1989.

[36] Griffiths, P., Harris, J., *Principles of algebraic geometry.* Reprint of the 1978 original. Wiley Classics Library. John Wiley & Sons, Inc., New York, 1994.

[37] Gunning, R. C., *Riemann surfaces and generalized theta functions*. Ergebnisse der Mathematik und ihrer Grenzgebiete, Band 91. Springer-Verlag, Berlin-New York, 1976.

[38] Gunning, R. C., *Lectures on Riemann surfaces.* Princeton Mathematical Notes, Princeton University Press, Princeton, N.J., 1966.

[39] Hadamard, J., *Non-Euclidean geometry in the theory of automorphic functions*, AMS, 1999.

[40] Han, Q., Lin, F., *Elliptic partial differential equations*. Second edition. Courant Lecture Notes in Mathematics, 1. Courant Institute of Mathematical Sciences, New York; American Mathematical Society, Providence, RI, 2011.

[41] Hancock, H., *Lectures on the theory of elliptic functions: Analysis*. Dover Publications, Inc., New York 1958

[42] Hartman, P., *Ordinary differential equations*. Reprint of the second edition. Birkhäuser, Boston, Mass., 1982.

[43] Hoffman, K., *Banach spaces of analytic functions*. Reprint of the 1962 original. Dover Publications, Inc., New York, 1988.

[44] Hurwitz, A., Courant, R., *Vorlesungen über allgemeine Funktionentheorie und elliptische Funktionen*. Interscience Publishers, Inc., New York, (1944).

[45] Israel, G., Nurzia, L., *The Poincaré-Volterra theorem: a significant event in the history of the theory of analytic functions*. Historia Math. 11 (1984), no. 2, 161–192.

[46] Jänich, K. *Einführung in die Funktionentheorie*, zweite Auflage, Springer, 1980.

[47] Jones, G., Singerman, D. *Complex functions. An algebraic and geometric viewpoint*. Cambridge University Press, Cambridge, 1987.

[48] Jost, J., *Compact Riemann surfaces. An introduction to contemporary mathematics*. Third edition. Universitext. Springer-Verlag, Berlin, 2006.

[49] Jost, J., *Riemannian geometry and geometric analysis*. Fourth edition. Universitext. Springer-Verlag, Berlin, 2005.

[50] Katok, S., *Fuchsian groups*. Chicago Lectures in Mathematics. University of Chicago Press, Chicago, IL, 1992.

[51] Klein, F., *On Riemann's theory of algebraic functions and their integrals*. A supplement to the usual treatises. Translated from the German by Frances Hardcastle Dover Publications, Inc., New York 1963

[52] Koosis, P., *Introduction to H_p spaces*. Second edition. With two appendices by V. P. Havin. Cambridge Tracts in Mathematics, 115. Cambridge University Press, Cambridge, 1998.

[53] Kostov, V. P., *The Deligne-Simpson problem – a survey*, J. Algebra 281 (2004), 83–108.

[54] Lang, S., *Elliptic functions*. With an appendix by J. Tate. Second edition. Graduate Texts in Mathematics, 112. Springer-Verlag, New York, 1987.

[55] Lang, S., *Complex analysis*. Fourth edition. Graduate Texts in Mathematics, 103. Springer-Verlag, New York, 1999.

[56] Lang, S., *Algebra*. Revised third edition. Graduate Texts in Mathematics, 211. Springer-Verlag, New York, 2002.

[57] Lawler, G., *Conformally invariant processes in the plane*. Mathematical Surveys and Monographs, 114. American Mathematical Society, Providence, RI, 2005.

[58] Lawler, G., Limic, V., *Random walk: a modern introduction*. Cambridge Studies in Advanced Mathematics, 123. Cambridge University Press, Cambridge, 2010.

[59] Lehner, J., *Discontinuous groups and automorphic functions*, AMS, 1964.

[60] Levin, B. Ya., *Lectures on Entire Functions*, Translations of Mathematical Monographs, Volume 150, AMS 1996.

[61] Madsen, I., Tornehave, J., *From calculus to cohomology. de Rham cohomology and characteristic classes*. Cambridge University Press, Cambridge, 1997.

[62] Majstrenko, P., *On a theorem of Poincaré and Volterra*. Proc. London Math. Soc. (2) 53 (1951), 57–64.

[63] McKean, H., Moll, V., *Elliptic curves. Function theory, geometry, arithmetic*. Cambridge University Press, Cambridge, 1997.

[64] Mumford, D., *Tata lectures on theta I, II, III*, reprints of the original edition, Birkhäuser, 2007.

[65] Muscalu, C., Schlag, W. *Classical and multilinear harmonic analysis*. Vol. I., II. Cambridge Studies in Advanced Mathematics, 137, 138. Cambridge University Press, Cambridge, 2013.

[66] Narasimhan, R., *Compact Riemann surfaces*. Lectures in Mathematics ETH Zürich. Birkhäuser Verlag, Basel, 1992.

[67] Nevanlinna, R., *Uniformisierung*, Die Grundlehren der mathematischen Wissenschaften in Einzeldarstellungen, Band 64, Springer, zweite Auflage, 1967.

[68] Pyateskii-Shapiro, I. I., *Automorphic functions and the geometry of classical domains*. Translated from the Russian. Mathematics and Its Applications, Vol. 8 Gordon and Breach Science Publishers, New York-London-Paris, 1969.

[69] Radó, T., *Über die Begriffe der Riemannschen Fläche*. Acta Litt. Sci. Szeged 2 (1925), 101–121.

[70] Remmert, R., *Funktionentheorie. II*. Grundwissen Mathematik, 6. Springer-Verlag, Berlin, 1991.

[71] Rosenberg, S., *The Laplacian on a Riemannian manifold. An introduction to analysis on manifolds*. London Mathematical Society Student Texts, 31. Cambridge University Press, Cambridge, 1997.

[72] Rosenblum, M., Rovnyak, J., *Topics in Hardy classes and univalent functions*, Birkhäuser Advanced Texts, Basel, 1994.

[73] Rudin, W., *Real and complex analysis*. Third edition. McGraw-Hill Book Co., New York, 1987.

[74] Schiff, J., *Normal families*. Universitext. Springer-Verlag, New York, 1993.

[75] Sogge, C. D., *Hangzhou Lectures on Eigenfunctions of the Laplacian*. Annals of Mathematics Studies. Princeton, 2014.

[76] Springer, G., *Introduction to Riemann surfaces*. Addison-Wesley Publishing Company, Inc., Reading, Mass., 1957.

[77] Stein, E., Shakarchi, R. *Complex analysis*, Princeton Lectures in Analysis II, Princeton University Press, 2003.

[78] Stein, E., Weiss, G. *Introduction to Fourier analysis on Euclidean spaces*. Princeton Mathematical Series, No. 32. Princeton University Press, Princeton, N.J., 1971.

[79] Taylor, J. L., *Complex Variables*, Undergraduate Texts, Vol. 16, AMS, Providence, R.I., 2011.

[80] Titchmarsh, E., *The theory of functions*, Oxford, second edition, 1939.

[81] Titchmarsh, E., *The theory of the Riemann zeta-function*. Second edition. The Clarendon Press, Oxford University Press, New York, 1986.

[82] Ullrich, P., *The Poincaré–Volterra theorem: from hyperelliptic integrals to manifolds with countable topology*. Arch. Hist. Exact Sci. 54 (2000), no. 5, 375–402.

[83] Varadarajan, V. S., *Reflections on quanta, symmetries, and supersymmetries*, Springer, 2011.

[84] Varolin, D., *Riemann surfaces by way of complex analytic geometry*. Graduate Studies in Mathematics, 125. American Mathematical Society, Providence, RI, 2011.

[85] Walker, R. J., *Algebraic curves*. Reprint of the 1950 edition. Springer-Verlag, New York-Heidelberg, 1978.

[86] Watson, G. N., *A treatise on the theory of Bessel functions*, 2nd ed., Cambridge University Press, Cambridge, 1996

[87] Werner, W., *Percolation et modéle d'Ising*. Cours Spécialisés, 16. Société Mathématique de France, Paris, 2009.

[88] Weyl, H., *Die Idee der Riemannschen Fläche*. Fünfte Auflage. B. G. Teubner, Stuttgart, 1974.

Index